Organic Reactions

Organic Reactions

VOLUME V

JOHN WILEY & SONS, INC.
NEW YORK   LONDON   SYDNEY

PREFACE TO THE SERIES

In the course of nearly every program of research in organic chemistry the investigator finds it necessary to use several of the better-known synthetic reactions. To discover the optimum conditions for the application of even the most familiar one to a compound not previously subjected to the reaction often requires an extensive search of the literature; even then a series of experiments may be necessary. When the results of the investigation are published, the synthesis, which may have required months of work, is usually described without comment. The background of knowledge and experience gained in the literature search and experimentation is thus lost to those who subsequently have occasion to apply the general method. The student of preparative organic chemistry faces similar difficulties. The textbooks and laboratory manuals furnish numerous examples of the application of various syntheses, but only rarely do they convey an accurate conception of the scope and usefulness of the processes.

For many years American organic chemists have discussed these problems. The plan of compiling critical discussions of the more important reactions thus was evolved. The volumes of *Organic Reactions* are collections of about twelve chapters, each devoted to a single reaction, or a definite phase of a reaction, of wide applicability. The authors have had experience with the processes surveyed. The subjects are presented from the preparative viewpoint, and particular attention is given to limitations, interfering influences, effects of structure, and the selection of experimental techniques. Each chapter includes several detailed procedures illustrating the significant modifications of the method. Most of these procedures have been found satisfactory by the author or one of the editors, but unlike those in *Organic Syntheses* they have not been subjected to careful testing in two or more laboratories. When all known examples of the reaction are not mentioned in the text, tables are given to list compounds which have been prepared by or subjected to the reaction. Every effort has been made to include in the tables all such compounds and references; however, because of the very nature of the reactions discussed and their frequent use as one of the several steps of syntheses in which not all of the intermediates have been isolated, some instances may well have been missed.

v

Nevertheless, the investigator will be able to use the tables and their accompanying bibliographies in place of most or all of the literature search so often required.

Because of the systematic arrangement of the material in the chapters and the entries in the tables, users of the books will be able to find information desired by reference to the table of contents of the appropriate chapter. In the interest of economy the entries in the indices have been kept to a minimum, and, in particular, the compounds listed in the tables are not repeated in the indices.

The success of this publication, which will appear periodically in volumes of about twelve chapters, depends upon the cooperation of organic chemists and their willingness to devote time and effort to the preparation of the chapters. They have manifested their interest already by the almost unanimous acceptance of invitations to contribute to the work. The editors will welcome their continued interest and their suggestions for improvements in *Organic Reactions*.

CONTENTS

SUBJECTS OF PREVIOUS VOLUMES

CHAPTER 1

THE SYNTHESIS OF ACETYLENES

Thomas L. Jacobs

University of California

Los Angeles

CONTENTS

1

INTRODUCTION

Many advances have been made in recent years in the methods for the synthesis of acetylenes, and many of these compounds are now rather readily available in the pure state.

Acetylene was first prepared by Davy,[1] who treated potassium acetylide with water; propyne, the first substituted acetylene, was obtained in 1861 by the action of sodium ethoxide on bromopropene [2] or of ethanolic potassium hydroxide on propylene dibromide.[3] At the present time alkynes are usually synthesized by the alkylation of sodium acetylide or substituted metallic acetylides, often in liquid ammonia,

[1] Davy, Ann., 23, 144 (1837).
[2] Sawitsch, Compt. rend., 52, 399 (1861); Ann., 119, 185 (1861).
[3] Morkownikoff, Bull. soc. chim. France, 14, 90 (1861); Ann., 118, 332 (1861).

and 1-alkynes are also obtained in good yield by dehydrohalogenation of suitable halides with sodium amide or in certain cases by ethanolic alkali.

The present discussion will be limited to methods for the creation of a carbon-carbon triple bond and to the alkylation of metallic acetylides. No attempt will be made to deal with the multitude of processes in which sodium or other metallic derivatives of acetylenes or acetylene-magnesium bromide react with carbonyl compounds with the formation of products containing triple bonds. Neither will the closely related base-catalyzed condensations of acetylene or monosubstituted acetylenes with ketones to produce carbinols, the formation of diacetylenes by oxidation of metallic acetylides, or the replacement of the acetylenic hydrogen by halogen by the action of hypohalite be discussed.

THE SYNTHESIS OF ACETYLENES BY DEHYDROHALOGENATION

Dehydrohalogenation produces acetylenic compounds from dichlorides or dibromides of olefins, chloro- or bromo-olefins, and the mono- or di-chloro compounds prepared from aldehydes or ketones. Potassium hydroxide and sodium amide are employed most commonly to effect the reaction, although sodium hydroxide, alkali metal alkoxides, alkaline-earth carbonates or hydroxides, and amines have found occasional use. Alcoholic potassium hydroxide is now seldom employed in the aliphatic series because of the tendency of the triple bond to migrate away from the end of the chain under its influence, but aromatic acetylenes are still prepared conveniently by its use, often in higher yield than with sodium amide. Sodium amide causes the rearrangement of the triple bond to the 1-position because the insoluble sodium alkynide is formed; excellent yields of 1-alkynes are realized using this reagent. Aliphatic α,β-acetylenic acids can seldom be prepared by dehydrohalogenation because alkoxy acids, ketones, or polymers are the principal products. Mild conditions must be employed with arylpropiolic acids to avoid decarboxylation.

Potassium Hydroxide

Alcoholic, usually ethanolic, potassium hydroxide has been the most widely used reagent for the synthesis of acetylenes, but no critical study of optimum conditions for the reaction has been made. Bromides react more readily than chlorides, and the formation of a bromoethylene from a dibromide occurs more easily than the preparation of an acetylene from the bromoethylene, so that it is sometimes advantageous with sensitive dibromides to remove the first molecule of hydrogen bromide in the cold with dilute ethanolic alkali or other bases. With aliphatic compounds it is sometimes necessary to use sealed tubes or autoclaves and temperatures near 170°, but extended refluxing is usually sufficient with aryl chloro- or bromo-ethylenes. The reaction is more rapid at high concentrations of alkali, and excess alkali is usually employed. Ethanolic potassium hydroxide saturated at room temperature is about 4 N (around 20%), but solutions of more than twice this strength can be prepared by saturation at the boiling point. Some workers [4] specify equal weights of ethanol and alkali, and recent directions [5] for tolan call for 90 g. of potassium hydroxide in 150 ml. of ethanol, but in most reports the concentration is not given. Powdered potassium hydroxide moistened with ethanol is satisfactory for the preparation of *tert*-butylacetylene from the halides derived from pinacolone.[6] With some compounds high concentrations give decreased yields, as illustrated by the dehydrohalogenation of the acetal of 2,3-dibromopropanal to propargyl acetal.[7] Ordinary 95% ethanol is often satisfactory although absolute ethanol is sometimes specified. Water is always present since it is a product of the reaction and since commercially available potassium hydroxide contains about 86% alkali along with some potassium carbonate and considerable water. The reaction time varies widely. Thus, 1-bromo-1-furylethylene gives a maximum yield (25%) of furylacetylene on heating for three minutes at 100° with a slight excess of 18% ethanolic potassium hydroxide,[8] but stilbene dibromide gives tolan in good yield and free from bromo compound only after twenty-four hours' refluxing with a 40% solution.[5]

Other solvents have been used. The yield of acetylenedicarboxylic acid from α,β-dibromosuccinic acid is higher with *methanolic* than with ethanolic potassium hydroxide.[9] A methanol solution saturated at room temperature is about 6 N. It darkens less rapidly than an ethanol solution but has a lower boiling point. *Butyl alcohol* was used by Tapley and Giesey [10] as the solvent in the dehydrohalogenation of propylene dibromide, and many workers have adopted this procedure for propyne. It has been used occasionally for other acetylenes.[10c] *Diethylene glycol*

[4] Johnson and McEwen, *J. Am. Chem. Soc.*, **48**, 469 (1926).

[5] Smith and Falkof, *Org. Syntheses*, **22**, 50 (1942).

[6] (a) Ivitsky, *Bull. soc. chim. France*, [4] **35**, 357 (1924); (b) Gray and Marvel, *J. Am. Chem. Soc.*, **47**, 2796 (1925).

[7] Grard, *Ann. chim.*, [10] **13**, 336 (1930).

[8] Moureu, Dufraisse, and Johnson, *Ann. chim.*, [10] **7**, 14 (1927).

[9] Abbott, Arnold, and Thompson, *Org. Syntheses*, **18**, 3 (1938); *Coll. Vol.* **2**, 10 (1943).

[10] (a) Tapley and Giesey, *J. Am. Pharm. Assoc.*, **15**, 115 (1926); (b) Heisig and Davis, *J. Am. Chem. Soc.*, **57**, 339 (1935); (c) Cleveland and Murray, *J. Chem. Phys.*, **11**, 450 (1943).

has been employed in the synthesis of propyne,[11] but no record of the preparation of other acetylenes in this solvent has been found. *Ethylene glycol* has been used as the solvent in the synthesis of methyl propargyl ether.[12] A 5% solution of potassium hydroxide in *Cellosolve* (the monoethyl ether of ethylene glycol) is very effective for the dehydrochlorination of polyvinyl chloride,[13] and such a solution is superior to ethanolic alkali for converting 1-bromo-1-methylcyclobutane to methylcyclobutene.[14] Potassium hydroxide in *pyridine* has been used to prepare β-naphthylphenylacetylene from the corresponding chloroethylene,[15] for neither methanolic nor molten alkali is effective. *Aqueous* alkali is sometimes preferable to ethanolic for dehydrohalogenation of halogenated acids,[16] as in the preparation of phenylacetylenephosphonic acid,[16a] 4,4'-dinitrotolan-2,2'-disulfonic acid,[16c] 5-bromo-2-furylpropiolic acid,[16d] and several substituted phenylpropiolic acids.[16b,16e]

Dehydrohalogenation by distillation at partially reduced pressure from *solid potassium hydroxide* was first used by Krafft and Reuter [17] to prepare higher 1-alkynes from dibromides or bromoethylenes. Rapid distillation at low pressures gave mainly bromoölefins. It was claimed that no rearrangement occurred, although no critical study was made. The method has been applied successfully to the preparation of the sensitive acetylenic ethers from alkoxy- or aryloxy-bromoethylenes.[18] However, 1,2,3-tribromopropane gives 2,3-dibromopropene but almost no propargyl bromide [19] by distillation from solid sodium hydroxide or potassium hydroxide at atmospheric pressure.

Molten potassium hydroxide is a reagent which has found fairly wide application.[17] Phenylacetylene is most simply prepared by dropping ω-bromostyrene onto the molten alkali at 200–220°.[20] Pure potassium hydroxide melts at 360°,[21] but the monohydrate melts at 143°,[22] and the

[11] (a) Yost, Osborne, and Garner, *J. Am. Chem. Soc.*, **63**, 3492 (1941); (b) Skei, Ph.D. Thesis, University of California at Los Angeles, 1942, p. 121.

[12] Heilbron, Jones, and Lacey, *J. Chem. Soc.*, **1946**, 27.

[13] Marvel, Sample, and Roy, *J. Am. Chem. Soc.*, **61**, 3241 (1939).

[14] Shand, Schomaker, and Fischer, *J. Am. Chem. Soc.*, **66**, 636 (1944).

[15] Ruggli and Reinert, *Helv. Chim. Acta*, **9**, 67 (1926).

[16] (a) Bergmann and Bondi, *Ber.*, **66**, 278 (1933); (b) Linstead and Noble, *J. Chem. Soc.*, **1937**, 933; (c) Ruggli and Peyer, *Helv. Chim. Acta*, **9**, 929 (1926); (d) Gilman, Hewlett, and Wright, *J. Am. Chem. Soc.*, **53**, 4192 (1931); (e) Schofield and Simpson, *J. Chem. Soc.*, **1945**, 512.

[17] Krafft and Reuter, *Ber.*, **25**, 2243 (1892).

[18] (a) Slimmer, *Ber.*, **36**, 289 (1903); (b) Jacobs, Cramer, and Weiss, *J. Am. Chem. Soc.*, **62**, 1849 (1940); (c) Jacobs, Cramer, and Hanson, *ibid.*, **64**, 223 (1942).

[19] Lespieau and Bourguel, *Org. Syntheses, Coll. Vol.* **1**, 209, 2nd ed., 1941; Lespieau, *Ann. chim. phys.*, [7] **11**, 232 (1897); *Bull. soc. chim. France*, [4] **29**, 528 (1921).

[20] Hessler, *Org. Syntheses, Coll. Vol.* **1**, 438, 2nd ed., 1941.

[21] von Hevesy, *Z. physik. Chem.*, **73**, 667 (1910).

[22] Pickering, *J. Chem. Soc.*, **63**, 890 (1893).

ordinary reagent grade usually contains enough water to melt at about 200°. For many reactions it is simpler to use a mixture of 2 parts of potassium hydroxide and 1 part of sodium hydroxide, which melts below 200°.[23] The eutectic of these alkalies lies close to 50% by weight and melts at 187°,[21] but the presence of water lowers the melting temperature. Glass vessels are not attacked appreciably by solid potassium hydroxide, but molten alkali is very corrosive and glass flasks (especially Pyrex) can be used safely no more than three or four times. If a Wood's metal bath is used for heating, the run can be completed even if the flask is eaten through below the bath level, but an oil bath is very rapidly saponified and usually foams over when the flask breaks. It is said that the use of steel or copper flasks reduces the yield slightly,[20] but a 70% yield of phenylacetylene is reported using a copper vessel and a stream of dry air to remove the phenylacetylene vapors.[23a] Copper flasks have been used successfully in other reactions.[12]

A mineral-oil suspension of powdered potassium hydroxide has been used to give a high yield of alkynes (partially rearranged.) [24] The method has not been applied to the synthesis of arylacetylenes.

Sodium Amide

Meunier and Desparmet were the first to use sodium amide to produce a triple bond; they dropped ethylene dibromide onto the *powdered reagent* and obtained acetylene.[25] Later, they studied the dehydrohalogenation of higher homologs of ethylene dibromide. These results were submitted to the French Chemical Society in a sealed communication. After Bourguel [26] independently made the same discovery, Meunier and Desparmet published the details of their work.[27] Bourguel has supplied carefully tested directions for the synthesis by this procedure of a variety of 1-alkynes.[26, 28, 29]

The following types of halogen compounds are suitable starting materials: $RCHXCH_2X$, RCH_2CHX_2, RCX_2CH_3, $RCX=CH_2$, and $RCH=CHX$. The halide is added dropwise to an excess of finely pulverized sodium amide *in an inert solvent* at 110–160°. Ammonia is given off vigorously at first, and the reaction is complete when this

[23] (a) Rupe and Rinderknecht, *Ann.*, **442**, 61 (1925); (b) Hurd and Cohen, *J. Am. Chem. Soc.*, **53**, 1068 (1931).

[24] (a) Guest, *J. Am. Chem. Soc.*, **50**, 1744 (1928); (b) Bachman and Hill, *ibid.*, **56**, 2730 (1934); (c) Hall and Bachman, *Ind. Eng. Chem.*, **28**, 57 (1936).

[25] Meunier and Desparmet, *Bull. soc. chim. France*, [4] **1**, 342 (1907).

[26] Bourguel, *Compt. rend.*, **176**, 751 (1923).

[27] Meunier and Desparmet, *Bull. soc. chim. France*, [4] **35**, 481 (1924).

[28] Bourguel, *Ann. chim.*, [10] **3**, 191, 325 (1925).

[29] Lespieau and Bourguel, *Org. Syntheses, Coll. Vol.* **1**, 191, 2nd ed., 1941.

evolution becomes very slow; the reaction requires about twenty hours at 110°, three to four hours at 130°, and only fifteen minutes after all the halide is added at 160°. A temperature of 150–165° is most satisfactory, and a purified petroleum oil, none of which boils below 250°, is the most readily available solvent. Different ligroin fractions, the lightest boiling at 150–180° and the heaviest at 125–140°/14 mm., have been used,[28] with no advantages recorded for any particular fraction. Xylene and toluene have been employed, but the long refluxing is a disadvantage especially with the latter. Usually the mixture is heated for two hours after all the halide is added to ensure completion of the reaction. The acetylene forms a solid complex with excess sodium amide, and volatile impurities such as olefins may be removed under reduced pressure or by distillation of part of the solvent when it is not too high boiling. The acetylene is then liberated with dilute hydrochloric acid or acetic acid.[30, 31] The yields are usually 60–85% as summarized in Table I. Bourguel did not use a mechanical stirrer, though efficient stirring was employed when the reaction was carried out in mineral-oil suspensions.

TABLE I

DEHYDROHALOGENATION WITH SODIUM AMIDE [28]

Acetylene	Starting Material	Yield %
1-Butyne [32]	Bromobutene mixture	60
1-Pentyne	$C_2H_5CH=CClCH_3$	62
	$C_3H_7CCl_2CH_3$	45
	$C_3H_7CBr=CH_2$	55
	$C_2H_5CCl=CHCH_3$ ⎱ mixture $C_2H_5CCl_2C_2H_5$ ⎰	30
1-Hexyne	$C_4H_9CBr=CH_2$	60
1-Heptyne	$C_6H_{13}CHCl_2$	60
	$C_3H_7CCl=CHC_2H_5$	15 *
1-Octyne	$C_5H_{11}CHBrCHBrCH_3$	25
	$C_5H_{11}CBr=CHCH_3$	55
	$C_6H_{13}CBr=CH_2$	75
Phenylacetylene	$C_6H_5CBr=CH_2$	75
	$C_6H_5CHBrCH_2Br$	40, 60
3-Phenyl-1-propyne	$C_6H_5CH_2CBr=CH_2$	75
3-Cyclohexyl-1-propyne	$C_6H_{11}CH_2CBr=CH_2$	87

* The yield of disubstituted acetylene, mainly 3-heptyne, was 40%.

[30] Levina and Ivanov, J. Gen. Chem. U.S.S.R., 7, 1866 (1937) [C.A., 32, 507 (1938)].
[31] Levina and Kulikov, J. Gen. Chem. U.S.S.R., 10, 1189 (1940) [C.A., 35, 2881 (1941)]
[32] Bourguel, Bull. soc. chim. France, [4] 41, 1475 (1927).

The lower yield of 3-cyclohexylpropyne obtained with mineral oil as a medium [29] as compared with a petroleum fraction boiling at 180–220° [28] may be accounted for by the difficulty of removing the reaction product from the former medium. Table II gives the yields reported with mineral oil and certain other solvents.

TABLE II

DEHYDROHALOGENATION WITH SODIUM AMIDE

Acetylene	Starting Material	Yield %	Reference
1-Butyne	2,2-Dichlorobutane	40 *	33
3-Methyl-1-butyne	3-Methyl-2-butanone	6 †	34
	1- and 2-Bromo-3-methylbutene	25 †	34
	1,2-Dibromo-3-methylbutane	28–34	35, 36
1-Heptyne	1-Chloroheptene	60–70; ‡ 54	4, 37
	Chloro compounds from heptaldehyde	50–80	27
4,4-Dimethyl-1-pentyne	2-Bromo-4,4-dimethyl-1-pentene	37	38
3-Ethyl-3-methyl-1-pentyne	2-Chloro-3-ethyl-3-methyl-1-pentene	45	39
1-Nonyne	Chloro compounds from 2-nonanone	50–80	27
1-Decyne	2-Bromo-1-decene	68	4, 29
1-Undecyne	Chloro compounds from 2-undecanone	50–80	27
1-Hexadecyne	1,2-Dibromohexadecane	65	40
Cyclopentylacetylene	Cyclopentyl methyl ketone	9 §	41
Cyclohexylacetylene	Cyclohexanol (5 steps)	6 §	41
3-Cyclohexyl-1-propyne	2-Bromo-3-cyclohexyl-1-propene	66	29
4-Cyclohexyl-1-butyne	4-Cyclohexyl-1,2-dibromobutane	65 ‖	30
3-Cyclopentyl-1-propyne	3-Cyclopentyl-2-bromo-1-propene	65	41
3-(cis-β-Decalyl)-1-propyne	3-(cis-β-Decalyl)-1,2-dibromopropane	77 ‖	31
3-(trans-β-Decalyl)-1-propyne	3-(trans-β-Decalyl)-1,2-dibromopropane	86 ‖	31
p-Tolylacetylene	α-Chloro-p-methylstyrene	30	42
2,4-Dimethylphenyl acetylene	α-Chloro-2,4-dimethylstyrene	75	43
Mesitylacetylene	α-Chloro-2,4,6-trimethylstyrene	71	43
4-Phenyl-1-butyne	2-Bromo-4-phenyl-1-butene	63	4, 29
	1,2-Dibromo-4-phenylbutane	55	44, 444
Tolan	α-Chlorostilbene	34	45

* Allowing for 25% recovery of chlorobutene.
† The medium was not stated.
‡ Contained 30% of disubstituted acetylenes.
§ The medium was decalin.
‖ The medium was kerosene.

REFERENCES TO TABLE II

[33] Stoll and Rouvé, *Helv. Chim. Acta*, **21**, 1542 (1938).
[34] Grédy, *Bull. soc. chim. France*, [5] **2**, 1951 (1935).
[35] Dedusenko, *Trudy Akad. Nauk S.S.S.R.*, *Azerbaïdzhan Filial*, **1940**, No. 3, 87; *Khim. Referat. Zhur.*, **4**, No. 1, 48 (1941) [*C.A.*, **37**, 1697 (1943)].
[36] Dedusenko, *Trudy Khim. Inst. Azerbaidzhan. Filiala Akad. Nauk*, **4**, No. 1, 15 (1940); *Khim. Referat. Zhur.*, **4**, No. 9, 53 (1941) [*C.A.* **38**, 1466 (1944)].
[37] Guest, *J. Am. Chem. Soc.*, **47**, 860 (1925).
[38] Ozanne and Marvel, *J. Am. Chem. Soc.*, **52**, 5267 (1930).
[39] Davis and Marvel, *J. Am. Chem. Soc.*, **53**, 3840 (1931).
[40] Mulliken, Wakeman, and Gerry, *J. Am. Chem. Soc.*, **57**, 1605 (1935).
[41] Grédy, *Ann. chim.*, [11] **4**, 5 (1935).
[42] Willemart, *Bull. soc. chim. France*, [4] **45**, 644 (1929).
[43] Vaughn and Nieuwland, *J. Am. Chem. Soc.*, **56**, 1207 (1934).
[44] Levina and Panov, *J. Gen. Chem. U.S.S.R.*, **11**, 533 (1941) [*C.A.*, **35**, 6936 (1941)].
[45] Paillard and Wieland, *Helv. Chim. Acta*, **21**, 1356 (1938).

It has been suggested [28] that the solid complex obtained in dehydrohalogenations with sodium amide contains some product different from the simple sodium acetylide, for it cannot be carbonated or methylated in high yield and the ammonia liberated during its formation is less than required by the following equation.

$$RCBr{=}CH_2 + 2NaNH_2 \rightarrow RC{\equiv}CNa + NaBr + 2NH_3$$

However, 2-pentynoic acid was obtained in 46% yield by treating 1,2-dibromobutane with sodium amide in kerosene at 145°, diluting the reaction mixture with ether, and passing in carbon dioxide with cooling.[46] When the starting material was the chlorinated mixture obtained from 2-pentanone and phosphorus pentachloride, the yield of acid dropped to 2–3%.

Of special importance for the success of the synthesis is the *quality* of the sodium amide. On exposure to the air, the reagent acquires a protective coating of sodium hydroxide. The dehydrohalogenation is then brought about by the sodium hydroxide and is accompanied by rearrangement of the triple bond. Such coated sodium amide is incapable of converting a monosubstituted acetylene into its sodium derivative even at 100°, whereas with a pure reagent this reaction occurs rapidly in ether at 30° although the quantity of ammonia evolved indicates no more than 85–90% conversion. Bourguel [28] used sodium amide of good commercial grade in his experiments and took great care to grind and store it out of contact with moisture. Accurate directions have appeared for the preparation of sodium amide from

[46] Favorskiï and Mokhnach, *Bull. Far East. Branch Acad. Sci. U.S.S.R.*, **9**, 3 (1934) [*C.A.*, **29**, 3981 (1935)]; *J. Gen. Chem. U.S.S.R.*, **5**, 1668 (1935) [*C.A.*, **30**, 3404 (1936)].

molten sodium and anhydrous ammonia.[47] A rapid and convenient method for obtaining the reagent in liquid ammonia has been described [48] (p. 48). By adding this solution to mineral oil at room temperature and heating to drive off the ammonia, a reactive, finely divided suspension is obtained. The sodium oxide which is present appears to have no deleterious effect. A yellow color due to peroxide formation often develops in old sodium amide which has been exposed to air. This material is dangerously explosive and should be discarded at once.[47]

Sodium amide in mineral oil has been reported [43] to be superior to ethanolic potassium hydroxide for the synthesis of mesityl- and 2,4-dimethylphenyl-acetylene, but it reacts too vigorously with halogen-substituted α-chlorostyrenes, and ethanolic alkali is better.[43, 49] For p-tolylacetylene the yields reported using potassium hydroxide [50, 51] are better than those with sodium amide, and the same is true for tolan [5, 45] and even for isopropylacetylene.[36]

The sodium amide method has been recommended for the synthesis of 3-aryl-1-propynes; [52] the yields were said to approach 75%. In view of the ease of rearrangement of these compounds to 1-aryl-1-propynes, (see p. 17), great care is necessary in the final hydrolysis of the reaction mixture.

Liquid ammonia offers a satisfactory medium for dehydrohalogenations,[48a] although there is some indication that with dibromides olefin formation is an important side reaction. The method is not often used since ammonia is somewhat less convenient to handle than other solvents. Table III gives some of the results.

[47] Dennis and Browne, Inorganic Syntheses, I, 74 (1939); J. Am. Chem. Soc., 26, 587, 597 (1904); Bergstrom and Fernelius, Chem. Revs., 12, 52 (1933); Bergstrom, Org. Syntheses, 20, 86 (1940).
[48] (a) Vaughn, Vogt, and Nieuwland, J. Am. Chem. Soc., 56, 2120 (1934); (b) Greenlee and Henne, Inorganic Syntheses, 2, 128 (1946).
[49] Dufraisse and Dequesnes, Bull. soc. chim. France, [4] 49, 1880 (1931).
[50] Smith and Hoehn, J. Am. Chem. Soc., 63, 1175 (1941).
[51] Robin, Ann. chim., [10] 16, 421 (1931).
[52] Bert, Dorier, and Lamy, Compt. rend., 181, 555 (1925).

TABLE III *

ACTION OF SODIUM AMIDE ON HALOGEN COMPOUNDS IN LIQUID AMMONIA

Halogen Compound	Product	Yield %	
		Overall	Accounted for †
1-Iodo-1-hexyne	1-Hexyne	31	34
1,2-Dibromo-1-heptene	1-Heptyne	55	
2-Bromo-1-octyne	1-Octyne	73	90
1,2-Dibromodecane	1-Decyne	54	78
2-Bromo-1-pentadecene	1-Pentadecyne [53]	10	
α-Chlorostyrene	Phenylacetylene	57	
β-Bromostyrene	Phenylacetylene	75	83
Styrene dibromide	Phenylacetylene [54]	52, 64	
p-Methyl-α-chlorostyrene	p-Tolylacetylene	49	64
Stilbene dibromide	Stilbene	86	

* This table is taken from Vaughn, Vogt, and Nieuwland, ref. 48a, except as indicated.
† The figures in this column are the yields after allowing for recovered starting material.

Other Alkaline Reagents

Other alkaline reagents are sometimes used for dehydrohalogenation, but these have usually been less satisfactory for preparing acetylenes although they often have advantages for preparing olefins. *Sodium hydroxide* is relatively insoluble in ethanol, but aqueous or dilute ethanolic solutions have been used.[16b, d, e, 55, 56, 57] *Sodium ethoxide* was used in the original propyne synthesis;[2] it has been employed occasionally in the synthesis of substituted tolans (p. 40) or other arylacetylenes [58, 59] but rarely for alkynes.[60, 61, 62] An unusually interesting example of the

[53] Ryden, Glavis, and Marvel, *J. Am. Chem. Soc.*, **59**, 1014 (1937).
[54] Campbell and O'Connor, *J. Am. Chem. Soc.*, **61**, 2897 (1939).
[55] Ruggli, Caspar, and Hegedüs, *Helv. Chim. Acta*, **20**, 250 (1937).
[56] Bashford, Emeléus, and Briscoe, *J. Chem. Soc.*, **1938**, 1358.
[57] Hatch and Moore, *J. Am. Chem. Soc.*, **66**, 285 (1944); Hatch and Evans, Brit. pat. 582,764 [*C.A.*, **42**, 583 (1948)].
[58] Adams and Theobald, *J. Am. Chem. Soc.*, **65**, 2208, 2383 (1943).
[59] Adams and Ludington, *J. Am. Chem. Soc.*, **67**, 794 (1945).
[60] Wislicenus and Hölz, *Ann.*, **250**, 230 (1889).
[61] Loevenich, Losen, and Dierichs, *Ber.*, **60**, 950 (1927).
[62] Bachman, *J. Am. Chem. Soc.*, **57**, 1088 (1935).

use of sodium ethoxide or hydroxide is the preparation of diacetylene from 1,4-dichloro-2-butyne.[62a]

Ketene acetals have been prepared [63] by dehydrohalogenation of haloacetals with *potassium tert-butoxide* in *tert*-butyl alcohol, which does not add to the reactive double bond, but no report of the use of this reagent for acetylene synthesis has appeared.[64] The use of *sodium anilide*,[65] *potassium benzylate*,[66] and *sodium ethylmercaptide* [61, 62] can be mentioned, but only the first showed synthetic promise. The preparation of 1-nitro-1-butyne and 1-nitro-1-pentyne by treatment of the corresponding 1-bromo-1-nitroölefins with *methylamine* and *diethylamine* respectively has been reported.[67] Dibromosuccinic acid gives acetylenedicarboxylic acid when treated with aqueous solutions of *pyridine* or *quinoline*,[68] but, in general, amines are not basic enough to remove hydrogen halide from a haloethylene.[61, 69] 1,2-Dibromo-3-cyclohexyl-propane gives 3-cyclohexyl-1-propyne in 27% yield when treated with ethanolic potassium hydroxide but gives cyclohexylallene in unspecified yield when distilled with quinoline. Aqueous *potassium carbonate* has been used occasionally [70] and *alkaline-earth carbonates* or *hydroxides* have been employed to prepare acetylenedicarboxylic or halogenated phenylpropiolic acids.[71] Bromomaleic and bromofumaric acids yield propiolic acid merely by heating with water at 140°.[71d] It has been shown that *sodium* in *liquid ammonia* removes halogen quantitatively

---

[62a] *Synthetic Fiber Developments in Germany*, Textile Research Institute, New York, 1946, p. 540.

[63] Beyerstedt and McElvain, *J. Am. Chem. Soc.*, **58**, 529 (1936).

[64] (a) Potassium *tert*-butoxide was less satisfactory than distillation from powdered potassium hydroxide for the dehydrohalogenation of bromophenoxyethylene to phenoxy-acetylene, although a low yield was obtained. Unpublished work, Jacobs and Whitcher. (b) Addition of *tert*-butyl alcohol to a triple bond may be involved in the formation of β-*tert*-butoxycrotonic acid by the action of potassium *tert*-butoxide on α-bromocrotonic acid. Owen, *J. Chem. Soc.*, **1945**, 385.

[65] Bodroux, *Compt. rend.*, **208**, 1022 (1939).

[66] Risseghem, *Bull. soc. chim. Belg.*, **47**, 261 (1938).

[67] Loevenich, Koch, and Pucknat, *Ber.*, **63**, 636 (1930).

[68] Dubreuil, *Bull. soc. chim. France*, [3] **31**, 914 (1904); *Compt. rend.*, **137**, 1063 (1903).

[69] Levina and Trakhtenberg, *J. Gen. Chem. U.S.S.R.*, **6**, 764 (1936) [*C.A.*, **30**, 6338 (1936)].

[70] (a) Orekhoff and Tiffeneau, *Bull. soc. chim. France*, [4] **37**, 1410 (1925); (b) Carlier and Einhorn, *Ber.*, **23**, 2894 (1890), reported that treatment of β-(2-quinolyl)acrylic acid dibromide with aqueous alkaline carbonate gave 2-quinolylacetylene; (c) Alberts and Bachman, *J. Am. Chem. Soc.*, **57**, 1284 (1935), were unable to duplicate the result reported in (b).

[71] (a) Jackson and Hill, *Ber.*, **11**, 1671 (1878); Hill, *Am. Chem. J.*, **3**, 98 (1881); (b) Wallach, *Ann.*, **203**, 83 (1880); (c) Lossen, *Ann.*, **272**, 127 (1893); (d) Lossen and Mendthal, *Ann.*, **348**, 308 (1906).

from many types of organic halides, but acetylenes are seldom the principal products and some olefin is always present.[62,72]

Phenylacetylene has been prepared by vapor-phase dehydrohalogenation over *soda lime* at high pressures,[73] and 1,1-dichloro- and 1,2-dibromo-heptane give low yields of 1-heptyne by this method.[24a, b, 74] The alkyne polymerizes rapidly at 300° and is cracked at 400°; below 300°, no rearrangement of the triple bond occurs.[24b] The dichloride is decomposed almost completely by passage over *aluminum silicate* at 470°.[74] Dichloroacetylene is best prepared by passing trichloroethylene over a *mixture of potassium hydroxide and calcium oxide* at 130°.[75,76,77]

Side Reactions

The Rearrangement of the Triple Bond. From a synthetic standpoint the greatest disadvantage of ethanolic potassium hydroxide as a dehydrohalogenating agent is its tendency to promote the shift of the triple bond away from the end of a chain. This rearrangement was discovered by Favorskiĭ,[78] who found that ethyl- and *n*-propyl-acetylenes give disubstituted acetylenes, isopropylacetylene gives unsymmetrical dimethylallene, and *tert*-butylacetylene gives no rearrangement even at 200° although much polymerization occurs. The experiments were usually carried out in a sealed tube with excess concentrated ethanolic alkali at 170°. The rate of the reaction increases with the concentration of the reagent and with the temperature, and no rearrangement was detected below 130–140° with 1-pentyne and 1-butyne. The temperature at which the rearrangement becomes negligible must vary with different compounds, and, since only very concentrated solutions of ethanolic potassium hydroxide have to be heated to 130–140° to effect refluxing, the extent of rearrangement in a practical synthesis is variable. No critical study has been made, and the preparation of monosubstituted acetylenes of reasonable but of unestablished purity by this method is

[72] (a) Chablay, *Ann. chim.*, [9] **1**, 469 (1914); (b) Kirrmann, *Compt. rend.*, **181**, 671 (1925); (c) Vaughn and Nieuwland, *Ind. Eng. Chem., Anal. Ed.*, **3**, 274 (1931); (d) Dean and Berchet, *J. Am. Chem. Soc.*, **52**, 2823 (1930); Vaughn, *ibid.*, **56**, 2064 (1934).

[73] (a) Morgan, *J. Chem. Soc.*, **29**, 162 (1876); (b) Peratoner, *Gazz. chim. ital.*, **22**, II, 65 (1892).

[74] Hill and Tyson, *J. Am. Chem. Soc.*, **50**, 172 (1928).

[75] Ott, Ottmeyer, and Packendorff, *Ber.*, **63**, 1941 (1930).

[76] Ott and Packendorff, *Ber.*, **64**, 1324 (1931).

[77] Ott, *Ber.*, **75**, 1517 (1942).

[78] (a) Favorskiĭ, *J. Russ. Phys. Chem. Soc.*, **19**, 414 (1887) (*Chem. Zentr.*, **1887**, 1539); *J. prakt. Chem.*, [2] **37**, 382 (1888); (b) Favorskiĭ, *ibid.*, [2] **37**, 531 (1888); **44**, 208 (1891). This discovery was announced before the Russian Society in 1886. See *Bull. soc. chim. France*, [2] **45**, 247 (1886).

reported occasionally; for example, 10-undecyne-1-al diethyl acetal [79a] and 4-pentynoic acid.[79b] The synthesis of disubstituted acetylenes, the purity of which was undetermined, has been reported many times, as illustrated by 4-methyl-2-pentyne [79c] and 2-methyl-4-hexyne.[79d] Ethanolic sodium hydroxide and sodium ethoxide effect the shift, but solid potassium hydroxide does not at the temperatures used. Allene or methylacetylene gives mainly ethyl isopropenyl ether, and dipropargyl is changed in low yield to dimethyldiacetylene. Favorskiĭ believed that the rearrangement goes to completion since his products gave no precipitate with ammoniacal silver or cuprous solutions; however, later workers obtained indications, with the more sensitive ethanolic silver nitrate, of incomplete conversion.[17, 80] Higher 1-alkynes rearrange mainly to 2-alkynes.[17, 80a, 81] It is reported [41] that samples of 2-octyne prepared by rearrangement of 1-octyne and by the methylation of sodium amylacetylide have identical physical properties and Raman spectra.

At 380°, 1-heptyne rearranges in the vapor state over soda lime to a disubstituted acetylene to a considerable extent, but the change is slight at 250°.[24a, 74] Over pumice at 350° less rearrangement but much decomposition occurs.

The reverse change of a disubstituted acetylene or allene into a monosubstituted acetylene by heating in a sealed tube with sodium at 100° has been effected.[82] The product, the sodium alkynide, was an almost dry powder which could be carbonated to the acetylenic acid or decomposed with water to the alkyne. Higher temperatures than 100° are generally found necessary for this reaction [17, 83] and some olefin is produced by hydrogenation.[82, 83] Sodium amide brings about the same change.[27, 28] The conditions for the rearrangement are not greatly different from those employed with sodium, but sodium amide is preferable because the triple bond is not reduced. The reaction is usually carried out with a suspension of the reagent in an inert solvent, and temperatures as low as 110° have been used, although the best results are obtained at 150–160°.

[79] (a) English and Velick, J. Am. Chem. Soc., 67, 1413 (1945); (b) Schjånberg, Ber., 71, 569 (1938); (c) Ipatieff, J. Russ. Phys. Chem. Soc., 27, 387 (1895); J. prakt. Chem., [2] 53, 145 (1896); (d) Petrov, Verentsova and Kokleeva, J. Gen Chem. U.S.S.R., 11, 1096 (1941) [C.A., 37, 3732 (1943)].

[80] (a) Béhal, Bull. soc. chim. France, [2] 49, 581 (1888); (b) Wislicenus and Schmidt, Ann., 313, 210 (1900).

[81] Krafft, Ber., 29, 2232 (1896).

[82] Favorskiĭ, J. Russ. Phys. Chem. Soc., 19, 553 (1887) (Chem. Zentr., 1888, 242); J. prakt. Chem., [2] 37, 417 (1888); J. Russ. Phys. Chem. Soc., 50, 43 (1918) [C.A., 18, 2498 (1924)].

[83] Béhal, Bull. soc. chim. France, [2] 50, 629 (1888).

When sodium amide is used for dehydrohalogenation a complete rearrangement of disubstituted to monosubstituted acetylenes does not always occur, but Bourguel [28] effected a clean separation of these products by working in a ligroin fraction which boiled higher than the acetylenes but low enough for partial removal by distillation. When the dehydrohalogenation was over, as indicated by cessation of ammonia evolution, the disubstituted acetylenes were removed with some of the solvent under reduced pressure before the sodium derivative of the monosubstituted acetylene was decomposed. Table IV indicates the yields

TABLE IV

REARRANGEMENT OF ACETYLENES BY SODIUM AMIDE *

Starting Material	Amt. g.	NaNH₂ g.	Temp. °C.	Time hr.	Solvent	Recovered Starting Material	Monosubstituted Acetylene g.	Yield %	
								Subtracting Recovered Starting Material	No Allowance for Recovery
2-Octyne	12	6	150	1½	Pseudocumene	Very little	9.5		80
2-Nonyne	18		160	2	Petroleum (b.p. 180–220°)	2.5 g. (14%)	13.0	84	72
3-Heptyne	10		170	4	Pseudocumene	4.0 g. (40%)	3 to 4	50 to 65	30 to 40
3-Octyne	22		170	9	Petroleum	9.5 g. (43%)	10.0	80	45
1-Phenyl-1-propyne	9		110	2	Toluene		6.0 †		67
1-Cyclohexyl-2-butyne	215	80	160	3 ‡	Petroleum (b.p. 220–250°)	8.0 g. (4%)	165.0	80	77
5-Cyclohexyl-2-pentyne	107	39	160	2½	Petroleum (b.p. 125–140°/ 15 mm.)	15.0 g. (14%)	81.0	88	76
6-Cyclohexyl-2-hexyne	48		160	2½	Petroleum (b.p. 125–140°/ 15 mm.)	9.0 g. (19%)	34.0	87	71

* Heating was discontinued when the evolution of ammonia became very slow. This usually occurred after 75% to 80% of the theoretical amount had been evolved. A slight excess of sodium amide was used (1.2 moles per mole of disubstituted acetylene) suspended in 300–400 ml. of solvent.

† No careful attempt was made to separate mono- from di-substituted acetylenes, although all the product was believed to be 1-alkyne.

‡ The first three-hour heating left 40 g. of disubstituted product, which, after reheating with fresh sodium amide, left only 8 g. of unchanged starting material.

and conditions in these experiments. It was observed that the rates of rearrangement vary with different compounds, but 3-alkynes always change more slowly than 2-alkynes. By essentially the same procedure, the allenes 1,2-pentadiene, 1,2-heptadiene, and 5-methyl-1,2-hexadiene give excellent yields of 1-pentyne, 1-heptyne, and 5-methyl-1-hexyne, respectively.[84] The reaction is practically complete within two hours at bath temperatures of 140°.

A heptyne mixture containing 80% disubstituted compounds may be rearranged [24a] by heating for twelve hours at 160° in a mineral-oil suspension of sodium amide with vigorous stirring, and an acetylene fraction (in unspecified yield) containing 64% of 1-heptyne is isolated.[85] This result is not inconsistent with those of Bourguel.[28] 6-Dodecyne and 5-decyne have been similarly rearranged at 210°.[86] This is the only recorded example of the shifting of a triple bond by five positions. In general, temperatures above 170° are undesirable because the sodium amide particles tend to clump together and the rearrangement is much slower. Sodium amide melts at 210°.[47]

Because of this rearrangement it is possible to use compounds with halogens three and four carbons from the end of the chain for the synthesis of monosubstituted acetylenes, but the yields are generally less satisfactory as Table I shows.

Successive methylation of a sodium acetylide by dimethyl sulfate and rearrangement of the methylalkylacetylene to a new monosubstituted acetylene is a satisfactory method of synthesizing relatively inaccessible higher acetylenes. Using this method Bourguel was able to prepare 200 g. of 6-cyclohexyl-1-hexyne from 500 g. of 3-cyclohexyl-1-propyne by three repetitions of the cycle.

Since 3-nonyne is not rearranged by standing for sixteen hours at −34° in a liquid ammonia solution containing sodium amide,[48a] it was suggested that easily rearranged disubstituted acetylenes might be synthesized by dehydrohalogenations in this medium, but no experimental work has been reported. Because 3-alkynes are less readily rearranged than 2-alkynes it would be interesting to observe the behavior of 2-nonyne or a similar compound in such a solution.

The rearrangement of the triple bond has been compared with a corresponding shift of the double bond.[24a] Olefins have been studied mainly in the vapor phase or in acids,[87] and there is no evidence that 1-alkenes tend to rearrange to 2-alkenes in the presence of alkaline reagents under conditions comparable to those of the acetylene isomerization. However, at 420°, 1-butene is converted to 2-butene to the

[84] Bouis, *Ann. chim.*, [10] **9**, 402 (1928).
[85] Analysis by the method of Hill and Tyson, ref. 74.
[86] Vaughn, *J. Am. Chem. Soc.*, **55**, 3453 (1933).
[87] The isomerization of olefins and acetylenes has been reviewed by Egloff, Hulla, and Komarewsky, *Isomerization of Pure Hydrocarbons*, American Chemical Society Monograph, Reinhold Publishing Corp., New York, 1942, especially Chapters 2 and 3. A brief account is given by Egloff, The Reactions of Aliphatic Hydrocarbons, Chapter I of *Organic Chemistry*, Gilman, 2nd ed., John Wiley & Sons, New York, 1943.

extent of 92% by passage over lime.[88] It is well known that alkaline reagents cause a rearrangement of allyl benzenes to propenylbenzenes.[89] Similarly benzylacetylene cannot be prepared using solid or ethanolic potassium hydroxide,[90, 91] and even the reaction of benzyl chloride and sodium acetylide yields methylphenylacetylene.[90] The rates of interconversion by ethanolic sodium ethoxide and the positions of equilibrium in a series of substituted 1,3-diphenylpropenes have been determined, and the mechanism of the reaction has been discussed.[92] In the acetylene series, 1-p-bromophenyl-3-phenyl-1- or 2-propynes ($BrC_6H_4C{\equiv}CCH_2C_6H_5$, $BrC_6H_4CH_2C{\equiv}CC_6H_5$) were found to be isolable compounds which were not isomerized by hot 15% potassium hydroxide solution or by the Grignard reagent.[93]

The interconversion of α,β- and β,γ-olefinic acids has been studied,[79 b, 94] but the corresponding rearrangements of acetylenic acids have not been reported.

The conversion of 1,4-dichloro-2-butyne to diacetylene [62a] has already been mentioned (p. 12); this is presumably the result of 1,4-dehydrohalogenation rather than rearrangement.

$$ClCH_2C{\equiv}CCH_2Cl \rightarrow CH_2{=}C{=}C{=}CHCl \rightarrow HC{\equiv}C{-}C{\equiv}CH$$

Removal of Adjacent Halogen Atoms. When the starting material for acetylene synthesis is a 1,2-dihalogen compound the alkaline reagent sometimes removes the halogen atoms to form an olefin. This reaction is relatively common with the dihalides of stilbenes [16 c, 70a, 95] or β-arylacrylic acids [70c, 96] and has been observed more often with tertiary amines than with ethanolic potassium hydroxide, although α-iodo-β-chlorobutyric acid gives crotonic acid with ethanolic potassium hydroxide and α-iodocrotonic acid with pyridine.[97] β-(2-Quinolyl)- and β-(4-

[88] I.G. Farbenind. A.-G., U. S. pat. 1,914,674 [*C.A.*, **27**, 4252 (1933)]; Ger. pat. 583,790 [*C.A.*, **28**, 1058 (1934)].

[89] Tiffeneau, *Compt. rend.*, **139**, 481 (1904); Agejewa, *J. Russ. Phys. Chem. Soc.*, **37**, 662 (1905) (*Chem. Zentr.*, **1905**, II, 1017); Klages, *Ber.*, **39**, 2587 (1906); and many others.

[90] Lespieau, *Bull. soc. chim. France*, [4] **29**, 528 (1921).

[91] Zeberg, *J. Gen. Chem. U.S.S.R.*, **5**, 1016 (1935) [*C.A.*, **30**, 1023 (1936)].

[92] Ingold and Piggott, *J. Chem. Soc.*, **121**, 2381 (1922); Ingold and Shoppee, *ibid.*, **1929**, 447; Shoppee, *ibid.*, **1930**, 968; **1931**, 1225. A review of this work and of a number of related investigations can be found in Baker, *Tautomerism*, George Routledge and Sons, Ltd., London, 1934; D. Van Nostrand Co., New York, 1934, p. 80.

[93] Johnson, Jacobs, and Schwartz, *J. Am. Chem. Soc.*, **60**, 1885 (1938).

[94] Linstead, *J. Chem. Soc.*, **1930**, 1603; Linstead and Noble, *ibid.*, **1934**, 610, 614.

[95] (a) Zincke and Fries, *Ann.*, **325**, 44 (1902); (b) Zincke and Wagner, *Ann.*, **338**, 236 (1905); (c) Pfeiffer, *Ber.*, **45**, 1810 (1912); (d) Pfeiffer and Kramer, *Ber.*, **46**, 3655 (1913); (e) Reinhardt, *Ber.*, **46**, 3598 (1913); (f) Harrison, *J. Chem. Soc.*, **1926**, 1232.

[96] (a) Pfeiffer and Langenberg, *Ber.*, **43**, 3039 (1910); (b) Perkin and Bellenot, *J. Chem. Soc.*, **49**, 440 (1886).

[97] Ingold and Smith, *J. Chem. Soc.*, **1931**, 2742.

pyridyl)-acrylic acids are obtained from their dibromides not only by the action of common bases but even by boiling with water or ethanol.[70c] Cyclic compounds such as 1,2-dibromocyclohexane which cannot yield an acetylene lose halogen to give cyclic olefins as one of several reactions with quinoline.[98]

The removal of adjacent halogens to form olefins is an important side reaction when dibromides are treated with sodium amide.[28] In Bourguel's technique the olefin is readily separated from the 1-alkyne, but the yields of the acetylene are often low and it is preferable to remove the first molecule of hydrogen bromide with ethanolic potassium hydroxide. Bromoölefins are not converted to olefins by sodium amide. Polymerization always accompanies the dehalogenation; 1,2-dibromopropane gives very little methylacetylene, some propylene, and mainly polymer even though sodium amide free from sodium is used.

Addition of Alcohols. Acetylenes in which the triple bond is activated by conjugation with such groups as phenyl or carboxyl add primary alcohols readily in the presence of sodium alkoxides.[99] Addition is also observed with propargyl acetal [100] and ethers of acetylenic glycols.[101] With phenylacetylene this reaction gives alkyl styryl ethers in high yield,[99a, c] and the direction of addition is the reverse of that observed with reagents in the presence of acid. Alcohols add 1,4 to vinylacetylene in the presence of sodium alkoxides, and the products rearrange to 1-alkoxy-2-butynes.[102] Secondary alcohols add slowly, and tertiary alcohols even more slowly. Rearrangement is the principal reaction observed when 1-alkynes are treated with ethanolic alkali,[78, 99c] although Moureu isolated from 1-heptyne a little high-boiling material which may have been formed by addition of ethanol. Allene or methylacetylene gives mainly ethyl isopropenyl ether.[78b]

Small amounts of vinyl ethers have been reported occasionally in the synthesis of arylacetylenes by the reaction of ethanolic potassium hydroxide, and this reagent has been used instead of sodium ethoxide to promote the addition of ethanol.[78, 99a] It appears that the presence of some water decreases the ease of addition and that vinyl ether formation is not ordinarily an important side reaction during dehydrohalogenation to produce arylacetylenes, although it might be expected to interfere with the use of sodium ethoxide (p. 11).

[98] Harries and Splawa-Neyman, *Ber.*, **42**, 693 (1909); Harries, *Ber.*, **45**, 809 (1912); Willstätter and Hatt, *Ber.*, **45**, 1464 (1912).

[99] (a) Nef, *Ann.*, **308**, 264 (1899); (b) Moureu, *Compt. rend.*, **137**, 259 (1903); (c) Moureu, *Bull. soc. chim. France*, [3] **31**, 493, 526 (1904); (d) Moureu and Lazennec, *Compt. rend.*, **142**, 338 (1906); *Bull. soc. chim. France*, [3] **35**, 526, 531 (1906).

[100] Claisen, *Ber.*, **36**, 3664 (1903).

[101] Gauthier, *Ann. chim.*, [8] **16**, 289 (1909).

[102] Jacobson, Dykstra, and Carothers, *J. Am. Chem. Soc.*, **56**, 1169 (1934).

Limitations in the Synthesis of Acetylenic Acids. Although substituted cinnamic acid dibromides or their esters are readily converted to phenylpropiolic acids,[103] the reaction is usually accompanied by some decarboxylation. To minimize this side reaction the temperature is kept as low as possible, especially during acidification of the alkaline reaction mixture. The decarboxylation occurs readily and has been used for the synthesis of a number of substituted phenylacetylenes.[16, 104] α-Alkylcinnamic acid dibromides yield 1-phenyl-1-alkynes directly and in good yield when treated with ethanolic potassium hydroxide.[105]

Aliphatic acids with a triple bond adjacent to the carboxyl group cannot be prepared from the dibromides of the corresponding olefinic acids or from the α-haloölefinic acids. The action of alcoholic alkali on α-bromocrotonic or α,β-dibromobutyric acid gives α- and β-alkoxycrotonic acids in proportions depending upon the alcohol.[64 b, 106] The attempted synthesis of 2-pentynoic acid from 2-pentenoic acid dibromide failed,[79 b] and propiolic acid has not been obtained from α,β-dihalopropionic or α-haloacrylic acid although α-ethoxyacrylic acid, pyruvic acid, glyceric acid, and polymers have been reported.[107] The conversion of α-bromoacrylic acid to acetylene and carbon dioxide by dehydrohalogenation and decarboxylation has been noted.[107 b, 108]

Certain β-halo-α,β-unsaturated acids will yield acetylenic acids, for tetrolic acid is usually prepared from ethyl acetoacetate by the action of phosphorus pentachloride followed by potassium hydroxide;[109] but the yield is often low, and such by-products as acetone, ethoxycrotonic acid, and polymers are produced. The literature contains conflicting reports on the conversion of 3-bromo-2-pentenoic acid to 2-pentynoic acid.[46, 79 b] Most α,β-acetylenic carboxylic acids are now prepared by carbonation of metallic derivatives of 1-alkynes so that decarboxylation of these acids has no synthetic value. However, the decarboxylation has been reported to take place with excellent yields.[110]

[103] For phenylpropiolic acid see Abbott, *Org. Syntheses*, **12**, 60 (1932); *Coll. Vol.* **2**, 515 (1943); Reimer, *J. Am. Chem. Soc.*, **64**, 2510 (1942).

[104] (a) Otto, *J. Am. Chem. Soc.*, **56**, 1393 (1934); (b) Fulton and Robinson, *J. Chem. Soc.*, **1933**, 1463; (c) Weltzien, Micheel, and Hess, *Ann.*, **433**, 247 (1923); (d) Wollring, *Ber.*, **47**, 111 (1914); (e) Gattermann, *Ann.*, **347**, 347 (1906); (f) Straus, *Ann.*, **342**, 190 (1905); (g) Reychler, *Bull. soc. chim. France*, [3] **17**, 513 (1897); (h) Müller, *Ann.*, **212**, 122 (1882); *Ber.*, **20**, 1212 (1887); (i) Baeyer, *Ber.*, **13**, 2254 (1880); (j) Glaser, *Ann.*, **154**, 137 (1870).

[105] Bogert and Davidson, *J. Am. Chem. Soc.*, **54**, 334 (1932).

[106] Pfister, Robinson, and Tishler, *J. Am. Chem. Soc.*, **67**, 2269 (1945).

[107] (a) Otto, *Ber.*, **23**, 1108 (1890); Otto and Beckurts, *Ber.*, **18**, 239 (1885); (b) Lossen and Kowski, *Ann.*, **342**, 124 (1905); (c) Wagner and Tollens, *Ann.*, **171**, 340 (1874).

[108] Mauthner and Suida, *Monatsh.*, **2**, 98 (1881).

[109] See table, p. 23.

[110] Moureu and André, *Ann. chim.*, [9] **1**, 116 (note) (1914).

Acetylenedicarboxylic acid [9] resembles phenylpropiolic acid in that it is prepared from α,β-dibromosuccinic acid without difficulty and its acid potassium salt is readily decarboxylated to propiolic acid.[111]

Other Side Reactions. Polymerization is encountered in the synthesis of a number of acetylenic compounds, and autoxidation may occur,[112, 113] although usually it is not important. The formation of polymeric material under the influence of ethanolic potassium hydroxide, sodium ethoxide, and similar reagents may perhaps be the result of polymerization of vinyl ethers formed by addition of alcohol to the triple bond.

Preparation of the Halogen Compounds for Dehydrohalogenation to Acetylenes

Four general methods have been employed for synthesis of halogen compounds useful for preparing acetylenes: (1) olefins to olefin dibromides, (2) cinnamic acids to ω-bromostyrenes, (3) ketones with phosphorus pentachloride to dihalides, (4) 2-bromoallyl bromide or 3-chloroallyl chloride with Grignard reagents to halogenated olefins. The first method requires no comment. The second has been reviewed in a previous chapter in *Organic Reactions*.[114] The third and fourth will be discussed below.

Phosphorus Pentachloride and Carbonyl Compounds. The reaction of phosphorus pentachloride with carbonyl compounds[115] has been widely used to prepare chlorides for acetylene synthesis. The products of the reaction include monochloroethylenes as well as the expected dichlorides; hydrogen chloride is always produced. Favorskiĭ[116] has re-

$$RCOCH_2R' + PCl_5 \rightarrow RCCl_2CH_2R' + POCl_3$$

$$RCOCH_2R' + PCl_5 \rightarrow RCCl{=}CHR' + HCl + POCl_3$$

viewed the work prior to 1913 and has carefully studied the reaction with aliphatic ketones. Maximum yields of chlorides suitable for acetylene synthesis are obtained by adding the ketone dropwise to a slight excess

[111] (a) Bandrowski, *Ber.*, **13**, 2340 (1880); (b) Baeyer, *Ber.*, **18**, 674, 2269 (1885); (c) Perkin and Simonsen, *J. Chem. Soc.*, **91**, 816 (1907); (d) Ingold, *J. Chem. Soc.*, **127**, 1199 (1925); (e) for an alternative preparation see Straus and Voss, *Ber.*, **59**, 1681 (1926); Straus, Heyn, and Schwemer, *Ber.*, **63**, 1086 (1930).

[112] Young, Vogt, and Nieuwland, (a) *J. Am. Chem. Soc.*, **56**, 1822 (1934); (b) *ibid.*, **58**, 55 (1936); (c) *J. Chem. Soc.*, **1935**, 115.

[113] Campbell and Eby, *J. Am. Chem. Soc.*, **63**, 216 (1941).

[114] The Perkin Reaction, Johnson, *Org. Reactions*, **1**, 210–265 (1942).

[115] Friedel, *Compt. rend.*, **67**, 1192 (1868); *Ann. chim.*, [4] **16**, 310 (1869).

[116] Favorskiĭ, *J. prakt. Chem.*, [2] **88**, 641 (1913); *J. Russ. Phys. Chem. Soc.*, **44**, 1339 (1912) [*C.A.* **7**, 984 (1913)].

of phosphorus pentachloride in an all-glass apparatus at 0° so that the evolution of hydrogen chloride is not vigorous. The reaction occurs only at higher temperatures with diisopropyl ketone or pentamethyl-acetone, and under these conditions α-chloroketones are formed as the result of a chlorination reaction. Pinacolone is converted to a mixture of chloroölefin and dichloride which is readily transformed into *tert*-butylacetylene.[6a, 116] The yield of chloro compounds has been reported as essentially quantitative, and the yield of *tert*-butylacetylene as 65%. Other workers have not always obtained such good results,[4, 6b] although over 90% yields of chloro compounds have been obtained.[117] By use of finely powdered phosphorus pentachloride, maintenance of the temperature at 0–5°, and stirring, the yield of mono- and di-chlorides is 91%, from which an 80% yield of the acetylene is obtained.[117b] The reaction of pinacolone with phosphorus pentachloride has been extensively studied.[117c, d] The only product isolated from ethyl *tert*-butyl ketone and phosphorus pentachloride at 70° is 2-chloro-4,4-dimethyl-3-pentanone, $(CH_3)_3CCOCHClCH_3$.[118]

Phosphorus pentabromide produces from all types of ketones mainly α-bromoketones and cannot be used to prepare bromides suitable for acetylene synthesis.[116] This may be the result of the action of halogen formed by dissociation of the phosphorus pentabromide. However, the ketones are more readily brominated by phosphorus pentabromide than by bromine, so that, if the free halogen is the reagent, a phosphorus halide must be a catalyst for the reaction.

Even at 0° the products of the reaction of phosphorus pentachloride with aliphatic ketones include small amounts of dichloro compounds of the type RCHClCHClR' and of acetylenes as well as the expected dichloro compounds RCH_2CCl_2R' and monochloroölefins.[119] The chloroethylenes from methyl ketones are largely 2-chloro-2-alkenes, $RCH{=}CClCH_3$.[119] However, butanone was said to give a mixture of chlorobutenes containing an appreciable amount of 2-chloro-1-butene.[120]

The action of phosphorus pentachloride on arylacetones, $ArCH_2COCH_3$, gives a mixture of chloroölefins, $ArCH{=}CClCH_3$ and $ArCH_2CCl{=}CH_2$. If either of these pure chloroölefins is allowed to stand, it slowly changes to an equilibrium mixture of the two.[121] An aromatic aliphatic ketone

[117] (a) de Graef, *Bull. soc. chim. Belg.*, **34**, 427 (1925); (b) Bartlett and Rosen, *J. Am. Chem. Soc.*, **64**, 543 (1942); (c) Delacre, *Bull. soc. chim. France*, [3] **35**, 343 (1906); *Acad. roy. Belg., Classe sci., Mém.*, [2] **1**, 1 (1904–1906); (d) Risseghem, *Bull. soc. chim. Belg.*, **31**, 62 (1922).
[118] Vassliev, *Bull. soc. chim. France*, [4] **43**, 563 (1928).
[119] Bourguel, *Bull. soc. chim. France*, [4] **35**, 1629 (1924).
[120] Charpentier, *Bull. soc. chim. France*, [5] **1**, 1407 (1934).
[121] Zaki and Iskander, *J. Chem. Soc.*, **1943**, 68.

such as acetophenone yields mainly chloroethylene and polymer, but a little 1,1-dichloroethylbenzene can be isolated. Phosphorus trichloride dibromide [122] gives a mixture of products including phenacyl bromide and phenacyl dibromide. A 54% yield of chlorostyrene is obtained [123] using petroleum ether as a solvent and mixing the phosphorus pentachloride with coarsely broken glass. The autoxidizability of the product is reported. Phosphorus oxychloride or a mixture of this with phosphorus trichloride has been used as a solvent in the reaction of acetobromomesitylene or acetoisodurene with phosphorus pentachloride.[58, 59] ω-Chloroketones and phosphoric esters are reported as by-products.

In general the reaction of aromatic methyl ketones with phosphorus pentachloride is a satisfactory method of preparing intermediates for acetylene syntheses, since the starting materials are readily available by the Friedel and Crafts or other reactions, and there is no possibility of rearrangement of the triple bond in the final step. The reaction is usually carried out at about 70°. Aliphatic acetylenes are obtainable in this way in low yield only, except for a few compounds like *tert*-butylacetylene. Cyclohexylacetylene is readily obtainable by this method, but the yield of cyclopentylacetylene appears to be low. Table V gives some of the more recent results obtained. The preparation of *p*-tolylacetylene by this method is described in the section on laboratory procedures (p. 50).

Reaction of Grignard Reagents with Halogen-Substituted Allyl Halides. The reaction of 2,3-dibromopropene with Grignard reagents was first used by Lespieau [90] to prepare halogen compounds for acetylene syntheses. The reaction has been carefully studied,[28] and detailed directions for the synthesis of 3-cyclohexyl-2-bromopropene have been

[122] Taylor, *J. Chem. Soc.*, **1937**, 304.
[123] Dufraisse and Viel, *Bull. soc. chim. France*, [4] **37**, 874 (1925).

TABLE V

Yields in the Reaction of Phosphorus Pentachloride with Carbonyl Compounds and Conversion of the Products to Acetylenes

Acetylene	Yield of Chloro Compound %	Yield of Acetylene from Chloro Compound %	Overall Yield %	Reference
Phenylacetylene	Quantitative yield of crude product	37–43	37–43	99a
p-Tolylacetylene	68	48	33	50
	75	57	43	51
2,4-Dimethylphenylacetylene	82	75 *	61	43
Mesitylacetylene	78	71 *	55	43, 58
2,3,4,6-Tetramethylphenylacetylene	73 †	65	47	58
p-Chlorophenylacetylene	60	36	22	43
p-Bromophenylacetylene	70	53	37	49
3-Bromo-2,4,6-trimethylphenylacetylene	63	57	36	58
β-Naphthylacetylene			35	51
2,4-Dimethyl-3-chloro-6-methoxyphenylacetylene	60	60	36	59
3-Ethynyl-2-methylnaphthalene			45	124
Tolan	80	34	27	45
Phenyl-β-naphthylacetylene	75–93 †	58	44–54	15
β-Pyridylacetylene	50	42	21	70c
Cyclopentylacetylene			9 *	41
Cyclohexylacetylene	70–80	46	32–37	125
tert-Butylacetylene	45–100	59–80	27–73	117
3-Ethyl-3-methyl-1-pentyne	65	45 *	29	39
1-Heptyne	70	60 *‡	24	28, 74
4-Methyl-2-pentyne			26	79c
5-Methyl-2-hexyne	61			79d
2,6-Dimethyl-3-heptyne	52	38	20	79d
Tetrolic acid	52	16	15.5 §	126
1-(p-Methoxyphenyl)-1-propyne	24 ‖	75	18	127

* The sodium amide method was used for dehydrohalogenation.
† Crude product.
‡ Hill and Tyson, ref. 74, prepared 1,1-dichloroheptane in 70% yield but used it for vapor-phase dehydrohalogenation. Bourguel, ref. 28, obtained 60% yields of the acetylene using a rather pure chloro compound, and an overall yield of 24% in runs in which the chloro product was not purified carefully.
§ The overall yield was obtained in a larger run.
‖ 2-Chloro-1-(p-anisyl)-1-propene from p-anisylacetone. p-Methoxypropiophenone was converted to 1-chloro-1-(p-anisyl)-1-propene in 44% yield, but this chloride was not dehydrohalogenated.

124 Karrer, Epprecht, and König, Helv. Chim. Acta, 23, 272 (1940).
125 Sweet and Marvel, J. Am. Chem. Soc., 54, 1184 (1932).
126 Feist, Ann., 345, 100 (1906).
127 Hobday and Short, J. Chem. Soc., 1943, 609.

described.[28,128] If the Grignard solution is added to the dibromopropene,

$$C_6H_{11}MgBr + BrCH_2CBr\!\!=\!\!CH_2 \rightarrow C_6H_{11}CH_2CBr\!\!=\!\!CH_2 + MgBr_2$$

yields of 45–65% are usually obtained, but addition of the bromo compound to the organometallic derivative leads to the formation of complex substances and greatly reduces the yield of the desired product. Allene is one of the principal by-products. The presence also of a saturated bromo compound is attributed to the addition of the Grignard reagent to the double bond of $RCH_2CBr\!\!=\!\!CH_2$,[90] though some doubt about the saturated character of the by-product has recently been raised.[129]

Syntheses with 1,3-dihalopropenes are complicated by the possibility of an allylic rearrangement which may lead to a mixture of products. The reaction of such allyl compounds with aliphatic Grignard reagents

$$BrCH_2CH\!\!=\!\!CHBr \rightleftarrows CH_2\!\!=\!\!CHCHBr_2$$

is very complicated,[130] but nearly quantitative yields of 3-aryl-1-chloro-1-propenes have been reported [52,131] from arylmagnesium halides. α-Naphthylmagnesium bromide and 1,3-dibromopropene in toluene at 100° [131c] give a 50% yield of product. The addition of 1,3- and 2,3-dibromo- and 1,3-dichloro-propenes to aryl Grignard reagents at low temperatures in ether results in lower yields than those reported above.[132] The abnormal reaction of 1,2,3-tribromopropene with phenylmagnesium bromide will be discussed (p. 44). When the five-carbon homolog of bromoallyl bromide (mainly $C_2H_5CH\!\!=\!\!CBrCH_2Br$) is first converted to 3-bromo-3-hexene and then to 3-hexyne some 1-alkyne, presumably 3-methyl-1-pentyne, is obtained owing to an allylic rearrangement.[133]

$$C_2H_5CH\!\!=\!\!CBrCH_2Br \rightleftarrows C_2H_5CHBrCBr\!\!=\!\!CH_2 \xrightarrow{CH_3MgBr} C_2H_5\overset{\overset{\displaystyle CH_3}{|}}{C}HCBr\!\!=\!\!CH_2$$

$$\xrightarrow{KOH} C_2H_5\overset{\overset{\displaystyle CH_3}{|}}{C}HC\!\!\equiv\!\!CH$$

[128] Lespieau and Bourguel, *Org. Syntheses, Coll. Vol.* **1**, 186, 2nd ed., 1941.

[129] Private communication, Young and Linden, University of California, Los Angeles.

[130] Kirrmann, *Bull. soc. chim. France*, [4] **47**, 834 (1930); Kirrmann and Grard, *Compt. rend.*, **190**, 876 (1930); Kirrmann, Pacaud, and Dosque, *Bull. soc. chim. France*, [5] **1**, 860 (1934); Kirrmann and Renn, *Compt. rend.*, **202**, 1934 (1936).

[131] (a) Bert, *Bull. soc. chim. France*, [4] **37**, 879 (1925); (b) *Compt. rend.*, **180**, 1504 (1925); (c) Bert and Dorier, *Bull. soc. chim. France*, [4] **37**, 1600 (1925); (d) *ibid.*, [4] **39**, 1610 (1926).

[132] Braun and Kuhn, *Ber.*, **58**, 2168 (1925).

[133] Lespieau and Wiemann, *Bull. soc. chim. France*, [4] **45**, 627 (1929).

The halogen-substituted allyl halides such as 1,3-dichloropropene are readily prepared [19, 134] by well-known methods.

1-ALKYNES FROM METALLIC DERIVATIVES OF ACETYLENE

The alkylation of sodium acetylide in liquid ammonia by alkyl halides was first reported by Lebeau and Picon.[135, 136] In this work alkyl iodides

$$RX + NaC\equiv CH \rightarrow RC\equiv CH + NaX$$

were employed, but other alkyl halides have been used and the bromides usually give the best yields. Alkyl sulfates [137, 138] and esters of p-toluene-sulfonic acid [139] have also been tried; dimethyl and diethyl sulfates are recommended for the synthesis of propyne and 1-butyne.[140, 141] The reaction is limited to the introduction of primary alkyl groups, RCH_2CH_2-, which are not branched on the second carbon. In the hands of an experienced operator yields of 70–90% are usually obtained. The method has been extensively investigated and improved.[142, 143, 144] Some results obtained by its use are given in Table VI.

[134] Hill and Fischer, *J. Am. Chem. Soc.*, **44**, 2582 (1922); Bert and Dorier, *Bull. soc. chim. France*, [4] **39**, 1573 (1926).

[135] Lebeau and Picon, *Compt. rend.*, **156**, 1077 (1913).

[136] Picon, *Compt. rend.*, (a) **158**, 1184, 1346 (1914); (b) **168**, 894 (1919); (c) **169**, 32 (1919).

[137] Meinert and Hurd, *J. Am. Chem. Soc.*, **52**, 4540 (1930).

[138] Hurd and Meinert, *J. Am. Chem. Soc.*, **53**, 289 (1931).

[139] Kranzfelder and Sowa, *J. Am. Chem. Soc.*, **59**, 1490 (1937).

[140] Campbell and Eby, *J. Am. Chem. Soc.*, **63**, 2683 (1941).

[141] See Table VI, note ‡, p. 26.

[142] Vaughn, Hennion, Vogt, and Nieuwland, *J. Org. Chem.*, **2**, 1 (1937).

[143] Nieuwland and Vogt, *The Chemistry of Acetylene*, Chapters II and III, Reinhold Publishing Corp., New York, 1945.

[144] (a) Greenlee, Dissertation, Ohio State University, 1942; (b) Henne and Greenlee, *J. Am. Chem. Soc.*, **65**, 2020 (1943); **67**, 484 (1945).

TABLE VI

1-ALKYNES FROM SODIUM ACETYLIDE AND ALKYL BROMIDES [144]

1-Alkyne	Yield * %	Reaction time hr.	Moles of Bromide	Moles of $HC{\equiv}CNa$
1-Propyne	84 †	5	4.25	4
1-Butyne	89 ‡	3	‡	1
1-Pentyne	85	5	17.1	20
1-Hexyne	89	6½	4.5	5
1-Heptyne	56	4	2 to 3	Slight excess
	73	6	2 to 3	Slight excess
	83	13	2 to 3	Slight excess
5-Methyl-1-hexyne	68 §	6		4.5
1-Octyne	72	22	14	20

* Based on alkyl bromide, which was the limiting factor except as noted.
† A slight excess of methyl bromide was used. The yield based on sodium was 89%.
‡ Diethyl sulfate was used instead of ethyl bromide. The reaction was vigorous so that addition was slow. The yield given is of crude material. Some difficulties were encountered in purification, and some material was lost. The yield of pure product was 65%, but it should be possible to improve this.
§ Insufficient reaction time. The yield was 47% on isoamyl bromide taken, and the recovery of bromide was 31%. The freezing-point curve was poor, probably owing to isomers resulting from impure isoamyl bromide.

The Preparation of Sodium Acetylide and Other Metallic Acetylides

Sodium acetylide is prepared commonly by passing acetylene into a solution of sodium in liquid ammonia at the boiling point. The reaction is slow because the mechanical difficulty of dissolving a gas in a boiling solution is increased by the vigorous exothermic reaction and consequent dilution of the acetylene by solvent vapors and ethylene.[144] This difficulty has been surmounted most successfully by using a metallic reflux condenser of adequate capacity cooled with Dry Ice.[48b,144a] The acetylene that does not react when first passed through the solution is dissolved and returned to the flask by the condensing ammonia. Excellent directions for this method of preparation have been published.[145] If a suitable condenser is not available, it is probably simplest to introduce a large piece of sodium gradually into a saturated solution of acetylene in liquid ammonia with vigorous stirring as described by Hennion.[146]

[145] Greenlee and Henne, *Inorganic Syntheses*, **2**, 75 (1946). See also reference 143, Chapter 2, for a discussion of the synthesis of sodium acetylide.
[146] Hennion, *Proc. Indiana Acad. Sci.*, **47**, 116 (1938) [*C.A.*, **32**, 9039 (1938)].

The addition of a solution of sodium in liquid ammonia to a saturated solution of acetylene in liquid ammonia has been successful,[142, 143] but it is hazardous since the sodium solution cannot be handled in an ordinary separatory funnel. Small amounts of sodium acetylide have been prepared [135] by passing acetylene into the sodium solution cooled in Dry Ice. The preparation has also been carried out in an autoclave at room temperature, but there is danger of violent explosions, especially if a trace of air is present.[142, 143] Any of these procedures for preparing sodium acetylide from metallic sodium has two disadvantages: the upper walls of the flask are quickly covered by metallic sodium which is difficult to wash down, and one-third of the acetylene is wasted as ethylene.

$$3HC\equiv CH + 2Na \rightarrow 2NaC\equiv CH + H_2C\equiv CH_2$$

A preferable method employing sodium amide in place of sodium was discovered by Picon [147] and developed by others.[48b, 144, 145] In practice the method is less troublesome and somewhat more adaptable. The sodium acetylide prepared in this way contains small amounts of iron and other impurities, but these do not appear to interfere with its use in synthesis. In fact the impurities may be beneficial, since it is reported that the acetylide obtained in this way is considerably more reactive than that obtained using sodium.[148] The details of the procedure are given on p. 48.

A reactive form of sodium acetylide has been prepared from acetylene and a suspension of sodium naphthalene in dimethyl ether. The sodium derivatives of other aromatic hydrocarbons can be substituted for sodium naphthalene, and the dimethyl ether can be replaced by ethers of ethylene glycol or of various polyhydroxyl compounds.[148a]

The acetylides of other alkali and alkaline-earth metals have been prepared but offer no advantages for the synthesis of 1-alkynes.[149] Patents have been issued for the synthesis of mono- and di-substituted acetylenes from calcium carbide and organic halogen or hydroxyl compounds, mostly at high temperatures.[149c, d, e]

[147] Picon, *Compt. rend.*, **173**, 155 (1921); *Bull. soc. chim. France*, [4] **29**, 709 (1921).

[148] Heilbron, Jones, and Weedon, *J. Chem. Soc.*, **1945**, 81.

[148a] Scott, Hansley, and Walker, *J. Am. Chem. Soc.*, **58**, 2442 (1936); U. S. pats. 2,171,867 and 2,171,868 [*C.A.*, **34**, 115, 116 (1940)].

[149] A review of these is given in reference 143, pp. 40–48, 78–79. References dealing especially with their use in alkyne synthesis include: (a) Vaughn and Danehy, *Proc. Indiana Acad. Sci.*, **44**, 144 (1934) [*C.A.*, **30**, 429 (1936)]; (b) Campbell and Campbell, *Proc. Indiana Acad. Sci.*, **50**, 123 (1940) [*C.A.*, **35**, 5457 (1941)]; (c) Soc. pour l'ind. chim. à Bâle, Brit. pat. 298,090 [*C.A.*, **23**, 2722 (1929)]; (d) Dutt, Fr. pat. 677,338 [*C.A.*, **24**, 2956 (1930)]; (e) Corson, Brit. pat. 279,095 [*C.A.*, **22**, 2755 (1928)]; Fr. pat. 642,170 [*C.A.*, **23**, 1135 (1929)].

The Alkylation of Sodium Acetylide

The alkylation of sodium acetylide by alkyl halides is limited to the introduction of primary alkyl groups, RCH_2CH_2-. Secondary and tertiary halides and primary halides with branching on the second carbon, R_2CHCH_2-, give only traces of 1-alkyne; the principal product is the alkene formed by dehydrohalogenation.[136, 150] The reactivity of the alkyl halides with sodium acetylide increases with the atomic weight of the halogen and decreases with increasing size of the alkyl group. Methyl chloride gives propyne in 54% yield in sixteen hours, all the halide being used, but n-butyl chloride yields only 30% of 1-hexyne after twenty-five hours.[144a] Aryl halides cannot be employed; they either fail to react (chlorobenzene) or undergo ammonolysis only (o-chloronitrobenzene).[142] Products other than 1-alkynes are obtained with vinyl chloride,[142] 1-bromo-1-butyne,[144a] and chloromethyl ether.[144a] Yields of 60–75% of ethers of 3-butyn-1-ol have been obtained from a number of ethers of ethylene bromohydrin $ROCH_2CH_2Br$.[151] Ethylene bromohydrin gives mainly acetaldehyde.[151]

Allyl halides react with sodium acetylide[144, 152] to give a mixture of unidentified compounds containing eight and eleven carbon atoms. This anomalous result is attributed to metalation of the methylene group of 1-penten-

$$CH_2=CHCH_2Br + NaC\equiv CH \rightarrow CH_2=CHCH_2C\equiv CH + NaBr$$

$$CH_2=CHCH_2C\equiv CH + NaC\equiv CH \rightarrow CH_2=CHCHNaC\equiv CH + HC\equiv CH$$

$$CH_2=CHCHNaC\equiv CH + CH_2=CHCH_2Br \rightarrow \underset{\underset{CH_2CH=CH_2}{|}}{CH_2=CHCHC\equiv CH} + NaBr$$

4-yne. The eleven-carbon compound $\underset{\underset{C\equiv CH}{|}}{CH_2=CHC(CH_2CH=CH_2)_2}$

would be formed from $\underset{\underset{C\equiv CH}{|}}{CH_2=CH-CHCH_2CH=CH_2}$ by further reac-

tion with sodium acetylide and allyl bromide. Analogous products were obtained from methallyl chloride.[144]

Alkyl bromides, especially if pure, give the best results, since they are more reactive than chlorides yet produce smaller amounts of amines than the iodides. The synthesis has been carried out in an autoclave at higher pressures and temperatures,[136c, 142, 143] but, except with

[150] Picon, *Compt. rend.*, **168**, 825 (1919).
[151] McCusker and Kroeger, *J. Am. Chem. Soc.*, **59**, 213 (1937).
[152] Lespieau and Journaud, *Bull. soc. chim. France*, [4] **49**, 423 (1931).

chlorides, the best results are obtained at atmospheric pressure at the boiling point of liquid ammonia.

The chlorides and even the bromides are not readily separated from the alkynes, and efficient fractionating columns must be used in purifying the products. A column of 25-plate efficiency gives 1-heptyne and 1-octyne of high purity.[144, 153] No satisfactory chemical method of removing the halogen compound has been discovered.[142, 143] A large excess of sodium acetylide is ineffective in reducing the amount of the impurity, but with very efficient stirring less halide is found in the product.

The yields are lowered by entrainment and vaporization of the alkyne during the addition of water to the liquid ammonia solution at the end of the reaction unless adequate precautions are taken, such as the use of an efficient Dry Ice-cooled condenser [48b, 144] (p. 48). The removal of the ammonia before hydrolysis is not advisable, for the hot concentrated sodium hydroxide produced on addition of water may then rearrange the 1-alkyne. Thus, in the reaction of butyl bromide and sodium acetylide, removal of ammonia followed by addition of water gave a product boiling at 71–72° containing only 79% of 1-hexyne.[154]

Organic solvents do not improve the yield in the synthesis and are often detrimental, although small amounts of ether may increase the rate of reaction slightly. The yields are not altered by substitution of cadmium, aluminum, or iron containers for the usual glass flask; stirrers of Monel metal, nickel, Nichrome, brass, and glass have been used.

The application of the liquid ammonia method to dihalides has been successful.[144, 155] 1,6-Heptadiyne and 1,8-nonadiyne are obtained without difficulty from trimethylene and pentamethylene bromides in 40–43% and 84% yields, respectively.[144] The crude yield of the former is 70–74%, but 13% of low-boiling material, possibly 2-penten-4-yne, is present, and the product is difficult to purify on account of polymerization. 1-Bromo-3-chloropropane gives a 57% yield of 5-chloro-1-pentyne.[144] Compounds having halogens on adjacent carbon atoms usually undergo dehydrohalogenation,[142, 143, 144] and methylene chloride gives unidentified material.[144]

Alkyl sulfates may be used in the alkylation instead of halides [137, 138] and are superior for the synthesis of propyne and 1-butyne.[140, 141] It should be remembered that only one of the alkyl groups in an alkyl

---

[153] The physical constants of the pure alkynes are given in references 140 and 144. They are also given in *Selected Values of Properties of Hydrocarbons*, American Petroleum Institute Research Project 44, National Bureau of Standards, Washington, D. C.

[154] See the private communication from Hurd cited by Vaughn, Hennion, Vogt, and Nieuwland, *J. Org. Chem.*, **2**, 11 (1937).

[155] Lespieau and Journaud, *Compt. rend.*, **188**, 1410 (1929).

sulfate reacts. It is noteworthy that diisopropyl sulfate gives 29–50% yields of isopropylacetylene.[139]

The methyl, propyl, and butyl esters of p-toluenesulfonic acid will alkylate sodium acetylide in liquid ammonia in 37–47% yields, but solid esters such as the amyl cannot be used.[139] No alkylation is obtained with tributyl phosphate, amyl acetate, or butyl acetate.

Sodium acetylide, prepared from acetylene and sodium naphthalene in a suitable ether solvent, furnishes propiolic acid in 69% yield on carbonation and is reported to undergo alkylation with alkyl halides.[148a]

Side Reactions in the Alkylation of Sodium Acetylide

The by-products in this alkylation reaction are as follows: olefins, amines, ethers, alcohols, disubstituted acetylenes, and acetylene. ,

Olefins. As mentioned above, secondary and tertiary alkyl halides, and primary alkyl halides branched on the second carbon, give mainly dehydrohalogenation to olefins in the alkylation reaction. When carefully purified primary bromides, RCH_2CH_2Br, are used this olefin formation is unimportant.[144] The alkenes may arise in part as a result of the action of the alkyl halides with sodium amide, sodium hydroxide, or sodium alkoxides present in low concentration, but sodium acetylide is a strong base and might be expected to cause some dehydrohalogenation. Since the olefins have two fewer carbons than the desired acetylenes the separation is not difficult.

Amines. The reaction of ethyl bromide or iodide with liquid ammonia to produce a mixture of ethyl amines [156] has been found [142,143] to represent a general reaction of alkyl halides and to occur in 1-alkyne syntheses. Iodides react most readily and chlorides least. The amines obtained as by-products in the acetylene preparation consist of about equal parts of primary and secondary with variable amounts of tertiary. At atmospheric pressure and 34° this side reaction is unimportant with bromides, but at high pressures and temperatures it is significant. Alkyl sulfates give higher yields of amines as by-products.

Ethers and Alcohols. The presence of moisture may result in the formation of ethers and alcohols by the following reaction.

$$H_2O \xrightarrow{NaC_2H} NaOH \xrightarrow{RX} ROH \xrightarrow{NaC_2H} RONa \xrightarrow{RX} ROR$$

The Williamson synthesis of ethers has been shown to proceed smoothly in liquid ammonia.[157] Alcohols may also be present as impurities in the

[156] Picon, Bull. soc. chim. France, [4] 35, 979 (1924).
[157] Vaughn, Vogt, and Nieuwland, J. Am. Chem. Soc., 57, 510 (1935).

alkyl halides and lead to ether formation.[144] Ethers were isolated in
1% to 5% yields by fractionation of the residues from the distillation of
1-alkynes,[142,143] and alcohols were ordinarily present in amounts less
than 1%. Pure bromides give no significant quantities of ethers although
commercial bromides sometimes give several per cent.

Disubstituted Acetylenes. A small amount of disubstituted acetylene
usually can be isolated from the reaction of sodium acetylide with an
alkyl halide in liquid ammonia. When butyl and amyl bromides are
used, 2–3% and occasionally up to 30% of dialkylacetylenes may be
formed.[142,143] Much less of these by-products has been reported by
others,[144] and it has been suggested they arise from the presence of sodium
carbide. The presence of sodium carbide in metallic acetylides prepared
in liquid ammonia is disputed.[158,159] Certain results [144,145] suggest that
an equilibrium exists between sodium acetylide and sodium carbide.

$$2NaC{\equiv}CH \rightleftarrows NaC{\equiv}CNa + HC{\equiv}CH$$

Such an equilibrium is well established for the Grignard reagent from
acetylene (p. 32).

Acetylene. Some acetylene usually is produced in the final stages of
this synthesis,[160] but it is readily removed if the product is properly
fractionated.

Other Impurities. The following have been listed [142,143] as possible
by-products: rearranged hydrocarbons resulting from the action of
strong bases such as sodium acetylide, dimethylethynylcarbinol from
incomplete removal of acetone from the acetylene, peroxides produced
by the action of air or sodium peroxide, and polymers. A small amount
of polymerization usually occurs when the higher-boiling alkynes are
distilled. These side reactions are ordinarily unimportant, although the
rapidity with which the physical constants of acetylenes are changed by
peroxide formation on exposure to air has been stressed.[112,113,153]

Acetylene Mono- and Di-magnesium Bromide

Acetylenemagnesium bromide and acetylenedimagnesium bromide
have been used in the synthesis of many acetylenic compounds. A
mixture of these which behaves mainly as the dimagnesium derivative
was first prepared by Iozitsch [161] and is easily obtained at ordinary

[158] Moissan, *Compt. rend.*, **127**, 911 (1898).
[159] See reference 142, p. 17, and 143, pp. 41, 44.
[160] Heisig and Hurd, *J. Am. Chem. Soc.*, **55**, 3485 (1933).
[161] The extensive work of Iozitsch is noteworthy: *J. Russ. Phys. Chem. Soc.*, **34**, 242
(1902); **35**, 431, 1269 (1903); **38**, 252, 656 (1906); *Bull. soc. chim. France*, [3] **30**, 210 (1903);
[3] **32**, 552 (1904); [3] **34**, 181 (1905); [4] **4**, 981, 1203 (1908).

pressures;[162] its reactions with many carbonyl compounds have been studied. The proportion of monomagnesium derivative in the mixture is influenced by the amount of acetylene, but even when excess acetylene is present some glycol is produced in the reaction with an aldehyde.[161, 163] By using excess acetylene under pressure with efficient stirring it is possible to obtain a solution which behaves mainly as the monomagnesium derivative.[164, 165] The preparation of such a reagent using a shaking machine has been described.[166] The reaction between acetylene and ethylmagnesium bromide is allowed to proceed at ordinary pressure and temperature until ethane is no longer evolved (seven to eight hours), and the reaction is completed by several hours' stirring and refluxing under acetylene pressure of half an atmosphere. On carbonation this solution gives a 62% yield of propiolic acid and a 10% yield of acetylenedicarboxylic acid.[164] The reaction has been improved so that an 87% yield of propiolic acid can be obtained.[165]

The composition of the Grignard solution prepared at atmospheric pressure has been investigated.[167] It is not safe to estimate the proportions of mono- and di-magnesium derivatives present from the amounts of mono- and di-substituted acetylenes obtained in alkylation or addition reactions because the following reactions can also account for disubstituted compounds.

$$RX + HC \equiv CMgBr \rightarrow RC \equiv CH + MgXBr$$

$$RC \equiv CH + HC \equiv CMgBr \rightarrow RC \equiv CMgBr + HC \equiv CH$$

$$RC \equiv CMgBr + RX \rightarrow RC \equiv CR + MgXBr$$

The alkylation of the Grignard reagent of acetylene has not been studied extensively, although it appears to give rather satisfactory yields of 1-alkynes under the special conditions already mentioned.[164, 165] Benzyl bromide gives a 70% yield of 3-phenylpropyne, 8% of 1,4-di-

[162] Wieland and Kloss, *Ann.*, **470**, 201 (1929), have described the preparation and use of such a solution.

[163] Oddo, *Atti. accad. naz. Lincei*, [5] **13**, II, 187 (1904) (*Chem. Zentr.*, **1904**, II, 943); *Gazz. chim. ital.*, **34**, II, 429 (1904); **38**, I, 625 (1908).

[164] Grignard, Lapayre, and Tchéoufaki, *Compt. rend.*, **187**, 517 (1928).

[165] Tchéoufaki, *Contribs. Inst. Chem. Natl. Acad. Peiping*, **1**, 127 (1934) [*C.A.*, **29**, 2513 (1935)].

[166] Dane, Höss, Bindseil, and Schmitt, *Ann.*, **532**, 39 (1937).

[167] Zal'kind and Rosenfeld, *Ber.*, **57**, 1690 (1924); Kleinfeller and Lohmann, *Ber.*, **71**, 2608 (1938). The latter workers used a kinetic method and concluded that, contrary to common belief, the monomagnesium derivative is formed first. The following reactions account for their results.

$$C_2H_2 + C_2H_5MgBr \rightleftarrows HC \equiv CMgBr + C_2H_6$$

$$2HC \equiv CMgBr \rightleftarrows BrMgC \equiv CMgBr + C_2H_2$$

phenyl-2-butyne, and 12% of acetylene, while butyl bromide produces 72% of 1-hexyne. The solution obtained when only 1 mole of acetylene has been absorbed in 1 mole of ethyl- or phenyl-magnesium bromide produces 39% of 1-hexyne and 30% of 5-decyne by reaction with butyl bromide and only 20% of 3-hexyne with ethyl bromide. The reactions with butyl bromide are carried out at 80–90°. When the acetylenic Grignard reagent is prepared by the procedure of Iozitsch [161] and allowed to react with primary alkyl halides, the products include saturated hydrocarbons and olefins as well as disubstituted acetylenes which are produced in low yields only.[168] Butyl bromide gives C_4H_{10}, C_4H_8, a polymer of the latter, and a little 5-decyne. Isoamyl bromide behaves similarly, but no 9-octadecyne is isolated when n-octyl bromide is used. No 1-alkynes were reported. Wieland and Kloss [162] obtained only disubstituted acetylenes under comparable conditions from benzohydryl chloride and triphenylmethyl chloride.

The reaction of allyl bromide with the monobromomagnesium reagent was reported to give allylacetylene in 75% yield,[164] but this result could not be duplicated.[169] The reaction of allyl bromide with alkylacetylenic Grignard reagents occurs only in the presence of catalysts such as cuprous or cupric salts (p. 34).[170] These catalysts have not been tried with the Grignard reagent from acetylene.

THE SYNTHESIS OF DISUBSTITUTED ACETYLENES

The synthesis of pure disubstituted acetylenes with two aliphatic groups attached to the triple bond cannot be accomplished by the usual dehydrohalogenating agents since these reagents cause a rearrangement of the acetylenic linkage. Such compounds are best prepared from metallic derivatives of acetylenes and alkyl halides in liquid ammonia or alkyl sulfates in ether or other solvents.

Alkylation in Organic Solvents. Nef [171] reported the methylation of phenylacetylene by heating it with methyl iodide and potassium hydroxide, and Morgan [73a] obtained 1-phenyl-1-butyne by ethylating sodium phenylacetylide with ethyl iodide. Both reactions were carried out in sealed tubes at about 140°, and low yields resulted. Except in liquid ammonia, the sodium derivatives of acetylenes are remarkably inert toward alkyl halides, and vigorous, deep-seated decomposition

[168] Malinovskiĭ and Fedoseev, *Trudy Gor'kov Gosudarst. Pedagog. Inst.*, **1940**, No. 5, 43; *Khim. Referat. Zhur.*, **4**, No. 2, 40 (1941) [*C.A.*, **37**, 3046 (1943)].

[169] Grignard and Lapayre, *Compt. rend.*, **192**, 250 (1931).

[170] Danehy, Killian, and Nieuwland, *J. Am. Chem. Soc.*, **58**, 611 (1936).

[171] Nef, *Ann.*, **310**, 333 (1900).

occurs at temperatures sufficiently high to bring about a reaction.[172] Silver, cuprous, and mercuric acetylides are also inert toward alkyl halides.

Acetylenic Grignard reagents are less reactive than alkyl- or aryl-bromomagnesium compounds as measured by their tendency to add to benzonitrile,[173] and the reaction of these reagents with saturated aliphatic halides is without synthetic value, although very low yields of dialkylethynes from alkynylmagnesium bromides and tertiary alkyl halides have been reported.[174] The yield of 3,3-dimethyl-4-nonyne from hexynylmagnesium bromide and tert-amyl bromide was only 3%. With more reactive halides the synthetic results are better. Phenylethynyl-magnesium bromide reacts with triphenylmethyl chloride,[162] benzohydryl bromide,[162] and α-furfuryl chloride [175] to give satisfactory yields of the expected disubstituted acetylenes. Its reaction with allyl bromide to form 1-phenyl-4-penten-1-yne, $C_6H_5C \equiv CCH_2CH = CH_2$, in 70% yield has been described [169, 176] but could be duplicated [170] only in the presence of catalysts such as cuprous or cupric halides or cuprous cyanide. Alkynylmagnesium bromides failed to react with allyl bromide on standing with frequent stirring for twenty-three days or by refluxing for two to twelve hours in benzene or di-n-amyl ether without catalysts. Cuprous chloride and bromide are the best catalysts, giving high yields of the enyne $RC \equiv CCH_2CH = CH_2$ with n-amyl-, n-butyl-, phenyl-, and vinyl-ethynylmagnesium bromides. 1-Octen-4-yne is readily formed from allyl chloride and pentynylmagnesium bromide in the presence of cuprous salts.[144] It has been suggested that the difference in the results of the earlier and later investigators might have been due to impurities in the magnesium in the initial experiments. These catalysts are not effective in promoting a reaction between acetylenic Grignard reagents and alkyl halides of normal reactivity.[170] However, methylene iodide and phenylethynylmagnesium bromide were reported to give an 8% yield of 1,5-diphenyl-1,4-pentadiyne,[176] $C_6H_5C \equiv CCH_2C \equiv CC_6H_5$, but methylene bromide failed to react.[177] Likewise, chloromethyl ethers and chloromethyl esters were unreactive [177] either with acetylenic Grignard reagents or with the sodium derivatives.

In the preparation of Grignard reagents from monosubstituted acetylenes, ethylmagnesium bromide appears to be superior to methyl-magnesium iodide; the use of 3 moles of ether for each mole of metallic

[172] Johnson, Schwartz, and Jacobs, *J. Am. Chem. Soc.*, **60**, 1882 (1938).
[173] Gilman, St. John, St. John, and Lichtenwalter, *Rec. trav. chim.*, **55**, 577 (1936).
[174] Campbell and Eby, *J. Am. Chem. Soc.*, **62**, 1798 (1940).
[175] Gilman, Van Ess, and Burtner, *J. Am. Chem. Soc.*, **55**, 3461 (1933).
[176] Grignard and Lapayre, *Bull. soc. chim. France*, [4] **43**, 141 (1928).
[177] Hennion and Bell, *J. Am. Chem. Soc.*, **65**, 1847 (1943).

derivative has been recommended.[178] Phenylmagnesium bromide is also satisfactory, but since no gas is evolved the course of the reaction is less easily followed.

1,4-Diynes have been prepared by the reaction of substituted propargyl bromides and sodium alkynides at 140°.[179] Although the corre-

$$RC\equiv CNa + BrCH_2C\equiv CR' \rightarrow RC\equiv CCH_2C\equiv CR' + NaX$$

sponding acetylenic Grignard reagents fail to react on boiling for six hours in toluene, the use of catalysts [170] might make this reaction successful. The yields are only 15–20% even though the bromo compounds react to the extent of 80–90%. By-products include polymers and tri- and tetra-acetylenes, for the central methylene group is sufficiently acidic to form sodium derivatives $(RC\equiv CCHNaC\equiv CR')$ that may react with part of the bromide. Attempts to prepare aryl-aliphatic or diaryl-1,4-diacetylenes failed, and only polymers resulted.[179] The saturated Grignard reagents, on the other hand, were reported to give at ordinary temperatures almost quantitative yields of disubstituted acetylenes with propargyl bromides of the type $RC\equiv CCH_2Br$; the synthesis of 4-decyne from 1-bromo-2-octyne and ethylmagnesium bromide was cited as an example.[179] The yield of benzylphenylacetylene by this procedure was only 27%.[93] The method has been used to prepare 4-octyne from ethylmagnesium bromide and 1,4-dibromo-2-butyne.[180a] It has also been applied to tertiary propargyl chlorides $RC\equiv CC(R'R'')Cl$, which react with concentrated Grignard solutions at 60–80° to give the disubstituted acetylenes in 60–74% yields.[174] Although some care was taken to establish the carbon skeletons of these acetylenes, similar reactants have more recently been reported to give allenes in fair yields.[180b] An allylic rearrangement of the halogen of the propargyl

$$(CH_5)_2CClC\equiv CCH_3 + RMgX \rightarrow (CH_3)_2C=C=CRCH_3$$

halide may also complicate the synthesis at earlier stages.[180c]

$$R_2CXC\equiv CR \rightleftarrows R_2C=C=CRX$$

1,5-Diacetylenes may be prepared by coupling two molecules of substituted propargyl bromide using magnesium or sodium, magnesium giving 50–60% yields.[181] If excess sodium is used some reduction occurs

[178] Tchao Yin Lai, *Bull. soc. chim. France*, [4] **53**, 682 (1933).

[179] Tchao Yin Lai, *Bull. soc. chim. France*, [4] **53**, 1533, 1537 (1933).

[180a] Johnson, *J. Chem. Soc.*, **1946**, 1009.

[180b] Zakhareva, *J. Gen. Chem. U.S.S.R.*, **17**, 1277 (1947) [*C.A.*, **42**, 3722 (1948)].

[180c] Johnson, *The Chemistry of the Acetylenic Compounds*, Vol. I, The Acetylenic Alcohols, Edward Arnold and Co., **1946**, p. 63.

[181] Tchao Yin Lai, *Bull. soc. chim. France*, [4] **53**, 1543 (1933).

36 ORGANIC REACTIONS

to a γ-enyne. Sodium amide polymerizes these diynes, presumably by
first rearranging them to β-diynes.

The alkylation of alkyl or aryl acetylenes by alkyl sulfates or sulfonates in ether or high-boiling inert solvents is an excellent synthetic
method for preparing disubstituted acetylenes. Gilman and Beaber [182]
appear to have been the first to apply this reaction when they prepared
4-chloro-1-phenyl-1-butyne, $(C_6H_5C \equiv CCH_2CH_2Cl)$, by interaction of
phenylethynylmagnesium bromide and β-chloroethyl p-toluenesulfonate.
A number of monosubstituted acetylenes have been methylated in about
80% yield by treating the sodium derivatives with excess dimethyl
sulfate.[28] These yields are based on the unrecovered alkyne. Various
esters of aromatic sulfonic acids react readily with sodium alkynides or
acetylenic Grignard reagents [93, 172, 183] in ether, tetralin, or mineral oil. It
is often advantageous to substitute dibutyl ether or toluene for diethyl
ether as the solvent. The bromomagnesium alkynide has the disadvantage that two moles of the sulfonic ester are necessary. The

$$RC \equiv CMgBr + 2p\text{-}CH_3C_6H_4SO_3R' \rightarrow$$
$$RC \equiv CR' + R'Br + (p\text{-}CH_3C_6H_4SO_3)_2Mg$$

reaction of phenylethynylsodium with benzyl or β-chloroethyl p-
toluenesulfonate fails to give benzylphenylacetylene or β-chloroethyl-
phenylacetylene, although these compounds are readily prepared using
phenylethynylmagnesium bromides.[93, 172]

The very sensitive phenoxyethynylmagnesium bromide gives satisfactory yields of 1-phenoxyhexyne with butyl p-toluenesulfonate, but
the yield of 1-phenoxybutyne with ethyl p-toluenesulfonate is low.[18b]
Disubstituted acetylenes have been prepared in good yield by the reaction of acetylenic Grignard reagents with alkyl sulfates in ether.[184]
Table VII summarizes the synthetic data on disubstituted acetylenes
prepared by these methods.

Alkylations in Liquid Ammonia. The first alkylation of the sodium
derivative of a monosubstituted acetylene in liquid ammonia was carried
out by Heisig,[10b, 185] who treated propynylsodium with methyl iodide or
dimethyl sulfate. Alkyl sulfates, sulfonates, and bromides were used
for alkylation of vinylethynylsodium in liquid ammonia.[186] The yields
were moderate except with heptyl bromide, which gave 80% of 1-heptyl-
2-vinylacetylene. Propyl-, butyl-, amyl-, and phenyl-ethynylsodium

[182] Gilman and Beaber, J. Am. Chem. Soc., 45, 839 (1923).
[183] Truchet, Ann. chim., [10] 16, 309 (1931).
[184] Thorn, Hennion, and Nieuwland, J. Am. Chem. Soc., 58, 796 (1936).
[185] Heisig, J. Am. Chem. Soc., 53, 3245 (1931).
[186] Jacobson and Carothers, J. Am. Chem. Soc., 55, 1622 (1933).

TABLE VII

DISUBSTITUTED ACETYLENES PREPARED BY VARIOUS METHODS

Acetylene	Solvent *	Yield † %	Method ‡	Reference
4-Methyl-2-pentyne	Ether	28	1	36
2-Heptyne	Ether	S	1	184
2-Methyl-3-hexyne	Ether	39	1	35, 36
4,4-Dimethyl-2-pentyne	Ether	55	2	117a
2-Octyne	Ether	81	2	28
3-Octyne	Ether	70	1	184
	Ether	S	1	184
2-Nonyne	Ether	79	2	28
	Tetralin	33	4	183
3-Nonyne	Ether	S	1	184
	Tetralin	50	4	183
3-Decyne	Vaseline oil	47	4	183
4-Decyne	Tetralin		4	183
5-Undecyne	Vaseline oil	70	4	183
3-Dodecyne	Dibutyl ether	63	4	172
6-Dodecyne	Benzene	23	4	183
1-Chloro-4-tridecyne	Dibutyl ether	65	4	172
1-Hexen-3-yne	Ether	S	1	184
5,8-Tridecadiyne	Ether	13	1	177
1-Cyclohexyl-2-butyne	Ether	83	2	28
5-Cyclohexyl-2-pentyne	Ether	85	2	28
6-Cyclohexyl-2-hexyne	Ether	80	2	28
1-Phenyl-1-propyne	Tetralin	44	4	183
1-Phenyl-1-butyne	Benzene	56	4	183
	Dibutyl ether	77	4	172
1-Phenyl-4-chloro-1-butyne	Ether	45–75	3	182, 172
1-Phenyl-1-pentyne	Vaseline oil	65	4	183
1-Phenyl-5-chloro-1-pentyne	Dibutyl ether	75	4	172
1-Phenyl-1-hexyne	Vaseline oil	57	4	183
	Toluene	65–70	4	172
1,3-Diphenylpropyne	Ether	72	3	93
1-p-Bromophenyl-3-phenyl-1-propyne	Ether	26	3	93
3-p-Bromophenyl-1-phenyl-1-propyne	Ether	50	3	93
1-Phenoxy-1-butyne	Ether	15	3	18b
1-Phenoxy-1-hexyne	Ether	52	3	18b

* The sodium derivatives were usually prepared in ether and the higher-boiling solvent was added for the last part of the reaction only. The acetylide can be prepared in toluene and probably in other solvents if the temperature is maintained at 35–40°, but at higher temperatures the derivative is gelatinous and difficult to stir.

† S indicates that the yield was reported as satisfactory.

‡ Methods: (1) Grignard reagent and sulfate; (2) sodium alkynide and sulfate; (3) Grignard reagent and sulfonate; (4) sodium alkynide and sulfonate.

were alkylated with a variety of alkyl halides and sulfates.[142, 143] Bromides were reported to be the most effective alkylating agents, followed by iodides, sulfates, and chlorides in that order. The molecular weight of the alkyl group did not appear to influence the yield in the narrow range studied. The yields using bromides were between 42% and 58%, and the reaction could be carried out at atmospheric pressure or in an autoclave.

The preparation of a 1-alkyne from an alkyl halide and sodium acetylide, its conversion to an alkynylsodium with sodium amide, and the reaction of this derivative with alkyl halide to give a disubstituted acetylene can be conducted successively in one liquid ammonia solution to yield dialkylethynes in excellent yields and with saving of time.[187] The success of this method was attributed to the greater solubility of sodium acetylide relative to sodium amide and to the greater reactivity of 1-alkynes towards sodium amide. For symmetrical acetylenes it is sufficient to mix sodium acetylide, sodium amide, and alkyl halide in the molar ratio 1:1:2 with vigorous stirring. The following reactions take place.

$$HC{\equiv}CNa + RX \rightarrow RC{\equiv}CH + NaX$$

$$RC{\equiv}CH + NaNH_2 \rightarrow RC{\equiv}CNa + NH_3$$

$$RC{\equiv}CNa + RX \rightarrow RC{\equiv}CR + NaX$$

Bromides are the most satisfactory alkylating agents at atmospheric pressure, and chlorides give only low yields. Chlorides are more effective in an autoclave, but without stirring the yields remain lower than from bromides at ordinary pressures.

Unsymmetrical acetylenes can also be produced without the isolation of the intermediate 1-alkynes by adding an alkyl bromide to sodium acetylide in liquid ammonia, treating the solution after some time with a liquid ammonia suspension of sodium amide, and finally adding the second alkyl halide.

These methods are limited to alkyl halides of moderate molecular weight.[188] With n-octyl bromide the yield of 9-octadecyne, $CH_3(CH_2)_7C{\equiv}C(CH_2)_7CH_3$, is only 15%, although 75% of 1-decyne, $CH_3(CH_2)_7C{\equiv}CH$, is also produced. The yield of 9-octadecyne increases to 27% at 8 atmospheres and only 15% of 1-decyne is isolated. Decyl bromide gives only decylamine and 1-dodecyne at atmospheric or higher pressures.

The introduction of a heavier alkyl radical first has been sug-

[187] Bried and Hennion, *J. Am. Chem. Soc.*, **59**, 1310 (1937).
[188] Bried and Hennion, *J. Am. Chem. Soc.*, **60**, 1717 (1938).

gested,[54,140] and several new disubstituted acetylenes have been prepared in this way.

The use of two liquid ammonia condensers [189] mounted one above the other has been proposed.[187] A metal condenser cooled with Dry Ice [48b] is more effective and enables one to avoid the troublesome transfer of the sodium amide in liquid ammonia by passing into such a suspension just half enough acetylene to convert it to sodium acetylide. The resulting mixture is probably disodium acetylide ammonolyzed to an unknown extent. A simplified two-step process for preparing disubstituted

$$NaC\!\!\equiv\!\!CNa + NH_3 \rightleftarrows NaC\!\!\equiv\!\!CH + NaNH_2$$

acetylenes in which the intermediate 1-alkyne is dried but not purified after hydrolysis, and is converted to the alkynide by addition to sodium amide in liquid ammonia, has been devised.[144]

Table VIII summarizes the more recent results on the synthesis of disubstituted acetylenes by these methods.

Sodium amide is superior to metallic sodium for the formation of sodium alkynides in liquid ammonia as it is for the formation of sodium acetylide (p. 27). The reduction of higher acetylenes to olefins by the metal [190] has been observed. The report that the hydrogenation [142,143] is less extensive than with acetylene has not been confirmed in other laboratories.[144,190] Some reduction also occurs when sodium is used to form acetylides in inert solvents such as ether,[191] but this side reaction is less important here than in liquid ammonia. The use of sodium amide in inert solvents has been recommended because the reaction is more rapid and there is no danger of hydrogenation.[28] Furthermore, it is difficult to accomplish a complete removal of the metallic sodium because of the tendency of some of the derivatives to form a protective coating on the metal. The quality of the sodium amide is an important consideration (p. 9).

Sodium derivatives have been prepared in liquid ammonia, this solvent being replaced with benzene, toluene, or ether before alkylating; [177] this procedure appears to offer no special advantages.

Acetylenic Grignard reagents can be alkylated in low yield in liquid ammonia solution.[192]

[189] Vaughn and Pozzi, *J. Chem. Educ.*, **8**, 2433 (1931).

[190] Lebeau and Picon, *Compt. rend.*, **157**, 137, 223 (1913). It was reported that phenylacetylene gave ethylbenzene.

[191] (a) Lagermark and Eltekov, *J. Russ. Phys. Chem. Soc.*, **11**, 125 (1879); *Ber.*, **12**, 854 (1879); (b) Favorskiĭ, *J. Russ. Phys. Chem. Soc.*, **19**, 553 (1887) [*Chem. Zentr.*, **19**, 242 (1888)]; (c) Moureu and Delange, *Bull. soc. chim. France*, [3] **25**, 302 (1901); (d) Fuson and Meek, *J. Org. Chem.*, **10**, 551 (1945).

[192] Hennion and Wolf, *Proc. Indiana Acad. Sci.*, **48**, 98 (1939) [*C.A.*, **33**, 6794 (1939)].

TABLE VIII

DISUBSTITUTED ACETYLENES PREPARED IN LIQUID AMMONIA

Disubstituted Acetylene	Yield * %	Reference	Disubstituted Acetylene	Yield * %	Reference
2-Butyne	36	10b, 185, 144	7-Methyl-3-octyne	35	54
2-Pentyne †	59	144	5-Decyne	69	140, 187
2-Hexyne	—	140	8-Methyl-4-nonyne	35	54
3-Hexyne ‡	75	144, 140, 187	5-Undecyne	60	54
2-Octyne §	58	144, 140	6-Dodecyne	30	187
3-Octyne ‖	64	144, 140, 187	7-Tetradecyne	38	188
4-Octyne	60–66	54, 144, 140, 187	9-Octadecyne	15–27	188
4-Octyne ¶	81	144, 54	1-Phenylpropyne ††	50	54
3-Nonyne **	35	54	2,7-Nonadiyne ‡‡	76	144

* Based on alkyl bromides. When two different halides were used the yield was based on the heavier, which was introduced first. The one-step process was used except as noted.

† Two-step process using dimethyl sulfate first and transferring the propyne and ammonia as a gas to the second flask containing sodium amide in liquid ammonia.

‡ This is the only experiment employing the new technique of metering into a sodium amide suspension just half as many moles of acetylene. Bried and Hennion, ref. 187, obtained only 47% by the standard one-step method. Using diethyl sulfate the yield was 37% but the product was unusually pure (ref. 144).

§ Two-step process. Yield based on 1-heptyne and allowing twelve hours. Recovery of 1-heptyne was 20%. A longer reaction time was recommended. Using 1-propyne and amyl bromide the yield was 56% and the 2-octyne was very difficult to separate from the bromide.

‖ In the simplified two-step process a yield of 67% was obtained and 16% of 1-hexyne was isolated (ref. 144).

¶ Two-step process.

** The two-step process gave a 54% yield (ref. 142).

†† Based on phenylacetylene. Dimethyl sulfate was used. A yield of 43% was reported using methyl iodide (ref. 142).

‡‡ Based on 1,6-heptadiyne; 3% was recovered and 5% of 1,6-octadiyne was isolated.

THE SYNTHESIS OF DIARYLACETYLENES (TOLANS)

Tolan and substituted tolans appear to be very readily formed, and various special methods have been found for their preparation. The standard synthesis from stilbene dibromide and ethanolic potassium hydroxide has been modified many times between the first report in 1868 [193] and the modern version of 1942.[5] Tolan has been synthesized in 75% yield by a neat but expensive method which involves the oxidation of benzil dihydrazone with yellow mercuric oxide.[194] There appears to be no possibility of the formation of stilbene in this preparation, which

[193] Limpricht and Schwanert, *Ann.*, **145**, 330 (1868).
[194] Curtius and Thun, *J. prakt. Chem.*, [2] **44**, 171 (1891); Schlenk, Bergmann, and Rodloff, *Ann.*, **463**, 76 (1928).

is an advantage when high purity is paramount since stilbene and tolan form a solid solution not readily separable.[195]   Di-p-tolylacetylene [196] and α-naphthylphenylacetylene [197] were prepared by the same method in very high yields.[196]

The preparation of diphenylacetylenes by the dehydrohalogenation and rearrangement of unsymmetrical diarylhaloethylenes or ethanes was first reported in 1894.[198]   The yield of tolan from diphenylchloro-

$$\text{Ar}_2\text{C}{=}\text{CHCl} + \text{NaOC}_2\text{H}_5 \xrightarrow[200°]{180-} \text{ArC}{\equiv}\text{CAr} + \text{NaCl} + \text{C}_2\text{H}_5\text{OH}$$

ethylene was only 9%, the principal product being 2,2-diphenylvinyl ethyl ether.   The yields of di-p-tolylacetylene and of di-p-anisylacetylene from the corresponding chlorides were 85% and 55%, respectively.   A disadvantage of the method is the necessity of using a sealed tube for the reaction.   The starting materials are prepared in good yields by condensing dichloroacetal with benzene, toluene, or anisole and removing hydrogen chloride from the resulting 1,1-diaryl-2,2-dichloroethane by ethanolic potassium hydroxide.   Potassium amyloxide was used to prepare 3,4,3′,4′-tetramethoxytolan from 1,1-bis-(3,4-dimethoxyphenyl)-2-chloroethylene.[199]

When potassium amide in liquid ammonia was substituted for the ethanolic sodium ethoxide in this reaction,[200] the scope and usefulness were greatly broadened.   Yields of 85–90% of the purified diphenyl-

$$(\text{C}_6\text{H}_5)_2\text{C}{=}\text{CHX} + \text{KNH}_2 \rightarrow \text{C}_6\text{H}_5\text{C}{\equiv}\text{CC}_6\text{H}_5 + \text{KX} + \text{NH}_3$$

acetylenes are obtained when the aryl groups are phenyl, o-, m-, or p-tolyl, o-, m-, or p-methoxyphenyl, 3,4-dimethylphenyl, and xenyl; but with p-ethyl, propyl, or butyl substituents on the ring an oily impurity is formed and the yields are reduced to 50–70%.   No significant variation in yield is observed with bromo or chloro compounds as starting materials or with 1,1-diaryl-2,2-dihaloethanes, although the dichloroethanes do appear to give slightly poorer results.   The position of attachment of the benzene ring is not changed during the migration, and the structures of several of the tolans were proved by synthesizing them from the corresponding stilbene dibromides with ethanolic potassium hydroxide and by reducing them to known dibenzyls.   Sodium amide is as effective

[195] Pascal and Normand, *Bull. soc. chim. France*, [4] **13**, 151 (1913).

[196] Curtius and Kastner, *J. prakt. Chem.*, [2] **83**, 225 (1911).

[197] A synthesis by Jenny mentioned by Ruggli and Reinert, ref. 15.

[198] (a) Fritsch, *Ann.*, **279**, 319 (1894); (b) Buttenberg, *Ann.*, **279**, 324 (1894); (c) Wiechell, *Ann.*, **279**, 337 (1894).

[199] Fritsch, *Ann.*, **329**, 37 (1903).

[200] Coleman and Maxwell, *J. Am. Chem. Soc.*, **56**, 132 (1934); Coleman, Holst, and Maxwell, *ibid.*, **58**, 2310 (1936).

as potassium amide in this synthesis [200] and, since it is more readily prepared, would seem to be the reagent of choice. 1,1-Diphenyl-2,2-dichloroethane gives tolan in 80% yield with sodium amide.[84] This method is probably the best available for the synthesis of tolan derivatives since diarylbromoethenes are easily prepared from the unsymmetrical diarylethenes which are available from diarylmethylcarbinols.

Tolan derivatives may be prepared in unspecified yield by treating unsymmetrical diaryldichloro- or diarylbromochloro-ethenes with sodium in benzene.[201] Under the same conditions diaryltrichloroethanes give 95% yields of the substituted stilbenes and only 2% of tolans. The action of ethanolic sodium ethoxide on unsymmetrical diphenyl- or ditolyl-dichloroethene yields mainly diarylacetic acids, but, with di-p-anisyl- or di-p-phenetyl-dichloroethenes, 80% yields of the tolans are obtained and about 20% of unchanged dihaloethene is recovered.[202]

An unusual synthesis of o,o'- or p,p'-dinitrotolan occurs when o- or p-nitrobenzal chloride is treated with ethanolic sodium ethoxide.[95, 203] With the *ortho* compound [203] considerable heat is generated and the yields are 36–39%. The reaction is believed to go through the corresponding tolan dihalide, which has been isolated from p-nitrobenzal chloride.[95e] m-Nitrobenzal chloride [203] gives only an acetal in this reaction. A similar reaction for the formation of o- or p-stilbenes from nitrobenzyl halides is well known and has been reported for benzyl chloride itself.[204] 2-Dibromomethylanthraquinone gives a 97% yield of 2,2-dianthraquinonylacetylene dibromide merely by heating to 230–240°,[205] and this loses bromine to form the acetylene in 89% yield when refluxed with diethylaniline. The same acetylene is obtained by refluxing 2-tribromomethylanthraquinone with copper bronze in nitrobenzene.[206]

The union of halogenated carbons to form a triple bond occurs readily in the production of 1,1,4,4-tetraphenyl-2-butyne or similar substituted compounds from 1,1-diaryl-2,2,2-trihaloethanes.[207] The reaction, which is seldom clean-cut, is accomplished electrolytically in hot ethanolic hy-

$$2Ar_2CHCCl_3 \rightarrow Ar_2CHC{\equiv}CCHAr_2$$

drochloric acid at a lead cathode. Catalytic reduction and reduction by

[201] Harris and Frankforter, *J. Am. Chem. Soc.*, **48**, 3144 (1926).

[202] Fritsch and Feldmann, *Ann.*, **306**, 72 (1899).

[203] Kliegl and Haas, *Ber.*, **44**, 1209 (1911).

[204] Tschitschibabin, *J. Russ. Phys. Chem. Soc.*, **34**, 130 (1902) (*Chem. Zentr.*, **1902**, 1, 1301).

[205] Ullmann and Klingenberg, *Ber.*, **46**, 712 (1913).

[206] Eckert, *Monatsh.*, **35**, 289 (1914).

[207] Brand et al., (*a*) *Z. Elektrochem.*, **16**, 669 (1910); (*b*) *Ber.*, **46**, 2935, 2942 (1913); (*c*) *Ber.*, **54**, 1987, 2007, 2017 (1921); (*d*) *Ber.*, **57**, 846 (1924); (*e*) *Ber.*, **72**, 1029, 1036 (1939); (*f*) *J. prakt. Chem.*, **115**, 335, 351 (1927); (*g*) *ibid.*, **127**, 219, 240 (1930).

metal combinations appear to give tetraaryl-2,2,3,3-tetrahalobutanes or 2,3-dihalo-2-butenes, and the latter usually are converted to the tetraaryl-2-butynes by reaction with zinc and acetic acid. 1,1-Di-p-tolyl-

$$Ar_2CHCCl_3 \rightarrow Ar_2CHCCl_2CCl_2CHAr_2 \quad \text{or} \quad Ar_2CHCCl\!=\!CClCHAr_2$$

2,2,2-tribromoethane is converted into tetratolyl-2-butyne in one step with zinc and acetic acid.

Somewhat similar reactions appear to occur when benzotrichloride or a substituted benzotrichloride is heated with copper powder in benzene. The yields of 1,2-diaryltetrachloroethanes are low. o-Chlorobenzotrichloride gives both stereoisomeric dichloroethylenes.[208, 209] Heating the o,o'-dichlorotolan dichlorides with zinc dust at 200° gives an 80% yield of o,o'-dichlorotolan. Di-(p-chlorophenyl)-tetrachloroethane gives the corresponding tolan when refluxed with zinc dust in acetic acid.

OTHER METHODS OF PREPARING ACETYLENES

The removal of adjacent halogens from 1,2-dihaloethylenes by metals has been used to prepare acetylenic compounds, but the method is not of great synthetic value. Dibromofumaric acid loses bromine more readily than dibromomaleic acid when treated with zinc in moist ether at 60–70° to give acetylenedicarboxylic acid in good yield.[210] A number of α,β-dichlorostyrenes, prepared from ω-chloroacetophenones by treatment with phosphorus pentachloride, react with sodium in ether to form the sodium derivatives of the corresponding acetylenes; with water these give the acetylenes in yields reported to be "good." [211]

$$C_6H_5COCH_2Cl \rightarrow C_6H_5CCl\!=\!CHCl \rightarrow C_6H_5C\!\equiv\!CNa$$

Sodium phenoxyacetylide [18a] and cyclooctyne [212] are obtained in the same way from 1,2-dibromo-1-phenoxyethylene or tribromophenoxyethylene and 1,2-dibromocyclooctene. Zinc dust in acetone effects the removal of bromine from tolan dibromide and diphenyldiacetylene tetrabromide.[104f] The yield of diphenyldiacetylene is 85%. It is clear that whenever an acetylene dibromide is the starting material the method cannot be of synthetic value unless some source for the dibromide other

[208] Kenner and Witham, *J. Chem. Soc.*, **97**, 1960 (1910).

[209] Fox, *Ber.*, **26**, 653 (1893).

[210] Michael, *J. prakt. Chem.*, [2] **46**, 209 (1892); [2] **52**, 344 (1895).

[211] (a) Kunckell and Gotsch, *Ber.*, **33**, 2654 (1900); (b) Kunckell and Koritzky, *Ber.*, **33**, 3261 (1900); (c) Kunckell and Eras, *Ber.*, **33**, 3264 (1900); **36**, 915 (1903); (d) Kunckell, Eras, Müller, and Hildebrandt, *Ber. deut. pharm. Ges.*, **23**, 188 (1913) (*Chem. Zentr.*, **1913**, I, 1768). The constants of mesitylacetylene have been corrected, ref. 43.

[212] Domnin, *J. Gen. Chem. U.S.S.R.*, **8**, 851 (1938) [*C.A.*, **33**, 1282 (1939)].

than the acetylene can be found. Dibromoethylenes have been prepared from $RCH_2CBr{=}CH_2$ (obtained by a Grignard reagent and 2,3-dibromopropene) by adding bromine and removing hydrogen bromide with ethanolic sodium ethoxide.[90] The product is treated with zinc and ethanol to form the acetylene, but the yields are low. A similar method gave only 8% of 3-hexyne.[66] The most serious difficulty lies in the substitution which occurs during the addition of bromine to the bromoethylene. It may be possible that some olefin is formed along with the acetylene during the removal of the halogens, since s-dibromo-bis(p-tolylmercapto)ethylene is converted to s-bis(p-tolylmercapto)ethylene by zinc and acetic acid.[213]

$$p\text{-}CH_3C_6H_4SCBr{=}CBrSC_6H_4CH_3\text{-}p \rightarrow p\text{-}CH_3C_6H_4SCH{=}CHSC_6H_4CH_3\text{-}p$$

A novel method of preparing 3-phenyl-1-propyne by adding phenylmagnesium bromide to 1,2,3-tribromopropene has been described.[90] The reaction is not the result of the action of unchanged magnesium but requires excess Grignard reagent, and biphenyl is produced. By adding

$$4C_6H_5MgBr + BrCH_2CBr{=}CHBr \rightarrow$$

$$C_6H_5CH_2C{\equiv}CMgBr + C_6H_5C_6H_5 + C_6H_6 + 3MgBr_2$$

the tribromopropene to the Grignard reaction the yield is increased from 40% to 52%.[4]

Lithium phenylacetylide is produced almost quantitatively from ω-chloro- or ω-bromo-styrene by phenyllithium or butyllithium.[214] The reaction does not appear to be a simple dehydrohalogenation.[214a]

Acetylenes have been obtained by the pyrolysis of bis-quaternary ammonium hydroxides.[215] From butane-1,2-bis-trimethylammonium hydroxide a 44% yield of ethylacetylene and a 56% yield of methylallene result, while from the 2,3-compound 42–47% of 1,3-butadiene and 58–53% of a mixture of methylallene and dimethylacetylene are obtained.

The formation of benzoylmesitylacetylene by the reaction of phenylmagnesium bromide and 2,4,6-trimethyl-β-methoxycinnamonitrile [216] may also be mentioned.

$$2,4,6\text{-}(CH_3)_3C_6H_2C(OCH_3){=}CHCN + C_6H_5MgBr \rightarrow$$

$$2,4,6\text{-}(CH_3)_3C_6H_2C{\equiv}CCOC_6H_5$$

[213] Fromm and Siebert, Ber., 55, 1014 (1922).

[214] (a) Wittig and Harborth, Ber., 77, 315 (1944); (b) Wittig and Witt, Ber., 74, 1474 (1941); (c) Gilman, Langham, and Moore, J. Am. Chem. Soc., 62, 2327 (1940); (d) Gilman and Haubein, ibid., 67, 1420 (1945).

[215] Hurd and Drake, J. Am. Chem. Soc., 61, 1943 (1939).

[216] Fuson, Ullyot, and Hickson, J. Am. Chem. Soc., 61, 410 (1939).

THE DETECTION, DETERMINATION, AND PURIFICATION OF MONOSUBSTITUTED ACETYLENES

The detection of monosubstituted acetylenes and their separation from mixtures with disubstituted acetylenes or other hydrocarbons is customarily accomplished by means of metallic derivatives. Ammoniacal silver nitrate or cuprous chloride solutions are often used to form silver or cuprous acetylides, although early investigators [217] showed that mixtures containing small amounts of monosubstituted acetylenes give no precipitate with these reagents. It requires 20% of 1-octyne with the silver reagent and 10% of 1-heptyne with the cuprous solution to give a positive acetylene test. A 5% solution of silver nitrate in 95% ethanol gives an instantaneous precipitate of a white, crystalline compound $RC{\equiv}CAg_2NO_3$ when treated with even traces of 1-alkynes,[217] so that they can be separated almost quantitatively from mixtures by its use.[17, 81] From 3.5 g. of 1-hexadecyne in 10 ml. of ethanol and a solution of 5.35 g. of silver nitrate in 5 ml. of water and 45 ml. of ethanol, 7.4 g. of a silver derivative results, a yield of 94.3%. The reagent has been adapted to the quantitative determination of monosubstituted acetylenes in a gas mixture.[218] A simple volumetric procedure involving the titration of the free nitric acid produced in the reaction is used.

$$RC{\equiv}CH + 2AgNO_3 \rightarrow RC{\equiv}CAg_2NO_3 + HNO_3$$

A procedure for determining 1-heptyne by this method has been described,[74] but no data are given on the accuracy of the method. Results 2% low for 1-heptyne and 2.8% low for 1-hexyne were obtained using compounds carefully purified through their silver derivatives.[219] The procedure has been used by many workers and is the standard industrial method for the analysis of monosubstituted acetylenes. A gravimetric method is unsatisfactory because the silver complex adsorbs silver ions and decomposes above 100°, making thorough drying difficult; [74] the results are 2–3% higher than by the volumetric procedure. Acidic, basic, and sulfur impurities must be removed from the mixture in the volumetric procedure. The ethanolic silver solution should not be heated since this produces violently explosive silver fulminate.

Phenylacetylene has been determined [220] by precipitation of the cuprous derivative from ethanolic solution with ammoniacal cuprous chloride.[221, 104f] After vigorous shaking the precipitate is filtered and

[217] Béhal, *Ann. chim.*, [6] **15**, 408 (1888).
[218] Chavastelon, *Compt. rend.*, **125**, 245 (1897).
[219] Hurd and Christ, *J. Org. Chem.*, **1**, 141 (1936).
[220] Hein and Meyer, *Z. anal. Chem.*, **72**, 30 (1927).
[221] Ilosvay Nagy Ilosva, *Ber.*, **32**, 2697 (1899).

washed with water, ethanol, and ether, is dried, and is either weighed or dissolved in ferric sulfate-sulfuric acid solution and titrated with permanganate. With known weights of pure phenylacetylene the results

$$2C_8H_5Cu + Fe_2(SO_4)_3 + H_2SO_4 \rightarrow 2FeSO_4 + 2CuSO_4 + 2C_8H_6$$

of the two procedures are in agreement and are 0.38% and 0.90% high. No determinations on hydrocarbon mixtures of known phenylacetylene content were given. The precipitation of the cuprous derivative of 1-heptyne with aqueous ammoniacal cuprous chloride is slow, and with concentrated ammonia solutions incomplete.[74]

Silver acetylides are rather soluble in concentrated silver nitrate solution because of the formation of a complex between the silver acetylide and silver ion [222] (Table IX). Dilution of the solution caused a

TABLE IX

SOLUBILITY OF ACETYLENES IN 50% AQUEOUS SILVER NITRATE

Acetylene	Volume %
1-Butyne	15
1-Pentyne	10
1-Heptyne	6
Phenylacetylene	8
Dialkylacetylenes	0

silver derivative to precipitate. Raman spectra studies indicate that the triple bond is involved in the complex formation, and the suggestion has been made that the complexes may be similar to those formed by olefins.[223] It is odd that dialkylacetylenes do not form such coordination compounds. Very probably the somewhat erratic results observed in the determination of acetylenes as their metallic derivatives arise from the variable solubility of the complexes in the solution.

A method has been published for the determination of acetylenes based on their reaction with methanol in the presence of mercuric oxide-boron trifluoride catalyst, to produce ketals which are subsequently hydrolyzed to ketones.[223a]

In neutral or acidic solution mercuric salts give addition products of

[222] Taufen, Murray, and Cleveland, *J. Am. Chem. Soc.*, **63**, 3500 (1941).

[223] Winstein and Lucas, *J. Am. Chem. Soc.*, **60**, 836 (1938); Keller, *Chem. Revs.*, **28**, 229 (1941).

[223a] Wagner, Goldstein, and Peters, *Ind. Eng. Chem., Anal. Ed.*, **19**, 103 (1947).

varying composition with monosubstituted acetylenes, but in alkaline solution mercuric derivatives analogous to cuprous or silver alkynides are formed. These mercuric acetylides are prepared easily in yields of 85–95% [4] by adding a solution of the acetylene in ethanol to excess alkaline mercuric iodide [99a] or cyanide.[224] The derivatives are useful for the identification of monosubstituted acetylenes because they are easily purified and have characteristic melting points.

The purification of monosubstituted acetylenes through their cuprous, silver, or mercuric derivatives has been widely used. It is common practice to decompose the first two of these with dilute hydrochloric acid, although this reagent with the cuprous or silver derivative of 1-heptyne leads to a product containing traces of halogen.[225] Diacetylene has been recovered from its copper derivative by treatment with potassium cyanide,[111b] and chloro- or bromo-acetylene is obtained similarly from its mercuric derivative.[224] Furylacetylene has been purified through its copper salt by refluxing with aqueous sodium cyanide with 90% recovery; phenylacetylene was purified similarly with an 85% recovery.[8] Pure 1-hexyne is obtained with only 27% loss by refluxing the recrystallized silver nitrate complex with sodium cyanide solution.[112b] When ammonium thiocyanate is used to decompose the complex, the yield is only 40%, but the losses are said to be largely mechanical.[219] The formation of an acetylenic Grignard reagent is not sufficiently complete to make this derivative of value for purification.[226]

The synthesis of 1-alkynes using sodium amide [28] assures freedom from disubstituted acetylenes if conducted properly, and in some instances an acetylenic mixture obtained by dehydrohalogenation with potassium hydroxide has been converted to 1-alkyne by treatment with sodium amide in a similar fashion.[227]

In general the purification of monosubstituted acetylenes through their metallic derivatives is a satisfactory process entailing moderate losses. It appears to be the best method of separating these compounds from disubstituted acetylenes. Since some of these metallic derivatives, notably those of acetylene and diacetylene, are very explosive when dry, even moderate quantities should be kept moist with the solvent at all times.

Disubstituted acetylenes are occasionally purified by removal of monosubstituted isomers as metallic derivatives. Thus 1-butyne was removed from 2-butyne by passing the gaseous mixture through 50% aqueous ethanolamine containing cuprous chloride.[11a]

[224] Hofmann and Kirmreuther, *Ber.*, **41**, 314 (1908); **42**, 4232 (1909).
[225] Moureu, *Ann. chim.*, [8] **7**, 541 (1906) note; see Straus and Kühnel, *Ber.*, **65**, 154 (1932).
[226] Hurd, Meinert, and Spence, *J. Am. Chem. Soc.*, **52**, 1138 (1930).
[227] Levina and Potapova, *J. Gen. Chem. U.S.S.R.*, **7**, 353 (1937) [*C.A.*, **31**, 4652 (1937)].

EXPERIMENTAL PROCEDURES

Carefully tested directions for the synthesis of the following acetylenic compounds have appeared in *Organic Syntheses*.

Acetylenedicarboxylic acid from α,β-dibromosuccinic acid with methanolic potassium hydroxide.[9]

3-Cyclohexylpropyne from 3-cyclohexyl-2-bromopropene with sodium amide.[29]

Phenylacetylene from ω-bromostyrene with molten potassium hydroxide.[20]

Phenylpropargyl aldehyde from cinnamic aldehyde.[228]

Phenylpropiolic acid from ethyl cinnamate dibromide with ethanolic potassium hydroxide.[103]

Tolan from stilbene dibromide.[5]

Stearolic acid from methyl oleate dibromide with potassium hydroxide in amyl alcohol.[228a]

1-Hexyne from Sodium Acetylide and *n*-Butyl Bromide in Liquid Ammonia [229]

The apparatus consists of a 5-l. three-necked flask equipped with a mercury-sealed stirrer and an efficient Dry Ice-cooled condenser. The stirrer may be a well-balanced glass loop or a wire stirrer.[230] The condenser [48b] consists of a several-turn vertical coil of 1:7 gradient made of block tin tubing not less than ½ in. in internal diameter, fitting snugly inside a double-walled jacket made of a tin can inserted inside a slightly larger can and separated from it by a layer of asbestos. The top of the annular space is sealed with plaster of Paris, and the coil is soldered in at top and bottom. (To arrest corrosion the condenser is cleaned and dried after each run.) Glass condensers, although considerably less efficient, may be used in small runs. Two liquid-ammonia condensers [189] mounted one above the other have also been used.[142]

About 2 l. of commercial anhydrous liquid ammonia is placed in the 5-l. flask, and 1.5 g. of powdered, hydrated ferric nitrate (0.3 g. for each

[228] Allen and Edens, *Org. Syntheses*, **25**, 92 (1945).

[228a] Adkins and Burks, *Org. Syntheses*, **27**, 76 (1947).

[229] These directions are a condensation of those found in the Ph.D. Thesis of Greenlee, Ohio State University, 1942 (see ref. 144). The preparations of sodium amide and of sodium acetylide given in *Inorganic Syntheses*, **2**, 128, 75 (1946), specify more concentrated solutions which probably work equally well in the final step.

[230] Hershberg, *Ind. Eng. Chem., Anal. Ed.*, **8**, 313 (1936); *Org. Syntheses*, **17**, 31 (1937); *Coll. Vol.* **2**, 117 (1943).

gram atom of sodium) is added. After vigorous stirring for several minutes, 2 g. of sodium is added; a vigorous reaction occurs, and the solution becomes black from the colloidal particles of iron. When the reaction subsides the blue color of sodium is visible around the edges of the mixture and hydrogen is slowly evolved. To improve visibility the frost on the outside of the flask may be removed with ethanol. A brisk stream of dry air is bubbled through the solution for fifteen to twenty seconds. This converts some of the sodium to sodium peroxide which activates the catalyst. The evolution of hydrogen is more rapid for a short time but soon ceases, and 114 g. of sodium (a total of 116 g. or 5 gram atoms plus 1 g.) is added in 15- to 23-g. quantities, enough time being allowed between additions for complete conversion to sodium amide (disappearance of the blue color). The stirrer is operated slowly during this procedure, and at the end it is run at high speed for a few minutes to wash down sodium spattered on the upper walls of the flask. The sodium amide can be seen around the walls of the flask as tiny colorless crystals like grains of sand; the liquid is still dark from the iron catalyst. A rapid stream of tank acetylene which has been passed through concentrated sulfuric acid and then through a tower of soda lime and anhydrous calcium chloride is introduced at a point below the stirrer, which is run at moderate speed. The reaction mixture immediately becomes milky and clears up shortly before the theoretical amount of acetylene has been added, when it turns dark again. No gases are evolved during the addition of acetylene.

The acetylene addition tube is replaced by a dropping funnel, and 617 g. (4.5 moles) of n-butyl bromide is added rather rapidly. The solvent refluxes somewhat more vigorously for about two hours, and the solution is stirred rapidly for a total of six and one-half hours. Water is then added at moderate rate from the dropping funnel until the flask is nearly full; some acetylene is evolved during the process. Two layers are formed, and the lower (aqueous ammonia) is siphoned off and discarded. The upper layer is shaken with water, ice-cold 1:1 hydrochloric acid (which removes finely divided iron), and dilute sodium carbonate solution, and is dried over calcium chloride. The crude product (350 g., 95% yield) is fractionated through a column having about six theoretical plates, and the fraction that boils at 70.5–71°/750 mm. (uncor.) is collected; this weighs 320 g. (87% yield). Refractionation of fore-run and residue gives an additional 10 g. of material with the same boiling point and refractive index (total yield 89%). Pure 1-hexyne has the following constants: b.p. 71.4°/760 mm., m.p. −132.09°, d_4^{20} 0.7156, n_D^{20} 1.3990.

p-Tolylacetylene [50]

(*a*) **Preparation of 1-*p*-Tolyl-1-chloroethylene.** To 189 g. (0.9 mole) of phosphorus pentachloride in a 250-ml. Claisen flask fitted with a dropping funnel and drying tube and cooled in a bath of ice and salt, 110 g. (0.82 mole) of *p*-tolyl methyl ketone is added during one hour. The reaction mixture is left in the cooling bath for an hour and at room temperature for twelve hours. Phosphorus oxychloride is removed under reduced pressure, and the residue is distilled through a small column. The product is an oil, b.p. 81–83°/10 mm., yield 85 g. (68%). At 70° a 75% yield is obtained. The use of pure phosphorus pentachloride and rapid distillation are important.[51]

(*b*) **Conversion of 1-*p*-Tolyl-1-chloroethylene to *p*-Tolylacetylene.** A mixture of 85 g. (0.56 mole) of 1-*p*-tolyl-1-chloroethylene, prepared as above, and 50 g. (0.78 mole) [231] of potassium hydroxide in 100 ml. of absolute ethanol is refluxed for twenty-four hours. The mixture is poured into a liter of ice water, the oil separated, and the aqueous layer extracted with ether. The oil and ether are combined and dried over potassium hydroxide; the ether is removed, and the residue is distilled under reduced pressure; b.p. 79–82°/31–33 mm.; yield 31 g. (48%).

p-Bromophenylacetylene [49]

(*a*) **Preparation of 1-(4-Bromophenyl)-1-chloroethylene and 1-(4-Bromophenyl)-1,1-dichloroethane.** A mixture of 95 g. (0.48 mole) of *p*-bromoacetophenone and 107 g. (0.51 mole) of phosphorus pentachloride in a 500-ml. round-bottomed flask provided with a reflux condenser is heated to 70° in an oil bath. Rapid evolution of hydrogen chloride begins when the *p*-bromoacetophenone melts, and the reaction is over in about ten minutes. The clear yellow liquid is distilled under reduced pressure. After the phosphorus oxychloride has been removed (b.p. 45–50°/18 mm.), 19 g. (18%) of the monochloroethylene derivative, b.p. 118–122°/18 mm., and 62.5 g. (52%) of the dichloroethane, b.p. 126–127°/18 mm., are obtained. These fractions need not be separated for the next reaction.

(*b*) **Conversion of the Chloroethylene and Dichloroethane to the Acetylene.** A mixture of 82 g. (0.34 mole) of chloro compounds obtained above and 400 g. of ethanolic potassium hydroxide (25% by titration, 1.8 moles) in a 1-l. round-bottomed flask provided with a reflux condenser, is refluxed for three hours in an oil bath and poured into a liter

---

[231] The potassium hydroxide contains about 13% of water and other impurities.

of ice water. The oil is separated, and the aqueous portion is extracted with ether. The oil and ether are combined and dried over potassium hydroxide or potassium carbonate. The ether is removed, and the product is distilled under reduced pressure from a Claisen flask having a wide side arm, b.p. 88–90°/16 mm. The p-bromophenylacetylene crystallizes in the receiver and is recrystallized from ethanol. The yield is 32.5 g. (53%) of colorless crystals, m.p. 64–65°. There is no advantage in dropwise addition of the chloro compound to the ethanolic potassium hydroxide.

1-Phenyl-1-hexyne [172]

To 11.5 g. (0.5 gram atom) of sodium wire in 200 ml. of toluene in a 1-l. three-necked round-bottomed flask, equipped with a reflux condenser, mercury-sealed stirrer, and dropping funnel, is added slowly with stirring 51 g. (0.5 mole) of phenylacetylene.[20] The flask is kept at 35–40°, since above this temperature the sodium derivative forms a gelatinous mass. To the suspension of the acetylide is added with stirring during two hours 114 g. (0.5 mole) of n-butyl p-toluenesulfonate [232] while the temperature is maintained at 70°. After three hours at 80° the reaction mixture is cooled and treated with water; ether is added if an emulsion forms, and the ether-toluene solution is washed and dried over solid potassium hydroxide or potassium carbonate. The product is distilled under reduced pressure, and, after a small fore-run of phenylacetylene, 51–55 g. (65–70%) of 1-phenyl-1-hexyne is obtained, b.p. 109–110°/12 mm. On redistillation the compound boils at 94–95°/4 mm.; d_4^{20} 0.9024 and n_D^{20} 1.5347.

The sodium derivative of phenylacetylene may also be prepared with sodium amide. The reagent is finely powdered under mineral oil and transferred to the flask as a suspension. Anhydrous ether is then added, and the oil is removed by several washings with ether. An alternative method is to prepare the sodium amide in liquid ammonia and displace this solvent with ether.[177] An excess of sodium amide and of butyl p-toluenesulfonate results in a 57% yield of 1-phenyl-1-hexyne.[183]

Dibutyl ether may be used instead of toluene in the preparation, or the sodium derivative may be prepared in ether with sodium and the ether replaced by a higher-boiling solvent. Mineral oil may be added for the last part of the reaction.

---

[232] Roos, Gilman, and Beaber, *Org. Syntheses, Coll. Vol.* **1**, 145, 2nd ed., 1941.

The Purification of 1-Hexyne [112b]

To a solution of 41 g. (0.5 mole) of 1-hexyne in 160 ml. of 95% ethanol is added slowly and with stirring a solution of 170 g. (1 mole) of silver nitrate in 250 ml. of water. The white precipitate of $C_4H_9C{\equiv}CAg_2NO_3$ is filtered, washed with water, and recrystallized from 1.8 l. of 95% ethanol. The crystals are washed thoroughly with water and refluxed for three hours with a solution of 115 g. of sodium cyanide in 250 ml. of water. The regenerated 1-hexyne is dried over calcium chloride and distilled; b.p. 70.5–70.7° cor./747 mm., yield 30 g. (73%).

TABULAR SURVEY OF ACETYLENES SYNTHESIZED BY THE METHODS DESCRIBED IN THIS CHAPTER

Only those acetylenes are included that have been prepared by methods covered in this review and that have been reported in *Chemical Abstracts* through 1947. If other methods are of synthetic value for one of these compounds, they are included, but the references may not be complete. An attempt has been made to include mainly references dealing with synthesis, and with the more common acetylenes only recent references or those of definite synthetic value are listed. Where information is available, yields have been calculated allowing for recovered starting material. The methods of synthesis are indicated as follows.

1. Dehydrohalogenation with ethanolic potassium hydroxide or other alkaline reagents except alkali amides.

2. Dehydrohalogenation with sodium amide or potassium amide.

3. Alkylation of metallic derivatives of acetylenes in ether or other inert solvents.

4. Alkylation in liquid ammonia.

5. Other methods discussed in this review.

6. Methods not discussed in this review.

A question mark (?) indicates some uncertainty in the structure or synthesis. A star (★) indicates that the yield was of crude material.

SYNTHESIS OF ACETYLENES 53

Formula	Compound	Method	Yield %	References *

C₂

Formula	Compound	Method	Yield %	References *
C₂Br₂	Dibromoacetylene	1	15	233, 234
		6	—	235
		6	28	236
C₂Cl₂	Dichloroacetylene	1	65	75, 76, 77, 237
		6	—	235, 238
C₂HBr	Bromoacetylene	1	Good, 45	224, 239, 240, 241, 99a, 242, 243, 244, 2, 56
C₂HCl	Chloroacetylene	1	Good	224, 56, 245, 246, 247
		6	—	71b
C₂HI	Iodoacetylene	6	—	248
C₂I₂	Diiodoacetylene	1	25	249
		6	86–93	250, 251, 252, 253, 254, 255, 256, 257, 111b
		6	54–63	258, 259

C₃

Formula	Compound	Method	Yield %	References *
C₃HBrO₂	Bromopropiolic acid	1	—	71a
		6	74	235
C₃HClO₂	Chloropropiolic acid	1	—	71b
		6	19	235
C₃HIO₂	Iodopropiolic acid	1	80	99a
		6	—	260, 111b
C₃H₂Br₂	1,3-Dibromo-1-propyne	1	—	261
C₃H₂O₂	Propiolic acid	6	70–87	111, 262, 263, 264, 164, 165 148a
C₃H₃Br	1-Bromo-1-propyne	1	25	61
		6	—	10c
C₃H₃Br	3-Bromo-1-propyne	6	65	265, 266, 267, 268
C₃H₄	Propyne	1	67–85	10, 226, 160, 11b, 65, 269, 270
		4	84	135, 137, 139, 142, 143, 144, 185, 271, 272, 273

See p. 52 for explanation of symbols and methods in this table.
* References 233–519 are listed on pp. 72–78.

Formula	Compound	Method	Yield %	References *
C_3H_4O	2-Propyn-1-ol	1	66–69	57, 266, 268, 274, 275, 368
		6	—	276
		6	10	277
C_3H_4O	Methoxyacetylene	1	—	278
C_3H_5N	3-Amino-1-propyne	1	Poor	276

C_4

C_4H_2	1,3-Butadiyne	1	80–90	180a, 279
		6	Poor	111b, 280, 281, 270
$C_4H_2O_4$	Acetylenedicarboxylic acid	1	73–88	9, 111a, b, 68, 71c, d, 210, 262, 282, 283, 284, 285, 286, 287
		6	Poor, 34	161, 164, 214d
$C_4H_4O_2$	2-Butynoic acid	1	16–87	126, 288, 289, 290, 291, 292, 293, 210, 294, 295, 296, 297, 298, 299
		5	—	298, 299
		6	—	161, 300
C_4H_5BrO	1-Bromo-3-methoxy-1-propyne	1	—	261, 301
$C_4H_5NO_2$	1-Nitro-1-butyne	1	—	67
C_4H_6	1-Butyne	1	34	4
		2	60	32, 33
		4	65–78	144a, 142, 143, 136a, 302, 138, 139, 149a, c, d, 273
	2-Butyne	1	65	80b, 78, 269, 60, 41, 11a
		4	81 *	271, 303, 304, 10b, 185
C_4H_6O	3-Butyn-2-ol	1	—	305, 306
		6	57	307, 308, 309

See p. 52 for explanation of symbols and methods in this table.
* References 233–519 are listed on pp. 72–78.

Formula	Compound	Method	Yield %	References *
C_4H_6O	3-Butyn-1-ol	1	—	305, 310
		6	65	311, 277
	3-Methoxy-1-propyne	1	80	12, 274, 312, 313
		2	61	26, 28
	Ethoxyacetylene	1	50–55	18c, 278, 314
$C_4H_6O_2$	2-Butyne-1,4-diol	5	—	316, 399
		6	—	305, 161, 315, 317, 180a

C_5

Formula	Compound	Method	Yield %	References *
$C_5H_4O_4$	2-Pentyne-1,5-dioic acid	1	—	318
C_5H_6	1-Penten-3-yne	4	38	186
		6	59–73	319
	1-Penten-4-yne (?)	3	70–75	164, 169, 170, 144, 152
$C_5H_6O_2$	2-Pentynoic acid	6	45–49	79b, 320, 288, 46, 78, 321, 322
	3-Pentynoic acid	1	10–15	79b
	4-Pentynoic acid	1	40	79b, 323, 111c
C_5H_7Cl	5-Chloro-1-pentyne	4	57	144
$C_5H_7NO_2$	1-Nitro-1-pentyne (?)	1	—	67
C_5H_8	1-Pentyne	1	55	24c, 78, 84, 90, 324
		2	30–62	28
		4	90	144, 142, 143, 136a, 304, 86, 139
	2-Pentyne	1	35	325, 78, 324, 326, 327
		3	40	32, 41
		4	59	144
	3-Methyl-1-butyne	1	18–60	125, 327, 328, 78, 329, 330, 35, 36
		2	25–34	34, 35, 36
		4	29–50	139
C_5H_8O	1-Pentyn-3-ol	1	—	305
		6	50	331, 309
	4-Pentyn-1-ol	1	Poor	332
	n-Propoxyacetylene	1	75	314
	3-Ethoxy-1-propyne	1	88 ★	333, 334, 335, 312

See p. 52 for explanation of symbols and methods in this table.
* References 233–519 are listed on pp. 72–78.

Formula	Compound	Method	Yield %	References *
C_5H_8O	3-Ethoxy-1-propyne (?)	2	81	26, 28
	1-Methoxy-2-butyne	3	15	28
		6	61	102, 336
	4-Methoxy-1-butyne	1	—	305, 337
		4	60–75	151
$C_5H_8O_2$	Propynal dimethylacetal	1	—	338
$C_5H_{10}BrN$	Ethynyltrimethylammonium bromide	1	—	339, 340

C_6

Formula	Compound	Method	Yield %	References *
C_6H_3BrO	5-Bromo-2-ethynylfuran	1	—	341
		5	32	16d
C_6H_4O	2-Furylacetylene	1	25	8, 342
C_6H_6	1,5-Hexadien-3-yne	6	—	343, 344
	1,4-Hexadiyne	1	—	344
	1,5-Hexadiyne	1	—	344, 274, 345, 346, 347, 348, 349, 350, 305, 78, 316
	2,4-Hexadiyne	1	—	316, 78
		6	42	271, 344
$C_6H_6O_4$	Propargylmalonic acid	1	—	111c
C_6H_7Br	1-(or 2-)-Bromo-1-hexen-5-yne	1	—	305, 344, 346
C_6H_8	1-Hexen-3-yne	3	Satisfactory	184
		4	24–31	186
	1-Hexen-5-yne	1	—	351
C_6H_8O	1-Hexyn-5-one	1	Poor	323
$C_6H_8O_2$	2-Methyl-4-pentynoic acid	1	—	323, 111c
C_6H_9BrO	2-Bromoethyl 3-butynyl ether	4	—	151
C_6H_{10}	1-Hexyne	1	75	24c, 352, 78
		2	60	28, 48a,
		3	72	164, 165
		4	90	144, 142, 143, 135, 219, 86, 149a, 54, 139, 140, 112b
	2-Hexyne	1	—	78, 352, 353
		3	—	28, 41

See p. 52 for explanation of symbols and methods in this table.
* References 233–519 are listed on pp. 72–78.

Formula	Compound	Method	Yield %	References *
	2-Hexyne (*Continued*)	4	—	140
	3-Hexyne	1	Poor	66, 133
		3	20	165
		4	75	144, 187, 140
		5	8	66
	4-Methyl-1-pentyne	1	50	354
		5	—	90
	4-Methyl-2-pentyne	1	—	79c
		3	36	34, 36
	3,3-Dimethyl-1-butyne	1	27–73	117,6,116,78,10c, 355, 356
$C_6H_{10}O$	3-Hexyn-1-ol	1	71	357, 358
		6	28	33, 357
	n-Butoxyacetylene	1	34–56	18c, 314
	4-Ethoxy-1-butyne	4	60–75	151
	5-Methoxy-1-pentyne	4	70	332
$C_6H_{10}O_2$	2-Butynal dimethyl acetal	1	70–80	359, 360
	1,4-Dimethoxy-2-butyne	3	63	101, 305

C₇

Formula	Compound	Method	Yield %	References *
$C_7H_3BrO_3$	5-Bromo-2-furylpropiolic acid	1	69 ★	16d
C_7H_5N	3-Pyridylacetylene	1	42	70c
C_7H_8	1,6-Heptadien-3-yne	3	Good	170
	1,6-Heptadiyne	4	40–43	144, 155
$C_7H_8O_4$	Methylpropargylmalonic acid	1	—	111c
C_7H_{10}	5-Methyl-3-hexen-1-yne	1	33	361
	Cyclopentylacetylene	2	9	41
	Cycloheptyne (?)	1	—	362, 363
$C_7H_{10}O$	2-Ethoxy-1-penten-4-yne (?)	1	—	364
C_7H_{12}	1-Heptyne	1	0–88 ★	24a, b, 37, 65, 74, 80a, 328, 329, 352, 365, 366, 191c, 367, 369, 370
		2	60	28, 4, 27, 37, 48a
		4	83	144, 142, 143, 136c, 219, 54, 149a, b, 139, 140
		5	Good	110, 225

See p. 52 for explanation of symbols and methods in this table.
* References 233–519 are listed on pp. 72–78.

Formula	Compound	Method	Yield %	References *
C₇H₁₂	2-Heptyne	1	—	217, 296, 371
		3	Satisfactory	184, 41
		4	38	142, 143
	3-Heptyne	1	—	217, 372
		2	40	28
	5-Methyl-1-hexyne	1	42	373, 84
		4	68–70	144, 136
	5-Methyl-2-hexyne	1	—	79d
	2-Methyl-3-hexyne	3	39	35, 36
	4,4-Dimethyl-1-pentyne	1	—	82
		2	37	38
	4,4-Dimethyl-2-pentyne	1	—	82, 374
		3	55	117a
C₇H₁₂O₂	Propynal diethyl acetal	1	35	7, 100, 338, 375

C₈

Formula	Compound	Method	Yield %	References *
C₈H₄Cl₂	2,6-Dichlorophenylacetylene	1	—	376
C₈H₅Br	Bromoethynylbenzene	1	Satisfactory	99a, 377
		6	88	235, 378, 379, 380
	4-Bromophenylacetylene	1	53	49, 43, 381
C₈H₅Cl	Chloroethynylbenzene	1	—	99a
		6	67, 70	183, 382
	2-Chlorophenylacetylene	5	66	16a
	4-Chlorophenylacetylene	1	75	43, 381
C₈H₅I	Iodoethynylbenzene	5	—	383, 73b
		6	92	384, 385, 183, 99a, 377, 386, 251, 387
C₈H₅NO₂	2-Nitrophenylacetylene	5	Good	104i, 388, 16e
	3-Nitrophenylacetylene	1	—	389
		5	—	390, 104d
	4-Nitrophenylacetylene	5	Quant.	391, 104h, 392, 381
C₈H₆	Phenylacetylene	1	67	20, 23, 105, 45, 99a, 377, 393, 394

See p. 52 for explanation of symbols and methods in this table.
* References 233–519 are listed on pp. 72–78.

Formula	Compound	Method	Yield %	References *
	Phenylacetylene (Continued)	2	83	183, 28, 26, 65, 48a, 54
		5	82	214, 72e
$C_8H_6ClO_3P$	2-Chlorophenylethynylphosphonic acid	1	68 *	16a
C_8H_6O	Phenoxyacetylene	1	60–80	18
	2-Hydroxyphenylacetylene	6	55	394a
$C_8H_7O_3P$	Phenylethynylphosphonic acid	1	—	16a
$C_8H_8O_2$	1,6-Heptadiyne-4-carboxylic acid	1	—	323, 395
C_8H_{10}	3-Ethynyl-1,5-hexadiene (?)	3	—	164
	3-Ethynyl-1,5-hexadiene	4	85–93 *	144, 152
	1,7-Octadiyne	1	—	396
	1-Ethynyl-1-cyclohexene	2	—	397, 398
$C_8H_{10}O$	bis(3-Butynyl) ether	4	60–75	151
$C_8H_{10}O_2$	2,6-Octadiyne-1,8-diol	5	—	316, 399, 400
$C_8H_{10}O_4$	Ethyl acetylenedicarboxylate	1	13	401, 283
		5	Poor	210
		6	Good	402, 111b
$C_8H_{11}Cl$	Chloroethynylcyclohexane	6	48	382
C_8H_{12}	1-Octen-3-yne	4	—	186
	1-Octen-4-yne	3	32	144 (170)
	6-Methyl-3-hepten-1-yne	1	—	361
	1-Cyclopentylpropyne	3	50	41
	3-Cyclopentylpropyne	2	65	41
	Cyclohexylacetylene	1	46	125, 403, 404, 227
		2	6 †	41
	Cycloöctyne	5	32	212
C_8H_{14}	1-Octyne	1	—	80a, 296, 329, 405
		2	75	28, 86, 48a
		4	72	144, 142, 143, 406, 140
	2-Octyne	1	—	83, 217, 296, 366
		3	81	28, 41
		4	84	144, 142, 143, 140

See p. 52 for explanation of symbols and methods in this table.

* References 233–519 are listed on pp. 72–78.

† This is the overall yield from cyclohexanol and is not to be compared with the 46% yield of method 1 which is for the last step only.

Formula	Compound	Method	Yield %	References *
C_8H_{14}	3-Octyne	2	23	28
		3	70	184
		4	67	144, 187, 142, 143, 192, 140
	4-Octyne	4	60–81	144, 187, 54, 142, 143, 406, 140
		5	58	180a
	3-Ethyl-3-methyl-1-pentyne	2	45	39
$C_8H_{14}O$	Butyl 3-butynyl ether	4	60–75	151
	Isoamyl propargyl ether	1	—	333
	1-Methoxy-2-heptyne	3	42	177
$C_8H_{14}O_2$	3-Butynyl-2-ethoxyethyl ether	4	60–75	151
	1,4-Diethoxy-2-butyne	3	45	101
	2,5-Dimethoxy-3-hexyne	3	21	101
	2-Butynal diethyl acetal	1	—	359, 360

C_9

Formula	Compound	Method	Yield %	References *
$C_9H_4Cl_2O_2$	2,6-Dichlorophenylpropiolic acid	1	—	376
$C_9H_4N_2O_6$	2,4-Dinitrophenylpropiolic acid	1	24	407
$C_9H_5BrO_2$	4-Bromophenylpropiolic acid	1	80	408, 409
$C_9H_5ClO_2$	2-Chlorophenylpropiolic acid	1	68	16a
C_9H_5N	2-Ethynylbenzonitrile	5	25	16b
$C_9H_5NO_4$	2-Nitrophenylpropiolic acid	1	79	407, 104h, i. 410, 16e
	3-Nitrophenylpropiolic acid	1	—	390, 389, 104d
	4-Nitrophenylpropiolic acid	1	—	96b, 391, 104h
		6		411
$C_9H_6N_2O_4$	1-(2,4-Dinitrophenyl)-1-propyne	1	—	121
C_9H_6O	Phenylpropynal	6	70–81	228, 100, 338, 412, 413, 414, 415

See p. 52 for explanation of symbols and methods in this table.
* References 233–519 are listed on pp. 72–78.

Formula	Compound	Method	Yield %	References *
$C_9H_6O_2$	3,4-Methylenedioxy-phenylacetylene	1	60	377, 416
	Phenylpropiolic acid	1	76–80	103, 417, 383, 418, 104j, 419, 420, 294, 421
		6	Good	104j, 422, 99a, 423, 214c
C_9H_7BrO	2- (or 3-) Bromo-4-meth-oxyphenylacetylene	5	—	424
	4-Bromophenyl propargyl ether	1	50	425
C_9H_7Cl	1-Chloroethynyl-4-methylbenzene	1	—	211a
		6	52	382
C_9H_7ClO	1-Chloroethynyl-4-meth-oxybenzene	1	—	211c
		6	52	382
$C_9H_7NO_2$	1-(4-Nitrophenyl)-1-propyne	1	—	121
$C_9H_7NO_3$	2-Nitro-5-methoxyphenyl-acetylene	5	48	16e
C_9H_8	p-Tolylacetylene	1	48–57	50, 51, 4
		2	64	48a, 42, 72e
		5	—	211a, d, 381, 104e
	1-Phenyl-1-propyne	1	70 *	105, 426, 427, 428, 90, 429, 91
		3	50–77	183, 41, 54, 16a, 171
		5	35	214a
	3-Phenyl-1-propyne	2	75	28, 131d, 26
		3	70	164, 165
		5	52	4, 90, 429
C_9H_8O	Phenyl propargyl ether	1	53	425, 430, 431
	2-Methoxyphenyl-acetylene	2	Poor	431a
	4-Methoxyphenyl-acetylene	5	67	16a
	4-Methoxyphenyl-acetylene	5	62	16a, 104c, g, 211, 377
C_9H_9N	Phenylpropargylamine	1	45	432
		2	—	433
C_9H_{12}	1,8-Nonadiyne	4	84	144, 155
	2,7-Nonadiyne	4	76	144
	1-Ethynyl-5-methyl-cyclohexene	2	—	397, 398

See p. 52 for explanation of symbols and methods in this table.
* References 233–519 are listed on pp. 72–78.

Formula	Compound	Method	Yield %	References *
C_9H_{12}	1-Propynyl-1-cyclohexene	3	—	397, 398
C_9H_{14}	1-Nonen-4-yne	3	88	170
	1-Cyclopentyl-2-butyne	3	65	41
	1-Ethynyl-3-methylcyclo-hexane	2	—	397, 398
	1-Cyclohexyl-1-propyne	3	24	41
	3-Cyclohexyl-1-propyne	1	66	434, 90, 69
		2	66–87	29, 28, 41
$C_9H_{14}O_2$	Butylpropargyl acetate	3	16	177
C_9H_{16}	1-Nonyne	1	—	435
		2	84	28, 27, 183
		4	46	86, 142, 143
	2-Nonyne	3	80	28, 183, 41, 184
	3-Nonyne	3	60	183, 184
		4	54	142, 143, 48a, 54
	4-Nonyne	4	45	142, 143
	7-Methyl-3-octyne	4	35	54
	2,6-Dimethyl-3-heptyne	1	38	79d
$C_9H_{16}O$	1-Ethoxy-2-heptyne	3	27–35	177, 436

$$C_{10}$$

Formula	Compound	Method	Yield %	References *
$C_{10}H_5NO_6$	2-Nitro-4,5-methylenedi-oxyphenylpropiolic acid	1	76 ★	16e
$C_{10}H_7NO_5$	3-Nitro-4-methoxyphenyl-propiolic acid	1	—	437
	2-Nitro-5-methoxyphenyl-propiolic acid	1	70–78 ★	16e
$C_{10}H_8Br_2O$	x,x-Dibromo-2-methoxy-1-(1-propynyl)benzene	1	—	438
$C_{10}H_8O_2$	3,4-Methylenedioxy-1-(1-propynyl)benzene	1	—	439
	m-Tolylpropiolic acid	1	—	104h
	p-Tolylpropiolic acid	1	—	104e
$C_{10}H_8O_3$	2-Methoxyphenyl-propiolic acid	1	51	16a, 440, 440a
	3-Methoxyphenyl-propiolic acid	1	96	441
	4-Methoxyphenyl-propiolic acid	1	—	16a, 104g, 104c, 442

See p. 52 for explanation of symbols and methods in this table.
* References 233–519 are listed on pp. 72–78.

Formula	Compound	Method	Yield %	References *
$C_{10}H_9BrO$	x-Bromo-2-methoxy-1-(1-propynyl)benzene	1	—	438
$C_{10}H_9Cl$	1-Phenyl-4-chloro-1-butyne	3	46	172
	1-Chloroethynyl-4-ethyl-benzene	1	—	211b
	1-Chloroethynyl-2,5-dimethylbenzene	1	—	211a
$C_{10}H_9ClO$	1-Chloroethynyl-2-meth-oxy-5-methylbenzene	1	—	211d
$C_{10}H_9N_3$	1-Phenyl-4-triazo-1-butyne †	3	—	443
$C_{10}H_{10}$	1-Phenyl-1-butyne	1	70	105
		3	77	172, 183, 73, 44
	4-Phenyl-1-butyne	1	—	373
		2	63	4, 29, 52, 44, 444
	3-(2-Methylphenyl)-1-propyne	2	75	52
	3-(4-Methylphenyl)-1-propyne	2	75	52
	4-Ethylphenylacetylene	5	—	211b, d
	2,4-Dimethylphenyl-acetylene	2	75	43, 445, 86
$C_{10}H_{10}O$	2-Ethoxyphenylacetylene	1	—	446
	1-(4-Methoxyphenyl)-1-propyne	1	75	127, 447
	2-Methoxy-5-methyl-phenylacetylene	5	—	211d
	3-Methoxy-1-phenyl-1-propyne	3	—	336
	2-Hydroxy-4-phenyl-3-butyne	1	—	89
		6	70	448, 449, 415
$C_{10}H_{10}O_2$	3,4-Dimethoxyphenyl-acetylene	5	41	104b
$C_{10}H_{11}N$	Methylphenylprop-argylamine	1	50	450, 265
$C_{10}H_{14}$	1,9-Decadiyne	4	44	451
	1-Propynyl-5-methyl-cyclohexene	3	—	397, 398

See p. 52 for explanation of symbols and methods in this table.
* References 233–519 are listed on pp. 72–78.
† The product is unstable and loses nitrogen. It was isolated as a dibromide.

Formula	Compound	Method	Yield %	References *
$C_{10}H_{14}O_2$	1,8-Dimethoxy-2,6-octadiyne	3	—	305, 316
$C_{10}H_{16}$	1-Decen-4-yne	3	Good	170
	1-Cyclohexyl-2-butyne	3	78	28, 41
	4-Cyclohexyl-1-butyne	2	80	28, 30
	1-(3-Methylcyclohexyl)-1-propyne	3	—	397, 398
	3-(3-Methylcyclohexyl)-1-propyne	2	—	397, 398
$C_{10}H_{16}Cl_2O_2$	1,6-Dichloro-2,5-diethoxy-3-hexyne	3	—	452
$C_{10}H_{16}O_2$	Butylpropargyl propionate	3	21	177
	Amylpropargyl acetate	3	10	177
$C_{10}H_{18}$	1-Decyne	1	—	435
		2	68	4, 29, 86, 48a
		4	53	142, 143, 188, 136c
	3-Decyne	3	47	183
	4-Decyne	3	Good	179, 183
		4	42	142, 143
	5-Decyne	3	30	164, 168
		4	69	187, 142, 143, 54, 192, 140
	8-Methyl-4-nonyne	4	35	54
	2,2,5,5-Tetramethyl-3-hexyne	6	55	356
$C_{10}H_{18}O$	Butylpropargyl propyl ether	3	34	177, 436
$C_{10}H_{18}O_2$	1,4-Di-n-propoxy-2-butyne	3	16	101
	2,5-Diethoxy-3-hexyne	3	14	101

C_{11}

Formula	Compound	Method	Yield %	References *
$C_{11}H_7N$	2-Quinolylacetylene (?)	1	—	70b, c
$C_{11}H_{10}$	5-Phenyl-1-penten-4-yne	3	70	176, 170
$C_{11}H_{10}O_3$	2-Ethoxyphenylpropiolic acid	1	50	453, 446
$C_{11}H_{10}O_4$	2,3-Dimethoxyphenyl-propiolic acid	1	—	454
	3,4-Dimethoxyphenyl-propiolic acid	1	—	104b

See p. 52 for explanation of symbols and methods in this table,
* References 233-519 are listed on pp. 72-78,

Formula	Compound	Method	Yield %	References *
$C_{11}H_{11}Br$	3-Bromo-2,4,6-trimethyl-phenylacetylene	1	57	58
$C_{11}H_{11}Cl$	1-Chloroethynyl-2,4,6-tri-methylbenzene	1	—	211b
	1-Chloroethynyl-4-iso-propylbenzene	1	—	211b
	5-Chloro-1-phenyl-1-pentyne	3	75	172
$C_{11}H_{11}ClO$	3-Chloro-6-methoxy-2,4-dimethylphenylacetylene	1	60	59
$C_{11}H_{11}ClO_3$	3-Chloro-6-methoxy-2,4-dimethylphenylpropiolic acid	6	55	59
$C_{11}H_{12}$	2,4,6-Trimethylphenyl-acetylene	2	71	43, 86, 58, 191d
	2,4,6-Trimethylphenyl-acetylene (?)	5	—	211b, 43
	4-Isopropylphenyl-acetylene	5	—	211b
	3-(2,4-Dimethylphenyl)-1-propyne	2	75	52
	3-(2,5-Dimethylphenyl)-1-propyne	2	75	52
	1-Phenyl-1-pentyne	1	70 *	105
		3	65	183
$C_{11}H_{12}O$	1-Phenyl-1-pentyn-3-ol	1	—	89
		6	—	415
$C_{11}H_{13}N$	Ethylphenylpropargyl-amine	1	30	265
	Benzylmethylpropargyl-amine	1	—	450
	4-Ethynyl-4-vinyl-1,6-heptadiene (?)	4	Poor	152
$C_{11}H_{14}O_2$	2,10-Undecadiyn-1-oic acid	6	24	451
$C_{11}H_{16}$	1,10-Undecadiyne	1	Good	455
$C_{11}H_{18}$	1-Undecen-3-yne	4	80	186
	5-Cyclohexyl-1-pentyne	2	88	28
	5-Cyclohexyl-2-pentyne	3	85	28
	1-(3-Methylcyclohexyl)-1-butyne	3	—	397, 398

See p. 52 for explanation of symbols and methods in this table.
* References 233–519 are listed on pp. 72–78.

Formula	Compound	Method	Yield %	References *
$C_{11}H_{18}$	1-(3-Methylcyclohexyl)-2-butyne	3	—	397, 398
	4-(3-Methylcyclohexyl)-1-butyne	5	—	397, 398
$C_{11}H_{18}O_2$	9-Undecynoic acid	1	Quant.	456, 81, 457
	10-Undecynoic acid	1	49–77	458, 81, 451
$C_{11}H_{20}$	1-Undecyne	1	Poor	328, 459, 460, 435
		2	50–80	27
		4	51	142, 143, 86
	2-Undecyne	1	—	460, 461, 462
	5-Undecyne	3	70	183
		4	60	54
	3,3-Dimethyl-4-nonyne	3	3	174
		6	73	174

$$C_{12}$$

$C_{12}H_6O_4$	Benzene-1,3-dipropynoic acid	1	50–55	463
$C_{12}H_7BrO_4$	Benzene-1-bromoacrylic-3-propiolic acid	1	—	463
$C_{12}H_8$	α-Naphthylacetylene	1	—	464
	β-Naphthylacetylene	1	35	51, 465
$C_{12}H_{11}BrO_2$	3-Bromo-2,4,6-trimethyl-phenylpropiolic acid	1	75	58
$C_{12}H_{12}$	4-Phenyl-1-hexen-5-yne	5	34	466
$C_{12}H_{13}BrO$	1-Phenyl-3-ethoxy-4-bromo-1-butyne	3	60	466a
$C_{12}H_{13}Cl$	1-Chloroethynyl-5-iso-propyl-2-methylbenzene	1	—	211b
$C_{12}H_{14}$	2,3,4,6-Tetramethyl-phenylacetylene	1	65	58
	2-Methyl-5-isopropyl-phenylacetylene	5	—	211b, d
	3-(4-Isopropylphenyl)-1-propyne	2	75	52
	1-Phenyl-1-hexyne	1	70	105
		3	65–70	172, 183
$C_{12}H_{14}O$	Phenylpropargyl propyl ether	3	—	336

Formula	Compound	Method	Yield %	References *
$C_{12}H_{14}O$	1-Phenyl-3-ethoxy-1-butyne	3	50	466a
$C_{12}H_{14}O_4$	2,10-Dodecadiyne-1,12-dioic acid	6	18	451
$C_{12}H_{18}O_4$	2-Dodecyne-1,12-dioic acid	6	61	451
$C_{12}H_{20}$	6-Cyclohexyl-1-hexyne	2	87	28
	6-Cyclohexyl-2-hexyne	3	80	28
$C_{12}H_{22}$	1-Dodecyne	1	24	467, 17
		2	34	86
		4	57	188
	2-Dodecyne	1	—	17, 468
	3-Dodecyne	3	63	172
	6-Dodecyne	3	23	183
		4	58	142, 143, 187
	2,9-Dimethyl-5-decyne	3	Poor	168
$C_{12}H_{22}O_2$	1,4-Diisobutoxy-2-butyne	3	18	101

C_{13}

Formula	Compound	Method	Yield %	References *
$C_{13}H_8O_2$	α-Naphthylpropiolic acid	1	85	469, 470
		6	—	465
$C_{13}H_{10}$	2-Ethynyl-3-methyl-naphthalene	1	45	124
	3-(1-Naphthyl)-1-propyne	2	50	131c
$C_{13}H_{10}O$	3-(2-Furyl-1-phenyl)-1-propyne	3	35	175
$C_{13}H_{16}$	3-(5-Isopropyl-2-methyl-phenyl)-1-propyne	2	75	52
	1-Phenyl-1-heptyne	1	70	105
$C_{13}H_{16}O_2$	Phenylpropynal diethyl acetal	1	80–86	228, 338, 412
		6	68	414
$C_{13}H_{20}$	5,8-Tridecadiyne	3	13	177
	3-(trans-2-Decalyl)-propyne	2	86	31
	3-(cis-2-Decalyl)propyne	2	77	31
$C_{13}H_{23}Cl$	1-Chloro-4-tridecyne	3	65	172

C_{14}

Formula	Compound	Method	Yield %	References *
$C_{14}H_8Br_2$	4,4'-Dibromodiphenyl-acetylene	1	74	483

See p. 52 for explanation of symbols and methods in this table.
* References 233–519 are listed on pp. 72–78.

Formula	Compound	Method	Yield %	References *
$C_{14}H_8Cl_2$	2,2'-Dichlorodiphenyl-acetylene	1	—	471
		5	80	209
	4,4'-Dichlorodiphenyl-acetylene	5	—	208
$C_{14}H_8N_2O_4$	2,4-Dinitrodiphenyl-acetylene	1	94 *	95c, d, 407
	2,2'-Dinitrodiphenyl-acetylene	1	78	472, 473
		5	36–39	203, 474, 475
	3,4'-Dinitrodiphenyl-acetylene	1	70	95f
	4,4'-Dinitrodiphenyl-acetylene	1	90–95	95d, e, 476, 477
		5	—	95e
$C_{14}H_8N_2O_4S_2$	bis(2-Nitrophenylthio)-acetylene	1	—	478
$C_{14}H_8N_2O_{10}S_2$	4,4'-Dinitrodiphenyl-acetylene-2,2'-disulfonic acid	1	66	16c
$C_{14}H_9NO_2$	2-Nitrodiphenylacetylene	1	63–73	55, 407
$C_{14}H_{10}$	Diphenylacetylene	1	66–69	5, 479, 480, 477, 481, 482
		2	90–95	200, 54, 45
		5	75	194
$C_{14}H_{10}O_3$	4-Methoxy-1-naphthyl-propiolic acid	1	—	484
$C_{14}H_{14}$	(2-Cyclohexen-1-yl)-phenylacetylene	3	—	398
$C_{14}H_{16}Cl_4O_2$	3,5,3',5'-Tetrachloro-4,4'-dihydroxydiphenyl-acetylene	1	—	95a, b
$C_{14}H_{16}O_2$	n-Butylpropargyl benzoate	3	10	177
$C_{14}H_{17}Cl$	1-Chloroethynyl-2,4,6-triethylbenzene	1	—	211d
$C_{14}H_{18}$	2,4,6-Triethylphenyl-acetylene	5	—	211d
$C_{14}H_{20}$	(2-Cyclohexen-1-yl)cyclo-hexylacetylene	3	—	398
$C_{14}H_{22}O$	Di-(n-butylpropargyl) ether	3	21	177
$C_{14}H_{25}Cl$	1-Chloro-1-tetradecyne	6	40	382

See p. 52 for explanation of symbols and methods in this table.
* References 233–519 are listed on pp. 72–78.

Formula	Compound	Method	Yield %	References *
$C_{14}H_{26}$	1-Tetradecyne	1	—	17
	2-Tetradecyne	1	—	17, 468
	7-Tetradecyne	4	38	188
$C_{14}H_{26}O_2$	1,4-Diisoamyloxy-2-butyne	3	14	101

C_{15}

Formula	Compound	Method	Yield %	References *
$C_{15}H_9BrO$	4-Bromobenzoylphenylacetylene	1	40	485
$C_{15}H_9ClO$	2-Chlorophenylbenzoylacetylene	1	90	485
$C_{15}H_{10}O$	Benzoylphenylacetylene	1	30	485
		6	78	23b, 99a, 373, 393, 485a, b
$C_{15}H_{10}O_2$	4-Biphenylpropiolic acid	1	—	486, 487
$C_{15}H_{11}Br$	1-(4-Bromophenyl)-3-phenyl-1-propyne	3	26	93
	3-(4-Bromophenyl)-1-phenyl-1-propyne	3	50	93
$C_{15}H_{12}$	1,3-Diphenylpropyne	3	70	93, 488
$C_{15}H_{12}O$	4-Methoxydiphenylacetylene	1	—	489
$C_{15}H_{22}$	1-(2-Cyclohexen-1-yl)-3-cyclohexylpropyne	3	Good	398
$C_{15}H_{24}$	6,9-Pentadecadiyne	3	15	179
$C_{15}H_{26}$	Cyclopentadecyne	1	—	490
$C_{15}H_{28}$	1-Pentadecyne	2	Poor	53
$C_{15}H_{28}O_2$	10-Undecyn-1-al diethyl acetal	1	24–25	79a

C_{16}

Formula	Compound	Method	Yield %	References *
$C_{16}H_{12}$	1,4-Diphenyl-1-buten-3-yne	5	—	104f
$C_{16}H_{12}O_2$	p-Methoxyphenylbenzoylacetylene	1	30	485
		6	33	377, 490a

See p. 52 for explanation of symbols and methods in this table.
* References 233–519 are listed on pp. 72–78.

Formula	Compound	Method	Yield %	References *
$C_{16}H_{12}O_2$	p-Methoxybenzoylphenyl-acetylene	1	50	485
		6	60	490a, b, c
$C_{16}H_{14}$	1,4-Diphenyl-2-butyne	3	8	164
	2,2'-Dimethyldiphenyl-acetylene	2	90–95	200
	3,3'-Dimethyldiphenyl-acetylene	2	89	200
	4,4'-Dimethyldiphenyl-acetylene	1	—	491
		2	86–95	200
		5	Quant.	196, 198b
$C_{16}H_{14}O_2$	2,2'-Dimethoxydiphenyl-acetylene	2	—	200
	3,3'-Dimethoxydiphenyl-acetylene	2	—	200
	4,4'-Dimethoxydiphenyl-acetylene	1	80	201, 198c, 492
		2	90–95	200
$C_{16}H_{14}S_2$	bis(p-Tolylmercapto)-acetylene	1	—	213
	bis(Benzylmercapto)-acetylene	1	—	478
$C_{16}H_{26}$	1,15-Hexadecadiyne	1	—	455
	6,9-Hexadecadiyne	3	15	179
$C_{16}H_{28}O_2$	7-Hexadecynoic acid	1	—	493
$C_{16}H_{30}$	1-Hexadecyne	1	—	17, 81, 494
		2	65	40
	2-Hexadecyne	1	—	17, 468, 495
	C_{17}			
$C_{17}H_{12}$	1,5-Diphenyl-1,4-penta-diyne	3	10	176
$C_{17}H_{12}O_2$	2,5-Diphenyl-2-penten-4-ynoic acid	1	—	496
$C_{17}H_{24}O_2$	3-(8-Nonynyl)veratrole	4	51	497
$C_{17}H_{28}$	7,10-Heptadecadiyne	3	18	179
$C_{17}H_{30}$	Cycloheptadecyne	1	—	490
	C_{18}			
$C_{18}H_{12}$	β-Naphthylphenyl-acetylene	1	58	15

See p. 52 for explanation of symbols and methods in this table.
* References 233–519 are listed on pp. 72–78.

Formula	Compound	Method	Yield %	References *
	β-Naphthylphenyl- acetylene (*Continued*)	5	—	197
C₁₈H₁₈	4,4'-Diethyldiphenyl- acetylene	2	73	200
	3,4,3',4'-Tetramethyl- diphenyldiacetylene	2	90–95 *	200
C₁₈H₁₈O₂	4,4'-Diethoxydiphenyl- acetylene	1	—	198c
C₁₈H₁₈O₄	3,4,3',4'-Tetramethoxy- diphenylacetylene	1	45–50	199
C₁₈H₃₂O₂	5-Octadecynoic acid	1	—	498
	6-Octadecynoic acid	1	—	498, 499, 500, 501, 502, 503, 504, 505
	7-Octadecynoic acid	1	—	498
	8-Octadecynoic acid	1	—	503
	9-Octadecynoic acid	1	33–42	506, 507, 508, 509, 228a
	10-Octadecynoic acid	1	—	503
C₁₈H₃₂O₃	12-Hydroxy-9-octade- cynoic acid	1	—	510, 511, 512, 513
C₁₈H₃₄	1-Octadecyne	1	—	17
		4	—	136c
	2-Octadecyne	1	—	17, 468
	9-Octadecyne	4	15	188

C₁₉–C₄₀

Formula	Compound	Method	Yield %	References *
C₁₉H₃₆	1-Nonadecyne	2	73	514
C₂₀H₂₂	4,4'-Di-*n*-propyldiphenyl- acetylene	2	55	200
	Dimesitylacetylene	1	—	515
C₂₀H₃₆O₂	11-Eicosynoic acid	1	—	493
C₂₁H₁₆	1,3,3-Triphenyl-1-propyne	3	80	162
C₂₂H₁₄	Di-1-naphthylacetylene	5	—	196
C₂₂H₂₆	4,4'-Di-*n*-butyldiphenyl- acetylene	2	55	200
C₂₂H₄₀O₂	13-Docosynoic acid	1	75–90	516, 517, 518, 508
C₂₃H₁₈	5,5,5-Triphenyl-1-penten- 3-yne	3	71	519
C₂₃H₃₆O₂	3-(8-Pentadecynyl)vera- trol	4	85	497

See p. 52 for explanation of symbols and methods in this table.
* References 233–519 are listed on pp. 72–78.

Formula	Compound	Method	Yield %	References *
$C_{23}H_{40}$	10,13-Tricosadiyne	3	Poor	179
$C_{26}H_{18}$	4,4'-Diphenyldiphenyl-acetylene	2	91 *	200
$C_{27}H_{20}$	1,3,3,3-Tetraphenyl-1-propyne	3	60–70	162
$C_{28}H_{18}Br_4$	1,1,4,4-Tetra-p-bromo-phenyl-2-butyne	5	Poor	207
$C_{28}H_{18}Cl_4$	1,1,4,4-Tetra-p-chloro-phenyl-2-butyne	5	13	207
$C_{28}H_{22}$	1,1,4,4-Tetraphenyl-2-butyne	3	40–50	162
		5	—	207
$C_{30}H_{14}O_4$	Di-2-anthraquinonyl-acetylene	1	89	205
		5	—	206
$C_{30}H_{26}$	1-Phenyl-3,3,3-tri-p-tolyl-1-propyne	3	80	162
$C_{32}H_{30}$	1,1,4,4-Tetra-p-tolyl-2-butyne	5	—	207
$C_{32}H_{30}O_4$	1,1,4,4-Tetra-p-methoxy-phenyl-2-butyne	5	—	207
$C_{36}H_{38}O_4$	1,1,4,4-Tetra-p-ethoxy-phenyl-2-butyne	5	35	207
$C_{40}H_{30}$	1,1,1,4,4,4-Hexaphenyl-2-butyne	3	20–25	162

See p. 52 for explanation of symbols and methods in this table.
* References 233–519 are listed on pp. 72–78.

REFERENCES FOR TABULAR SURVEY

[233] Lemoult, Bull. soc. chim. France, [3] 33, 193 (1905); Compt. rend., 136, 1333 (1903); 137, 55 (1903); 139, 131 (1904).

[234] Lawrie, Am. Chem. J., 36, 487 (1906).

[235] Straus, Kollek, and Heyn, Ber., 63, 1868 (1930).

[236] Nekrassov, Ber., 60, 1756 (1927).

[237] Metz, J. prakt. Chem., [2] 135, 142 (1932).

[238] Böeseken and Carrière, Verslag Akad. Wetenschap., Amsterdam, 22, 1186 (1914) [C.A., 8, 3296 (1914)].

[239] Sabanejeff, J. Russ. Phys. Chem. Soc., 17, 175 (1885) [Beilstein, Handbuch der org. Chem., 4th ed., 1, 245].

[240] Sabanejeff, Ann., 216, 251 (1883).

[241] Nef, Ann., 298, 355 (1897).

[242] Reboul, Ann., 124, 267 (1862).

[243] Reboul, Ann., 125, 81 (1863).

[244] Fontaine, Ann., 156, 260 (1870).

245 Ingold, *J. Chem. Soc.*, **125**, 1528 (1924).
246 Sastry, *J. Soc. Chem. Ind.*, **35**, 450 (1916).
247 Ott, Dittus, and Weissenburger, *Ber.*, **76**, 84 (1943).
248 Grignard and Tchéoufaki, *Compt. rend.*, **188**, 357 (1929).
249 Nef, *Ann.*, **298**, 341 (1897).
250 Biltz and Küppers, *Ber.*, **37**, 4412 (1905).
251 Dehn, *J. Am. Chem. Soc.*, **33**, 1598 (1911).
252 Biltz, *Ber.*, **30**, 1200 (1897).
253 Tamblyn and Forbes, *J. Am. Chem. Soc.*, **62**, 99 (1940).
254 Howell and Noyes, *J. Am. Chem. Soc.*, **42**, 991 (1920).
255 Berend, *Ann.*, **135**, 257 (1865).
256 Maquenne, *Bull. soc. chim. France*, [3] **7**, 777 (1892); [3] **9**, 643 (1893).
257 Dussol, *Bull. soc. chim. France*, [4] **35**, 1618 (1924).
258 Vaughn and Nieuwland, *J. Am. Chem. Soc.*, **54**, 787 (1932).
259 Vaughn, U. S. pat. 2,124,218 [*C.A.*, **32**, 7058 (1938)].
260 Homolka and Stolz, *Ber.*, **18**, 2282 (1885).
261 Lespieau, *Ann. chim.*, [7] **11**, 232 (1897).
262 Moureu and Bongrand, *Ann. chim.*, [9] **14**, 47 (1920).
263 Skosarewski, *J. Russ. Phys. Chem. Soc.*, **36**, 863 (1904) (*Chem. Zentr.*, **1904**, II, 1024).
264 Oddo, *Gazz. chim. ital.*, **38**, I, 625 (1908).
265 Braun, Kühn, and Siddiqui, *Ber.*, **59**, 1081 (1926).
266 Henry, *Ber.*, **6**, 728 (1873).
267 Henry, *Ber.*, **7**, 761 (1874).
268 Pauling, Gordy, and Saylor, *J. Am. Chem. Soc.*, **64**, 1753 (1942).
269 Pauling, Springall, and Palmer, *J. Am. Chem. Soc.*, **61**, 927 (1939).
270 Price and Walsh, *Trans. Faraday Soc.*, **41**, 381 (1945).
271 Conn, Kistiakowsky, and Smith, *J. Am. Chem. Soc.*, **61**, 1868 (1939).
272 Maass and Russell, *J. Am. Chem. Soc.*, **43**, 1227 (1921).
273 Morehouse and Maass, *Can. J. Research*, **5**, 306 (1931).
274 Henry, *Ber.*, **5**, 449 (1872).
275 Henry, *Ber.*, **5**, 569 (1872).
276 Paal and Heupel, *Ber.*, **24**, 3035 (1891).
277 Hennion and Murray, *J. Am. Chem. Soc.*, **64**, 1220 (1942).
278 Favorskiĭ and Shostakovskiĭ, *J. Gen. Chem. U.S.S.R.*, **13**, 1 (1943) [*C.A.*, **38**, 330 (1944)].
279 Keyssner and Eichler, Ger. pat. 740,637 [*C.A.*, **40**, 586 (1946)]; see also reference 62a.
280 Noyes and Tucker, *Am. Chem. J.*, **19**, 123 (1897).
281 Straus and Kollek, *Ber.*, **59**, 1664 (1926).
282 Bandrowski, *Ber.*, **10**, 838 (1877).
283 Michael and Bucher, *Ber.*, **29**, 1792 (1896).
284 Backer and van der Zanden, *Rec. trav. chim.*, **47**, 776 (1928).
285 Eichelberger, *J. Am. Chem. Soc.*, **48**, 1320 (1926).
286 Farmer, Ghosal, and Kon, *J. Chem. Soc.*, **1936**, 1804.
287 Ruggli, *Helv. Chim. Acta*, **3**, 559 (1920).
288 Lindstrom and McPhee, *J. Am. Chem. Soc.*, **65**, 2387 (1943).
289 Friedrich, *Ann.*, **219**, 322 (1883).
290 Geuther, *Zeit. für Chem.*, **7**, 237 (1871); *J. prakt. Chem.*, [2] **3**, 431 (1871).
291 Kahlbaum, *Ber.*, **12**, 2335 (1879).
292 Wislicenus, *Ann.*, **248**, 281 (1888).
293 Michael, *J. prakt. Chem.*, [2] **38**, 6 (1888).
294 Michael, *Ber.*, **34**, 4215 (1901).
295 Fittig and Clutterbuck, *Ann.*, **268**, 96 (1892).
296 Desgrez, *Ann. chim.*, [7] **3**, 209 (1894).
297 Desgrez, *Bull. soc. chim. France*, [3] **11**, 391 (1894).
298 Szenic and Taggesell, *Ber.*, **28**, 2665 (1895).
299 Pinner, *Ber.*, **28**, 1877 (1895).

300 Pinner, *Ber.*, **8,** 898, 1561 (1875); **14,** 1081 (1881).
301 Lespieau, *Bull. soc. chim. France*, [3] **13,** 629 (1895).
302 Tchao Yin Lai, *Bull. soc. chim. France*, [4] **53,** 687 (1933).
303 Walling, Kharasch, and Mayo, *J. Am. Chem. Soc.*, **61,** 1711 (1939).
304 Morehouse and Maass, *Can. J. Research*, **11,** 637 (1934).
305 Lespieau, *Ann. chim.*, [8] **27,** 137 (1912).
306 Lespieau, *Compt. rend.*, **150,** 113 (1910).
307 Kreimeier, U. S. pat. 2,106,181 [*C.A.*, **32,** 2547 (1938)].
308 Lespieau, *Bull. soc. chim. France*, [4] **39,** 991 (1926).
309 Zal'kind and Gverdtsiteli, *J. Gen. Chem. U.S.S.R.*, **9,** 971 (1939) [*C.A.*, **33,** 8569 (1939)].
310 Lespieau and Pariselle, *Compt. rend.*, **146,** 1035 (1908).
311 Kreimeier, U. S. pat. 2,106,182 [*C.A.*, **32,** 2547 (1938)].
312 Liebermann, *Ann.*, **135,** 266 (1865).
313 Leonardi and de Franchis, *Gazz. chim. ital.*, **33,** I, 316 (1903).
314 Favorskiĭ and Shchukina, *J. Gen. Chem. U.S.S.R.*, **15,** 394 (1945) [*C.A.*, **40,** 4657 (1946)].
315 Lespieau, *Compt. rend.*, **150,** 1761 (1910).
316 Lespieau, *Ann. chim.*, [9] **2,** 280 (1914).
317 Dupont, *Ann. chim.*, [8] **30,** 485 (1913).
318 Burton and Pechmann, *Ber.*, **20,** 145 (1887).
319 Sargent, Buchman, and Farquhar, *J. Am. Chem. Soc.*, **64,** 2692 (1942).
320 Zoss and Hennion, *J. Am. Chem. Soc.*, **63,** 1151 (1941).
321 Dupont, *Compt. rend.*, **148,** 1522 (1909).
322 Iozitsch, *J. Russ. Phys. Chem. Soc.*, **29,** 90 (1897) (*Chem. Zentr.*, **1897,** I, 1012).
323 Gardner and Perkin, *J. Chem. Soc.*, **91,** 848 (1907).
324 Kurkuritschkin, *J. Russ. Phys. Chem. Soc.*, **35,** 873 (1903) (*Chem. Zentr.*, **1904,** I, 576).
325 Mowat and Smith, *J. Chem. Soc.*, **1938,** 19.
326 Risseghem, *Bull. soc. chim. Belg.*, **28,** 187 (1914–1919); *Compt. rend.*, **158,** 1694 (1914).
327 Eltekow, *Ber.*, **10,** 1905, 2058 (1877).
328 Bruylants, *Ber.*, **8,** 406, 410 (1875).
329 Béhal, *Ann. chim.*, [6] **15,** 267 (1888).
330 Flavitky and Krylow, *Ber.*, **10,** 1102 (1877); *J. Russ. Phys. Chem. Soc.*, **10,** 342 (1878).
331 McGrew and Adams, *J. Am. Chem. Soc.*, **59,** 1497 (1937).
332 Lespieau, *Compt. rend.*, **194,** 287 (1932).
333 Henry, *Ber.*, **5,** 274 (1872).
334 Liebermann and Kretschmer, *Ann.*, **158,** 230 (1871).
335 Baeyer, *Ann.*, **138,** 196 (1866).
336 Iozitsch and Orelkin, *J. Russ. Phys. Chem. Soc.*, **42,** 373, 1081 (1910) [Beilstein, 4th ed., Supp. Vol. 1, p. 235].
337 Lespieau, *Compt. rend.*, **144,** 1161 (1907).
338 Claisen, *Ber.*, **31,** 1021 (1898).
339 Bode, *Ges. z. Förd. d. ges. Naturw. z. Marburg*, **13/3** (*Chem. Zentr.*, **1889,** I, 713).
340 Bode, *Ann.*, **267,** 268 (1892).
341 Gibson and Kahnweiler, *Am. Chem. J.*, **12,** 314 (1890).
342 Moureu and Johnson, *Bull. soc. chim. France*, [4] **33,** 1241 (1923).
343 Nieuwland, Calcott, Downing, and Carter, *J. Am. Chem. Soc.*, **53,** 4197 (1931).
344 Griner, *Ann. chim.*, [6] **26,** 305 (1892).
345 Henry, *Ber.*, **6,** 955 (1873).
346 Henry, *Ber.*, **14,** 399 (1881).
347 Perkin, *J. Chem. Soc.*, **67,** 255 (1895).
348 Brühl, *Ber.*, **25,** 2638 (1892).
349 Berthelot, *Ann. chim.*, [5] **23,** 188 (1881).
350 Lespieau and Vavon, *Compt. rend.*, **148,** 1331 (1909).
351 Henry, *Jahresbericht Fort. Chem.*, 380 (1878); *Compt. rend.*, **87,** 171 (1878).
352 Welt, *Ber.*, **30,** 1493 (1897).

[353] Hecht, *Ber.*, **11**, 1050 (1878).

[354] Risseghem, *Bull. soc. chim. Belg.*, **42**, 229 (1933).

[355] Thompson and Margnetti, *J. Am. Chem. Soc.*, **64**, 573 (1942).

[356] Hennion and Banigan, *J. Am. Chem. Soc.*, **68**, 1202 (1946).

[357] Takei, Ono, and Sinosaki, *Ber.*, **73**, 950 (1940).

[358] Bohnsack, *Ber.*, **74**, 1575 (1941).

[359] Claisen, *Ber.*, **44**, 1161 (1911).

[360] Viguier, *Ann. chim.*, [8] **28**, 433 (1913).

[361] Grignard, *Bull. soc. chim. France*, [3] **21**, 574, 576 (1899).

[362] Markownikow, *J. Russ. Phys. Chem. Soc.*, **27**, 285 (1895); **34**, 904 (1902) (*Chem. Zentr.*, **1903**, I, 567); *Ann.*, **327**, 59 (1903).

[363] Favorskiĭ, *Bull. soc. chim. France*, [5] **3**, 1727 (1936).

[364] Combes, *Ann. chim.*, [6] **12**, 199 (1887).

[365] Limpricht, *Ann.*, **103**, 80 (1857).

[366] Rubien, *Ann.*, **142**, 294 (1867).

[367] Kuz'min, *Soobshchenie o Nauch.-Issledovatel. Rabote Kiev. Ind. Inst.*, **2**, 17 (1940); *Khim. Referat. Zhur.*, **4**, No. 2, 41 (1941) [*C.A.*, **37**, 3046 (1943)].

[368] Wenner and Reichstein, *Helv. Chim. Acta*, **27**, 24 (1944).

[369] Nametkin, Isagulyants, and Eliseeva, *Sintezy Dushistykh Veshchestv, Sbornik Stateĭ*, 281 (1939) [*C.A.*, **36**, 3783 (1942)].

[370] Bryusova and Kuznetsova, *Sintezy Dushistykh Veshchestv, Sbornik Stateĭ*, 291 (1939) [*C.A.*, **36**, 3783 (1942)].

[371] Béhal and Desgrez, *Compt. rend.*, **114**, 1074 (1892).

[372] Favorskiĭ, *J. prakt. Chem.*, [2] **51**, 533 (1895).

[373] André, *Ann. chim.*, [8] **29**, 540 (1913); *Bull. soc. chim. France*, [4] **9**, 193 (1911).

[374] Favorskiĭ, *J. Russ. Phys. Chem. Soc.*, **50**, 557 (1920) (*Chem. Zentr.*, **1923**, III, 998).

[375] Reitzenstein and Bönitsch, *J. prakt. Chem.*, [2] **86**, 1 (1912).

[376] Reich, *Bull. soc. chim. France*, [4] **21**, 217 (1917).

[377] Manchot, *Ann.*, **387**, 257 (1912).

[378] Iozitsch, *J. Russ. Phys. Chem. Soc.*, **35**, 1269 (1903) [*Bull. soc. chim. France*, [3] **34**, 181 (1905)].

[379] Grignard and Courtot, *Bull. soc. chim. France*, [4] **17**, 228 (1915).

[380] Grignard, Bellet, and Courtot, *Ann. chim.*, [9] **4**, 28 (1915).

[381] Zal'kind and Fundyler, *J. Gen. Chem. U.S.S.R.*, **9**, 1725 (1939) [*C.A.*, **34**, 3719 (1940)].

[382] Ott and Bossaller, *Ber.*, **76**, 88 (1943).

[383] Liebermann and Sachse, *Ber.*, **24**, 4112 (1891).

[384] Vaughn and Nieuwland, *J. Am. Chem. Soc.*, **55**, 2150 (1933).

[385] Wilson and Wenzke, *J. Am. Chem. Soc.*, **56**, 2025 (1934).

[386] Iozitsch, Seslawin, and Koschelew, *J. Russ. Phys. Chem. Soc.*, **42**, 1490 (1910) [*Bull. soc. chim. France*, [4] **10**, 1294 (1911)].

[387] Prévost, *Compt. rend.*, **200**, 942 (1935).

[388] Baeyer, *Ber.*, **15**, 50 (1882).

[389] Reich, *Arch. sci. phys. et nat.*, [4] **45**, 191 (March), 259 (April) (1918), Geneva University Laboratory [*C.A.*, **12**, 1876 (1918)].

[390] Reich and Koehler, *Ber.*, **46**, 3727 (1913).

[391] Drewsen, *Ann.*, **212**, 150 (1882).

[392] Wieland, *Ann.*, **328**, 233 (1903).

[393] Kohler and Barrett, *J. Am. Chem. Soc.*, **46**, 747 (1924).

[394] Hessler, *J. Am. Chem. Soc.*, **44**, 425 (1922).

[394a] Reichstein and Baud, *Helv. Chim. Acta*, **20**, 892 (1937).

[395] Perkin and Simonsen, *J. Chem. Soc.*, **91**, 840 (1907).

[396] Lespieau and Deluchat, *Compt. rend.*, **183**, 889 (1926).

[397] Mousseron, *Compt. rend.*, **217**, 155 (1943).

[398] Mousseron and Jullien, *Bull. soc. chim. France*, **1946**, 239.

[399] Lespieau, *Compt. rend.*, **158**, 707 (1914).

[400] Lespieau, *Compt. rend.*, **158**, 1187 (1914).

[401] Pum, *Monatsh.*, **9**, 446 (1888); **14**, 491 (1893).
[402] Ruhemann and Beddow, *J. Chem. Soc.*, **77**, 1119 (1900).
[403] Darzens and Rost, *Compt. rend.*, **149**, 681 (1909).
[404] Jegorowa, *J. Russ. Phys. Chem. Soc.*, **43**, 1116 (1911) (*Chem. Zentr.*, **1912**, I, 1010).
[405] Béhal, *Bull. soc. chim. France*, [2] **47**, 33 (1887).
[406] Cleveland, *J. Chem. Phys.*, **11**, 1 (1943).
[407] Pfeiffer, *Ann.*, **411**, 72 (1916).
[408] Reimer and Tobin, *J. Am. Chem. Soc.*, **63**, 2490 (1941).
[409] Bergmann and Christiani, *Ber.*, **64**, 1481 (1931).
[410] Baeyer, Ger. pat. 11,857 [*Frdl.*, **1**, 128 (1877–1887)].
[411] Reich, *Compt. rend.*, **162**, 129 (1916).
[412] Kalff, *Rec. trav. chim.*, **46**, 594 (1927).
[413] Moureu and Delange, *Bull. soc. chim. France*, [3] **27**, 374 (1902).
[414] Moureu and Delange, *Bull. soc. chim. France*, [3] **31**, 1327 (1904).
[415] Brachin, *Bull. soc. chim. France*, [3] **35**, 1163 (1906).
[416] Lohaus, *J. prakt. Chem.*, [2] **119**, 235 (1928).
[417] Curtius and Kenngott, *J. prakt. Chem.*, [2] **112**, 314 (1926).
[418] Perkin, *J. Chem. Soc.*, **45**, 170 (1884).
[419] Barisch, *J. prakt. Chem.*, [2] **20**, 173 (1879).
[420] Sudborough and Thompson, *J. Chem. Soc.*, **83**, 1153 (1903).
[421] Michael, *Ber.*, **34**, 3640 (1901).
[422] Macallum, U. S. pat. 2,194,363 [*C.A.*, **34**, 4745 (1940)].
[423] Erlenmeyer, *Ber.*, **16**, 152 (1883).
[424] Eigel, *Ber.*, **20**, 2527 (1887).
[425] Powell and Adams, *J. Am. Chem. Soc.*, **42**, 646 (1920).
[426] Körner, *Ber.*, **21**, 276 (1888); *Ann.*, **227**, 248 (1885).
[427] Wohl and Jaschinowski, *Ber.*, **54**, 476 (1921).
[428] Tiffeneau, *Ann. chim.*, [8] **10**, 145 (1907); *Compt. rend.*, **135**, 1346 (1902).
[429] Lespieau and Garreau, *Compt. rend.*, **171**, 111 (1920).
[430] Dey, *J. Chem. Soc.*, **1937**, 1057.
[431] Henry, *Bull. soc. chim. France*, [2] **40**, 323 (1883); *Compt. rend.*, **96**, 1233 (1883).
[431a] Quelet and Golse, *Compt. rend.*, **223**, 159 (1946).
[432] Braun and Tauber, *Ann.*, **458**, 102 (1927).
[433] Dorier, *Compt. rend.*, **196**, 1677 (1933).
[434] Rességuier, *Bull. soc. chim. France*, [4] **7**, 431 (1910).
[435] Noerdlinger, *Kleine Mitt. Chem. Fabr. Flörsheim*, No. 37, November 1911 [*C.A.*, **6**, 2072 (1912)].
[436] Kranzfelder and Vogt, *J. Am. Chem. Soc.*, **60**, 1714 (1938).
[437] Einhorn and Grabfield, *Ann.*, **243**, 362 (1888).
[438] Hell and Bauer, *Ber.*, **36**, 1184 (1903).
[439] Shōichirō Nagai, *J. Coll. Eng. Tokyo Imp. Univ.*, [4] **11**, 83 (1921) [*C.A.*, **16**, 418 (1922)].
[440] Perkin, *J. Chem. Soc.*, **39**, 409 (1881).
[440a] Baddar, *J. Chem. Soc.*, **1947**, 224.
[441] Jones and James, *J. Chem. Soc.*, **1935**, 1600.
[442] Vorländer and Gahren, *Ber.*, **40**, 1966 (1907).
[443] Fridman, *Mem. Inst. Chem., Acad. Sci. Ukr.S.S.R.*, **4**, No. 3, 341 (1937) [*C.A.*, **32**, 5400 (1938)].
[444] Slobodin, *J. Gen. Chem. U.S.S.R.*, **9**, 272 (1939) [*C.A.*, **33**, 6258 (1939)].
[445] Grignard and Perrichon, *Ann. chim.*, [10] **5**, 5 (1926).
[446] Fittig and Claus, *Ann.*, **269**, 1 (1892).
[447] Ladenburg, *Ann. Supp.*, **8**, 87 (1872).
[448] Moureu, *Bull. soc. chim. France*, [3] **33**, 151 (1905).
[449] Moureu and Desmots, *Bull. soc. chim. France*, [3] **27**, 366 (1902).
[450] Braun, Fussgänger, and Kühn, *Ann.*, **445**, 201 (1925).

451 Lauer and Gensler, *J. Am. Chem. Soc.*, **67**, 1171 (1945).
452 Lespieau and Bresch, *Compt. rend.*, **156**, 710 (1913).
453 Michael and Lamb, *Am. Chem. J.*, **36**, 552 (1906).
454 Ruhemann, *Ber.*, **53**, 274 (1920).
455 Lespieau, *Bull. soc. chim. France*, [4] **37**, 421 (1925).
456 Krafft, *Ber.*, **11**, 1414 (1878).
457 Welander, *Ber.*, **28**, 1448 (1895).
458 Oskerko, *Ber.*, **70**, 55 (1937).
459 Giesecke, *Zeit. für Chem.*, **6**, 428 (1870) (*Chem. Zentr.*, **1870**, 610).
460 Thoms and Mannich, *Ber.*, **36**, 2544 (1903).
461 Mannich, *Ber.*, **35**, 2144 (1902).
462 Mannich, *Ber.*, **36**, 2551 (1903).
463 Ruggli and Staub, *Helv. Chim. Acta*, **19**, 962 (1936).
464 Leroy, *Bull. soc. chim. France*, [3] **6**, 385 (1891); *Compt. rend.*, **113**, 1056 (1891).
465 Leroy, *Bull. soc. chim. France*, [3] **7**, 644 (1892).
466 Levy and Cope, *J. Am. Chem. Soc.*, **66**, 1684 (1944).
466a Quelet and Golse, *Bull. soc. chim. France*, **1947**, 313.
467 Majima and Tahara, *Ber.*, **48**, 1606 (1915).
468 Krafft, *Ber.*, **17**, 1371 (1884).
469 West, *J. Am. Chem. Soc.*, **42**, 1656 (1920).
470 Wojack, Glupe, and Jatzkewitz, *Ber.*, **71**, 1372 (1938).
471 Gill, *Ber.*, **26**, 649 (1893).
472 Ruggli, *Ann.*, **392**, 92 (1912).
473 Pfeiffer, *Ber.*, **45**, 1819 (1912).
474 Ruggli and Zaeslin, *Helv. Chim. Acta*, **18**, 853 (1935).
475 Ruggli, Zaeslin, and Lang, *Helv. Chim. Acta*, **21**, 1240 (1938).
476 Ruggli and Lang, *Helv. Chim. Acta*, **19**, 996 (1936).
477 Ruggli and Lang, *Helv. Chim. Acta*, **21**, 38 (1938).
478 Fromm, Benzinger, and Schäfer, *Ann.*, **394**, 325 (1912).
479 Laitinen and Wawzonek, *J. Am. Chem. Soc.*, **64**, 1765 (1942).
480 Smith and Hoehn, *J. Am. Chem. Soc.*, **63**, 1180 (1941).
481 Söderbäck, *Ann.*, **443**, 142 (1925).
482 Weissberger and Sängewald, *Z. physik. Chem.*, **20B**, 145 (1933).
483 Barber and Slack, *J. Chem. Soc.*, **1944**, 612.
484 Ruhemann and Levy, *Ber.*, **53**, 265 (1920).
485 Bickel, *J. Am. Chem. Soc.*, **69**, 73, 2134 (1947).
485a Dufraisse, *Compt. rend.*, **158**, 1691 (1914); *Ann. chim.*, [9] **17**, 140 (1922).
485b Moureu and Delange, *Compt. rend.*, **134**, 45 (1902); *Bull. soc. chim. France*, [3] **27**, 378 (1902).
486 Knowles, *J. Am. Chem. Soc.*, **43**, 896 (1921).
487 Hey, *J. Chem. Soc.*, **1931**, 2476.
488 Campbell, Campbell, and McGuire, *Proc. Indiana Acad. Sci.*, **50**, 87 (1940) [*C.A.*, **35**, 5872 (1941)].
489 Orekhoff and Tiffeneau, *Bull. soc. chim. France*, [4] **37**, 1410 (1925).
490 Ruzicka, Hürbin, and Boekenoogen, *Helv. Chim. Acta*, **16**, 498 (1933).
490a Weygand and Bauer, *Ann.*, **459**, 123 (1927).
490b Watson, *J. Chem. Soc.*, **85**, 1319 (1904).
490c Stockhausen and Gattermann, *Ber.*, **25**, 3535 (1892).
491 Goldschmiedt and Hepp, *Ber.*, **6**, 1504 (1873).
492 Zincke and Münch, *Ann.*, **335**, 157 (1904).
493 Bodenstein, *Ber.*, **27**, 3397 (1894).
494 Krafft and Heizmann, *Ber.*, **33**, 3586 (1900).
495 Chydenius, *Ann.*, **143**, 267 (1867).
496 Thiele and Rössner, *Ann.*, **306**, 201 (1899).
497 Wasserman and Dawson, *J. Org. Chem.*, **8**, 73 (1943).

[498] Posternak, *Compt. rend.*, **162**, 944 (1916).
[499] Hilditch, *The Chemical Constitution of Natural Fats*, John Wiley & Sons, 2nd ed., 1947, p. 179.
[500] Arnaud, *Bull. soc. chim. France*, [3] **7**, 233 (1892); *Compt. rend.*, **114**, 79 (1892).
[501] Arnaud, *Bull. soc. chim. France*, [3] **27**, 484, 489 (1902).
[502] Arnaud and Posternak, *Compt. rend.*, **149**, 220 (1909).
[503] Arnaud and Posternak, *Compt. rend.*, **150**, 1130, 1245 (1910).
[504] Arnaud and Hasenfratz, *Compt. rend.*, **152**, 1603 (1911).
[505] Grützner, *Chem. Z.*, **17**, 1851 (1893) (*Chem. Zentr.*, **1894**, I, 320).
[506] Overbeck, *Ann.*, **140**, 39 (1866).
[507] Behrend, *Ber.*, **28**, 2248 (1895).
[508] Hoffmann-La Roche and Co., Ger. pat. 243,582 [*C.A.*, **6**, 2335 (1912)].
[509] Böeseken and Slooff, *Rec. trav. chim.*, **49**, 95 (1930).
[510] Ulrich, *Zeit. für Chem.*, **3**, 545 (1867) [Beilstein, *Handbuch der org. Chem.*, 4th ed., 3, 391].
[511] Grün and Woldenberg, *J. Am. Chem. Soc.*, **31**, 490 (1909).
[512] Mangold, *Monatsh.*, **15**, 307 (1894).
[513] Mühle, *Ber.*, **46**, 2091 (1913).
[514] Coffman, Tsao, Schniepp, and Marvel, *J. Am. Chem. Soc.*, **55**, 3792 (1933).
[515] Fuson, Southwick, and Rowland, *J. Am. Chem. Soc.*, **66**, 1109 (1944).
[516] Haussknecht, *Ann.*, **143**, 40 (1867).
[517] Holt, *Ber.*, **25**, 961 (1892).
[518] Grossmann, *Ber.*, **26**, 639 (1893).
[519] Carothers and Berchet, *J. Am. Chem. Soc.*, **55**, 1094 (1933).

CHAPTER 2

CYANOETHYLATION

Herman Alexander Bruson *

Resinous Products and Chemicals Company

Rohm and Haas Company, Inc.

CONTENTS

* Present address, Industrial Rayon Corporation, Cleveland, Ohio.

NATURE OF THE REACTION

A variety of organic and inorganic compounds possessing labile hydrogen atoms add readily to acrylonitrile with the formation of molecules containing a cyanoethyl grouping ($-CH_2CH_2CN$). This reaction is commonly known as "cyanoethylation" and resembles closely a Michael type of addition.

$$RH + CH_2{=}CHCN \rightarrow RCH_2CH_2CN$$

Typical compounds containing reactive hydrogen atoms which have been added to acrylonitrile are as follows:

I. Compounds having one or more —NH— groups such as ammonia, primary and secondary amines, hydrazine, hydroxylamine, imides, lactams, and amides.

II. Compounds having one or more —OH, —SH, or —AsH— groups such as water, alcohols, phenols, oximes, hydrogen sulfide, mercaptans, and arsines.

III. Certain acidic compounds, other than carboxylic acids, such as hydrogen cyanide, hydrogen chloride, hydrogen bromide, hypochlorous acid, and sodium bisulfite.

IV. Compounds possessing the grouping HCX_3 in which X is chlorine or bromine.

V. Sulfones having a $-CH_2-$ group between the $-SO_2-$ group and an olefinic linkage or an aromatic ring.

VI. Nitro compounds having a $-CH-$, $-CH_2-$, or CH_3- group contiguous to the $-NO_2$ group.

VII. Ketones or aldehydes having a $-CH-$, $-CH_2-$, or CH_3- group contiguous to the carbonyl group.

VIII. Compounds such as malonic esters, malonamide, cyanoacetamide, etc., in which a $-CH-$ or $-CH_2-$ group is situated between $-CO_2R$, $-CN$, or $-CONH-$ groups.

IX. Compounds such as benzyl cyanide or allyl cyanide in which a $-CH_2-$ group is situated between a cyano group and an aryl nucleus or an ethylenic linkage.

X. Compounds in which a $-CH-$ or $-CH_2-$ group is situated between two ethylenic carbon atoms of a carbocycle or of a heterocycle, such as cyclopentadiene, indene, fluorene, and 2-phenylindole.

The cyanoethylation reaction, except with certain amines, usually requires the presence of an alkaline catalyst. Typical catalysts which are useful for the purpose are the oxides, hydroxides, alkoxides, hydrides, cyanides, and amides of the alkali metals sodium and potassium, as well as the alkali metals themselves. The strongly basic quaternary ammonium hydroxides, in particular benzyltrimethylammonium hydroxide (Triton B), are particularly effective because of their solubility in organic media. Only small amounts of catalyst are required; usually from 1% to 5% of catalyst based on the weight of the acrylonitrile is sufficient. The cyanoethylation of certain amines requires an acidic catalyst.

Many of the reactions are strongly exothermic and require cooling to prevent excessive polymerization of the acrylonitrile. Inert solvents such as benzene, dioxane, pyridine, or acetonitrile are often useful to dissolve solid reactants or to moderate the reaction. *tert*-Butyl alcohol, although reactive with acrylonitrile at temperatures above 60°, is relatively inert at or near room temperature and is often useful as a solvent since it dissolves appreciable amounts of potassium hydroxide (up to about 4% at 25°) to give an effective catalyst solution.

In order to prevent sudden reactions which may get out of control, it is advisable to dissolve or disperse the catalyst in the hydrogen donor, with or without the use of an auxiliary solvent, and to add the acrylonitrile gradually with mechanical stirring while controlling the temperature of the reaction.

SCOPE AND LIMITATIONS

It is most convenient to discuss the scope and limitations of the cyanoethylation reaction in terms of the different classes of compounds which
add to acrylonitrile. This is done in the subsections which follow.

Cyanoethylation of Ammonia and Amines (Tables I–IV)

Ammonia and most amines add to acrylonitrile without the aid of a
catalyst.[1] In general, amines add more readily than any other class of
compounds, but the ease of addition varies considerably. With those
amines which react slowly an acidic or basic catalyst is desirable, and
with some amines a catalyst is essential. Primary amines may react
with one or two moles of acrylonitrile. Low temperatures favor the
addition of one molecule of amine with formation of a secondary amine,
an alkylcyanoethylamine; higher temperatures result in the addition of
the initial secondary amine to a second molecule of acrylonitrile with
formation of a tertiary amine, an alkyldicyanoethylamine, especially if
excess of acrylonitrile is present. Since secondary amines can yield

$$RNH_2 + CH_2{=}CHCN \rightarrow RNHCH_2CH_2CN$$

$$RNHCH_2CH_2CN + CH_2{=}CHCN \rightarrow RN(CH_2CH_2CN)_2$$

only a single product with acrylonitrile the temperature at which the
reaction takes place may be varied over a wide range.

Ammonia yields a mixture of mono-, di-, and tri-cyanoethylation
products,[1,2,3] though the last is formed much less readily than the other
two.

$$NH_3 + CH_2{=}CHCN \nearrow H_2NCH_2CH_2CN$$
$$\rightarrow HN(CH_2CH_2CN)_2$$
$$\searrow N(CH_2CH_2CN)_3$$

The yield of the three cyanoethylamines depends upon the proportions
of the reactants and the temperature. When five moles of anhydrous
liquid ammonia is heated with four moles of acrylonitrile in an autoclave
at 90° for thirty minutes, β-aminopropionitrile is obtained in only
12.5% yield, whereas the disubstituted amine, bis(2-cyanoethyl)amine,
is obtained in about 75% yield.[1] If the molar ratio of liquid ammonia

---

[1] Hoffmann and Jacobi, U. S. pat. 1,992,615 [C.A., **29**, 2548 (1935)].

[2] Whitmore, Mosher, Adams, Taylor, Chapin, Weisel, and Yanko, J. Am. Chem. Soc.,
66, 725 (1944).

[3] Wiedemann and Montgomery, J. Am. Chem. Soc., **67**, 1994 (1945).

CYANOETHYLATION 83

to acrylonitrile is 8:1, a 22% yield of β-aminopropionitrile and a 64% yield of the secondary amine can be obtained [2] by reaction at 40°. If one mole of acrylonitrile is gradually added to one mole of concentrated aqueous ammonia at a temperature between 30° and 35°, and the mixture is allowed to stand for three hours, bis(2-cyanoethyl)amine can be obtained in 85% yield by distilling the product in vacuum. On the other hand, rapid addition of acrylonitrile below the surface of an excess of aqueous ammonia preheated to 110° followed by a short reaction period and rapid cooling gives β-aminopropionitrile in more than 60% yield.[4]

An extensive study of the reaction of aqueous ammonia with acrylonitrile [5] has shown, as would be predicted on theoretical grounds, that increasing the ratio of aqueous ammonia to acrylonitrile favors formation of the primary amine. When the molar ratio of aqueous ammonia to acrylonitrile is 20:1 and cooling is employed, a 39% yield of the primary amine and a 39% yield of the secondary amine can be secured.[5] By operating without cooling and under pressure the exothermic reaction carries the temperature to 71°, and, under these conditions, a molar ratio of 7.5 moles of aqueous ammonia to one mole of acrylonitrile yields 38.3% of the primary amine and 53.2% of the secondary amine.

At higher temperatures hydrolysis and disproportionation of the various aminopropionitriles occur. At 150° aqueous ammonia and acrylonitrile yield 35% of β-aminopropionic acid after eight hours.[6] It has also been pointed out by Kirk [7] that β-aminopropionic acid is formed upon heating bis(2-cyanoethyl)amine with aqueous ammonia at 200° in an autoclave; and Küng [8] has shown that β-aminopropionitrile is formed by pyrolysis of bis(2-cyanoethyl)amine or tris(2-cyanoethyl)-amine.

Methylamine adds to acrylonitrile in the cold to give a 78% yield of β-methylaminopropionitrile;[9] even in the presence of methanol, which itself adds to acrylonitrile when alkaline catalysts are used, the amine adds readily. Upon heating methylamine and acrylonitrile in a sealed tube at 80° for six hours, the di-cyanoethylation product is formed.[9]

Ethylamine with an equimolar quantity of acrylonitrile below 30° gives a 90% yield of β-ethylaminopropionitrile.[2] When heated with excess acrylonitrile, a 60% yield of bis(2-cyanoethyl)ethylamine [2] is obtained. Similarly, n-propylamine and isopropylamine give, respec-

[4] Ford, Buc, and Greiner, J. Am. Chem. Soc., 69, 845 (1947).
[5] Buc, Ford, and Wise, J. Am. Chem. Soc., 67, 92 (1945).
[6] Carlson and Hotchkiss, U. S. pat. 2,335,997 [C.A., 38, 2972 (1944)]; U. S. pat. 2,377,401 [C.A., 39, 4333 (1945)].
[7] Kirk, U. S. pat. 2,334,163 [C.A., 38, 2667 (1944)].
[8] Küng, U. S. pat. 2,401,429 [C.A., 40, 5447 (1946)].
[9] Cook and Reed, J. Chem. Soc., 1945, 399.

tively, 92% and 95% yields of n-propylaminopropionitrile [10] and iso-propylaminopropionitrile; [11] n-butylamine, sec-butylamine, and tert-butylamine give 98%, 83%, and 56% yields, respectively, of the mono-cyanoethylated derivatives.[10] In general, small amounts of the di-cyano-ethylated compounds are obtained as by-products.

Piperidine is a very reactive secondary amine and adds to acrylonitrile with evolution of heat.[2,12] Morpholine is only slightly less reactive.[2] Diethylamine, however, adds more slowly than morpholine, although no difficulty is encountered in obtaining a nearly quantitative yield of product merely by heating the reactants together.[2] Di-n-propylamine gives a 90% yield of the cyanoethylation product, but diisopropylamine gives only a 12% yield; di-n-butylamine gives a 96% yield, and diiso-butylamine a 51% yield.

The rate of addition of dialkylamines decreases progressively with the size of the alkyl groups.[2] For example, an equimolar mixture of acrylo-nitrile and di-n-amylamine when warmed to 50° and allowed to stand overnight gives a 60% yield of β-di-n-amylaminopropionitrile,[13] whereas di-n-octylamine does not react with excess of acrylonitrile at 50° and requires a temperature of 100° to give an 80% yield of β-di-n-octyl-aminopropionitrile after one hundred hours.[14] A branched-chain octyl-amine reacts more slowly than the straight-chain isomer; bis(2-ethyl-hexyl)amine and excess of acrylonitrile under the conditions just speci-fied give a 65% yield of β-bis(2-ethylhexyl)aminopropionitrile,[14] and a 77% yield after three hundred and sixty hours at 100°.[2] These results indicate that the rate of addition is primarily dependent upon the size and complexity of the amine.[2] The basicity of the amine is probably not an important factor since the ionization constants of diethylamine, piperidine, and morpholine are, respectively, 1.2×10^{-3}, 1.6×10^{-3}, and 2.4×10^{-6}, and all three react quite rapidly.[14]

The reversibility of cyanoethylation reactions, mentioned in the dis-cussion of the reaction of ammonia and acrylonitrile, is again illustrated by the gradual decomposition of the higher β-dialkylaminopropionitriles to dialkylamine and acrylonitrile or its polymer when heated near their boiling points. Cyanoethyldiethanolamine upon distillation yields di-ethanolamine and a polymer of acrylonitrile.[2] Similarly, cyanoethyl-cyclohexylamine gives 20% of cyclohexylamine.[1] It has also been observed that when equimolar amounts of secondary amine and acrylo-

[10] Tarbell, Shakespear, Claus, and Bunnett, J. Am. Chem. Soc., 68, 1217 (1946).
[11] Pearson, Jones, and Cope, J. Am. Chem. Soc., 68, 1227 (1946).
[12] Terentev and Terenteva, J. Gen. Chem. U.S.S.R., 12, 415 (1942) [C.A., 37, 3095 (1943)].
[13] Holcomb and Hamilton, J. Am. Chem. Soc., 64, 1309 (1942).
[14] Burckhalter, Jones, Holcomb, and Sweet, J. Am. Chem. Soc., 65, 2014 (1943).

nitrile react some of the unreacted starting materials are always recovered; the yield is never so high as when an excess of one of the reactants is used.[2]

The cyanoethylation reaction has been extended to many more complex primary and especially secondary amines. Thus, benzylamine gives $C_6H_5CH_2NHCH_2CH_2CN$;[15] γ-diethylaminopropylamine gives a 79% yield of $(C_2H_5)_2NCH_2CH_2CH_2NHCH_2CH_2CN$ and a 9% yield of $(C_2H_5)_2NCH_2CH_2CH_2N(CH_2CH_2CN)_2$; β-morpholinoethylamine gives $OC_4H_8NCH_2CH_2NHCH_2CH_2CN$ in 81.5% yield.[2] Hydrazine hydrate and acrylonitrile in equimolar quantities react in the cold to form $NH_2NHCH_2CH_2CN$ in 90% yield,[1] and hydroxylamine gives an almost quantitative yield of $HONHCH_2CH_2CN$.[1] At 95° such mixed secondary amines as methyl-n-propylamine, ethylisopropylamine, cyclopentylethylamine, sec-butyl-n-propylamine, n-butyl-sec-butylamine,[16] and benzylmethylamine[15] add readily to acrylonitrile. The cyclic bases pyrrolidine, 2-methylpiperidine, 3-methylpiperidine, 4-methylpiperidine, and 2,6-dimethylpiperidine are other examples of amines which add readily.[17] The cyclic imine, 2,2-dimethylethyleneimine, when refluxed for thirty hours with acrylonitrile gives 1-(2-cyanoethyl)-2,2-dimethylethyleneimine in 66% yield.[18] Such alkanolamines as ethanolamine, diethanolamine, propanolamine, and N-methyl-N-ethanolamine[14] are preferentially cyanoethylated on the basic nitrogen atom rather than on the hydroxyl group.[19]

Heterocyclic bases containing two imino groups, such as piperazine, hydrogenated pyrimidines, and hydrogenated perimidines, react with two molecules of acrylonitrile.[20, 21]

$$
\begin{array}{c}
\mathrm{NH} \\
\diagup \; \diagdown \\
\mathrm{CH_2} \quad \mathrm{CH_2} \\
| \qquad | \\
\mathrm{CH_2} \quad \mathrm{CH_2} \\
\diagdown \; \diagup \\
\mathrm{NH}
\end{array}
\; + 2\mathrm{CH_2}{=}\mathrm{CHCN} \rightarrow
\begin{array}{c}
\mathrm{NCH_2CH_2CN} \\
\diagup \; \diagdown \\
\mathrm{CH_2} \quad \mathrm{CH_2} \\
| \qquad | \\
\mathrm{CH_2} \quad \mathrm{CH_2} \\
\diagdown \; \diagup \\
\mathrm{NCH_2CH_2CN}
\end{array}
$$

Certain amines, especially those in the aromatic and heterocyclic series, react only very slowly with acrylonitrile in the absence of a catalyst. Methylaniline and 1,2,3,4-tetrahydroquinoline do not react appreciably

[15] King and McMillan, *J. Am. Chem. Soc.*, **68**, 1468 (1946).
[16] Corse, Bryant, and Shonle, *J. Am. Chem. Soc.*, **68**, 1906 (1946).
[17] Corse, Bryant, and Shonle, *J. Am. Chem. Soc.*, **68**, 1912 (1946).
[18] Tarbell and Fukushima, *J. Am. Chem. Soc.*, **68**, 2501 (1946).
[19] Hoffmann and Jacobi, U. S. pat. 2,017,537 [*C.A.*, **29**, 8003 (1935)].
[20] I.G. Farbenind. A.-G., Brit. pat. 457,621 [*C.A.*, **31**, 3068 (1937)].
[21] Behr, Kirby, MacDonald, and Todd, *J. Am. Chem. Soc.*, **68**, 1297 (1946).

with acrylonitrile when heated in a sealed tube at 200°,[2] but in the presence of glacial acetic acid (about 5% of the weight of the amine) they react at 120–140° to give good yields of the cyanoethylated derivatives. Cyanoethylation of n-butylcresidine, 2-methylindoline, 1,2,3,4,-10,11-hexahydrocarbazole,[22] and p-anisidine[23] is accelerated by acetic acid as catalyst. Bases appear to be ineffective as catalysts with this group of substances.[2]

Other acidic catalysts that have been proposed for the cyanoethylation of otherwise unreactive amines are oxalic acid, formic acid, chloroacetic acid, sulfuric acid, and salts of nickel, zinc, cobalt, copper, or other metals capable of forming ammoniates; the ammonia or amine salts of strong mineral acids are also successful catalysts.[1,2,22] Copper salts, in particular copper chloride, sulfate, oleate, borate, or acetate, appear to inhibit the polymerization of acrylonitrile at elevated temperatures and to result in an improvement of yields.[20]

Alkaline catalysts have been very widely employed. Heterocyclic bases such as pyrrole, carbazole, indole, dihydroacridine, decahydroquinoline, perimidine, and thiodiphenylamine are cyanoethylated smoothly in the presence of small amounts of sodium ethoxide.[20] The same catalyst is effective in the cyanoethylation of benzimidazole at room temperature in pyridine as a solvent.[20] α-Methylindole and α-phenylindole react with acrylonitrile when heated in the presence of sodium methoxide and copper borate to yield mono- and di-cyanoethylated products.[20] The second cyanoethyl group is introduced as a result of addition involving the active hydrogen in the 3-position.

Aqueous potassium hydroxide is a catalyst for cyanoethylation of 8-(3-aminopropylamino)-6-methoxyquinoline at room temperature.[24]

[22] I.G. Farbenind. A.-G., Brit. pat. 466,316 [C.A., **31**, 7887 (1937)].

[23] Elderfield, Gensler, Bembry, Kremer, Brody, Hageman, and Head, J. Am. Chem. Soc., **68**, 1262 (1946).

[24] Kissinger, Von, and Carmack, J. Am. Chem. Soc., **68**, 1563 (1946).

Triton B as a catalyst [25] permits cyanoethylation of carbazole even at ice-bath temperature; [2] heterocyclic bases, such as isatin,[26] pyrrole, 2-phenylindole, 2-phenyl-3-indolecarboxaldehyde, 3-indolecarboxaldehyde, and 2-methyl-3-indolecarboxaldehyde, are readily cyanoethylated on the nitrogen atom at moderate temperatures with this catalyst.[27] Triton B has proved useful as a catalyst in cyanoethylation of 2,3-dimethylpiperidine,[17] 2,4-dimethylpiperidine,[17] methylisopropylamine, n-butylmethylamine, sec-butylmethylamine, isobutylmethylamine, methyl-2-pentylamine, methyl-3-pentylamine, cyclopentylmethylamine, 2,3-dimethylbutylamine, 2,4-dimethylpentylamine, 4-methylheptylamine, ethylisobutylamine, isopropyl-n-propylamine, isobutyl-n-propylamine, and cyclopentyl-n-butylamine.[16]

Cyanoethylation of Amides, Imides, and Lactams (Table V)

The cyanoethylation of amides, imides, and lactams has been described by Wegler.[28] The addition of compounds of these classes to acrylonitrile takes place readily and can be considered very general. Amides may react with one or two moles of acrylonitrile. N-Alkyl acid amides, with an occasional exception, yield the expected products, as do imides and lactams. Aromatic and aliphatic sulfonamides have not been extensively studied, but some of them add to acrylonitrile in the same way as acid amides. Alkaline catalysts are employed.

The addition of formamide to acrylonitrile occurs readily in the presence of alkaline catalysts such as sodium or sodium hydroxide. At moderate temperatures and with an excess of formamide the reaction readily yields β-formylaminopropionitrile. At temperatures of 85° or higher, and particularly with an excess of acrylonitrile, di-cyanoethylation predominates to yield β-formyliminodipropionitrile.

$$HCONH_2 + CH_2{=}CHCN \rightarrow HCONHCH_2CH_2CN \rightarrow HCON(CH_2CH_2CN)_2$$

Formamide also can react with more than two moles of acrylonitrile; [29] a substance with five to six moles of combined acrylonitrile has been reported but the structure is not known. N-Methylformamide is not cyanoethylated even in the presence of alkali catalysts although the corresponding N-n-propyl-, N-n-butyl-, N-n-hexyl-, cyclohexyl-, and N-phenylformamides add easily to acrylonitrile.[30] It has been suggested

[25] Bruson, J. Am. Chem. Soc., 64, 2457 (1942).
[26] DiCarlo and Lindwall, J. Am. Chem. Soc., 67, 199 (1945).
[27] Blume and Lindwall, J. Org. Chem., 10, 255 (1945).
[28] Wegler, Ger. pat. 734,725 [C.A., 38, 3671 (1944)].
[29] Wegler, Ger. pat. 735,771 [C.A., 38, 3992 (1944)].
[30] Wegler, Report to I.G. Farbenind. A.-G., April 21, 1941 (captured enemy documents).

that methylformamide is sufficiently acidic to neutralize the alkaline catalysts and render them ineffective.[30]   N-Butylformamide will react with as many as four moles of acrylonitrile to give a product of unknown structure.

Acetamide in excess gives good yields of β-acetaminopropionitrile.[30] It shows less tendency than formamide to react with two moles of acrylonitrile.   In contrast to methylformamide, the cyanoethylation of N-methylacetamide proceeds satisfactorily.   Similarly, N-methylpropionamide in the presence of 0.5% by weight of sodium hydroxide is smoothly cyanoethylated at 70–80° to yield $CH_3CH_2CON(CH_3)CH_2CH_2CN$.[31] Benzamide and acetanilide react with one mole of acrylonitrile at 90–100° in a little dioxane and in the presence of 1% of sodium hydroxide as a catalyst.[31]   Under similar conditions, N,N'-bis-methyladipamide yields the di-cyanoethylation product $NCCH_2CH_2N(CH_3)CO(CH_2)_4$-$CON(CH_3)CH_2CH_2CN$.   Crotonamide [32] yields the di-cyanoethylation product $CH_3CH\!=\!CHCON(CH_2CH_2CN)_2$, instead of the product $CH_2\!=\!CHC(CH_2CH_2CN)_2CONH_2$ previously reported.[33]

The cyanoethylation of most imides and lactams proceeds at 90–95° in the presence of 1–2% of sodium hydroxide as a catalyst [30] to yield the corresponding N-(2-cyanoethyl) derivatives.   Galat [34] obtained a quantitative yield of N-(2-cyanoethyl)phthalimide by refluxing phthalimide and acrylonitrile for ten minutes in the presence of a small amount of Triton B.   Succinimide and phthalimide in a little dioxane at 95° with 1–2% of sodium hydroxide as a catalyst react to form the corresponding N-(2-cyanoethyl)imides.[30]   α-Pyrrolidone,[30] ω-caprolactam,[30] and 2-pyridone [35] may be cyanoethylated in the presence of alkaline catalysts such as sodium hydroxide or potassium carbazole.

Certain sulfonamides can be cyanoethylated in the same way.   Benzenesulfonamide and acrylonitrile, regardless of the relative amounts of reactants, form primarily the di-cyanoethylation product, $C_6H_5SO_2N$-$(CH_2CH_2CN)_2$.   p-Acetaminobenzenesulfon-N-methylamide is readily cyanoethylated on the sulfonamide group.   p-Acetaminobenzenesulfon-

$$CH_3CONHC_6H_4SO_2NHCH_3 \rightarrow CH_3CONHC_6H_4SO_2N(CH_3)CH_2CH_2CN$$

N,N-dimethylamide, $CH_3CONHC_6H_4SO_2N(CH_3)_2$, could not be cyanoethylated on the NH— group, even though acetanilide can be cyanoethylated.   The influence of the sulfonamide group on a p-amino group is shown also by the failure of the amino group in p-aminobenzenesulfon-

[31] I.G. Farbenind. A.-G., Fr. pat. 877,120 (1942).
[32] Bruson, unpublished work.
[33] Bruson and Riener, J. Am. Chem. Soc., 65, 18 (1943).
[34] Galat, J. Am. Chem. Soc., 67, 1414 (1945).
[35] Adams and Jones, J. Am. Chem. Soc., 69, 1804 (1947).

N,N-dimethylamide to cyanoethylate. Saccharin also resists cyanoethylation.

Some aliphatic sulfonamides have been studied; propanesulfon-N-methylamide yields $CH_3CH_2CH_2SO_2N(CH_3)(CH_2CH_2CN)$ almost quantitatively, whereas propanesulfonamide is reported not to add to acrylonitrile. Benzyl sulfonamide reacts with acrylonitrile in the presence of Triton B to yield N,N-*bis*(2-cyanoethyl)benzylsulfonamide,[36] $C_6H_5CH_2$-$SO_2N(CH_2CH_2CN)_2$, and not a product with cyanoethyl groups on the methylene carbon atom as was first suggested.[37] The cyanoethylation of aliphatic sulfonamides has been patented by McQueen.[38]

Cyanoethylation of Water and Alcohols (Tables VI–VIII and XIII)

Water reacts with acrylonitrile [37, 39, 40] in the presence of alkaline catalysts to give β,β'-dicyanoethyl ether, $NCCH_2CH_2OCH_2CH_2CN$. Ethylene cyanohydrin is probably an intermediate in this reaction.

Practically all primary and secondary alcohols react with acrylonitrile in the presence of alkaline catalysts to form cyanoethyl ethers. The

$$ROH + CH_2{=}CHCN \rightarrow ROCH_2CH_2CN$$

reactions take place at or below room temperature with the lower aliphatic alcohols, particularly when the more active basic catalysts such as sodium, sodium methoxide, sodium or potassium hydroxide, or Triton B are used. Usually 0.5% to 5% of catalyst based on the weight of alcohol is adequate. The presence of other functional groups such as dialkylamino, halogen, olefinic, ether, or cyano does not interfere with the reaction. Glycols and polyalcohols are readily poly-cyanoethylated. Tertiary alcohols, on the other hand, react with difficulty or not at all. It has been demonstrated, however, that ethynyl tertiary alcohols react readily, the acetylene linkage apparently activating the addition reaction. Only the esters of hydroxy acids have resisted cyanoethylation; attempts to add ethyl glycolate, ethyl lactate, and ethyl ricinoleate to acrylonitrile have failed.

Most of the simple aliphatic alcohols can be cyanoethylated at 35–60° in the presence of 0.5–1% of sodium or sodium hydroxide. Examples are methanol,[41] ethanol,[41, 42] 2-propanol,[41] allyl alcohol,[41] n-amyl alcohol,[41]

[36] Bruson and Riener, *J. Am. Chem. Soc.*, **70**, 215 (1948).
[37] Bruson and Riener, *J. Am. Chem. Soc.*, **65**, 23 (1943).
[38] McQueen, U. S. pat. 2,424,664 (1947).
[39] Bruson, U. S. pat. 2,382,036 [*C.A.*, **40**, 347 (1946)].
[40] Hopff and Rapp, Ger. pat. 731,708 [*C.A.*, **38**, 555 (1944)].
[41] American Cyanamid Co., Brit. pat. 544,421 [*C.A.*, **36**, 6548 (1942)].
[42] Koelsch, *J. Am. Chem. Soc.*, **65**, 437 (1943).

2-ethylhexanol,[41] dodecanol,[41] and octadecanol.[41]   n-Butyl alcohol and acrylonitrile react rapidly at 40° with 0.4% of sodium as a catalyst.[43] Triton B [44,45,46] has been used effectively for cyanoethylation of these simple alcohols as well as of more complex ones. Tertiary amines have also been reported as satisfactory catalysts.[47]

Various methods for cyanoethylating aliphatic alcohols have been evaluated by MacGregor and Pugh.[48] As a general procedure for all aliphatic alcohols, including the long-chained alcohols, it is recommended that acrylonitrile be added to a solution of 0.05% of sodium in the alcohol at room temperature and that the reaction be completed at 80°. For alcohols with not more than five carbon atoms, two other procedures are reported as satisfactory: (1) equimolar quantities of acrylonitrile and alcohol are shaken at room temperature with a 2% aqueous sodium hydroxide solution as catalyst; (2) an equimolecular quantity of acrylonitrile is gradually added with cooling and stirring to a solution of 0.5% of potassium hydroxide in the alcohol. After the exothermic reaction is over, the reaction mixture is heated at 80° on a steam bath until refluxing ceases. Yields of 80–90% result.

The cyanoethylation of alcohols is an equilibrium reaction. The position of the equilibrium is more favorable to the addition product with primary than with secondary alcohols. Thus, 2-propanol gives a lower yield (69%) of cyanoethylation product than methanol, ethanol, or 1-butanol, which give 89%, 78%, and 86% yields, respectively.[44] Caution must be observed in the isolation of the β-alkoxypropionitriles by distillation, particularly those derived from secondary alcohols or from primary alcohols with more than seven carbon atoms. The alkaline catalyst must be destroyed by acidification or neutralization since the products are readily dissociated by heat in the presence of alkalies into the original alcohol and a polymer of acrylonitrile.[48]

Tertiary alcohols have not been extensively studied. tert-Butyl alcohol does not react with acrylonitrile at 30–40° and can, therefore, be used as a solvent for many cyanoethylation reactions which take place at low temperatures. At 80°, however, it reacts with acrylonitrile in the presence of 2% by weight of sodium hydroxide to form β-(tert-butoxy)propionitrile.[41] An acetylenic linkage attached to the tertiary alcohol carbon activates the addition. Thus, ethynyl dimethyl carbinol in the presence of sodium methoxide adds readily to acrylonitrile at 20°

[43] I.G. Farbenind. A.-G., Fr. pat. 796,001 [C.A., **30**, 5590 (1936)].
[44] Utermohlen, J. Am. Chem. Soc., **67**, 1505 (1945).
[45] Bruson, U. S. pat. 2,280,791 [C.A., **36**, 5589 (1942)].
[46] Bruson, U. S. pat. 2,280,792 [C.A., **36**, 5589 (1942)].
[47] Clifford and Lichty, Can. pat. 415,525 [C.A., **38**, 979 (1944)].
[48] MacGregor and Pugh, J. Chem. Soc., **1945**, 535.

to yield the expected ether.[49]   Acetylenic hydrogen atoms of acetylene,

$$
\begin{array}{ccc}
\quad CH_3 & \quad & \quad CH_3 \\
\quad | & \quad & \quad | \\
HC{\equiv}CCOH + CH_2{=}CHCN & \rightarrow & HC{\equiv}CCOCH_2CH_2CN \\
\quad | & \quad & \quad | \\
\quad CH_3 & \quad & \quad CH_3
\end{array}
$$

alkylacetylenes, or phenylacetylene do not react with acrylonitrile under the usual cyanoethylating conditions.

A wide variety of alcohols of the arylaliphatic,[44] alicyclic,[44,45] and heterocyclic series [44,46] are readily cyanoethylated.   For illustration may be mentioned benzyl alcohol,[44] cyclohexanol,[43] 3,4-dimethylcyclohexanol,[44] and menthol.[45]

Primary and secondary, but not tertiary, hydroxyl groups in glycols and polyhydric alcohols are cyanoethylated.[41,49-52]   Glycol is di-cyanoethylated in more than 80% yield; trimethylene, pentamethylene, and decamethylene glycols [37,50] also react readily.   1,4-Pentanediol gives an 83% yield of di-cyanoethylation product.[53]   Glycerol gives a tri-cyanoethyl derivative [37,50] in 74% yield, and pentaerythritol, mannitol, and sorbitol are reported to be completely cyanoethylated.[50]   A tertiary

$$
\begin{array}{l}
CH_2OCH_2CH_2CN \\
| \\
CHOCH_2CH_2CN \\
| \\
CH_2OCH_2CH_2CN
\end{array}
$$

alcohol group if present in a glycol resists cyanoethylation.[50]   In isobutylene glycol and 2-methyl-2,4-pentanediol, only the primary or secondary hydroxyl reacts.   Polyvinyl alcohol [54,55] yields products of varying degrees of cyanoethylation.

$$
\begin{array}{cc}
OH & OH \\
| & | \\
(CH_3)_2CCH_2OCH_2CH_2CN & (CH_3)_2CCH_2CH(CH_3)OCH_2CH_2CN
\end{array}
$$

Many alcohols with ether linkages present react easily.   Diethylene glycol,[37] triethylene glycol, tetraethylene glycol,[50] and the higher polyethylene glycols are readily cyanoethylated on one or both hydroxyl

[49] Bruson, U. S. pat. 2,280,790 [C.A., **36**, 5588 (1942)].
[50] Bruson, U. S. pat. 2,401,607 [C.A., **40**, 5450 (1946)].
[51] Treppenhauer, König, and Schröter, Ger. pat. 734,475 [C.A., **38**, 2966 (1944)].
[52] Carpenter, U. S. pat. 2,404,164 [C.A., **40**, 7232 (1946)].
[53] Christian, Brown, and Hixon, J. Am. Chem. Soc., **69**, 1961 (1947).
[54] I.G. Farbenind. A.-G., Fr. pat. 830,863 [C.A., **33**, 1838 (1939)].
[55] Houtz, U. S. pat. 2,341,553 [C.A., **38**, 4347 (1944)].

groups.[50]   The mono-methyl, -ethyl, -n-butyl, -allyl,[56] -phenyl, and substituted phenyl ethers of ethylene glycol react normally; [46] furfuryl alcohol,[56] tetrahydrofurfuryl alcohol,[44] and glyceryl α-ethers [50] also add to acrylonitrile.   Thiodiethylene glycol and acrylonitrile give a good yield of bis(2-cyanoethoxyethyl) sulfide.[37, 57]   Sugars,[54] starch,[58] and cellulose [54, 59, 60] may be considered in this general class of compounds and have been found to react to give products of various solubilities and other physical properties.   When cellulose is refluxed with an excess of acrylonitrile in the presence of 2% aqueous sodium hydroxide, a clear solution is obtained from which dilute ethanol precipitates a white flaky product containing three cyanoethyl groups per glucose unit.[60]   The cyanoethylation of cellulose xanthate and of viscose leads to interesting fibers.[61]

Unsaturated alcohols which have been added to acrylonitrile are numerous.   Sodium, sodium hydroxide, and sodium methoxide have normally been used as catalysts.   The reaction products from allyl,[41, 49] methallyl,[49] furfuryl,[49] oleyl,[49] and cinnamyl alcohols,[49] geraniol,[49] linaloöl,[49] citronellol,[49] and unsaturated ether alcohols [56] have been described.

The hydroxyl group in cyanohydrins reacts normally with acrylonitrile.   Formaldehyde cyanohydrin and acrylonitrile when heated with tributylamine as a catalyst give β-(cyanomethoxy)propionitrile,[62] $NCCH_2OCH_2CH_2CN$; lactonitrile gives a corresponding derivative, $CH_3CH(CN)OCH_2CH_2CN$.[62]   Ethylene cyanohydrin with sodium, sodium hydroxide,[37, 39, 41, 52, 63, 64] or sodium cyanide [62] as catalyst gives bis-2-cyanoethyl ether, $NCCH_2CH_2OCH_2CH_2CN$.   The same product can be obtained by the reaction between two moles of acrylonitrile and one mole of water.[37, 40, 54]

The halogenated alcohols ethylene chlorohydrin [65] and β-chloroethoxyethanol [46] add to acrylonitrile in the presence of a small amount of concentrated aqueous sodium hydroxide to give $ClCH_2CH_2OCH_2CH_2CN$ and $ClCH_2CH_2OCH_2CH_2OCH_2CH_2CN$, respectively.   The ω-fluoroalcohols, $F(CH_2)_nOH$, have also been cyanoethylated with acrylonitrile.[66]

[56] Schwoegler, U. S. pat. 2,403,686 [C.A., 40, 6499 (1946)].
[57] Hurd and Gershbein, J. Am. Chem. Soc., 69, 2328 (1947).
[58] Bock and Houk, U. S. pat., 2,316,128 [C.A., 37, 5812 (1943)].
[59] Bock and Houk, U. S. pats. 2,332,048 and 2,332,049 [C.A., 38, 1640 (1944)]; U. S. pat. 2,349,797 [C.A., 39, 1291 (1945)].
[60] Houtz, U. S. pat. 2,375,847 [C.A., 39, 4486 (1945)].
[61] Hollihan and Moss, J. Ind. Eng. Chem., 39, 929 (1947).
[62] Hansley, U. S. pat. 2,333,782 [C.A., 38, 2349 (1944)].
[63] Treppenhauer, König, and Bock, Ger. pat. 734,221 [C.A., 38, 1246 (1944)].
[64] König, Bock, and Treppenhauer, Ger. pat. 738,399 [C.A., 38, 3990 (1944)].
[65] Hopff, Ger. pat. 743,224 [C.A., 39, 2766 (1945)].
[66] Saunders, Nature, 160, 179 (1947).

Tertiary amino alcohols react readily with acrylonitrile when sodium methoxide, sodium hydroxide, or Triton B [67] is used as catalyst. Diethylaminoethanol [2] gives $(C_2H_5)_2NCH_2CH_2OCH_2CH_2CN$ in 79% yield; 1-diethylamino-4-pentanol [2] gives $(C_2H_5)_2NCH_2CH_2CH_2CH-(CH_3)OCH_2CH_2CN$ in 66% yield; and β-morpholinoethanol gives a 43% yield of $OC_4H_8NCH_2CH_2OCH_2CH_2CN$. Three cyanoethyl radicals are introduced into triethanolamine to give $tris$(2-cyanoethoxyethyl)-amine, $N(CH_2CH_2OCH_2CH_2CN)_3$.[67]

Cyanoethylation of Formaldehyde (Methylene Glycol) (Table X)

Formaldehyde or paraformaldehyde reacts in aqueous solution with acrylonitrile in the presence of alkaline catalysts in the form of the hydrate, $HOCH_2OH$, and cyanoethylation of this intermediate is reported to take place with the formation of the hemiformal of ethylene cyanohydrin or the formal of ethylene cyanohydrin,[68] depending upon the proportion of reagents.

$$HOCH_2OH + CH_2{=}CHCN \rightarrow HOCH_2OCH_2CH_2CN$$

$$HOCH_2OH + 2CH_2{=}CHCN \rightarrow NCCH_2CH_2OCH_2OCH_2CH_2CN$$

Only the latter compound has been isolated.

If the reaction between formaldehyde and acrylonitrile is carried out in the presence of an alcohol, the mixed formal of the alcohol and ethylene cyanohydrin results even though the alcohol used is a relatively unreactive tertiary alcohol.[69] The reactions go smoothly at

$$(CH_3)_3COH + CH_2O + CH_2{=}CHCN \rightarrow (CH_3)_3COCH_2OCH_2CH_2CN$$

35–45° in the presence of aqueous sodium hydroxide or Triton B as catalyst. Similar mixed formals are obtained from formaldehyde and acrylonitrile with such alcohols as methanol, allyl alcohol, benzyl alcohol, and 2-octanol.[69]

Cyanoethylation of Phenols (Table IX)

The reaction of acrylonitrile with the hydroxyl groups of phenols takes place at temperatures in the range of about 120–140°, particularly in the presence of alkaline catalysts such as the alkali metals and alkoxides or tertiary organic bases such as pyridine, quinoline, or dimethylaniline.[70] When acrylonitrile is gradually added at 130–140° to phenol

---

[67] Bruson, U. S. pat. 2,326,721 [C.A., **38**, 606 (1944)].
[68] Walker, U. S. pat. 2,352,671 [C.A., **39**, 223 (1945)].
[69] Bruson, U. S. pat. 2,435,869 (1948).
[70] Ufer, Ger. pat. 670,357 [C.A., **33**, 2907 (1939)].

containing 1% by weight of sodium and heating is continued under a reflux condenser for four to six hours at this temperature, a good yield of β-phenoxypropionitrile is obtained.[70]

$$C_6H_5OH + CH_2{=}CHCN \rightarrow C_6H_5OCH_2CH_2CN$$

In the same manner m-chlorophenol, β-naphthol, various cresols, xylenols, hydroxyanthraquinones, hydroxybiphenyls, hydroxyquinolines, and partially hydrogenated polynuclear phenols such as 5,6,7,8-tetrahydro-1(or 2)-hydroxynaphthalene react with acrylonitrile to yield the corresponding cyanoethyl ethers.[70] However, the cyanoethylation of β-naphthol in the presence of an *equimolecular amount of sodium hydroxide* suspended in benzene yields 2-hydroxy-1-(2-cyanoethyl)naphthalene in excellent yield.[71]

Polyhydric phenols such as pyrocatechol and hydroquinone can likewise be cyanoethylated in the presence of 1% by weight of sodium at 120–140° to yield the mono-cyanoethyl ether or the di-cyanoethyl ether, depending upon the proportions of acrylonitrile used.[70]

Acrylonitrile is reported to condense with resorcinol in the presence of hydrogen chloride and zinc chloride to yield the lactone of β-(2,4-dihydroxyphenyl)propionic acid which furnishes 2,4-dihydroxyphenylpropionic acid on hydrolysis.[72]

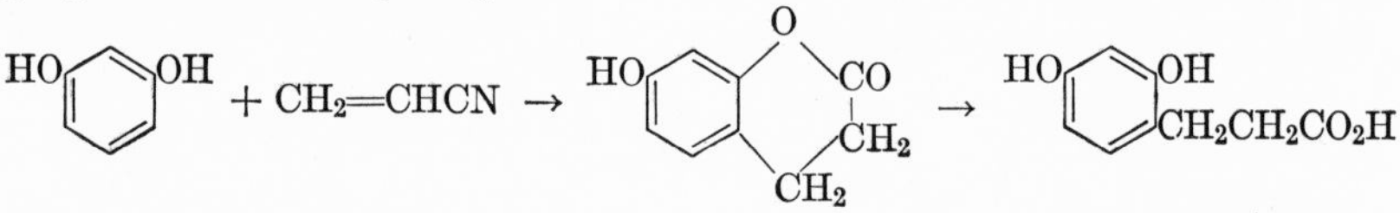

The cyanoethylation of resorcinol in the presence of Triton B gives a 40% yield of 1,3-*bis*(β-cyanoethoxy)benzene.[73] Upon refluxing salicylaldehyde with a large excess of acrylonitrile with Triton B as a catalyst, a small yield of 2-(β-cyanoethoxy)benzaldehyde is obtained together with 3-cyano-4-chromanol and 3-cyano-1,2-benzopyran.[73] In a similar

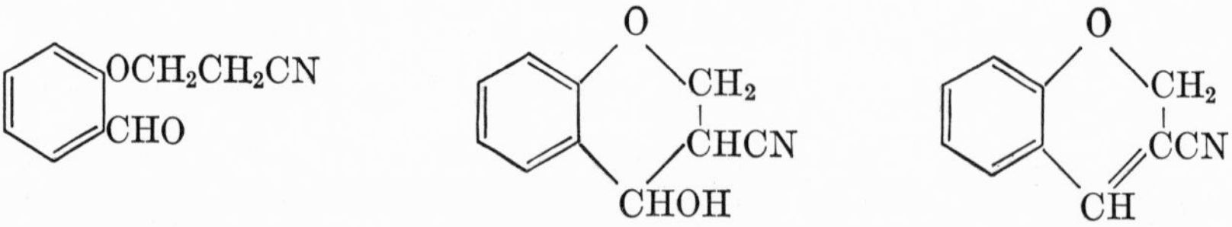

manner, phenol and m-methoxyphenol give 67.5% and 76% yields respectively of β-phenoxypropionitrile and m-methoxyphenoxypropionitrile.[73] Halogenated phenols such as o- and p-chlorophenol add only

[71] Hardman, U. S. pat. 2,421,837 [C.A., **41**, 5901 (1947)].
[72] Langley and Adams, J. Am. Chem. Soc., **44**, 2326 (1922).
[73] Bachman and Levine, J. Am. Chem. Soc., **70**, 599 (1948).

slowly to acrylonitrile, whereas p-nitrophenol and methyl salicylate apparently do not add at all.[73] The cyanoethylation of 6-bromo-2-naphthol gives a 10% yield of the corresponding cyanoethyl ether,[73] whereas 2-naphthol gives a 79% yield of β-(2-naphthoxy)propionitrile when the reaction is carried out in the presence of Triton B.[74]

Cyanoethylation of Oximes (Table IX)

The hydroxyl group of aldoximes and ketoximes adds to acrylonitrile in the presence of alkaline catalysts [37, 75] to form oximino ethers in 60–90% yields. The reactions take place at or near room temperature and are exothermic so that cooling and the use of an inert solvent such as dioxane are advisable.

A solution of acetone oxime, cyclohexanone oxime, or furfuraldehyde oxime in dioxane containing a small amount of sodium methoxide reacts smoothly at 25–35° with acrylonitrile to yield the corresponding cyano-ethyl ether. Liquid oximes, such as α-ethyl-β-propylacrolein oxime,

$$(CH_3)_2C{=}NOH + CH_2{=}CHCN \rightarrow (CH_3)_2C{=}NOCH_2CH_2CN$$

methyl n-hexyl ketoxime, and α-ethylhexaldoxime, do not require a solvent. Insoluble oximes such as dimethylglyoxime can be suspended in water containing a small amount of sodium hydroxide and cyano-ethylated by gradually adding acrylonitrile.

$$\begin{array}{c} CH_3C{=}NOH \\ | \qquad\qquad + 2CH_2{=}CHCN \rightarrow \\ CH_3C{=}NOH \end{array} \qquad \begin{array}{c} CH_3C{=}NOCH_2CH_2CN \\ | \\ CH_3C{=}NOCH_2CH_2CN \end{array}$$

Acetophenone oxime in benzene containing a small amount of Triton B adds acrylonitrile at 40–50° to give the corresponding cyanoethyl ether.

Benzoin oxime can be cyanoethylated on both the oximino group and the alcoholic hydroxyl group to yield the mixed ether.[37]

$$\begin{array}{c} C_6H_5C{=}NOCH_2CH_2CN \\ | \\ C_6H_5CHOCH_2CH_2CN \end{array}$$

Cyanoethylation of Hydrogen Sulfide, Mercaptans, and Thiophenols (Table IX)

Acrylonitrile reacts with hydrogen sulfide to yield bis-2-cyanoethyl sulfide [76] when heated in butanol at 80° in an autoclave. The reaction

[74] Bachman and Levine, *J. Am. Chem. Soc.*, **69**, 2343 (1947).
[75] Bruson and Riener, U. S. pat. 2,352,516 [*C.A.*, **38**, 5506 (1944)].
[76] Keysner, U. S. pat. 2,163,176 [*C.A.*, **33**, 7819 (1939)].

requires no catalyst but is accelerated by alkalies such as sodium hydroxide or Triton B. At atmospheric pressure and at 25° to 75° acrylo-

$$2CH_2\!\!=\!\!CHCN + H_2S \rightarrow NCCH_2CH_2SCH_2CH_2CN$$

nitrile does not react with hydrogen sulfide in the absence of an alkaline catalyst, but a trace of sodium methoxide or Triton B brings about an exothermic reaction and gives an 86–93% yield of bis-2-cyanoethyl sulfide.[77] The same product is formed when an aqueous solution of sodium sulfide or sodium hydrogen sulfide reacts with acrylonitrile at room temperature.[78,79]

Aliphatic mercaptans, dimercaptans, and thiophenols add readily to acrylonitrile in the presence of alkaline catalysts. Methyl, ethyl, propyl, isopropyl, butyl, tert-butyl, isobutyl, carbethoxymethyl, benzyl, and dodecyl mercaptans, thiophenol, and o-, m-, and p-thiocresol are reported to react in the presence of strong bases.[57,80] Piperidine has been used as a catalyst for the reactions involving ethyl mercaptan, benzyl mercaptan, β-mercaptoethanol, and ethylene dithiol.[81] Sodium methoxide is also effective and was employed in the addition of octyl, nonyl, and lauryl mercaptans to acrylonitrile.[82]

$$RSH + CH_2\!\!=\!\!CHCN \rightarrow RSCH_2CH_2CN$$

Other, more complex mercaptans which have been studied are 2-mercaptobenzothiazole,[80,83] 2-mercaptothiazoline, 2-mercapto-4-methylthiazole, and 2-mercaptobenzoxazole.[57] Hurd and Gershbein [57] have shown that benzyl, hydroxyethyl, and phenyl mercaptans add to acrylonitrile in the absence of alkalies to give excellent yields of cyanoethylation products. The sulfhydryl group in hydroxyethyl mercaptan reacts first. Alkali is required for cyanoethylation of the hydroxyl group. According to one report thiourea and thiocarbanilide add in the mercaptol form to acrylonitrile;[80] according to another report, however, thiourea and acrylonitrile do not react at 100° in the presence of alkali.[57]

The sodium salts of dialkyldithiocarbamic acids, such as dimethyl- and dibutyl-dithiocarbamic acid and piperidinodithiocarbamic acid, in aqueous solution add to acrylonitrile to yield the corresponding cyano-

[77] Gershbein and Hurd, J. Am. Chem. Soc., **69**, 242 (1947).
[78] Bruson, unpublished work.
[79] Hollihan and Moss, J. Ind. Eng. Chem., **39**, 223 (1947).
[80] Harman, U. S. pat. 2,413,917 [C.A., **41**, 2446 (1947)].
[81] Gribbins, Miller, and O'Leary, U. S. pat. 2,397,960 [C.A., **40**, 3542 (1946)].
[82] Rapoport, Smith, and Newman, J. Am. Chem. Soc., **69**, 694 (1947).
[83] Clifford and Lichty, U. S. pat. 2,407,138 [C.A., **41**, 488 (1947)].

ethylated derivatives.[80]   2-Diethylaminoethanethiol adds readily to

$$R_2N\overset{\overset{\displaystyle S}{\|}}{C}SH + CH_2{=}CHCN \rightarrow R_2N\overset{\overset{\displaystyle S}{\|}}{C}SCH_2CH_2CN$$

acrylonitrile without the use of a catalyst.[84]

$$(C_2H_5)_2NCH_2CH_2SH \rightarrow (C_2H_5)_2NCH_2CH_2SCH_2CH_2CN$$

Cyanoethylation of Arsines (Table XIII)

Mann and Cookson [85] have reported that phenylarsine reacts with acrylonitrile to give phenyl-*bis*-(2-cyanoethyl)arsine.

$$C_6H_5AsH_2 + 2CH_2{=}CHCN \rightarrow C_6H_5As(CH_2CH_2CN)_2$$

The reaction is very vigorous with alkaline catalysts such as traces of potassium hydroxide or sodium methoxide.[86]   Analogous reactions have been described with *p*-aminophenylarsine and with diphenylarsine to give $H_2NC_6H_4As(CH_2CH_2CN)_2$ and $(C_6H_5)_2AsCH_2CH_2CN$, respectively.[86]

Cyanoethylation of Inorganic Acids and Hydrogen Cyanide (Table XIII)

Hydrogen chloride, hydrogen bromide, hydrogen cyanide, hypochlorous acid, and sulfurous acid as sodium bisulfite have been added to acrylonitrile.   Many of the carboxylic acids such as formic, acetic, and benzoic have failed to add either in the presence or absence of alkaline catalysts.

When hydrogen chloride or hydrogen bromide is passed into acrylonitrile with cooling, the corresponding β-chloropropionitrile or β-bromopropionitrile is formed.[87, 88]

Hydrogen cyanide, however, adds to acrylonitrile only when an alkaline catalyst is present.[89]   In the presence of a small amount of potassium cyanide, acrylonitrile and hydrogen cyanide combine at atmospheric pressure to yield succinonitrile.[90]   If a large amount of water and sodium cyanide react with acrylonitrile at 80°, the product is largely succin-

[84] Clinton, Suter, Laskowski, Jackman, and Huber, *J. Am. Chem. Soc.*, **67**, 597 (1945).
[85] Mann and Cookson, *Nature*, **157**, 846 (1946).
[86] Cookson and Mann, *J. Chem. Soc.*, **1947**, 618.
[87] Moureu and Brown, *Bull. soc. chim. France*, (4) **27**, 903 (1920).
[88] Stewart and Clark, *J. Am. Chem. Soc.*, **69**, 713 (1947).
[89] *German Synthetic Fiber Developments*, p. 661, Textile Research Institute, New York, 1946.
[90] Kurtz, Ger. pat. 707,852 [*C.A.*, **37**, 2747 (1943)].

imide.[91]   The addition of hydrogen cyanide in the presence of alkalies to acrylonitrile has been patented by Carpenter.[92]

Hypochlorous acid does not undergo cyanoethylation. When acrylonitrile is dissolved in water and treated at 0–30° with chlorine or hypochlorous acid, α-chloro-β-hydroxypropionitrile is formed. An excess of calcium carbonate may be added to neutralize any free hydrochloric acid formed.[93]

$$HOCl + CH_2{=}CHCN \rightarrow HOCH_2CHClCN$$

Alkali bisulfites in aqueous solution readily add to the α,β-double bond of acrylonitrile to yield alkali metal salts of β-sulfopropionitrile.[94]

$$CH_2{=}CHCN + NaHSO_3 \rightarrow NCCH_2CH_2SO_3Na$$

Cyanoethylation of Haloforms (Table XIII)

Chloroform [95] and bromoform [96] add to acrylonitrile in the presence of Triton B or potassium hydroxide to give γ-trichlorobutyronitrile (11% yield) and γ-tribromobutyronitrile, respectively. Iodoform does

$$CHCl_3 + CH_2{=}CHCN \rightarrow Cl_3CCH_2CH_2CN$$

not add to acrylonitrile under the same conditions.

Cyanoethylation of Sulfones (Table XIII)

Mixed aromatic aliphatic sulfones in which the aliphatic carbon atom joined to the sulfur atom is attached to a multiple linkage add to acrylonitrile in the presence of alkaline catalysts.[36]   Such sulfones are illustrated by $C_6H_5SO_2CH_2C_6H_5$, $C_6H_5SO_2CH_2CH{=}CH_2$, and $C_6H_5SO_2CH_2CO_2C_2H_5$.   Two molecules of acrylonitrile react.[97]

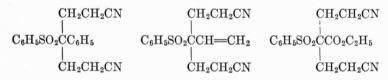

[91] Wolz, Ger. pat. 741,156 [C.A., 40, 1173 (1946)].
[92] Carpenter, U. S. pat. 2,434,606 [C.A., 42, 2615 (1948)].
[93] Tuerck and Lichtenstein, Brit. pat. 566,006 [C.A., 40, 5772 (1946)].
[94] Carpenter, U. S. pat. 2,312,878 [C.A., 37, 5199 (1943)].
[95] Bruson, Niederhauser, Riener, and Hester, J. Am. Chem. Soc., 67, 601 (1945).
[96] Niederhauser and Bruson, U. S. pat. 2,379,097 [C.A., 39, 4618 (1945)].
[97] Bruson, U. S. pat. 2,435,552 (1948)].

Cyanoethylation of Aliphatic Nitro Compounds (Table XI)

Acrylonitrile reacts with aliphatic nitro compounds having a methinyl, methylene, or methyl group contiguous to the nitro group. The usual alkaline catalysts, potassium hydroxide, sodium ethoxide, or Triton B, are required.[37, 98, 99, 100]

Nitromethane and acrylonitrile in equimolar quantities with sodium hydroxide as a catalyst react to give primarily the mono-cyanoethylation product, $O_2NCH_2CH_2CH_2CN$.[101] With excess acrylonitrile the crystalline $tris$(2-cyanoethyl)nitromethane, $O_2NC(CH_2CH_2CN)_3$, is the chief product, and is accompanied by varying amounts of mono- and di-cyanoethylation derivatives.[37, 102]

Nitroethane yields a mixture of mono- and di-cyanoethylation products, γ-nitrovaleronitrile, $CH_3CH(NO_2)CH_2CH_2CN$, and γ-nitro-γ-methylpimelonitrile, $CH_3C(NO_2)(CH_2CH_2CN)_2$.[101, 102] Similarly, 1-nitropropane reacts to give a mixture of $C_2H_5CH(NO_2)CH_2CH_2CN$ and $C_2H_5C(NO_2)(CH_2CH_2CN)_2$.

2-Nitropropane,[101, 102] nitrocyclohexane,[98, 99] and 9-nitroanthrone,[102] molecules in which only mono-cyanoethylation is possible, give the expected products, γ-methyl-γ-nitrovaleronitrile, 1-nitro-1-(β-cyanoethyl)cyclohexane, and 9-nitro-9-cyanoethylanthrone, respectively.

Cyanoethylation of Ketones (Table X)

Acrylonitrile reacts with ketones possessing methinyl, methylene, and methyl groups contiguous to the carbonyl group to introduce one, two, three, or more cyanoethyl groups.[108] The mode of operation and the catalysts are the same as those described for the cyanoethylation of alcohols or amines: the oxides, hydroxides, alkoxides, amides, or hydrides of the alkali metals, the alkali metals themselves, or especially

[98] I.G. Farbenind. A.-G., Fr. pat. 882,027 (1943).
[99] Wulff, Hopff, and Wiest, U. S. pat. appln. Ser. No. 404,150 (1943).
[100] Buckley and Lowe, Brit. pat. 584,086 [C.A., **41**, 3478 (1947)].
[101] Buckley and Lowe, Brit. pat. 586,099.
[102] Bruson, U. S. pat. 2,361,259 [C.A., **39**, 2079 (1945)].
[103] Bruson and Riener, J. Am. Chem. Soc., **64**, 2850 (1942).

Triton B; advantageously in the presence of inert solvents or diluents to control the reaction.

$$RCOCH_3 \rightarrow RCOC(CH_2CH_2CN)_3$$

Acetone and acrylonitrile in equimolecular proportions give a small yield of mono-cyanoethylation product, $CH_3COCH_2CH_2CH_2CN$.[104] With three moles of acrylonitrile in the presence of sodium hydroxide or Triton B as catalyst, the crystalline tri-cyanoethylation derivative, $CH_3COC(CH_2CH_2CN)_3$, is obtained in 75–80% yield,[103, 105] and upon further cyanoethylation a crystalline tetra addition product can be isolated, $NCCH_2CH_2CH_2COC(CH_2CH_2CN)_3$.

The unsymmetrical aliphatic methyl ketones, such as methyl ethyl ketone,[106] methyl n-propyl ketone, methyl isobutyl ketone, methyl n-amyl ketone, and methyl n-hexyl ketone, react with acrylonitrile in the presence of alkaline catalysts to cyanoethylate the methylene in preference to the methyl group.[103, 107] The mono-cyanoethylation product, $CH_3COCH(R)CH_2CH_2CN$, is not readily obtained in good yield since it is cyanoethylated further; with two moles of acrylonitrile the chief product is $CH_3COC(R)(CH_2CH_2CN)_2$. Excess of acrylonitrile gives a trisubstitution product, $NCCH_2CH_2CH_2COC(R)(CH_2CH_2CN)_2$, in which the methyl group has reacted; higher cyanoethylation derivatives from further reaction of the methyl group have been described.[103] Methyl isobutyl ketone reacts less readily than methyl n-amyl ketone.

Other aliphatic ketones have been studied. Diethyl ketone and excess acrylonitrile give chiefly a tri-cyanoethylation product,[103] $CH_3C-(CH_2CH_2CN)_2COCH(CH_2CH_2CN)CH_3$. Diisopropyl ketone reacts sluggishly, probably owing to steric hindrance, but the mono- and the di-substitution products, $(CH_3)_2C(CH_2CH_2CN)COCH(CH_3)_2$ and $(CH_3)_2C(CH_2CH_2CN)COC(CH_2CH_2CN)(CH_3)_2$, have been isolated.[107] Diisobutyl ketone does not react appreciably with acrylonitrile. Dibenzyl ketone and acrylonitrile combine to give a resinous mixture from which the tribasic acid, $C_6H_5C(CH_2CH_2CO_2H)_2COCH(CH_2CH_2-CO_2H)C_6H_5$, has been isolated after alkaline hydrolysis.[103] Phenylacetone yields the di-cyanoethylated product, γ-acetyl-γ-phenylpimelonitrile, $C_6H_5C(CH_2CH_2CN)_2COCH_3$, in 86% yield.[103]

Alicyclic ketones react like their aliphatic analogs but more readily. Cyclopentanone [108] and cyclohexanone [106] and its 4-substituted derivatives [103] react with four moles of acrylonitrile to give products with all

---

[104] Shannon, U. S. pat. 2,381,371 [C.A., **40**, 350 (1946)].
[105] Bruson, U. S. pat. 2,311,183 [C.A. **37**, 4500 (1943)].
[106] Wiest and Glaser, U. S. pat. 2,403,570 [C.A., **40**, 6498 (1946)].
[107] Bruson, U. S. pat. 2,386,736 [C.A., **40**, 7234 (1946)].
[108] Bruson, U. S. pat. 2,287,510 [C.A., **37**, 140 (1943)].

the hydrogens on the two carbon atoms adjacent to the carbonyl group replaced. The mono- and di-cyanoethylated products have been isolated, but poly-cyanoethylation takes place very readily and even with limited amounts of acrylonitrile the tetra addition product is formed. 2-Methylcyclohexanone is tri-cyanoethylated while α-tetralone [108] and 2,2,5,5-tetramethyltetrahydrofuran-3-one are di-cyanoethylated.

$$\text{(NCCH}_2\text{CH}_2)_2\text{C}\underset{\text{CO}}{\overset{\text{CH}_2-\text{CH}_2}{<}}\text{C(CH}_2\text{CH}_2\text{CN)}_2 \qquad \text{(NCCH}_2\text{CH}_2)_2\text{C}\underset{\text{CO}}{\overset{\text{CH}_2}{<}}\text{C(CH}_2\text{CH}_2\text{CN)}_2$$

$$\text{H}_3\text{C}\underset{\text{NCH}_2\text{CH}_2\text{C}}{\overset{\text{CH}_2}{<}}\text{C}\underset{\text{CO}}{>}\text{C(CH}_2\text{CH}_2\text{CN)}_2$$

$$\underset{\text{CH}_2}{\underset{\text{CH}_2}{\overset{\text{O}}{\overset{\text{C}}{<}}}}\text{C(CH}_2\text{CH}_2\text{CN)}_2 \qquad \text{(CH}_3)_2\text{C}\underset{\text{CO}}{\overset{\text{O}-\text{C(CH}_3)_2}{<}}\text{C(CH}_2\text{CH}_2\text{CN)}_2$$

Aromatic aliphatic ketones react very readily. The methyl ketones, exemplified by acetophenone and its homologs, p-methyl, p-methoxy-, p-chloro-, p-bromo-, and p-phenyl-acetophenone, give crystalline tri-cyanoethylation products, $\text{ArCOC(CH}_2\text{CH}_2\text{CN)}_3$, in good yields.[108] The addition products with one and two molecules of acrylonitrile are not described. 2-Naphthyl methyl ketone reacts similarly.[108] Even acetomesitylene, which frequently enters into reaction in its enol form, gives a 30% yield of the tri-cyanoethylation product.[103]

Propiophenone and desoxybenzoin represent molecules with only two hydrogens on the carbon attached to the carbonyl group and thus di-cyanoethylation derivatives result, γ-benzoyl-γ-methylpimelonitrile, $\text{C}_6\text{H}_5\text{COC(CH}_3)(\text{CH}_2\text{CH}_2\text{CN)}_2$, and $\text{C}_6\text{H}_5\text{COC(C}_6\text{H}_5)(\text{CH}_2\text{CH}_2\text{CN)}_2$.

Heterocyclic alkyl ketones are equally reactive. 2-Thienyl methyl ketone and 2-furyl methyl ketone yield crystalline tri-cyanoethylation products,[36, 109] and 2-thienyl ethyl ketone and 2-furyl ethyl ketone yield di-cyanoethylation products.[36]

$$\underset{\text{(O)}}{\overset{}{\boxed{}}_S}\text{COC(CH}_2\text{CH}_2\text{CN)}_3 \qquad \underset{\text{(O)}}{\overset{}{\boxed{}}_S}\text{COC(CH}_2\text{CH}_2\text{CN)}_2\text{CH}_3$$

[109] Bruson, U. S. pat. 2,394,962 [C.A., **40**, 2848 (1946)].

The methylene group in β-keto esters and their derivatives reacts with acrylonitrile in the presence of alkaline catalysts.[103, 107, 109, 110] Thus methyl or ethyl acetoacetate and the anilide, o-chloroanilide, and 2,5-dichloroanilide [107] give di-cyanoethylation products, $CH_3COC(CH_2CH_2CN)_2CO_2R$ and $CH_3COC(CH_2CH_2CN)_2CONHAr$.

Several 1,3-diketones which have been studied have failed to react with acrylonitrile; among these are 1,3-cyclohexanedione and methylene-bis-dihydroresorcinol.[32] The explanation offered is that the high degree of acidity effectively neutralizes the catalyst. It is essential that the reaction mixture be alkaline to moist litmus for the reaction to occur.[36] A similar explanation is given for the non-reactivity with acrylonitrile of 1-phenyl-3-methylpyrazolone, which exists primarily in the enol form.[32]

$$
\begin{array}{c}
CH\!\!=\!\!COH \\
| \qquad\quad \diagdown \\
\qquad\qquad\quad NC_6H_5 \\
| \qquad\quad \diagup \\
H_3CC\!\!=\!\!N
\end{array}
$$

On the other hand, certain 1,3-diketones in which one carbonyl group is part of an alicyclic ring react readily with acrylonitrile in the presence of aqueous potassium hydroxide or Triton B to introduce a cyanoethyl group between the two carbonyl groups.[32] 2-Acetylcyclopentanone, 2-acetylcyclohexanone, and 2-acetylcycloheptanone all react similarly. Boese has described the cyanoethylation of certain 2,4-diketones, notably acetylacetone, benzoylacetone, 3-benzylpentane-2,4-dione and 3-ethylpentane-2,4-dione.[111, 112]

$$
\begin{array}{ccc}
\begin{array}{c}
\quad CH_2 \\
\diagup \quad \diagdown \\
CH_2 \quad\; CH_2 \\
| \qquad\quad | \\
CH_2 \quad CHCOCH_3 \\
\diagdown \quad\; \diagup \\
\quad CO
\end{array}
&
+\; CH_2\!\!=\!\!CHCN \;\rightarrow
&
\begin{array}{c}
\quad CH_2 \\
\diagup \quad \diagdown \\
CH_2 \quad\; CH_2 \\
| \qquad\quad | \;\; CH_2CH_2CN \\
CH_2 \quad C\!\!<\!\! \\
\diagdown \quad\; \diagup \;\;\; COCH_3 \\
\quad CO
\end{array}
\end{array}
$$

Mesityl oxide, an α,β-unsaturated ketone, reacts with two moles of acrylonitrile in the presence of Triton B to give a 73% yield of a crystalline di- and a 10% yield of a liquid mono-cyanoethylation product. The latter upon further treatment with acrylonitrile is converted to the former. The structures of both products have been established,[33] the mono- as a derivative of the α,β-unsaturated form and the di- as a derivative of the β,γ-desmotrope. The mono-cyanoethylation product

---

[110] Wiest and Glaser, U. S. pat. 2,396,626 [*C.A.*, **40**, 3771 (1946)].
[111] Boese, U. S. pat. 2,438,961 (1948).
[112] Boese, U. S. pat. 2,438,894 (1948).

may result from an initial reaction with the desmotropic form followed

$$(CH_3)_2C\!\!=\!\!CHCOCH_3 \; \leftrightarrows \; CH_2\!\!=\!\!\underset{\underset{CH_3}{|}}{C}CH_2COCH_3$$

$$(CH_3)_2C\!\!=\!\!\underset{\underset{CH_2CH_2CN}{|}}{C}COCH_3 \qquad CH_2\!\!=\!\!\underset{\underset{CH_3}{|}}{C}\!-\!\!\overset{\overset{CH_2CH_2CN}{|}}{\underset{\underset{CH_2CH_2CN}{|}}{C}}COCH_3$$

by rearrangement to the α,β-unsaturated ketone.

The β,γ-unsaturated ketone, 2-cyclohexenylcyclohexanone, adds to acrylonitrile to yield a crystalline mono-cyanoethylation product in which the hydrogen of the methinyl group has reacted. Further cyanoethylation then occurs on the methylene group adjacent to the carbonyl.[36]

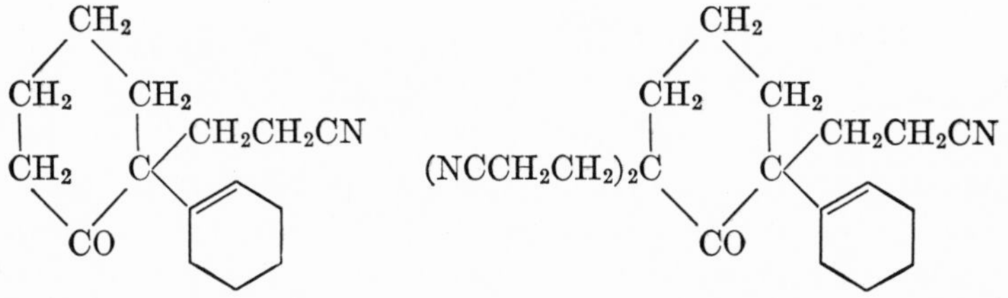

Acrylonitrile reacts with polyketones to cyanoethylate the methylene groups adjacent to the carbonyl groups. Polymeric ketones obtained from carbon monoxide and olefins, the polymers of methyl vinyl ketone and of methyl isopropenyl ketone, and copolymers of alkyl vinyl ketones with olefins and diolefins have been used in this reaction.[113]

Cyanoethylation of Aldehydes (Table X)

Acrylonitrile reacts in the presence of alkaline catalysts with those aldehydes in which the α-carbon atom has one or more hydrogen atoms.

Formaldehyde reacts as methylene glycol with acrylonitrile and yields derivatives which were discussed under alcohols (p. 93).

Acetaldehyde aldolizes and resinifies readily in the presence of alkalies and therefore yields a mixture of cyanoethylation products.[114] With concentrated aqueous sodium hydroxide or with sodium cyanide as catalyst, a mixture of γ-cyanobutyraldehyde and γ-formylpimelonitrile

[113] Mortenson, U. S. pat. 2,396,963 [C.A., **40**, 3937 (1946)].
[114] Bruson and Riener, U. S. pat. 2,353,687 [C.A., **38**, 6432 (1944)].

is produced in combined yield of 40–50% with the first catalyst and
38% with the second catalyst.[115, 116]

$$CH_3CHO + CH_2{=}CHCN \rightarrow NCCH_2CH_2CH_2CHO + \overset{\displaystyle CH_2CH_2CN}{\underset{\displaystyle CH_2CH_2CN}{CHCHO}}$$

Propionaldehyde and acrylonitrile give α-methyl-γ-cyanobutyralde-
hyde and γ-methyl-γ-formylpimelonitrile in 5% and 25% yields, respectively.[115, 116]

Dialkylacetaldehydes, such as isobutyraldehyde, diethylacetaldehyde,
and 2-ethylhexanal, are more stable to alkaline reagents and undergo
cyanoethylation readily.   Isobutyraldehyde and acrylonitrile with
saturated aqueous sodium hydroxide as catalyst at 65–80° give a 35–40%
yield of α,α-dimethyl-γ-cyano-n-butyraldehyde, $(CH_3)_2C(CH_2CH_2CN)$-
CHO.[116] It is reported that the same product is obtained by use of 20%
aqueous potassium cyanide as catalyst at a temperature of 80–90°.[117]
In the other dialkylacetaldehydes in which each of the alkyl groups has
at least two carbons, the yields of cyanoethylation products with 50%
aqueous potassium hydroxide as catalyst are about 80%.[118]

$$R_2CHCHO \rightarrow R_2C(CH_2CH_2CN)CHO$$

α-Ethyl-β-propylacrolein and acrylonitrile in equimolar quantities in
the presence of concentrated aqueous or methanolic potassium hydroxide
react, even though an α-hydrogen is lacking in the aldehyde, to give a
50% yield of product.   Apparently a hydrogen atom and the double
bond undergo a shift which permits the introduction of a cyanoethyl
group in the rearranged product.[114]

$$CH_3CH_2CH_2CH{=}\overset{\displaystyle C_2H_5}{C}{-}CHO + CH_2{=}CHCN \rightarrow CH_3CH_2CH{=}\overset{\displaystyle C_2H_5}{\underset{\displaystyle CH_2CH_2CN}{CHCCHO}}$$

The behavior of acrylonitrile with benzaldehyde in the presence of alkaline catalysts has not been explained.   Two products are formed: one
a liquid, b.p. 225–230°/5 mm., consisting of one molecule of benzaldehyde and two of acrylonitrile; and the other a colorless solid, m.p. 73°,
b.p. 270°/3 mm.[114]

[115] E. I. du Pont de Nemours & Co., Brit. pat. 576,427 (1946).
[116] Walker, U. S. pat. 2,409,086 [C.A., 41, 1235 (1947)].
[117] I.G. Farbenind. A.-G., Fr. pat. 886,846 (1943).
[118] Bruson and Riener, J. Am. Chem. Soc., 66, 56 (1944).

Cyanoethylation of Derivatives of Malonic and Cyanoacetic Acids (Table XI)

Acrylonitrile and the esters or amides of malonic acid react at 30–50° in the presence of alkaline catalysts, in particular sodium, sodium ethoxide, potassium hydroxide, or Triton B, to form mono- or di-cyanoethylation products.[37] Monoalkylated malonic esters are mono-cyanoethylated under the same conditions.[37, 119]

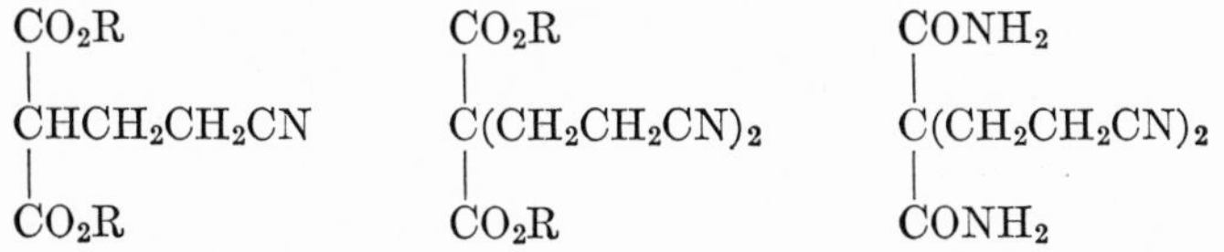

$$\begin{array}{ccc}
CO_2R & CO_2R & CONH_2 \\
| & | & | \\
CHCH_2CH_2CN & C(CH_2CH_2CN)_2 & C(CH_2CH_2CN)_2 \\
| & | & | \\
CO_2R & CO_2R & CONH_2
\end{array}$$

From equimolar quantities of acrylonitrile and ethyl malonate with sodium ethoxide as a catalyst, a 40–45% yield of a mono-cyanoethylation product results, $NCCH_2CH_2CH(CO_2C_2H_5)_2$.[120] This same product is obtained in small amounts when sodium is used as catalyst, but the di-cyanoethylated malonic ester, γ,γ-dicarbethoxypimelonitrile, is formed chiefly.[110] An 82.5% yield of this latter compound results from the condensation of two moles of acrylonitrile and one mole of malonic ester in the presence of Triton B; malonamide reacts equally well to give an analogous product.[37]

Of the monoalkylated diethyl malonates, ethyl, n-butyl, benzyl,[37] and cyclopentyl[119] have been studied, and they react smoothly with one mole of acrylonitrile, sodium alkoxide or Triton B being used as catalyst. All the products have the formula $RC(CH_2CH_2CN)(CO_2R)_2$.

Ethyl cyanoacetate and two moles of acrylonitrile give with Triton B essentially a quantitative yield of γ-carbethoxy-γ-cyanopimelonitrile, $C_2H_5O_2CC(CN)(CH_2CH_2CN)_2$.[37] Sodium, sodium hydroxide, and cyclohexylamine have also been used as catalysts in this reaction.[110] Cyanoacetamide and acrylonitrile with Triton B give a 70% yield of $NCC(CONH_2)(CH_2CH_2CN)_2$.[37]

Cyanoethylation of Arylacetonitriles (Table XII)

Benzyl cyanide and substituted benzyl cyanides, $ArCH_2CN$, react vigorously with acrylonitrile if traces of strong bases are present. It is usually difficult to isolate the mono-cyanoethylation products in good yield, but the di-cyanoethylation products are obtained in excellent yields.

[119] Lochte, Thomas, and Truitt, *J. Am. Chem. Soc.*, **66**, 551 (1944).
[120] Koelsch, *J. Am. Chem. Soc.*, **65**, 2458 (1943).

The reaction resembles that which takes place with certain aryl sulfones and related compounds described in the section on sulfones (p. 98).

Benzyl cyanide and acrylonitrile in equimolar proportions with sodium ethoxide as a catalyst give a 20–33% yield of α-phenylglutaronitrile, $C_6H_5CH(CH_2CH_2CN)CN$.[42] A solution of benzyl cyanide in tert-butyl alcohol with a little potassium hydroxide as a catalyst rapidly takes up two moles of acrylonitrile to form γ-cyano-γ-phenylpimelonitrile in 94% yield.[37, 121] With sodium as a catalyst, a 78.5% yield is reported.[110]

p-Nitrobenzyl cyanide in dioxane solution with Triton B catalyst gives a 91% yield of γ-cyano-γ-(p-nitrobenzyl)pimelonitrile.[37] p-Chlorobenzyl cyanide, p-isopropylbenzyl cyanide, and α-naphthylacetonitrile have also been di-cyanoethylated in good yield.[122]

Cyanoethylation of α,β-Unsaturated Nitriles (Table XII)

Crotononitrile reacts with acrylonitrile in the presence of basic catalysts, in particular Triton B, to give two products, α-ethylidene glutaronitrile and γ-cyano-γ-vinylpimelonitrile.[33, 123] The same products are obtained from allyl cyanide and acrylonitrile with Triton B. α-Ethylideneglutaronitrile is converted to γ-cyano-γ-vinylpimelonitrile by means of acrylonitrile and catalyst. The exact mechanism for the formation of these two products is not clear though the presumption is that allyl cyanide, which is desmotropic with crotononitrile, is probably the form which reacts with the acrylonitrile. The sequence of reactions may be formulated in the following way.

$$CH_3CH{=}CHCN \rightleftarrows CH_2{=}CHCH_2CN \xrightarrow{CH_2{=}CHCN}$$

$$
\left[
\begin{array}{c}
CH_2CH_2CN \\
| \\
CH_2{=}CHCHCN
\end{array}
\right]
\xrightarrow{CH_2{=}CHCN}
\begin{array}{c}
CH_2CH_2CN \\
| \\
CH_2{=}CHCCN \\
| \\
CH_2CH_2CN
\end{array}
$$

$$
\begin{array}{c}
\updownarrow \\
CH_2CH_2CN \\
| \\
CH_3CH{=}CCN
\end{array}
$$

The α,β-unsaturated nitrile represents the stable form after monocyanoethylation; the β,γ-unsaturated nitrile is the only possible form for the di-cyanoethylated derivatives.[33] The reaction resembles that of mesityl oxide described in the ketone section (p. 102).

121 Hester and Bruson, U. S. pat. 2,305,529 [C.A., 37, 3206 (1943)].
122 Rubin and Wishinsky, J. Am. Chem. Soc., 68, 828 (1946).
123 Bruson, U. S. pat. 2,352,515 [C.A., 38, 5622 (1944)].

β-Methylcrotononitrile, $(CH_3)_2C{=}CHCN$, and methallyl cyanide, $CH_2{=}C(CH_3)CH_2CN$, react in a similar manner to yield $(CH_3)_2C{=}C{-}(CH_2CH_2CN)CN$ and $CH_2{=}C(CH_3)C(CH_2CH_2CN)_2CN$.[33] Another example of a similar rearrangement is that which takes place upon reaction of cyclohexylideneacetonitrile and acrylonitrile to give α,α-di-(2-cyanoethyl)cyclohexenylacetonitrile.[33, 123]

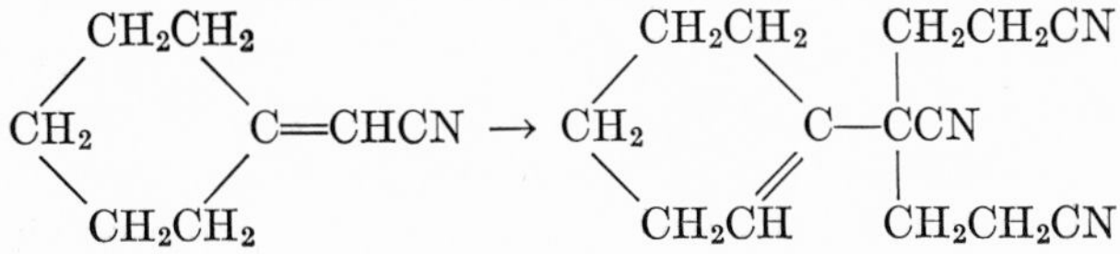

$$\begin{array}{ccc} & CH_2CH_2 & \\ \diagup & & \diagdown \\ CH_2 & & C{=}CHCN \\ \diagdown & & \diagup \\ & CH_2CH_2 & \end{array} \rightarrow \begin{array}{ccc} & CH_2CH_2 & CH_2CH_2CN \\ \diagup & & \diagdown \quad | \\ CH_2 & & C{-}CCN \\ \diagdown & & \diagup\!\!\!/ \quad | \\ & CH_2CH & CH_2CH_2CN \end{array}$$

Cyanoethylation of Cyclic Dienes (Table XIII)

Cyclopentadiene reacts with acrylonitrile in the absence of a catalyst to form a 1,4-adduct of the Diels-Alder type.[124] In the presence of Triton

$$\begin{array}{c} CH{=}CH \\ | \quad \diagdown CH_2 + CH_2{=}CHCN \rightarrow \\ CH{=}CH \end{array} \quad \begin{array}{ccc} CH{-}CH{-}CH_2 \\ \| \quad | \quad | \\ \quad \quad CH_2 \\ \quad | \\ CH{-}CH{-}CHCN \end{array}$$

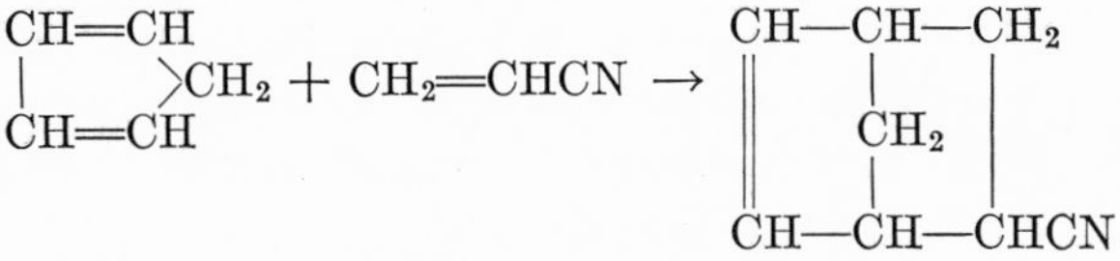

B, however, the Diels-Alder addition is completely repressed and all six hydrogen atoms in cyclopentadiene react to give a crystalline hexacyanoethylation derivative, accompanied by a mixture of lower polycyanoethylation products.[124]

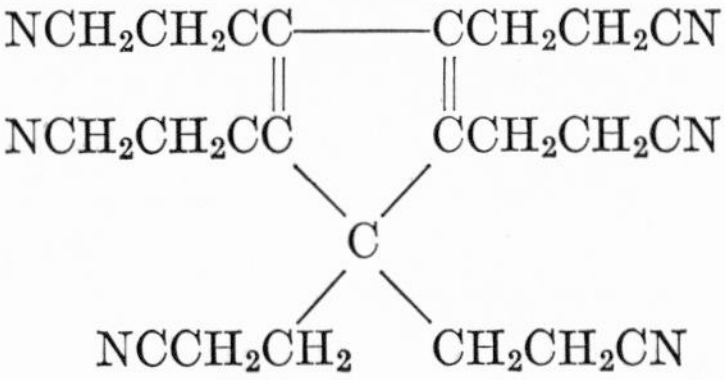

$$\begin{array}{cc} NCH_2CH_2CC\!\!-\!\!\!-\!\!\!-\!\!\!-CCH_2CH_2CN \\ \| \quad\quad\quad \| \\ NCH_2CH_2CC \quad\quad CCH_2CH_2CN \\ \diagdown\quad\quad\diagup \\ C \\ \diagup\quad\quad\diagdown \\ NCCH_2CH_2 \quad CH_2CH_2CN \end{array}$$

The fulvenes behave in a similar manner.[124] No Diels-Alder reaction occurs in the presence of Triton B when dimethylfulvene and acrylonitrile react. Only cyanoethylation products are formed.

Acrylonitrile and ω,ω-dimethylbenzofulvene with Triton B yield a crystalline mono-cyanoethylation product whose structure is uncertain.

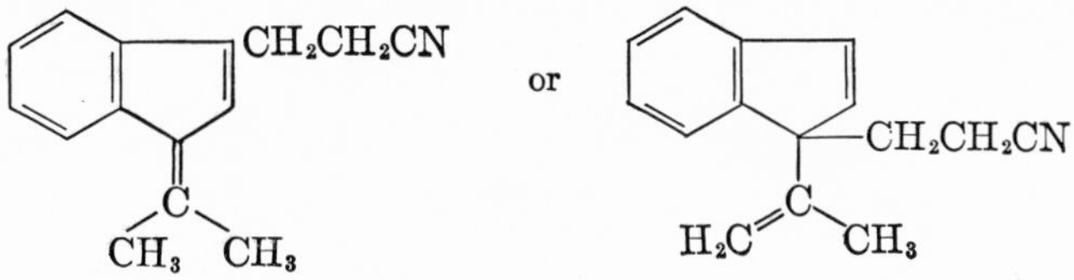

CH₂CH₂CN structure   or   —CH₂CH₂CN structure

[124] Bruson, *J. Am. Chem. Soc.*, **64**, 2457 (1942).

Indene with acrylonitrile and Triton B as catalyst yields primarily a crystalline *tris*(2-cyanoethyl)indene even when equimolar quantities of reactants are employed. A small amount of di-cyanoethylation product may be isolated. With three mole equivalents of acrylonitrile the yield of primary product is over 90%.[124] Fluorene and anthrone with acrylo-

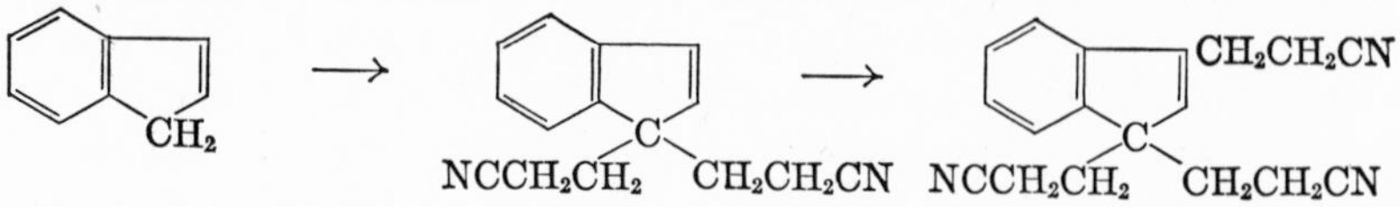

nitrile and Triton B give exclusively di-cyanoethylation products in 75–80% yields.[124, 125] The reactions of indene, fluorene, and anthrone

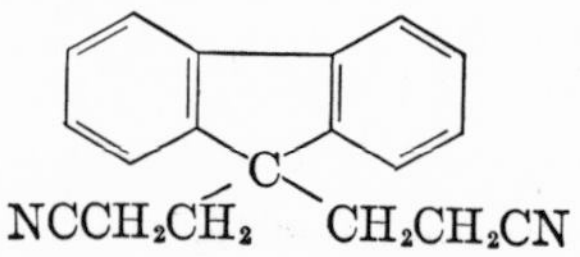

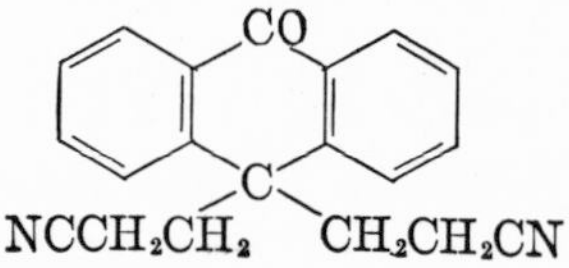

with acrylonitrile take place at room temperature with evolution of heat. In order to prevent excessive polymerization of the acrylonitrile and to allow cyanoethylation to go to completion, the use of inert solvents such as *tert*-butyl alcohol or dioxane, which dissolve the solid methylene compounds and moderate the reaction, is helpful.

EXTENSION OF THE REACTION TO HIGHER HOMOLOGS OF ACRYLO-NITRILE

Substituted acrylonitriles such as α-methylacrylonitrile and crotononitrile react less readily than acrylonitrile with the various classes of compounds considered in the preceding section of this chapter. It has not been possible to add aldehydes or ketones to α-methylacrylonitrile, although strongly basic amines such as piperidine do add to it.[32] Alcohols add to α-methylacrylonitrile, but the yields of alkoxy nitriles resulting are much lower than in the comparable reactions with acrylonitrile.[32] Crotononitrile is much more reactive than α-methylacrylonitrile. Alcohols,[126] amines, and nitroparaffins [32] add readily to crotononitrile, and fluorene can be added to it.[127]

β-Vinylacrylonitrile reacts readily with nitroparaffins, malonic ester, and highly enolized ketones such as acetoacetic ester under conditions similar to those used for cyanoethylation to yield addition products

[125] Bruson, U. S. pat. 2,280,058 [C.A., **36**, 5188 (1942)].
[126] Bruylants, *Bull. soc. chim. Belg.*, **31**, 225 (1922 [C.A., **17**, 1427 (1923)].
[127] Bruson, U. S. pat. 2,301,518 [C.A., **37**, 2101 (1943)].

containing the —CH$_2$CH=CHCH$_2$CN group in place of one or more of the reactive hydrogen atoms.[128]

EXPERIMENTAL CONDITIONS AND PROCEDURES

Acrylonitrile boils at 78° and is soluble in water to the extent of about 7.3% at 20°. Its vapor is toxic, and it should therefore be handled with due caution, preferably in a well-ventilated room or in a hood. Many cyanoethylation reactions are slow in starting and become strongly exothermic rather suddenly. It is advisable therefore to provide a cooling bath of ice water and to add the acrylonitrile dropwise with stirring to the other component advantageously in the presence of an inert solvent. Most cyanoethylation products are soluble in ethylene dichloride, and this solvent can be used to extract them from the reaction mixture or from any polyacrylonitrile that may be formed.

Ethylamine and Acrylonitrile; Preparation of β-Ethylaminopropionitrile and _bis_(2-Cyanoethyl)ethylamine.[2] One hundred and six grams (2 moles) of acrylonitrile is added to 200 g. (3 moles) of a 70% aqueous solution of ethylamine over a period of two hours while the temperature is kept below 30°. The reaction mixture is stirred at room temperature for five hours and finally heated on the steam bath for one hour. After the reaction mixture has stood overnight, the water is removed by adding 50 g. of anhydrous potassium carbonate and separating the aqueous layer. Distillation at 92–95°/30 mm. gives 177 g. (90%) of β-ethylaminopropionitrile.

When 130 g. (2 moles) of 70% ethylamine solution is added to 250 g. (4.7 moles) of acrylonitrile and the warm mixture heated on the steam bath for two hours and worked up as indicated above, 180.5 g. (60%) of _bis_(2-cyanoethyl)ethylamine, b.p. 202–205°/30 mm., is obtained.

Carbazole and Acrylonitrile; Preparation of 9-(β-Cyanoethyl)carbazole.[2] An intimate mixture of 167 g. (1.0 mole) of carbazole and 250 ml. (3.8 moles) of acrylonitrile is cooled in an ice bath, and 2 ml. of a 40% solution of benzyltrimethylammonium hydroxide (Triton B) is added to the well-stirred mixture. Upon addition of the catalyst a vigorous reaction ensues; the mixture warms up, and the pasty mass partially solidifies. The mixture is heated on the steam bath for one hour, and upon cooling a mass of crystals separates from the solution. These are removed by filtration and combined with a second crop of crystals obtained by concentrating the mother liquors. The yield is 188 g. (85.4%); m.p. 155.5°.

[128] Charlish, Davies, and Rose, _J. Chem. Soc._, **1948**, 227, 232.

p-Anisidine and Acrylonitrile; Preparation of β-(*p*-Anisidino)propionitrile.[23]   Equimolecular quantities of *p*-anisidine and acrylonitrile are refluxed with acetic acid (25 ml. per mole) for twelve hours. The mixture is dissolved in ether, washed successively with water and 5% bicarbonate solution, dried, and distilled. The yield of material boiling at 247°/0.7 mm. is 70%.

Butanol and Acrylonitrile; Preparation of β-*n*-Butoxypropionitrile.[44] A mixture of 148 g. (2.0 moles) of *n*-butanol and 2 g. of 40% benzyltrimethylammonium hydroxide (Triton B) is stirred under a reflux condenser while 106 g. (2 moles) of acrylonitrile is added at a rate such that the temperature does not exceed 45°. The mixture is stirred an hour after all the acrylonitrile has been added, made acidic with acetic acid, and fractionated in vacuum through a jacketed Vigreux column. The product boils at 98°/20 mm.; yield, 219 g. (86%).

Ethylene Cyanohydrin and Acrylonitrile; Preparation of *bis*-2-Cyanoethyl Ether.[37]   To a stirred mixture of 710 g. (10 moles) of ethylene cyanohydrin and 25 g. of 20% aqueous potassium hydroxide, 530 g. (10 moles) of acrylonitrile is added dropwise during the course of two and three-quarters hours while the reaction temperature is maintained at 40°. The mixture is stirred for eighteen hours at room temperature. It is then neutralized with dilute hydrochloric acid and evaporated to dryness in vacuum (30 mm.) on a steam bath. The residual oil, which weighs 1197 g., is distilled in vacuum to give 1126 g. (91%) of the product as a colorless liquid boiling at 155–165°/3 mm.

Formaldehyde, *tert*-Butyl Alcohol, and Acrylonitrile; Preparation of *tert*-Butyl 2-Cyanoethyl Formal.[69]   To a rapidly stirred suspension of 30 g. (1.0 mole) of paraformaldehyde, 100 g. of *tert*-butyl alcohol, and 5 g. of 30% methanolic potassium hydroxide, 53 g. (1.0 mole) of acrylonitrile is added dropwise during thirty minutes. The temperature rises spontaneously from 25° to about 45°, and the paraformaldehyde goes into solution. The mixture is stirred and heated for an hour and a half at 35–40° to complete the reaction. It is then filtered to remove a small amount of undissolved paraformaldehyde, and the filtrate is washed several times with water until it is no longer alkaline to litmus. The washed oil is then distilled in vacuum to yield 63 g. (40%) of the formal, $(CH_3)_3COCH_2OCH_2CH_2CN$, which boils at 100–102°/10 mm.

β-Naphthol and Acrylonitrile; Preparation of 1-(2-Cyanoethyl)-2-hydroxynaphthalene.[71]   A mixture of 55 ml. of benzene, 29 g. (0.2 mole) of β-naphthol, 9 g. of sodium hydroxide pellets, and 12 g. (0.22 mole) of acrylonitrile is heated on a steam bath under a reflux condenser for two hours. Then 100 ml. of cold water is added and the mixture stirred until all the alkali has dissolved. The aqueous layer is separated and acidified with acetic acid to yield 37 g. (93%) of product which, after recrystallization from ethanol, melts at 142°.

Sodium Sulfide and Acrylonitrile; Preparation of *bis*-2-Cyanoethyl Sulfide.[78] To a stirred solution of 480 g. (2.0 moles) of sodium sulfide nonahydrate and 400 g. of water, 212 g. (4.0 moles) of acrylonitrile is added dropwise while cooling to 12–20°. After the addition, which requires about one and one-quarter hours, the mixture is stirred at room temperature for four hours. The product usually crystallizes, especially if seeded and cooled. If it does not crystallize, the oil is taken up in benzene, washed with water, and dried in vacuum at 95°. The 247 g. of residual oil upon distillation in vacuum yields 240 g. (86%) of product boiling at 160–170°/0.5–1 mm. which crystallizes on cooling.

Hydrogen Cyanide and Acrylonitrile; Preparation of Succinonitrile.[90] A mixture of 300 g. (5.7 moles) of acrylonitrile and 3 g. of potassium cyanide is stirred under a good reflux condenser with 50 g. (1.9 moles) of liquid hydrogen cyanide. After the mixture has been warmed to 35° for a short time the reaction becomes exothermic and is held at 55–60° by cooling. When the reaction slows down, 105 g. (3.9 moles) of hydrogen cyanide is added dropwise. The reaction is completed by warming for two hours at 60–70°. The product is distilled directly in vacuum to give 424 g. (93%) of succinonitrile, b.p. 158–160°/20 mm.

Benzyl Phenyl Sulfone and Acrylonitrile; Preparation of 3-(3-Phenyl-1,5-dicyano)amyl Phenyl Sulfone.[97] To a stirred solution of 5.8 g. (0.025 mole) of benzyl phenyl sulfone, $C_6H_5CH_2SO_2C_6H_5$, 40 g. of acetonitrile, and 0.5 g. of Triton B at 32–38°, there is added 2.7 g. (0.05 mole) of acrylonitrile. The mixture is then stirred for eighteen hours at room temperature and neutralized with dilute hydrochloric acid. The product is washed with water and dried in vacuum at 95°. The 5 g. of residual oil crystallizes when mixed with ethanol and, after two recrystallizations from ethanol, forms colorless crystals, m.p. 180° (yield 55%).

Acetone and Acrylonitrile; Preparation of 1,1,1-*tris*(2-Cyanoethyl)-acetone.[103] To a stirred solution of 29 g. (0.5 mole) of acetone, 30 g. of *tert*-butyl alcohol, and 2.5 g. of 30% ethanolic potassium hydroxide solution cooled to 0–5°, a solution of 80 g. (1.5 moles) of acrylonitrile and 37 g. of *tert*-butyl alcohol is added dropwise during the course of one and a half hours while the reaction temperature is maintained at 0–5°. The mixture is then stirred for two hours at 5°, and the crystalline product is filtered with suction. The yield is 84 g. (79.5%), and the product melts at 154° after crystallization from hot water.

Methyl Acetoacetate and Acrylonitrile; Preparation of Methyl α,α-Di(2-cyanoethyl)acetoacetate.[103] To a solution of 58 g. (0.5 mole) of methyl acetoacetate, 100 g. of dioxane, and 7 g. of Triton B there is gradually added 53 g. (1.0 mole) of acrylonitrile at 30–40°. After stirring for one to three hours the crystalline product is filtered. The yield is 55 g. (50%), and the product melts at 154° after crystallization from acetone.

2-Ethylbutyraldehyde and Acrylonitrile; Preparation of 2-(2-Cyano-ethyl)-2-ethylbutyraldehyde.[114] To a stirred solution of 700 g. (7 moles) of freshly distilled 2-ethylbutyraldehyde and 20 g. of 50% aqueous potassium hydroxide solution, 408 g. (7.7 moles) of acrylonitrile is added dropwise during two hours at 55–58°. The mixture is stirred for ninety minutes longer, until the exothermic reaction has ceased, and finally is heated for one hour at 55° to complete the reaction. The product is acidified to congo red with dilute hydrochloric acid, washed twice with water, and dried under reduced pressure at 90°; the 1018 g. of residual oil is distilled in vacuum in a current of nitrogen. The product distils at 115–125°/4–6 mm. as a colorless oil. The yield is 821 g. (76.6%).

Ethyl Malonate and Acrylonitrile; Preparation of γ,γ-Dicarbethoxy-pimelonitrile.[37] To a stirred solution of 80 g. (0.5 mole) of ethyl malonate, 100 g. of dioxane, and 10 g. of Triton B, 53 g. (1 mole) of acrylonitrile is added dropwise during forty minutes while the reaction mixture is being cooled to 30–35°. The mixture is stirred for two hours at room temperature; then it is neutralized with dilute hydrochloric acid and poured into 1 l. of ice water. The product separates as an oil which rapidly solidifies to a white crystalline mass. The yield is 110 g. (82.7%), and the melting point is 62° after crystallization from ethanol.

Benzyl Cyanide and Acrylonitrile; Preparation of γ-Cyano-γ-phenyl-pimelonitrile.[37] A solution of 10.6 g. (0.2 mole) of acrylonitrile in 10 g. of tert-butyl alcohol is added dropwise to a stirred solution of 11.7 g. (0.1 mole) of benzyl cyanide, 25 g. of tert-butyl alcohol, and 1 g. of 30% of methanolic potassium hydroxide solution at 10–25°. The mixture is stirred for two hours at 10–25°, then neutralized with dilute hydrochloric acid and diluted with 25 ml. of ethanol to aid filtration of the crystalline product. The yield is 21 g. (94%). The melting point is 70° after crystallization from ethanol.

Fluorene and Acrylonitrile; Preparation of bis-9,9-(2-Cyanoethyl)-fluorene.[124] During one hour, 111.3 g. (2.1 moles) of acrylonitrile is added dropwise to a rapidly stirred solution of 166 g. (1.0 mole) of fluorene, 500 g. of dioxane, and 5 g. of Triton B, while the reaction temperature is maintained at 30–40° by occasional cooling with ice water. The solution is then stirred for three to six hours at room temperature to complete the reaction. At the end of this time, the dark brown solution is neutralized with dilute hydrochloric acid, and, without interruption of the stirring, 800 ml. of water is added to precipitate the product in granular form. The filtered and air-dried product weighs 250 g. Upon recrystallization from 500 ml. of ethanol, the product separates as faintly yellow crystals, m.p. 118–119°. The yield is 201 g. (74%). One more recrystallization from ethanol, using Norit, gives the pure compound as white needles, m.p. 121°.

TABLES OF CYANOETHYLATION REACTIONS

The following tables include the examples of cyanoethylation reactions described in the literature covered by *Chemical Abstracts* through 1947. A few articles that appeared in 1948 have been included. Attention is called to the fact that patents sometimes contain reports of cyanoethylation reactions but do not give the properties of the products. Products whose physical properties have not been reported are not included in the tables.

TABLE I

CYANOETHYLATION OF AMMONIA

Ratio of Moles of Ammonia to Moles of Acrylonitrile	Temp. °C.	Time Hr.	Yields of Products			Reference
			$H_2NC_2H_4CN$ %	$HN(C_2H_4CN)_2$ %	$N(C_2H_4CN)_3$ %	
20 *	30–33	24	39	39	—	5
15 *	30–33	24	36	40	—	5
10 *	30–33	24	35.6	53	—	5
7.5 *	30–33	24	32.6	54.5	—	5
5 *	30–33	24	23	58.6	—	5
2 *	30–33	24	9	67.6	—	5
1 *	30–33	3	—	85	—	32
0.55 *	30–33	24	0	87.2	—	5
0.5 *	30–33	24	0	85	—	5
0.53 *	30	—	1.7	88.5	6.0	3
0.56 *	30	—	5.8	83.5	1.0	3
5.9 *	30	—	23.9	58.9	3.3	3
7.5 †	30–33	24	30	57	—	5
5 †	30–33	24	19	—	—	5
7.5 ‡	30–33	24	26	66	—	5
1.25 §	90	0.5	12.5	75	—	1
8 §	40	—	22	64	—	2
7.5 ‖	—	24	38.3	53.2	—	5
5 ‖	—	24	34.4	58.5	—	5
4 ‖	—	24	35.5	57.8	—	5
3 ‖	—	24	33.2	61	—	5
2 ‖	—	24	24.6	68.6	—	5
3–10 *	110	2–5 min.	60–80	18	—	4

* 28–30% aqueous NH_3.
† 22% aqueous NH_3.
‡ 46% aqueous NH_3.
§ Liquid NH_3 in sealed tube.
‖ 28–30% aqueous NH_3 under pressure and no cooling.

TABLE II

CYANOETHYLATION OF PRIMARY AMINES

Amine	Ratio of Moles of Amine to Moles of Acrylonitrile	Temp. °C.	Time Hr.	Product	Yield %	Reference
Hydrazine *	1	Cooling	—	$H_2NNHCH_2CH_2CN$	90	1
Hydroxylamine hydrochloride †	0.7	30	2	$HONHCH_2CH_2CN$	100	1
Methylamine †	1.2	Cooling	24	$CH_3NHCH_2CH_2CN$	78	9
Methylamine ‡	1.1	80	6	$CH_3N(CH_2CH_2CN)_2$	—	9
Methylamine *	1.5	<30	24	$CH_3NHCH_2CH_2CN$	71	10
Ethylamine §§	1.5	Cooling	5 ‖	$C_2H_5NHCH_2CH_2CN$	90.4	2
Ethylamine §§	0.42	Boiling	2	$C_2H_5N(CH_2CH_2CN)_2$	60	2
Ethylamine *	1.5	<30	24	$C_2H_5NHCH_2CH_2CN$	84	10
n-Propylamine	1.5	<30	5 ‖	$n\text{-}C_3H_7NHCH_2CH_2CN$	92	10
Isopropylamine	1.5	<30	24	$iso\text{-}C_3H_7NHCH_2CH_2CN$	95	11
n-Butylamine	1	10–30	1	$n\text{-}C_4H_9NHCH_2CH_2CN$	100	1
n-Butylamine	1.5	<30	5 ‖	$n\text{-}C_4H_9NHCH_2CH_2CN$	98	10
sec-Butylamine	1.5	<30	5 ‖	$sec\text{-}C_4H_9NHCH_2CH_2CN$	83	10
tert-Butylamine	1.5	<30	5 ‖	$tert\text{-}C_4H_9NHCH_2CH_2CN$	56	10
n-Amylamine	1	50	—	$n\text{-}C_5H_{11}NHCH_2CH_2CN$	88	14
Cyclohexylamine	1	Reflux	1	$C_6H_{11}NHCH_2CH_2CN$	80	1
Cyclohexylamine	1.5	<30	5 ‖	$C_6H_{11}NHCH_2CH_2CN$	92	10
Benzylamine	1	—	—	$C_6H_5CH_2NHCH_2CH_2CN$	73	15
p-Anisidine ¶	1	Reflux	12	$CH_3OC_6H_4NHCH_2CH_2CN$	70	23

				Product		
Ethanolamine	—	—	—	HOCH$_2$CH$_2$N(CH$_2$CH$_2$CN)$_2$	—	2
Ethanolamine	1	Cooling	—	HOCH$_2$CH$_2$NHCH$_2$CH$_2$CN	100	19
γ-Diethylaminopropylamine	1	50	24 **	(C$_2$H$_5$)$_2$NCH$_2$CH$_2$CH$_2$NHCH$_2$CH$_2$CN	79.4	2
γ-Diethylaminopropylamine	—	—	—	(C$_2$H$_5$)$_2$NCH$_2$CH$_2$CH$_2$N(CH$_2$CH$_2$CN)$_2$	8.8	2
Morpholinoethylamine	—	—	—	OC$_4$H$_8$NCH$_2$CH$_2$CH$_2$NHCH$_2$CH$_2$CN	81.5	2
Morpholinopropylamine	1	25	6	OC$_4$H$_8$NCH$_2$CH$_2$CH$_2$NHCH$_2$CH$_2$CN	76	2
8-(3-Aminopropylamino)-6-methoxy-quinoline	—	—	—	8-[3-(2'-Cyanoethylamino)-propylamino]-6-methoxyquinoline	—	24
1-Naphthylamine ¶	0.5	160	16	N-(β-Cyanoethyl)-1-naphthylamine	—	22

* In aqueous solution.
† In methanol.
‡ In sealed tube.
§ A 70% aqueous solution.
‖ With later heating on the steam bath.
¶ In glacial acetic acid as catalyst.
** Allowed to stand forty-eight hours at room temperature after heating.

TABLE III

CYANOETHYLATION OF SECONDARY AMINES

Amine	Temp. °C.	Time Hr.	Product	Yield %	Reference
Diethyl-	50	24 *	$(C_2H_5)_2NCH_2CH_2CN$	97	2
Diethyl-	Reflux	8 †	$(C_2H_5)_2NCH_2CH_2CN$	74	2
Diethyl-	Reflux	0.5 ‡	$(C_2H_5)_2NCH_2CH_2CN$	93	2
Diethanol-	60	—	$(HOCH_2CH_2)_2NCH_2CH_2CN$	100	19
Diethanol-	30	8	$(HOCH_2CH_2)_2NCH_2CH_2CN$	94	2
N-Ethyl-ethanol-	50	24	$(C_2H_5)(HOCH_2CH_2)NCH_2CH_2CN$	72	14
Methyl-n-propyl-	95	24	$(CH_3)(n\text{-}C_3H_7)NCH_2CH_2CN$	93	16
Methylisopropyl- §	95	24	$(CH_3)(iso\text{-}C_3H_7)NCH_2CH_2CN$	76	16
Methylisobutyl- §	95	24	$(CH_3)(iso\text{-}C_4H_9)NCH_2CH_2CN$	78	16
Methyl-n-butyl- §	95	24	$(CH_3)(n\text{-}C_4H_9)NCH_2CH_2CN$	83	16
Methyl-sec-butyl- §	95	24	$(CH_3)(sec\text{-}C_4H_9)NCH_2CH_2CN$	87	16
Ethylisopropyl-	95	24	$(C_2H_5)(iso\text{-}C_3H_7)NCH_2CH_2CN$	31	16
Isopropyl-n-propyl- §	95	24	$(n\text{-}C_3H_7)(iso\text{-}C_3H_7)NCH_2CH_2CN$	80	16
Di-n-propyl- §	50	24 *	$(n\text{-}C_3H_7)_2NCH_2CH_2CN$	88	2, 14
Diisopropyl-	50	24 *	$(iso\text{-}C_3H_7)_2NCH_2CH_2CN$	12	14
Methyl-2-pentyl- §	95	24	$(CH_3)(C_5H_{11})NCH_2CH_2CN$	89	16
Methyl-3-pentyl- §	95	24	$(CH_3)(C_5H_{11})NCH_2CH_2CN$	81	16
Ethyl-isobutyl- §	95	24	$(C_2H_5)(iso\text{-}C_4H_9)NCH_2CH_2CN$	56	16
Methyl-2-(3-methylbutyl)- §§	95	24	$(CH_3)(C_5H_{11})NCH_2CH_2CN$	66	16
Methyl-4-(2-methylpentyl)- §§	95	24	$(CH_3)(C_6H_{13})NCH_2CH_2CN$	92	16
n-Butyl-n-propyl- §	95	24	$(C_4H_9)(C_3H_7)NCH_2CH_2CN$	61	16

Amine	Temperature	Time	Product	Yield %	Reference
sec-Butyl-n-propyl-	95	24	$(sec\text{-}C_4H_9)(C_3H_7)NCH_2CH_2CN$	34	16
Isobutyl-n-propyl- §	95	24	$(iso\text{-}C_4H_9)(C_3H_7)NCH_2CH_2CN$	49	16
4-Heptyl-methyl- §	95	24	$(C_7H_{15})(CH_3)NCH_2CH_2CN$	65	16
Di-n-butyl-	75	—	$(n\text{-}C_4H_9)_2NCH_2CH_2CN$	64	1
	50	24 *	$(n\text{-}C_4H_9)_2NCH_2CH_2CN$	91	2
	50	24 *	$(n\text{-}C_4H_9)_2NCH_2CH_2CN$	96	2
Diisobutyl-	50	24 *	$(iso\text{-}C_4H_9)_2NCH_2CH_2CN$	51	14
n-Butyl-sec-butyl-	95	24	$(n\text{-}C_4H_9)(sec\text{-}C_4H_9)NCH_2CH_2CN$	42	16
Di-n-amyl-	50	24	$(n\text{-}C_5H_{11})_2NCH_2CH_2CN$	90	2, 13
Di-n-hexyl-	50	24 *	$(n\text{-}C_6H_{13})_2NCH_2CH_2CN$	85	2
Di-n-octyl-	100	100 *	$(n\text{-}C_8H_{17})_2NCH_2CH_2CN$	80	14
Di-2-ethylhexyl-	100	100 *	$(C_8H_{17})_2NCH_2CH_2CN$	65	14
Di-2-ethylhexyl-			$(C_8H_{17})_2NCH_2CH_2CN$	77	2
Di-(γ-diethylaminopropyl)-	100 ‖	24 *	$[(C_2H_5)_2NCH_2CH_2CH_2]_2NCH_2CH_2CN$	78	2
γ-Diethylaminopropyl-	50	24 *	$(C_2H_5)_2NCH_2CH_2CH_2NHCH_2CH_2CN$	79.4	2
Benzyl-methyl-	—	—	$C_6H_5CH_2N(CH_3)CH_2CH_2CN$	93	15
Cyclopentyl-methyl- §	95	24	$(C_5H_9)(CH_3)NCH_2CH_2CN$	96	16
Cyclohexyl-methyl- §	95	24	$(C_6H_{11})(CH_3)NCH_2CH_2CN$	61	16
Cyclopentyl-ethyl-	95	24	$(C_5H_9)(C_2H_5)NCH_2CH_2CN$	48	16
Cyclopentyl-n-butyl- §	95	24	$(C_5H_9)(n\text{-}C_4H_9)NCH_2CH_2CN$	68	16
N-Methylaniline ¶	180	4	$C_6H_5N(CH_3)CH_2CH_2CN$	25	2
N-Methylaniline **	Reflux	12	$C_6H_5N(CH_3)CH_2CH_2CN$	Good	22

* Allowed to stand forty-eight hours at room temperature after heating.
† Distilled immediately after heating.
‡ Allowed to stand in refrigerator twenty-four hours after refluxing.
§ With benzyltrimethyl ammonium hydroxide catalyst (Triton B).
‖ With trace of Cu bronze.
¶ Hydrated copper sulfate catalyst.
** In glacial acetic acid as catalyst.

TABLE IV

CYANOETHYLATION OF SECONDARY HETEROCYCLIC AMINES

Amine	Temp. °C.	Time Hr.	Product	Yield %	Reference
2,2-Dimethylethyleneimine	Reflux	34	$(CH_3)_2C$——NCH_2CH_2CN / CH_2	66	18
Morpholine	50	24 *	N-(β-Cyanoethyl)morpholine	95	2, 13
Piperazine	—	20	bis-N,N'-(β-Cyanoethyl)piperazine	—	20, 21
Pyrrole †	Reflux	5	N-(β-Cyanoethyl)pyrrole	44	20
Pyrrole ‡	40 §	1	N-(β-Cyanoethyl)pyrrole	80 ‖	27
Pyrrole	—	—	N-(β-Cyanoethyl)pyrrole	86	17
Pyrrolidine	—	—	N-(β-Cyanoethyl)pyrrolidine	81	17
Piperidine	8–20	16	N-(β-Cyanoethyl)piperidine	92	2, 20
2-Methylpiperidine	—	—	N-(β-Cyanoethyl)-2-methylpiperidine	99	17
3-Methylpiperidine	—	—	N-(β-Cyanoethyl)-3-methylpiperidine	97	17
4-Methylpiperidine	—	—	N-(β-Cyanoethyl)-4-methylpiperidine	87	17
2,3-Dimethylpiperidine §§	—	—	N-(β-Cyanoethyl)-2,3-dimethylpiperidine	99	17
2,4-Dimethylpiperidine §§	—	—	N-(β-Cyanoethyl)-2,4-dimethylpiperidine	68	17
2,6-Dimethylpiperidine §§	—	—	N-(β-Cyanoethyl)-2,6-dimethylpiperidine	82	17
Morpholinoethylamine	—	—	β-(Morpholinoethylamino)propionitrile	81.5	2
Morpholinopropylamine	—	—	β-(Morpholinopropylamino)propionitrile	76	2
Perimidine †	Reflux	1.5	N-(β-Cyanoethyl)perimidine	—	20
Isatin §	30	48 ‖	N-(β-Cyanoethyl)isatin	50	26
Indole †	120–30 ¶	5	1-(β-Cyanoethyl)indole	77	20
2-Methylindole †	130 ¶	12–13	1-(β-Cyanoethyl)-2-methylindole	74	20

2,3-Dimethylindole †	130–40 ¶	12	1-(β-Cyanoethyl)-2,3-dimethylindole	82	20
5-Methoxy-2,3-dimethylindole	120–40	2	1-(β-Cyanoethyl)-2,3-dimethyl-5-methoxyindole	84	20
2-Phenylindole ‡	60	24 § **	1-(β-Cyanoethyl)-2-phenylindole	80	27
2-Phenylindole †	75	1–2	1-(β-Cyanoethyl)-2-phenylindole	100	20
2-Methylindoline **	140	15	N-(β-Cyanoethyl)-2-methylindoline	100	22
Benzimidazole †	28–80	2 ††	1-(β-Cyanoethyl)benzimidazole	93	20
Indole-3-aldehyde ‡	30	24 §	1-(β-Cyanoethyl)indole-3-aldehyde	70	27
2-Methylindole-3-aldehyde ‡	30	24 §	1-(β-Cyanoethyl)-2-methylindole-3-aldehyde	—	27
2-Phenylindole-3-aldehyde ‡	30	72 §	1-(β-Cyanoethyl)-2-phenylindole-3-aldehyde	90	27
Tetrahydroquinoline **	108–125	6	N-(β-Cyanoethyl)tetrahydroquinoline	75.5	2, 22
Decahydroquinoline †	200	2	N-(β-Cyanoethyl)decahydroquinoline	60	20
Carbazole †	75	1	N-(β-Cyanoethyl)carbazole	75	20
Carbazole §	0–100	1	N-(β-Cyanoethyl)carbazole	85.4	2
1,2,3,4,10,11-Hexahydrocarbazole **	130	12	N-(β-Cyanoethyl)hexahydrocarbazole	Good	22

* Allowed to stand forty-eight hours at room temperature after heating.
† With sodium ethoxide catalyst.
‡ In dioxane.
§ With Triton B catalyst.
‖ In ethanol.
¶ In sealed tube.
** In glacial acetic acid as catalyst.
†† In pyridine.

TABLE V

CYANOETHYLATION OF AMIDES, IMIDES, LACTAMS, AND SULFONAMIDES

Compound	Catalyst	Product	Yield %	Reference
Formamide	Na	$HCONHCH_2CH_2CN$	—	28, 30
Formamide	NaOH	$HCON(CH_2CH_2CN)_2$	—	28, 29
Acetamide	NaOH	$CH_3CONHCH_2CH_2CN$	—	30
Acetamide	Triton B	$CH_3CON(CH_2CH_2CN)_2$	72	38
N-n-Propylformamide	NaOH	$HCON(C_3H_7)CH_2CH_2CN$	—	30
N-n-Butylformamide	NaOH	$HCON(C_4H_9)CH_2CH_2CN$	—	30
N-n-Hexylformamide	NaOH	$HCON(C_6H_{13})CH_2CH_2CN$	—	30
N-Cyclohexylformamide	NaOH	$HCON(C_6H_{11})CH_2CH_2CN$	—	30
N-Phenylformamide	NaOH	$HCON(C_6H_5)CH_2CH_2CN$	—	30
N-Methylacetamide	NaOH	$CH_3CON(CH_3)CH_2CH_2CN$	—	30, 31
N-Methylpropionamide	NaOH	$CH_3CH_2CON(CH_3)CH_2CH_2CN$	—	30, 31
Benzamide	NaOH	$C_6H_5CONHCH_2CH_2CN$	—	31
Acetanilide	NaOH	$CH_3CON(C_6H_5)CH_2CH_2CN$	—	31
Crotonamide	Triton B	$CH_3CH{=}CHCON(CH_2CH_2CN)_2$	—	32, 33
N,N'-Dimethyladipamide	NaOH	$NCCH_2CH_2(CH_3)NCO(CH_2)_4CON(CH_3)CH_2CH_2CN$	—	31
Succinimide	NaOH	N-(β-Cyanoethyl)succinimide	—	30
Phthalimide	Triton B	N-(β-Cyanoethyl)phthalimide	100	34
α-Pyrrolidone	NaOH	N-(β-Cyanoethyl)pyrrolidone	—	31
ω-Caprolactam	NaOH	N-(β-Cyanoethyl)caprolactam	—	30, 31
2-Pyridone	NaOH	N-(β-Cyanoethyl)pyridone	95	35
Propanesulfomethylamide	NaOH	$CH_3CH_2CH_2SO_2N(CH_3)CH_2CH_2CN$	95	30
Butanesulfonamide	Triton B	$CH_3CH_2CH_2CH_2SO_2NHCH_2CH_2CN$	51	38
Butanesulfonamide	NaOH	$CH_3CH_2CH_2CH_2SO_2N(CH_2CH_2CN)_2$	55	38
Benzylsulfonamide	Triton B	$C_6H_5CH_2SO_2N(CH_2CH_2CN)_2$	90	36, 37
Benzenesulfonamide	NaOH	$C_6H_5SO_2N(CH_2CH_2CN)_2$	—	30
p-Acetylaminobenzenesulfonyl-N-methylamide	NaOH	$CH_3CONHC_6H_4SO_2N(CH_3)CH_2CH_2CN$	—	30

TABLE VI

Cyanoethylation of Monohydric and Polyhydric Alcohols

Alcohol	Catalyst	Temp. °C	Time Hr.	Product	Yield %	Reference
Methanol	Triton B or CH_3ONa	—	—	$CH_3OCH_2CH_2CN$	89	44
Methanol	CH_3ONa	30–35	1.5	"	—	41
Methanol	2% NaOH solution	—	—	"	90	48
Ethanol	2% NaOH solution	—	—	$C_2H_5OCH_2CH_2CN$	90	48
Ethanol	NaOH	35–70	0.25	"	78	41
Ethanol	$NaOCH_3$ or Triton B	—	—	"	—	44
Ethanol	$NaOCH_3$	30–35	—	"	89	42
2-Propanol	NaOH	60–80	1	$iso\text{-}C_3H_7OCH_2CH_2CN$	69	41
2-Propanol	$NaOCH_3$ or Triton B	—	—	"	—	44
2-Propanol	KOH	—	—	"	85	48
1-Butanol	KOH	25–45	2	$n\text{-}C_4H_9OCH_2CH_2CN$	88	48
1-Butanol	Triton B	40	—	"	86	44
1-Butanol	Na	30–35	12	"	—	43
tert-Butyl alcohol	Na	80	—	$tert\text{-}C_4H_9OCH_2CH_2CN$	82	41
1-Pentanol	NaOH	—	16	$n\text{-}C_5H_{11}OCH_2CH_2CN$	92	48
1-Pentanol	Na	35–40	—	"	86	41
2-Ethyl-1-hexanol	Na	30–35	—	$C_8H_{17}OCH_2CH_2CN$	—	41
2-Ethyl-1-hexanol	Na	—	1	"	88	48
2-Ethyl-1-hexanol	$NaOCH_3$	75	—	"	77	44
1-Octanol	Na	—	—	$n\text{-}C_8H_{17}OCH_2CH_2CN$	80	48
1-Decanol	Na	—	15	$n\text{-}C_{10}H_{21}OCH_2CH_2CN$	37	48
1-Dodecanol	$NaOC_2H_5$	50	1	$n\text{-}C_{12}H_{25}OCH_2CH_2CN$	—	41
1-Octadecanol	$NaOC_2H_5$	50–55	—	$n\text{-}C_{18}H_{37}OCH_2CH_2CN$	—	41
Benzyl alcohol	$NaOCH_3$	75	—	$C_6H_5CH_2OCH_2CH_2CN$	94	44

TABLE VI—*Continued*

CYANOETHYLATION OF MONOHYDRIC AND POLYHYDRIC ALCOHOLS

Alcohol	Catalyst	Temp. °C.	Time Hr.	Product	Yield %	Reference
Cyclohexanol	—	—	—	$C_6H_{11}OCH_2CH_2CN$	—	43
3,5-Dimethylcyclohexanol	$NaOCH_3$	75	—	$(CH_3)_2C_6H_9OCH_2CH_2CN$	51	44
Ethylene glycol	Na	40–50	3	$NCCH_2CH_2OC_2H_4OCH_2CH_2CN$	83	41, 52
Ethylene glycol	$NaOCH_3$	25–30	6	"	78	37, 50
Propylene glycol	$NaOCH_3$	25–30	6	$NCC_2H_4OCH_2CH(CH_3)OC_2H_4CN$	87	37, 50
Trimethylene glycol	$NaOCH_3$	25–30	6.5	$NCC_2H_4O(CH_2)_3OC_2H_4CN$	87	37, 50
2,3-Butylene glycol	$NaOCH_3$	20–25	6	$NCC_2H_4OCH(CH_3)CH(CH_3)OC_2H_4CN$	67	37, 50
1,3-Butylene glycol	$NaOCH_3$	25	7	$NCC_2H_4OCH_2CH_2CH(CH_3)OC_2H_4CN$	68	37, 50
Pentamethylene glycol	$NaOCH_3$	25	6	$NCC_2H_4O(CH_2)_5OC_2H_4CN$	80	37, 50
Decamethylene glycol	$NaOCH_3$	25	6	$NCC_2H_4O(CH_2)_{10}OC_2H_4CN$	80	37, 50
1,12-Dihydroxyoctadecane	$NaOCH_3$	40–45	5.5	$CH_3(CH_2)_5CH(CH_2)_{10}CH_2OC_2H_4CN$, OC_2H_4CN	—	50
$(CH_3)_2C(OH)CH_2OH$	$NaOCH_3$	25	5.5	$(CH_3)_2C(OH)CH_2OCH_2CH_2CN$	71	50
$(CH_3)_2C(OH)CH_2CHOHCH_3$	$NaOCH_3$	25	5.5	$(CH_3)_2C(OH)CH_2CH(CH_3)OC_2H_4CN$	58	50
1,2-Cyclohexanediol	$NaOCH_3$	25	7	cyclohexane ring: CH_2—$CHOC_2H_4CN$ / CH_2—CH_2 / CH_2—$CHOC_2H_4CN$	60	50
Glycerol	$NaOCH_3$	25	6	$CH_2OC_2H_4CN$ / $CHOC_2H_4CN$ / $CH_2OC_2H_4CN$	74	37, 50
Pentaerythritol	Aqueous NaOH	40–50	7	$C(CH_2OCH_2CH_2CN)_4$	—	50
Mannitol	Aqueous NaOH	40–50	5	Hexa-(β-cyanoethoxy)hexane	—	50

TABLE VII

CYANOETHYLATION OF UNSATURATED ALCOHOLS AND ETHER ALCOHOLS

Alcohol	Catalyst	Temp. °C	Time Hr.	Product	Yield %	Reference
Allyl —	NaOH	45–60	3.5	$CH_2=CHCH_2OCH_2CH_2CN$	—	41
Allyl —	Na₂O	15–25	7	"	—	49
Methallyl —	Na₂O	15–25	7	$CH_2=C(CH_3)CH_2OCH_2CH_2CN$	70	49
Vinyl dimethyl carbinol	NaOCH₃	10–20	6	$CH_2=CHC(CH_3)_2OCH_2CH_2CN$	—	49
Ethynyl dimethyl carbinol	NaOCH₃	17–25	7	$HC\equiv CC(CH_3)_2OCH_2CH_2CN$	72	49
Geraniol	Na₂O	25	7	$C_{10}H_{17}OCH_2CH_2CN$	60	49
Linaloöl	Na₂O	25–28	7	$C_{10}H_{17}OCH_2CH_2CN$	—	49
Citronellol	NaOCH₃	25	7	$C_{10}H_{19}OCH_2CH_2CN$	77	49
Cinnamyl —	NaOCH₃	20–25	6.5	$C_6H_5CH=CHCH_2OCH_2CH_2CN$	73	49
Oleyl —	Na₂O	20–25	7	$C_{18}H_{35}OCH_2CH_2CN$	45	49
Furfuryl —	Na₂O	20–30	8	β-(Furfuryloxy)propionitrile	67	49
$\overset{CH-CH}{\underset{O}{\diagdown\diagup}}CCH_2OCH_2CH_2OH$	Na	25	0.5	$\overset{CH-CH}{\underset{O}{\diagdown\diagup}}CCH_2OC_2H_4OCH_2CH_2CN$	40	56
$CH_2=CHCH_2OCH_2CH_2OH$	NaOCH₃	18–20	2	$CH_2=CHCH_2OC_2H_4OC_2H_4CN$	80	56
$CH_2=CHCH_2OCH_2CHOHCH_3$	Na	15–25	1	$CH_2=CHCH_2OCH_2CH(CH_3)OC_2H_4CN$	80	56
Tetrahydrofuryl —	NaOCH₃	75	—	$\overset{CH_2-CH_2}{\underset{O}{\diagup\diagdown}}CH_2 \quad CHCH_2OCH_2CH_2CN$	80	44
Tetrahydrofurfuryl —	Na₂O	15–25	6	"	44.5	46

TABLE VII—*Continued*

Cyanoethylation of Unsaturated Alcohols and Ether Alcohols

Alcohol	Catalyst	Temp. °C.	Time Hr.	Product	Yield %	Reference
$CH_3OCH_2CH_2OH$	$NaOC_2H_5$	25	5	$CH_3OCH_2CH_2OCH_2CH_2CN$	74	46
$CH_3OCH_2CH_2OH$	$NaOCH_3$	75	—	$CH_3OCH_2CH_2OCH_2CH_2CN$	87	44
$C_2H_5OCH_2CH_2OH$	Na_2O	25	8	$C_2H_5OCH_2CH_2OCH_2CH_2CN$	75	46
$n\text{-}C_4H_9OCH_2CH_2OH$	Triton B	30–45	1	$n\text{-}C_4H_9OCH_2CH_2OCH_2CH_2CN$	78	46
$C_6H_5OCH_2CH_2OH$	$NaOCH_3$	25	18	$C_6H_5OCH_2CH_2OCH_2CH_2CN$	75	46
$C_6H_5CH_2OCH_2CH_2OH$	Triton B	25–30	4	$C_6H_5CH_2OCH_2CH_2OCH_2CH_2CN$	76	46
p-tert-Amylphenoxyethanol	Triton B	25	18	$p\text{-}tert\text{-}C_5H_{11}C_6H_4OC_2H_4OC_2H_4CN$	67	46
p-tert-Octylphenoxyethanol	$NaOCH_3$	25–30	24	$p\text{-}tert\text{-}C_8H_{17}C_6H_4OC_2H_4OC_2H_4CN$	89	46
$CH_3OC_2H_4OCH_2CH_2OH$	$NaOCH_3$	25	7	$CH_3OC_2H_4OC_2H_4OCH_2CH_2CN$	63	46
$n\text{-}C_4H_9OC_2H_4OCH_2CH_2OH$	$NaOCH_3$	25	8	$n\text{-}C_4H_9OC_2H_4OC_2H_4OCH_2CH_2CN$	70	46
Glyceryl 1,3-dimethyl ether	$NaOCH_3$	25–35	6	$(CH_3OCH_2)_2CHOC_2H_4CN$	80	46
Diethylene glycol	50% NaOH	10–20	5	$NCC_2H_4OC_2H_4OC_2H_4OC_2H_4CN$	91	37, 50
$HOCH_2CH_2SCH_2CH_2OH$	$NaOC_2H_5$	25	7	$NCC_2H_4OC_2H_4SC_2H_4OC_2H_4CN$	92	37, 50
Triethylene glycol	$NaOC_2H_5$	25	16	$NCC_2H_4(OC_2H_4)_3OC_2H_4CN$	77	37, 50
Glyceryl α-methyl ether	$NaOCH_3$	25–30	6.5	$CH_3OCH_2CHOC_2H_4CN$ — $CH_2OC_2H_4CN$	61	50
Glyceryl α-butyl ether	$NaOCH_3$	25–30	6.5	$C_4H_9OCH_2CHOC_2H_4CN$ — $CH_2OC_2H_4CN$	43	49
Dipropylene glycol	$NaOCH_3$	25	17	bis(β-Cyanoethoxy)-2,2'-dipropyl ether	73	50

TABLE VIII

CYANOETHYLATION OF ALCOHOLS CONTAINING HALOGEN, NITRILE, OR OTHER FUNCTIONAL GROUPS

Alcohol	Catalyst	Temp. °C.	Time Hr.	Product	Yield %	Reference
ClCH₂CH₂OH	40% NaOH	40	10	ClCH₂CH₂OCH₂CH₂CN	—	65
FCH₂CH₂OH	—	—	—	FCH₂CH₂OCH₂CH₂CN	—	66
ClCH₂CH₂OCH₂CH₂OH	NaOH	20–35	2	ClCH₂CH₂OC₂H₄OCH₂CH₂CN	70	46
p-Chlorophenoxyethanol	Triton B	25–40	2	ClC₆H₄OC₂H₄OCH₂CH₂CN	72	46
NCCH₂CH₂OH	Na	40–45	3	NCCH₂CH₂OCH₂CH₂CN	91	41
NCCH₂CH₂OH	20% KOH	25–40	18	NCCH₂CH₂OCH₂CH₂CN	75	37
NCCH₂CH₂OH	KCN	80	0.2	NCCH₂CH₂OCH₂CH₂CN	—	62
NCCH₂OH	(C₄H₉)₃N	80–90	0.75	NCCH₂OCH₂CH₂CN	—	62
CH₃CHOHCN	NaOH	90	0.5	CH₃CH(CN)OCH₂CH₂CN	—	62
(C₂H₅)₂NCH₂CH₂OH	NaOCH₃	25	24	(C₂H₅)₂NCH₂CH₂OCH₂CH₂CN	67	67
(C₂H₅)₂NCH₂CH₂OH	NaOCH₃	25	24	(C₂H₅)₂NCH₂CH₂OCH₂CH₂CN	80	2
(C₂H₅)₂NCH₂CH₂CH₂OH	NaOCH₃	25	24	(C₂H₅)₂NCH₂CH₂CH₂OC₂H₄CN	75.4	2
(C₂H₅)₂NCH₂CH₂CH₂CHOHCH₃	NaOCH₃	25	24	(C₂H₅)₂N(CH₂)₃CH(CH₃)OC₂H₄CN	66	2
N-(β-Hydroxyethyl)morpholine	NaOCH₃	25	18	$\begin{matrix} CH_2CH_2 \\ O \qquad\qquad N\text{-}CH_2CH_2OCH_2CH_2CN \\ CH_2CH_2 \end{matrix}$	43	67

TABLE VIII—*Continued*

CYANOETHYLATION OF ALCOHOLS CONTAINING HALOGEN, NITRILE, OR OTHER FUNCTIONAL GROUPS

Alcohol	Catalyst	Temp. °C.	Time Hr.	Product	Yield %	Reference
N-(β-Hydroxyethyl)di-2-ethyl-hexylamine	NaOCH₃	55	1	$(C_8H_{17})_2NCH_2CH_2OCH_2CH_2CN$	47	67
$C_6H_5{>}NCH_2CH_2OH$ C_2H_5	NaOCH₃	25	18	$C_6H_5{>}NCH_2CH_2OCH_2CH_2CN$ C_2H_5	66.5	67
$NCH_2CHOHCH_2OH$ CH_3 CH_3	NaOH aqueous	45	4	$(CH_3)_2NCH_2CHOC_2H_4CN$ OCH_2CH_2CN	37	67
$NCH_2CHOHCH_2OH$ CH_3	NaOCH₃	25	21	$(CH_3)_2NCH_2CHOC_2H_4CN$ $CH_2OC_2H_4CN$	37	67
Triethanolamine	NaOCH₃	20–40	16	$N(CH_2CH_2OCH_2CH_2CN)_3$	97	67
Triisopropanolamine	KOC₂H₅	25	18	$N[CH_2CH(CH_3)OCH_2CH_2CN]_3$	—	67

TABLE IX

CYANOETHYLATION OF PHENOLS, OXIMES, HYDROGEN SULFIDE, MERCAPTANS, AND THIOPHENOLS

Compound	Catalyst	Temp. °C.	Time Hr.	Product	Yield %	Reference
Phenol	Na	130–40	4–6	$C_6H_5OCH_2CH_2CN$	—	70
Phenol	Triton B	Reflux	20	$C_6H_5OCH_2CH_2CN$	67.5	73
m-Chlorophenol	Na	120–30	3	β-(3-Chlorophenoxy)propionitrile	—	70
m-Methoxyphenol	Triton B	Reflux	20	β-(3-Methoxyphenoxy)propionitrile	76.5	73
Pyrocatechol	Na	130–40	5	β-(2-Hydroxyphenoxy)propionitrile	—	70
Resorcinol	Triton B	Reflux	20	1,3-Di-(β-cyanoethoxy)benzene	40	73
Hydroquinone	Na	120–30	5	1,4-Di-(β-cyanoethoxy)benzene	—	70
Salicylaldehyde	Triton B	Reflux	30	2-(β-Cyanoethoxy)benzaldehyde	1.3	73
Salicylaldehyde	Triton B	Reflux	30	3-Cyano-1,2-benzopyran	1.3	73
Salicylaldehyde	Triton B	Reflux	30	3-Cyano-4-chromanol	2	73
β-Naphthol	Na	Reflux	3	β-(2-Naphthoxy)propionitrile	—	70
β-Naphthol	NaOH (excess)	90	2	2-Hydroxy-1-(2-cyanoethyl)naphthalene	94	71
β-Naphthol	Triton B	Reflux	18	β-(2-Naphthoxy)propionitrile	79.2	74
6-Bromo-2-naphthol	Triton B	Reflux	20	3-(6'-Bromo-2'-naphthoxy)propionitrile	10	73
Acetone oxime	$NaOCH_3$	25–50	12	$(CH_3)_2C{=}NOCH_2CH_2CN$	61	37
Methyl ethyl ketoxime	$NaOCH_3$	25	18	$\begin{matrix} CH_3 \\ C_2H_5 \end{matrix}{>}C{=}NOCH_2CH_2CN$	71	37
Methyl n-hexyl ketoxime	$NaOCH_3$	25–30	20	$\begin{matrix} CH_3 \\ C_6H_{13} \end{matrix}{>}C{=}NOCH_2CH_2CN$	82	75

TABLE IX—*Continued*

CYANOETHYLATION OF PHENOLS, OXIMES, HYDROGEN SULFIDE, MERCAPTANS, AND THIOPHENOLS

Compound	Catalyst	Temp. °C.	Time Hr.	Product	Yield %	Reference
Acetophenone oxime	Triton B	40–50	2	C_6H_5\C=NOCH$_2$CH$_2$CN / CH$_3$	92	37
Cyclohexanone oxime	NaOCH$_3$	25	24	(cyclohexane ring) C=NOCH$_2$CH$_2$CN	—	75
Dimethylglyoxime	NaOH	25	24	CH$_3$C=NOCH$_2$CH$_2$CN / CH$_3$C=NOCH$_2$CH$_2$CN	60	37
α-Ethyl-β-propylacrolein oxime	NaOCH$_3$	25	18	CH$_3$CH$_2$CH$_2$CH=CCH=NOC$_2$H$_4$CN / C$_2$H$_5$	80	75
α-Ethylhexaldoxime	Triton B	25	4	CH$_3$(CH$_2$)$_3$CHCH=NOC$_2$H$_4$CN / CH—CH	—	75
Furfuraldoxime (syn)	NaOCH$_3$	25	2	(furan) CCH=NOCH$_2$CH$_2$CN	45	37
Benzoin oxime	Triton B	25	24	C_6H_5C=NOCH$_2$CH$_2$CN / C_6H_5CHOCH$_2$CH$_2$CN	96	37

Reactant	Catalyst	Temp.	Time	Product	Yield	Ref.
Hydrogen sulfide	—	80	10	NCCH₂CH₂SCH₂CH₂CN	Good	76
Hydrogen sulfide	Triton B or NaOCH₃	65–70	—	NCCH₂CH₂SCH₂CH₂CN	86–93	77
Methyl mercaptan	NaOCH₃	<35	16	CH₃SCH₂CH₂CN	91	57
Ethyl mercaptan	NaOCH₃	<35	16	C₂H₅SCH₂CH₂CN	83	57
Ethyl mercaptan (Na salt)	—	<35	1	C₂H₅SCH₂CH₂CN	85	80
Ethyl mercaptan	Piperidine	<35	2	C₂H₅SCH₂CH₂CN	80	81
n-Propyl mercaptan (Na salt)	—	<35	1	n-C₃H₇SCH₂CH₂CN	78	80
Isopropylmercaptan	NaOCH₃	<35	16	iso-C₃H₇SCH₂CH₂CN	95	57
n-Butylmercaptan (Na salt)	—	<55	1	n-C₄H₉SCH₂CH₂CN	80–90	80
n-Butylmercaptan	NaOCH₃	—	—	n-C₄H₉SCH₂CH₂CN	96	57
Isobutylmercaptan	NaOCH₃	<35	16	iso-C₄H₉SCH₂CH₂CN	85	57
tert-Butylmercaptan	NaOCH₃	<35	16	tert-C₄H₉SCH₂CH₂CN	95	57
Carbethoxymethylmercaptan	NaOCH₃	<35	16	C₂H₅O₂CCH₂SCH₂CH₂CN	85–89	57
Benzylmercaptan	None	<35	16	C₆H₅CH₂SCH₂CH₂CN	92	57
Benzylmercaptan	NaOCH₃	<35	16	C₆H₅CH₂SCH₂CH₂CN	92	57
Octylmercaptan	NaOCH₃	40–50	—	C₈H₁₇SCH₂CH₂CN	—	82
Nonylmercaptan	NaOCH₃	40–50	—	C₉H₁₉SCH₂CH₂CN	—	82
Laurylmercaptan	NaOCH₃	40–50	—	C₁₂H₂₅SCH₂CH₂CN	—	82
Laurylmercaptan	NaOH	25–42	16	C₁₂H₂₅SCH₂CH₂CN	—	80
Thiophenol	NaOH	31–43	16	C₆H₅SCH₂CH₂CN	90	80
Thiophenol	Triton B	<35	16	C₆H₅SCH₂CH₂CN	97	57
Thiophenol	None	<35	3	C₆H₅SCH₂CH₂CN	93	57
o-Thiocresol	NaOCH₃	<35	16	o-CH₃C₆H₄SCH₂CH₂CN	81	57
m-Thiocresol	Triton B	<35	16	m-CH₃C₆H₄SCH₂CH₂CN	97	57
p-Thiocresol	Triton B	<35	16	p-CH₃C₆H₄SCH₂CH₂CN	95	57
p-Thiocresol	NaOH	30–42	3	p-CH₃C₆H₄SCH₂CH₂CN	74	80
2-Naphthiol	Triton B	65	1	C₁₀H₇SCH₂CH₂CN	92	74

TABLE IX—*Continued*

CYANOETHYLATION OF PHENOLS, OXIMES, HYDROGEN SULFIDE, MERCAPTANS, AND THIOPHENOLS

Compound	Catalyst	Temp. °C.	Time Hr.	Product	Yield %	Reference
β-Naphthiol	NaOH	31–43	16	$C_{10}H_7SCH_2CH_2CN$	—	80
2-Mercaptoethanol	None	25	16	$HOCH_2CH_2SCH_2CH_2CN$	91	57
2-Mercaptoethanol	Triton B	25	16	$NCCH_2CH_2OC_2H_4SCH_2CH_2CN$	98.6	57
2-Mercaptoethanol	NaOH in Ethanol	25	16	$NCCH_2CH_2OC_2H_4SCH_2CH_2CN$	98.3	57
Ethylene dithiol	Piperidine	—	—	$NCCH_2CH_2SC_2H_4SCH_2CH_2CN$	—	81
Ethylene dithiol	Piperidine	—	—	$HSCH_2CH_2SCH_2CH_2CN$	26	81
Diethylaminoethanethiol	None	—	3	$(C_2H_5)_2NCH_2CH_2SCH_2CH_2CN$	92	84
Sodium dimethyl dithiocarbamate	—	<30	3	$(CH_3)_2NCSSCH_2CH_2CN$	—	80
Sodium di-n-butyldithiocarbamate	—	<30	—	$(C_4H_9)_2NCSSCH_2CH_2CN$	82.5	80
Sodium piperidinodithiocarbamate	—	<40	3	$C_5H_{10}NCSSCH_2CH_2CN$	61	80
2-Mercaptobenzothiazole (Na salt)	—	25	2	2-(β-Cyanoethylmercapto)benzothiazole	—	80
2-Mercaptobenzothiazole	NaOH	Reflux	0.5	2-(β-Cyanoethylmercapto)benzothiazole	63	83
2-Mercaptobenzothiazole	Triton B	<35	16	2-(β-Cyanoethylmercapto)benzothiazole	87	57
2-Mercaptothiazoline (Na salt)	—	<30	2	2-(β-Cyanoethylmercapto)thiazoline	70	80
2-Mercapto-4-methyl thiazole (Na salt)	—	<30	2	2-(β-Cyanoethylmercapto)-4-methylthiazole	—	80
2-Mercaptobenzoxazole	Triton B	<35	16	2-(β-Cyanoethylmercapto)benzoxazole	88	57

TABLE X

Cyanoethylation of Aldehydes and Ketones

Compound	Catalyst	Temp. °C.	Time Hr.	Product	Yield %	Reference
Formaldehyde	NaOH	Reflux	8	$NCCH_2CH_2OCH_2OCH_2CH_2CN$	30	68
Acetaldehyde	NaOH	Reflux	1	γ-Cyanobutyraldehyde γ-Formylpimelonitrile	40–50	116
Propionaldehyde	NaOH	Reflux	1	$CH_3CH(CHO)CH_2CH_2CN$	4.9	116
			2	$CH_3C(CHO)(CH_2CH_2CN)_2$	25.1	116
Isobutyraldehyde	NaOH	65–80	—	$(CH_3)_2C(CHO)CH_2CH_2CN$	35–40	114, 117
Isobutyraldehyde	NaCN	80–90	1	$(CH_3)_2C(CHO)CH_2CH_2CN$	50	114, 118
2-Ethylbutyraldehyde	KOH	55–60	1	$(C_2H_5)_2C(CHO)CH_2CH_2CN$	76.6	114, 118
2-Ethylhexaldehyde	KOH	55–60	1	$(C_2H_5)(n\text{-}C_4H_9)C(CHO)CH_2CH_2CN$	79	118
α-Ethyl-β-propylacrolein	KOH	45–55	2	$CH_3CH_2CH{=}CHC(C_2H_5)(CHO)CH_2CH_2CN$	49	103, 105
Acetone	NaOH	0–5	5–7	$CH_3COC(CH_2CH_2CN)_3$	77	104
Acetone	Triton B	Reflux	2	$CH_3COCH_2CH_2CH_2CN$	8.5	103
$CH_3COC(CH_2CH_2CN)_3$	KOH	40	2	$NCCH_2CH_2CH_2COC(CH_2CH_2CN)_3$	—	103
Methyl ethyl ketone	Na	5–10	—	$CH_3COC(CH_3)(CH_2CH_2CN)_2$	89	106
Methyl ethyl ketone	Triton B	30–40	48	$CH_3COC(CH_3)(CH_2CH_2CN)_2$	50	103
$CH_3COC(CH_3)(CH_2CH_2CN)_2$	Triton B	25–40	1	$(NCCH_2CH_2)_2CHCOC(CH_3)(CH_2CH_2CN)_2$	—	103
Methyl n-propyl ketone	Triton B	15	1	$CH_3COC(C_2H_5)(CH_2CH_2CN)_2$	43	103
Methyl n-propyl ketone	Triton B	15	2	$NCCH_2CH_2CH_2COC(C_2H_5)(CH_2CH_2CN)_2$	—	103
Methyl isobutyl ketone	KOH	5–10	2	$CH_3COC(CH_2CH_2CN)_2CH(CH_3)_2$	20	103
Methyl n-amyl ketone	KOH	5–10	2	$CH_3COC(CH_2CH_2CN)_2C_4H_9$	50	103
Methyl n-hexyl ketone	KOH	5–10		$CH_3COC(CH_2CH_2CN)_2C_5H_{11}$	50	103
Diethyl ketone	Triton B	30	24	2,4,4-tris(β-Cyanoethyl)-3-pentanone	—	103

TABLE X—*Continued*

CYANOETHYLATION OF ALDEHYDES AND KETONES

Compound	Catalyst	Temp. °C.	Time Hr.	Product	Yield %	Reference
Diisopropyl ketone	Triton B	25	2	$(CH_3)_2CHCOC(CH_3)_2CH_2CH_2CN$	40	107
Acetonylacetone	Triton B	25	20	$NCCH_2CH_2(CH_3)_2CCOC(CH_3)_2CH_2CH_2CN$	—	107
				$CH_3COC(CH_2CH_2CN)_2$	11	107
Mesityl oxide	Triton B	5–10	2	$CH_3COC(CH_2CH_2CN)_2$	10–15	33
				$(CH_3)_2C{=}C(CH_2CH_2CN)COCH_3$	73.5	33
Phorone	Triton B	25	20	$CH_2{=}C(CH_3)C(CH_2CH_2CN)_2COCH_3$	24	107
				Mono-cyanoethyl derivative	10	—
				Di-cyanoethyl derivative		
Methyl benzyl ketone	Triton B	20–25	1	$CH_3COC(C_6H_5)(CH_2CH_2CN)_2$	86	103
Desoxybenzoin	Triton B	45	3	$C_6H_5COC(C_6H_5)(CH_2CH_2CN)_2$	95	103
2-Acetylcyclopentanone	Triton B	30	24	2-(β-Cyanoethyl)-2-acetylcyclopentanone	67	32
2-Propionylcyclopentanone	Triton B	30	24	2-(β-Cyanoethyl)-2-propionylcyclopentanone	85	32
2-Butyrylcyclopentanone	Triton B	30	24	2-(β-Cyanoethyl)-2-butyrylcyclopentanone	83	32
2-Acetylcyclohexanone	KOH	30	24	2-(β-Cyanoethyl)-2-acetylcyclohexanone	67.4	32
2-Propionylcyclohexanone	Triton B	30	24	2-(β-Cyanoethyl)-2-propionylcyclohexanone	71	32
Acetophenone	Triton B	25–40	2–4	$C_6H_5COC(CH_2CH_2CN)_3$	57	103
Propiophenone	Triton B	25–30	5	$C_6H_5COC(CH_2CH_2CN)_2CH_3$	95	103
p-Methylacetophenone	Triton B	25–30	2–4	$p\text{-}CH_3C_6H_4COC(CH_2CH_2CN)_3$	90	103
p-Chloroacetophenone	Triton B	25–30	2–4	$p\text{-}ClC_6H_4COC(CH_2CH_2CN)_3$	90	103
p-Bromoacetophenone	Triton B	25–30	2–4	$p\text{-}BrC_6H_4COC(CH_2CH_2CN)_3$	85	103
p-Methoxyacetophenone	Triton B	25–30	2–4	$p\text{-}CH_3OC_6H_4COC(CH_2CH_2CN)_3$	80	103
Acetomesitylene	Triton B	25–30	2–4	$2,4,6\text{-}(CH_3)_3C_6H_2COC(CH_2CH_2CN)_3$	30	103
p-Acetylbiphenyl	Triton B	25–30	2–4	$C_6H_5C_6H_4COC(CH_2CH_2CN)_3$	90	103
2-Acetylnaphthalene	Triton B	25–30	2–4	$C_{10}H_7COC(CH_2CH_2CN)_3$	90	103

Compound	Catalyst	Temp.	Time	Product	Yield %	Ref.
Cyclopentanone	Triton B	35–40	18	2,2,5,5-Tetra(β-cyanoethyl)cyclopentanone	97	103
Cyclohexanone	Na	40		2,2,6,6-Tetra(β-cyanoethyl)cyclohexanone	84	106
Cyclohexanone	Triton B	35–40	18	2-(β-Cyanoethyl)cyclohexanone	10	103
Cyclohexanone	Triton B	35–40	18	Di(β-cyanoethyl)cyclohexanone		103
Cyclohexanone	KOH	35–40	18	2,2,6,6-Tetra(β-cyanoethyl)cyclohexanone	88	103
4-Methylcyclohexanone	KOH	35–40	18	2,2,6,6-Tetra(β-cyanoethyl)-4-methylcyclohexanone	80	103
4-tert-Amylcyclohexanone	KOH	35–40	18	2,2,6,6-Tetra(β-cyanoethyl)-4-tert-amylcyclohexanone	80	103
4-tert-Octylcyclohexanone	KOH	35–40	18	2,2,6,6-Tetra(β-cyanoethyl)-4-tert-octylcyclohexanone	80	103
4-Cyclohexylcyclohexanone	KOH	35–40	18	2,2,6,6-Tetra(β-cyanoethyl)-4-cyclohexylcyclohexanone	80	103
α-Tetralone	Triton B	30	24	2,2-Di(β-cyanoethyl)-1-tetralone		103
2-Methylcyclohexanone	Triton B	30	18	2,6-Tri(β-cyanoethyl)-6-methylcyclohexanone		103
2-Cyclohexenylcyclohexanone	Triton B	30	2	2-(β-Cyanoethyl)-2-cyclohexenylcyclohexanone	47.6	36
2-(β-Cyanoethyl)-2-cyclohexenylcyclohexanone	Triton B	30	10	2,6,6-Tri(β-cyanoethyl)-2-cyclohexenylcyclohexanone	55	36
2,2,5,5-Tetramethyltetrahydrofuran-3-one	Triton B	25	3	4,4-Di(β-cyanoethyl)-2,2,5,5-tetramethyltetrahydrofuran-3-one	71	103
2-Acetylfuran	Triton B	30	18	Tri(β-cyanoethyl)-2-acetylfuran	90	36
2-Propionylfuran	Triton B	30	24	γ-Furoyl-γ-methylpimelonitrile	90	36
2-Butyrylfuran	Triton B	30	24	γ-Furoyl-γ-ethylpimelonitrile	68	36
2-Acetylthiophene	Triton B	30	2	1,1,1-Tri(β-cyanoethyl)methyl 2-thienyl ketone	87.7	36
2-Propionylthiophene	Triton B	30	24	γ-Methyl-γ-thenoylpimelonitrile	98	36
Methyl acetoacetate	NaOCH₃	40	2	$CH_3COCH(CH_2CH_2CN)CO_2CH_3$		107
Methyl acetoacetate	Triton B	30–40	1	$CH_3COC(CH_2CH_2CN)_2CO_2CH_3$	50	103
Ethyl acetoacetate	Na	60	6	$CH_3COC(CH_2CH_2CN)_2CO_2C_2H_5$	25	110
Acetoacetanilide	Na	45–50	2	$CH_3COC(CH_2CH_2CN)_2CONHC_6H_5$	28	110
Acetoacet-o-chloroanilide	Na	40–50	3	$CH_3COC(CH_2CH_2CN)_2CONHC_6H_4Cl$		107
Acetoacet-2,4-dichloroanilide	Na	40–45	2.5	$CH_3COC(CH_2CH_2CN)_2CONHC_6H_3Cl_2$	70	107

TABLE XI

CYANOETHYLATION OF NITRO COMPOUNDS AND DERIVATIVES OF MALONIC AND CYANOACETIC ACIDS

Compound	Catalyst	Temp. °C.	Time Hr.	Product	Yield %	Reference
Nitromethane	K_2CO_3	40	2	$O_2NC(CH_2CH_2CN)_3$	52	99
Nitromethane	Triton B	30	18	$O_2NC(CH_2CH_2CN)_3$	45	37, 102
Nitroethane	K_2CO_3	40	1	$O_2NC(CH_3)(CH_2CH_2CN)_2$	67	99
Nitroethane	Triton B	20–25	2	$CH_3CH(NO_2)CH_2CH_2CN$	—	102
1-Nitropropane	Triton B	40–45	2	$CH_3CH_2CH(NO_2)CH_2CH_2CN$	20	102
2-Nitropropane	Triton B	30	18	$(CH_3)_2C(NO_2)CH_2CH_2CN$	90	102
2-Nitropropane	NaOH	—	—	$(CH_3)_2C(NO_2)CH_2CH_2CN$	—	100
Nitrocyclohexane	NaOH	—	—	1-Nitro-1-(β-cyanoethyl)cyclohexane	—	100, 102
α-Methoxy-β-nitropropylbenzene	NaOH	—	—	$C_6H_5CH\!-\!CH(NO_2)CH_2CH_2CN$ OCH_3CH_3	—	100
9-Nitroanthrone	Triton B	30	48	9-Nitro-9-(β-cyanoethyl)anthrone	77	102
Ethyl malonate	Na	30–40	12	$(C_2H_5O_2C)_2CHCH_2CH_2CN$	42	110
Ethyl malonate	Na	30–40	12	$(C_2H_5O_2C)_2C(CH_2CH_2CN)_2$	10	110
Ethyl malonate	Triton B	30	2	$(C_2H_5O_2C)_2C(CH_2CH_2CN)_2$	82.5	37
Ethyl malonate	$NaOC_2H_5$	65	4	$(C_2H_5O_2C)_2CHCH_2CH_2CN$	40–45	120
Ethyl cyanoacetate	Na	40	2	$C_2H_5O_2CC(CN)(CH_2CH_2CN)_2$	—	110
Ethyl cyanoacetate	Triton B	30	1	$C_2H_5O_2CC(CN)(CH_2CH_2CN)_2$	97	37
Cyanoacetamide	Triton B	30	1	$H_2NOCC(CN)(CH_2CH_2CN)_2$	74	37
Malonamide	Triton B	35–40	1	$(H_2NOC)_2C(CH_2CH_2CN)_2$	13	37
Ethyl ethylmalonate	Triton B	30	5	$(C_2H_5O_2C)_2C(C_2H_5)CH_2CH_2CN$	79	37
Ethyl n-butylmalonate	Triton B	30	6	$(C_2H_5O_2C)_2C(C_4H_9)CH_2CH_2CN$	60	37
Ethyl cyclopentylmalonate	$NaOC_2H_5$	50	2	$(C_2H_5O_2C)_2C(C_5H_9)CH_2CH_2CN$	60	119
Ethyl benzylmalonate	Triton B	30	3	$(C_2H_5O_2C)_2C(CH_2C_6H_5)CH_2CH_2CN$	78	37

TABLE XII

CYANOETHYLATION OF ARYLACETONITRILES AND UNSATURATED NITRILES

Compound	Catalyst	Product	Yield %	Refer-ence
Benzyl cyanide	NaOC$_2$H$_5$	C$_6$H$_5$CH(CN)CH$_2$CH$_2$CN	20–33	42
Benzyl cyanide	KOH	C$_6$H$_5$C(CN)(CH$_2$CH$_2$CN)$_2$	94	37, 121
Benzyl cyanide	Na	C$_6$H$_5$C(CN)(CH$_2$CH$_2$CN)$_2$	78.5	110
p-Nitrobenzyl cyanide	Triton B	O$_2$NC$_6$H$_4$C(CN)(CH$_2$CH$_2$CN)$_2$	91	37
p-Chlorobenzyl cyanide	KOH	ClC$_6$H$_4$C(CN)(CH$_2$CH$_2$CN)$_2$	80	122
p-Isopropylbenzyl cyanide	KOH	(CH$_3$)$_2$CHC$_6$H$_4$C(CN)(CH$_2$CH$_2$CN)$_2$	—	122
α-Naphthylacetonitrile	KOH	C$_{10}$H$_7$C(CN)(CH$_2$CH$_2$CN)$_2$	55	122
Crotononitrile	Triton B	α-Ethylideneglutaronitrile	15	33, 123
Crotononitrile	Triton B	γ-Cyano-γ-vinylpimelonitrile	20	33, 123
Allyl cyanide	Triton B	α-Ethylideneglutaronitrile	11	33, 123
Allyl cyanide	Triton B	γ-Cyano-γ-vinylpimelonitrile	33	33, 123
β-Methylcrotononitrile	Triton B	α-Isopropylideneglutaronitrile	—	33, 123
β-Methylcrotononitrile	Triton B	γ-Cyano-γ-isopropenylpimelonitrile	—	33, 123
Cyclohexylideneacetonitrile	Triton B	α,α-Di(2-cyanoethyl)cyclohexenyl-acetonitrile	38	33, 123

TABLE XIII

MISCELLANEOUS CYANOETHYLATIONS

Compound	Catalyst	Product	Yield %	Refer-ence
Cyclopentadiene	Triton B	1,1,2,3,4,5-Hexa(β-cyanoethyl)cyclopentadiene	20–30	124, 125
Indene	Triton B	Tri(β-cyanoethyl)indene	35	124, 125
Fluorene	Triton B	9,9-Di(β-cyanoethyl)fluorene	74	124, 125
Anthrone	Triton B	9,9-Di(β-cyanoethyl)anthrone	88	124, 125
2-Nitrofluorene	Triton B	9,9-Di(β-cyanoethyl)-2-nitrofluorene	70	124
ω,ω-Dimethylbenzofulvene	Triton B	β-Cyanoethyl dimethylbenzofulvene	25	124
Chloroform	Triton B	Cl$_3$CCH$_2$CH$_2$CN	11	95
Bromoform	Triton B	Br$_3$CCH$_2$CH$_2$CN	—	95
Benzyl phenyl sulfone	Triton B	C$_6$H$_5$SO$_2$C(C$_6$H$_5$)(CH$_2$CH$_2$CN)$_2$	60	36
p-Methylphenyl allyl sulfone	Triton B	CH$_3$C$_6$H$_4$SO$_2$CH(CH=CH$_2$)CH$_2$CH$_2$CN	—	97
p-Methylphenyl allyl sulfone	Triton B	CH$_3$C$_6$H$_4$SO$_2$C(CH=CH$_2$)(CH$_2$CH$_2$CN)$_2$	—	97
Ethyl p-methylphenyl-sulfonylacetate	KOH	CH$_3$C$_6$H$_4$SO$_2$C(CO$_2$C$_2$H$_5$)(CH$_2$CH$_2$CN)$_2$	—	97
Water	NaOH	NCCH$_2$CH$_2$OCH$_2$CH$_2$CN	45	39, 40
Hydrogen cyanide	Ca(OH)$_2$	NCCH$_2$CH$_2$CN	79	92
Phenylarsine	KOH	C$_6$H$_5$As(CH$_2$CH$_2$CN)$_2$	—	85
p-Aminophenylarsine	KOH	H$_2$NC$_6$H$_4$As(CH$_2$CH$_2$CN)$_2$	—	85
Diphenylarsine	KOH	(C$_6$H$_5$)$_2$AsCH$_2$CH$_2$CN	—	86

CHAPTER 3

THE DIELS-ALDER REACTION
QUINONES AND OTHER CYCLENONES

Lewis W. Butz

Bureau of Animal Industry,
*United States Department of Agriculture **

AND

Anton W. Rytina

Resinous Products Division, Rohm and Haas Company, Inc.

CONTENTS

* Present address, Chemistry Branch, Office of Naval Research.

INTRODUCTION

In addition to the dienophiles already discussed in Chapters 1 and 2 of Volume IV of *Organic Reactions*, quinones and other cyclenones react by 1,4-addition with conjugated dienes. A typical example is the reaction of butadiene with p-benzoquinone yielding the diketohexahydronaphthalene I.[1,2]

By means of reactions of this type it is possible to prepare cycloölefinic ketones containing two or more fused rings. The reactions are especially useful for the preparation of fused-ring ketones containing cyclopentane rings fused to cyclohexane rings; for example, 1,4-naphthoquinone and 1,1'-bicyclopentenyl yield the pentacyclic product II.[3]

The diene synthesis with quinones and other cyclenones may be extended to provide a route to the preparation of fused-ring aromatic

[1] Hopff and Rautenstrauch, U. S. pat. 2,262,002 [*C.A.*, **36**, 1046 (1942)].
[2] I.G. Farbenind. A.-G., Swiss pat. 143,258 (*Chem. Zentr.*, **1931**, I, 2937).
[3] Barnett and Lawrence, *J. Chem. Soc.*, **1935**, 1104.

systems. The primary adducts are usually hydroaromatic systems which may be converted to aromatic compounds by dehydrogenation accompanied by enolization. Aromatization may often be effected directly by carrying out the reactions at higher temperatures in an appropriate solvent such as nitrobenzene.

It is also possible to prepare fused-ring ketones containing angular substituents. The di- adduct III from butadiene and 2,5-dimethyl-1,4-benzoquinone contains two angular methyl groups.[4] The mono- adducts

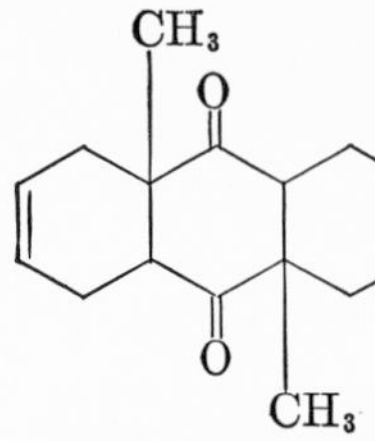

$$\text{CH}_3$$

III

from dienes and disubstituted p-benzoquinones with dissimilar substituents in the 2,5- or 2,6-positions present a special problem since they may each give rise to the two angular substituted products shown in the following general equations. It is impossible to predict the course

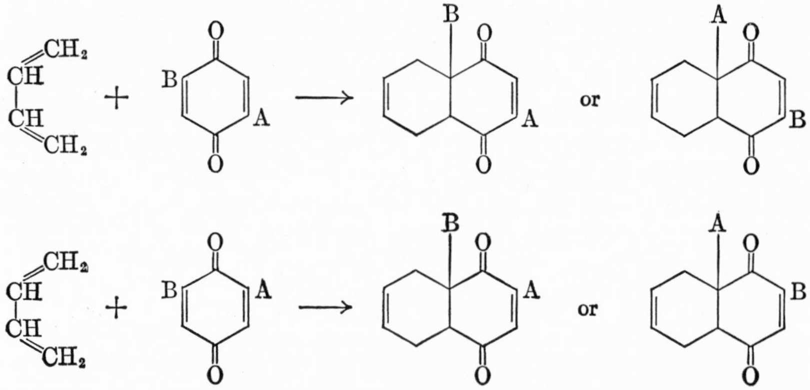

of additions of this type as the directing influences are imperfectly understood (see pp. 145–146).

Diene syntheses of the type described in this chapter may lead to the synthesis of compounds of steroidal structure. The reaction between 6-methoxy-1-vinyl-3,4-dihydronaphthalene and 1-methylcyclopentene-

[4] Adler, *Arkiv Kemi Mineral. Geol.*, **11B**, 49 (1935) [*C.A.*, **29**, 4004 (1935)].

4,5-dione furnishes a product which is believed to be IV or IVA.[5,6] The

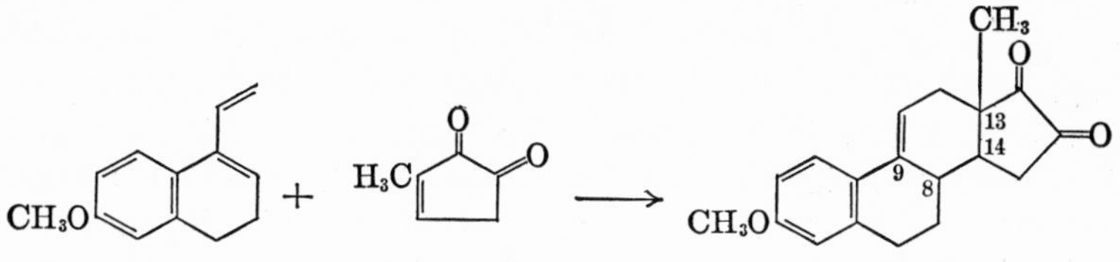

CH_3O + H_3C $\longrightarrow$ CH_3O

IV

or

CH_3O

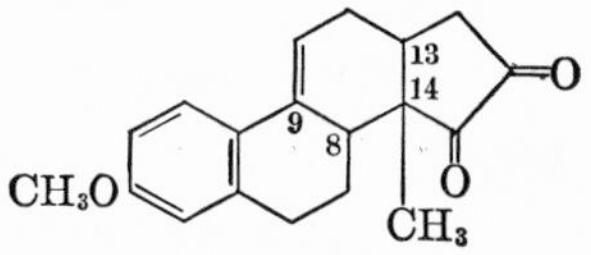

IVA

structure of the product is said to differ from that of the naturally occurring steroids only in the steric arrangements at ring junctions C8–C9 and C13–C14. However, the existence of a steroidal skeleton has not been proved and no choice between IV or IVA has been given so that this method offers promise rather than present utility.

The stereochemical configuration of Diels-Alder addition products has been discussed in Chapters 1 and 2 of Volume IV. This problem becomes exceedingly complex with products of the type discussed in this chapter, and it is virtually impossible to predict the stereochemical configurations of the adducts with any certainty. Even in the simpler situation described above in which several structural isomers may be obtained, the directing influences are imperfectly understood.[7]

Much of the experimental work connected with cyclenone additions is found only in the patent literature, and interested readers will find it necessary to consult the original patents for details.

SCOPE AND LIMITATIONS

The cyclenones which have been successfully employed in the Diels-Alder reaction include p-benzoquinone (Table I), mono-, di-, and trisubstituted p-benzoquinones (Tables II and III), o-quinones (Table IV), 1,4-naphthoquinone (Table V), substituted 1,4-naphthoquinones including 5,6,11,12-naphthacenediquinone (Table VI), mono- and di-keto derivatives of cyclopentene and cyclohexene (Table VII), and coumarin

[5] Dane and Schmitt, *Ann.*, **536**, 196 (1938).
[6] Dane and Schmitt, *Ann.*, **537**, 246 (1939).
[7] Orchin and Butz, *J. Org. Chem.*, **8**, 509 (1943).

(Table VII). The reactions of these cyclenones will be discussed in the order in which the cyclenones have just been mentioned. Under each cyclenone the various dienes will be considered in order of increasing complexity.

Diels-Alder additions to cyclenones have been run in a variety of solvents or in the absence of a solvent. Most of the reactions take place at atmospheric pressure; a few are carried out in bomb tubes. With many of the p-benzoquinones two moles of the diene can be added to one mole of the quinone. Generally, the addition of a second mole of diene requires higher temperatures and longer reaction times. When oxidizing solvents, such as nitrobenzene, are employed the adducts are frequently dehydrogenated

Diene Additions to p-Benzoquinone (Table I)

Four types of dienes add to p-benzoquinone: simple open-chain dienes, such as butadiene and 2,3-dimethylbutadiene; monocyclic dienes, such as cyclopentadiene and 1-vinylcyclohexene; dicyclic dienes, such as 1,1'-bicyclopentenyl; and fused-ring dienes, such as 4-vinyl-1,2-dihydronaphthalene and anthracene.

Butadiene reacts with p-benzoquinone in equimolar proportions to yield 1,4-diketo-1,4,4a,5,8,8a-hexahydronaphthalene (I).[1,2,8,9] Two moles of butadiene add to one mole of p-benzoquinone to give the diketodecahydroanthracene (V).[8] 2,3-Dimethylbutadiene and p-benzo-

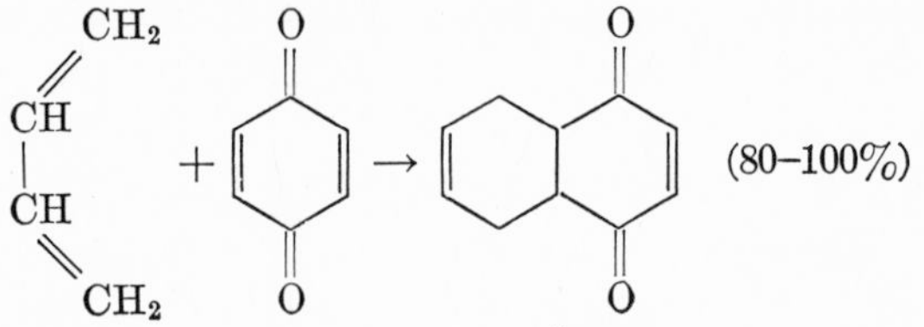

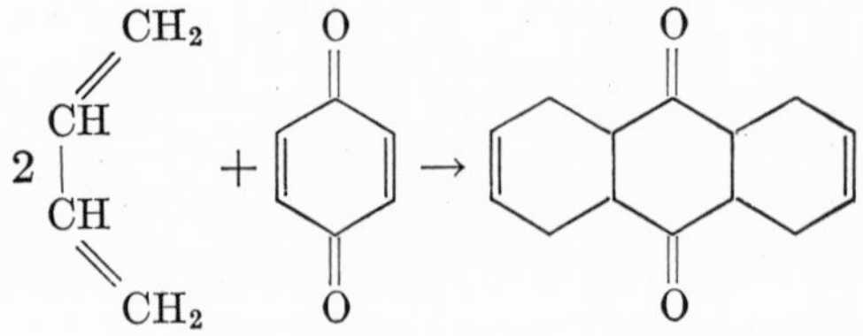

[8] Alder and Stein, *Ann.*, **501**, 247 (1933).
[9] Alder and Stein, *Angew. Chem.*, **50**, 510 (1937).

quinone react similarly to yield the mono- adduct (VI) nearly quantitatively [1] and the di- adduct (VII) in 60% yield.[10] When the formation of the di- adduct is attempted in nitrobenzene at 150°, dehydrogenation to the corresponding 9,10-anthraquinone takes place.[11] Two moles of

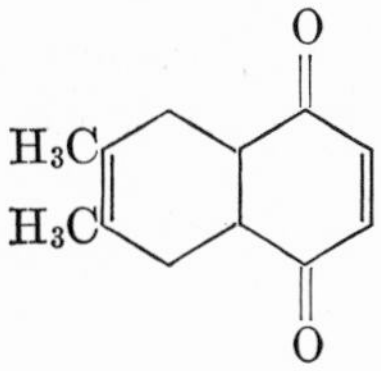

VI 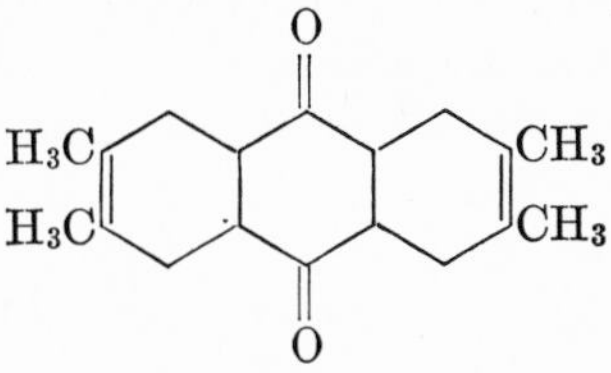   VII

1-phenylbutadiene and one mole of p-benzoquinone react to form a mixture of the mono- (VIII) and di- adducts (IX); [12] the structure of the di- adduct is very probably that given. At high temperature in nitrobenzene dehydrogenation takes place and X is formed in 39% yield.[13]

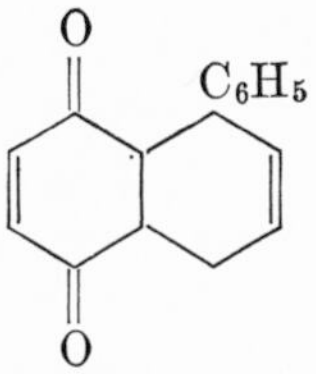

VIII 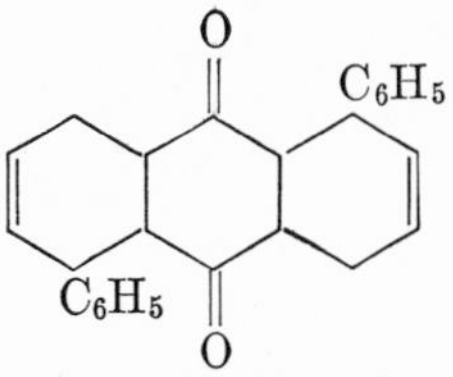   IX 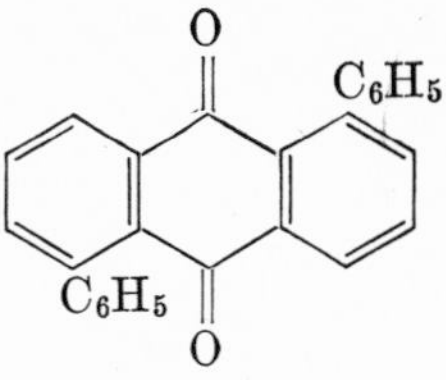   X

Equimolar quantities of cyclopentadiene and p-benzoquinone react in various solvents to form the expected adduct XI.[14, 15] At the melting

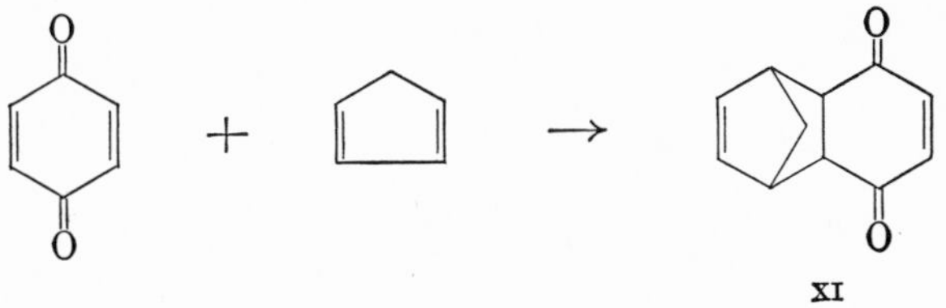

XI

point (157°) the adduct decomposes into the starting materials. In boiling acetic anhydride a similar decomposition occurs, but several other products are formed from the interaction of the starting materials,

[10] Morgan and Coulson, J. Chem. Soc., **1931**, 2329.
[11] I.G. Farbenind. A.-G., Fr. pat. (addition) 39,333 [C.A., **26**, 2202 (1932)].
[12] Weizmann, Bergmann, and Haskelberg, J. Chem. Soc., **1939**, 391.
[13] Bergmann, Haskelberg, and Bergmann, J. Org. Chem., **7**, 303 (1942).
[14] Albrecht, Ann., **348**, 31 (1906).
[15] Wassermann, J. Chem. Soc., **1935**, 1511.

the adduct (XI), and acetic anhydride.[16]   Two moles of cyclopentadiene when added to one mole of p-benzoquinone yield XII quantitatively.[8,14] From a reaction mixture containing three moles of 1,3-cyclohexadiene for each mole of p-benzoquinone, the adduct XIII may be obtained.[2,16] This product, unlike XI, yields the quinol diacetate (XIV) with acetic anhydride.[16]   When a fivefold excess of 1,3-cyclohexadiene and a much longer reaction time are employed, the di-adduct XV is the product.[8]

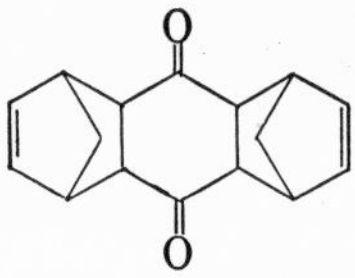

XII 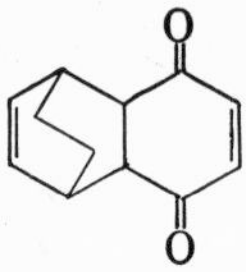   XIII 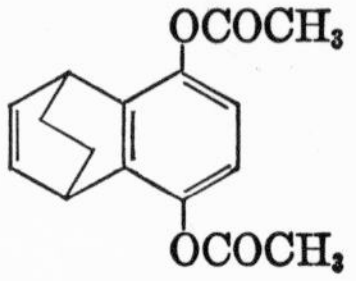   XIV 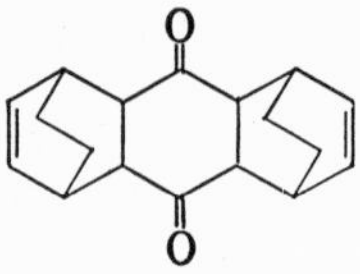   XV

The adduct XI, from cyclopentadiene and p-benzoquinone, reacts with 1,3-cyclohexadiene to yield XVI.[8]   When a 50% excess of 1-vinylcyclo-

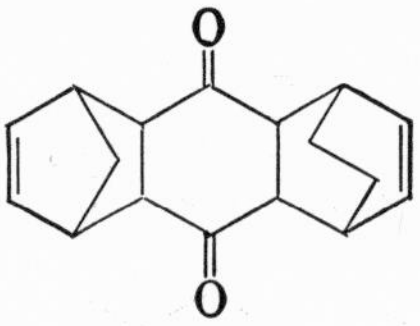

XVI

hexene adds to p-benzoquinone the adduct XVII results; at higher temperature, with a 100% excess of the diene, a 10% yield of the 1,2,5,6-dibenzhydroanthraquinone XVIII is obtained.[17]

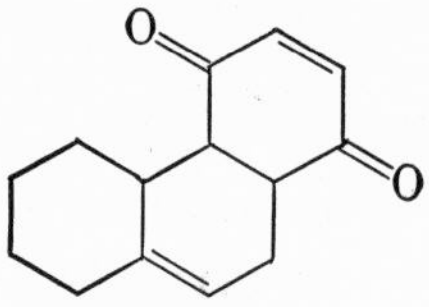

XVII 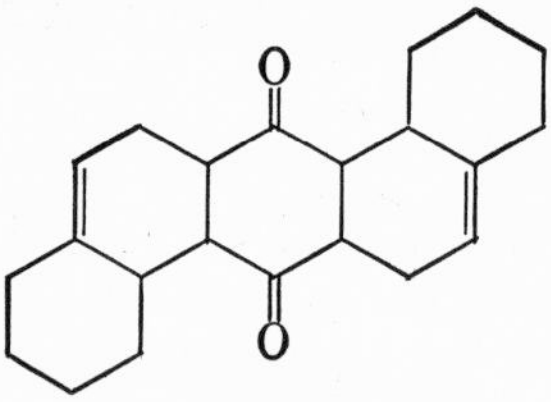   XVIII

The reaction of 1,1′-bicyclopentenyl or 1,1′-bicyclohexenyl with p-benzoquinone results in the formation of the tetracyclic products XIX [3] and XX [18,3] from one mole of diene, and the heptacyclic products, XXI [20] and XXII,[3,19,20] from two moles of diene.

[16] Diels, Alder, and Stein, Ber., **62,** 2337 (1929).
[17] Cook and Lawrence, J. Chem. Soc., **1938,** 58.
[18] Bergmann, Eschinazi, and Neeman, J. Org. Chem., **8,** 183 (1943).
[19] Weizmann, Bergmann, and Berlin, J. Am. Chem. Soc., **60,** 1331 (1938).
[20] Backer, Strating, and Huisman, Rec. trav. chim., **58,** 761 (1939).

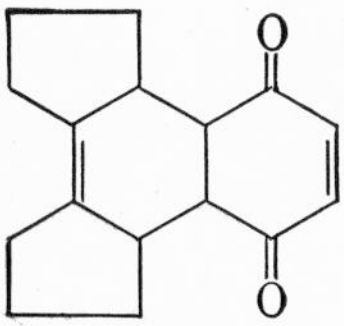

XIX

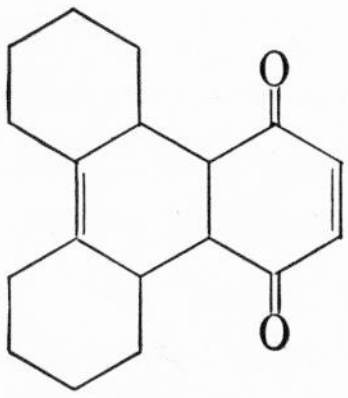

XX

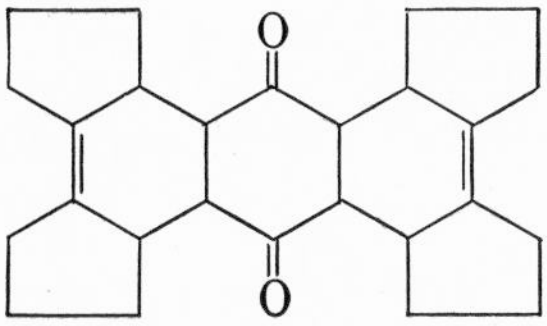

XXI

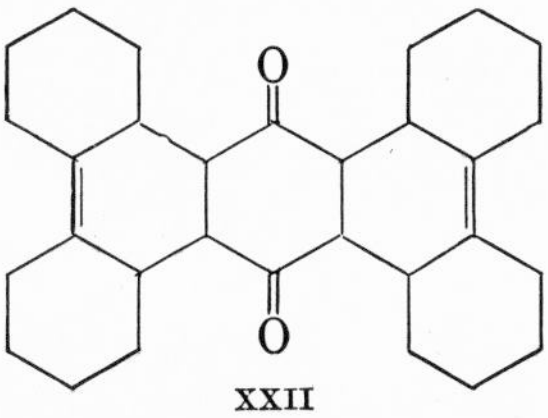

XXII

Cyclooctatetraene may be added to p-benzoquinone to obtain either the mono- (XXIII) or di-adduct (XXIV).[21] 4-Vinyl-1,2-dihydronaph-

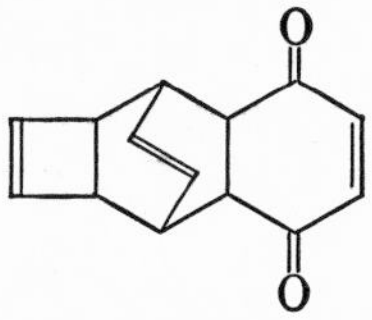

XXIII

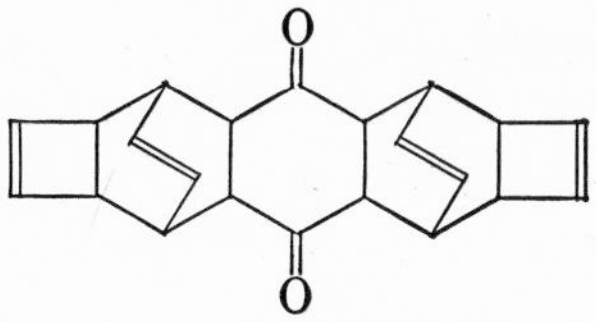

XXIV

thalene adds to p-benzoquinone, yielding what is probably the diketohydrochrysene XXV.[22] 7-Methoxy-4-vinyl-1,2-dihydronaphthalene and p-benzoquinone yield what is probably the methoxy analog XXVI.[23] The corresponding 4-ethynyl compound yields only an impure product.[23] The product from 4a-methyl-4-vinyl-1,2,4a,5,8,8a-hexahydronaphthalene and p-benzoquinone is a diketohydrochrysene (XXVII) in which the positions of the carbon-carbon double bonds have not been

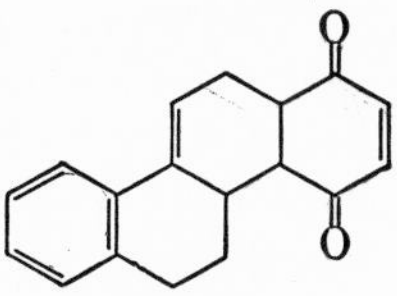

XXV

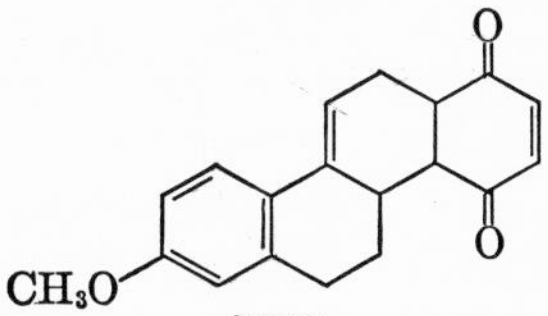

CH₃O   XXVI

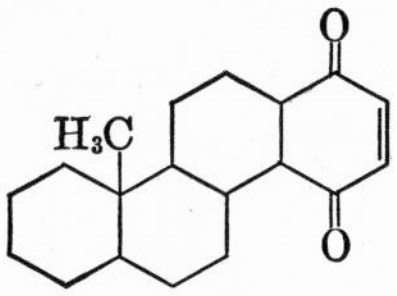

H₃C   XXVII

[21] Reppe, in *Synthetic Fiber Developments in Germany*, pp. 647, 650, 651, Textile Research Institute, Inc., New York, 1946.

[22] Dane, Höss, Bindseil, and Schmitt, *Ann.*, **532**, 42 (1937).

[23] Dane, Höss, Eder, Schmitt, and Schön, *Ann.*, **536**, 183 (1938).

established.[24]　Equimolar quantities of anthracene and p-benzoquinone furnish XXVIII in 93% yield.[25]

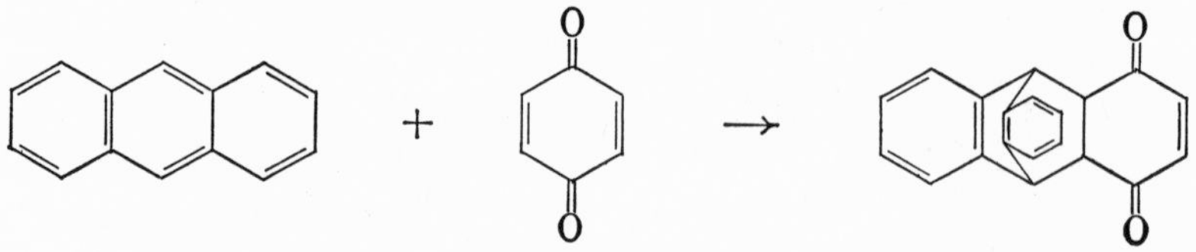

XXVIII

Diene Additions to Methyl-p-benzoquinone and Substituted Methyl-p-benzoquinones (Table II)

In carrying out Diels-Alder additions with methyl-p-benzoquinone or with substituted methyl-p-benzoquinones, use is made of solvents of the type employed with p-benzoquinone. Only simple dienes have been utilized, and, in general, greater excesses of the various dienes are used. In most reactions, temperatures below 100° are sufficient.

Excess butadiene and methyl-p-benzoquinone react to form the diketotetrahydronaphthalene XXIX.[26, 27]　1,3-Pentadiene and the same quinone furnish equal amounts of the structurally isomeric diketotetrahydronaphthalenes XXX and XXXI.[28]　At temperatures below 100°,

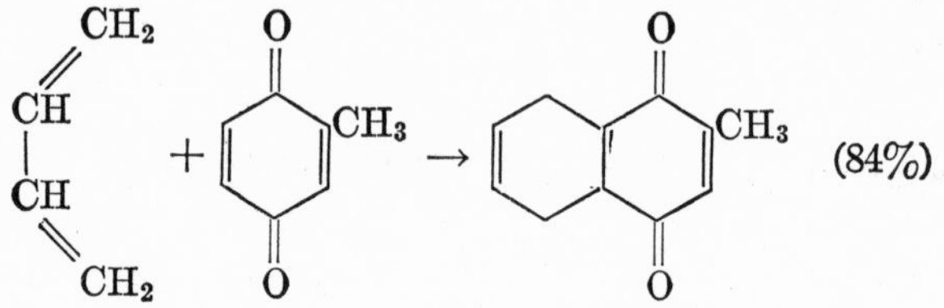

XXIX

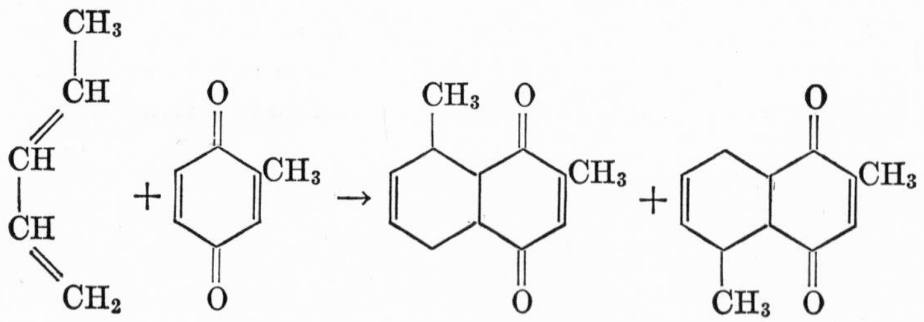

(22%)　　　　　　　(22%)
XXX　　　　　　　XXXI

[24] Gaddis and Butz, *J. Am. Chem. Soc.*, **69**, 1165 (1947).
[25] Clar, *Ber.*, **64**, 1676 (1931).
[26] Fieser and Chang, *J. Am. Chem. Soc.*, **64**, 2048 (1942).
[27] Chuang and Han, *Ber.*, **68**, 876 (1935).
[28] Tishler, Fieser, and Wendler, *J. Am. Chem. Soc.*, **62**, 2870 (1940).

excess 2,3-dimethylbutadiene and methyl-p-benzoquinone form XXXII, but at 150–170° the partially aromatized product XXXIII is obtained by a hydrogen shift.[29]

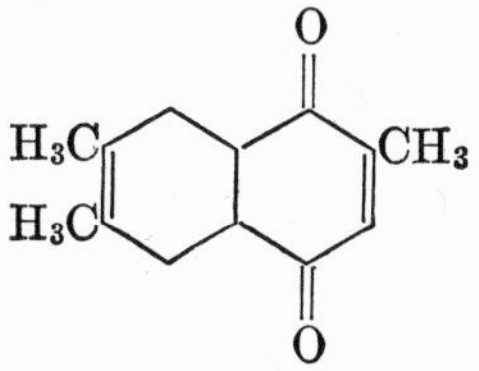

XXXII 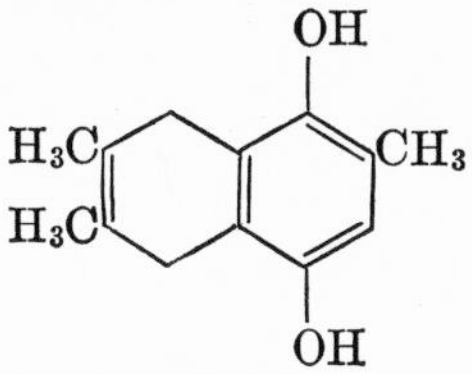   XXXIII

Butadiene,[30] 2,3-dimethylbutadiene,[30] and 1,3,5-hexatriene [31] add in a 1:1 ratio to 2,5-dimethyl-1,4-benzoquinone to give the expected products, which are distillable oils; the comparable product from 1,3-cyclohexadiene is a solid.[7] 2-Methoxy-5-methyl-1,4-benzoquinone gives a 75% yield of the angular methyl derivative XXXIV with butadiene,[7] while the same diene and 2-acetoxy-5-methyl-1,4-benzoquinone give the angular acetoxy compound XXXV and the angular methyl product XXXVI (isolated as XXXVII by hydrolysis).[32, 33] 2-Carbomethoxy- and

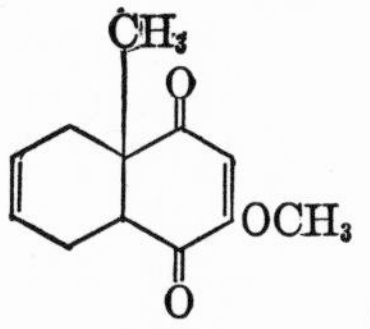

XXXIV 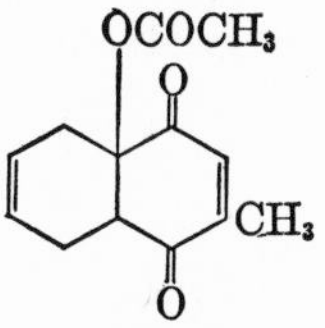   XXXV 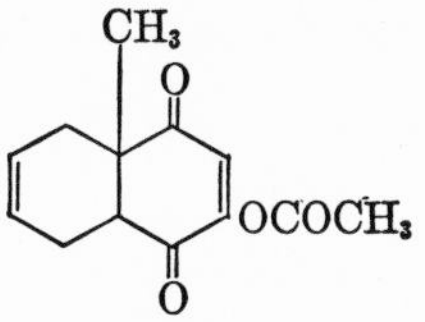   XXXVI 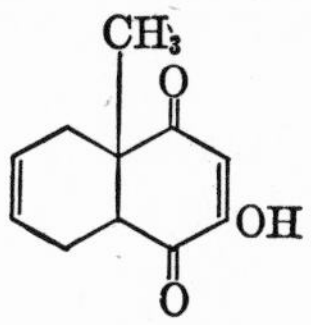   XXXVII

3-carbomethoxy-5-methyl-1,4-benzoquinone give only the angular carbomethoxy products XXXVIII and XXXIX and none of the angular methyl isomers.[34] The reaction between 1,3-cyclohexadiene and 2-acetoxy-5-methyl-1,4-benzoquinone gives three products: an angular acetate XL, a stereoisomeric angular acetate (6%), and a trace of what is probably the angular methyl derivative XLI.[33]

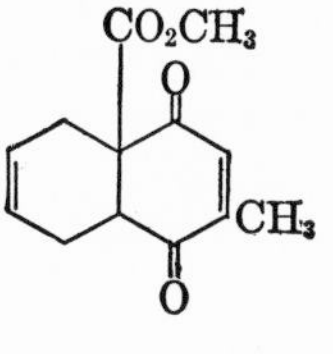

(55%)

XXXVIII   XXXIX   XL   XLI

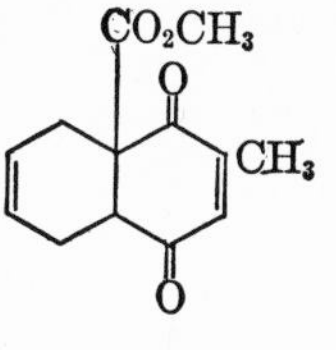

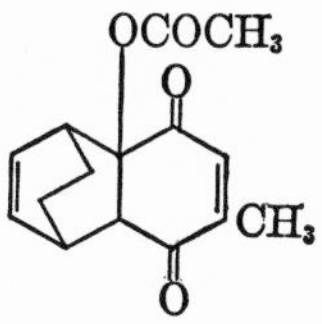

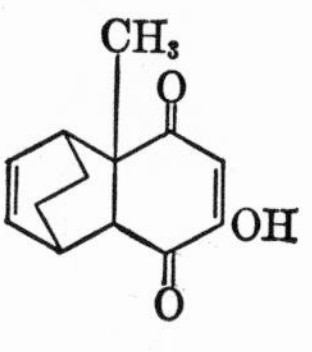

[29] Bergmann and Bergmann, *J. Org. Chem.*, **3**, 125 (1938).
[30] Fieser and Seligman, *Ber.*, **68**, 1747 (1935).
[31] L. Butz, unpublished results.
[32] Butz and Butz, *J. Org. Chem.*, **8**, 497 (1943).
[33] Butz and Butz, *J. Org. Chem.*, **7**, 199 (1942).
[34] Nudenberg, Gaddis, and Butz, *J. Org. Chem.*, **8**, 500 (1943).

2-Hydroxy-3,5-dimethyl-1,4-benzoquinone and butadiene give the angular methyl compound XLII in 100% yield.[5] This quinone and 7-methoxy-4-vinyl-1,2-dihydronaphthalene yield a single product which is probably one of the angular methyl derivatives XLIII or XLIIIA.[5]

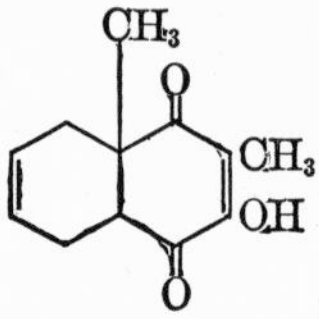

XLII 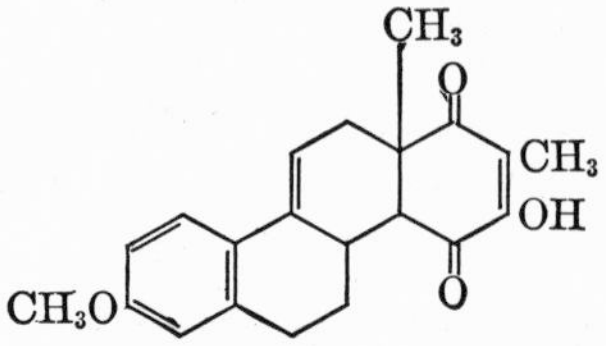   XLIII 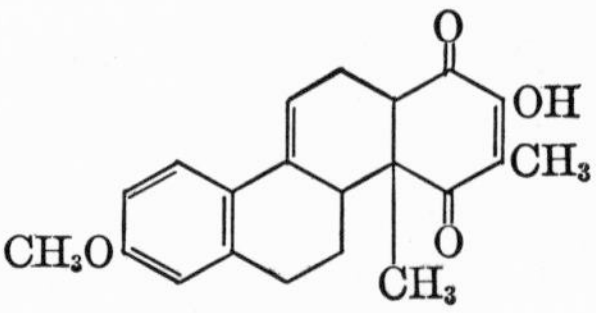   XLIIIA

Tetramethyl-p-benzoquinone and 1,3,5-hexatriene react at temperatures above 150°. The reaction is not of the Diels-Alder type; instead the quinone is reduced to the hydroquinone.[35]

Diene Additions to Substituted p-Benzoquinones Other than Methyl-p-benzoquinones (Table III)

Diene additions to these more complexly substituted p-benzoquinones are generally carried out in aromatic solvents such as benzene and xylene. The temperatures required are about the same as with the methyl-p-benzoquinones.

Excess 2,3-dimethylbutadiene (5.5 moles) reacts with 1 mole of phenyl-p-benzoquinone to yield a single product XLIV in 82% yield.[29] 1,1'-Bicyclohexenyl and phenyl-p-benzoquinone in the absence of a solvent give what is considered to be the expected adduct XLV, while in nitrobenzene the quinone XLVI is formed.[19] 2,5-Diphenyl-1,4-benzoquinone

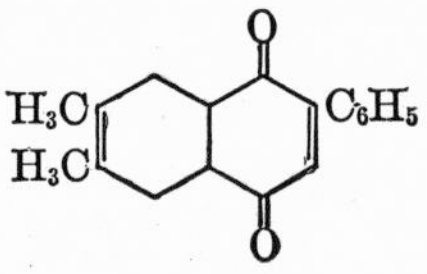

XLIV 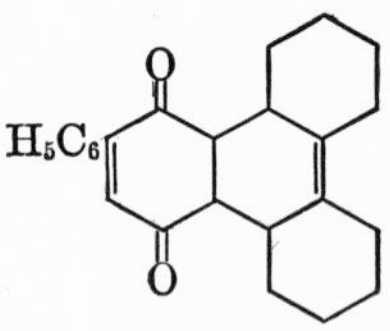   XLV 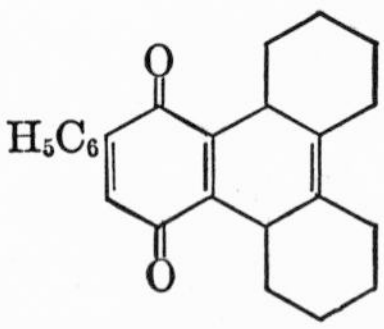   XLVI

reacts with butadiene, 2,3-dimethylbutadiene, and 1-phenylbutadiene to yield what are apparently the angular adducts XLVII, XLVIII, and XLIX in 77%, 79%, and 89% yields, respectively.[36]

[35] L. Butz and Gaddis, unpublished results.
[36] Allen, Bell, Clark, and Jones, *J. Am. Chem. Soc.*, **66**, 1617 (1944).

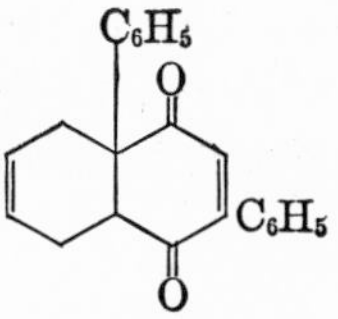

XLVII 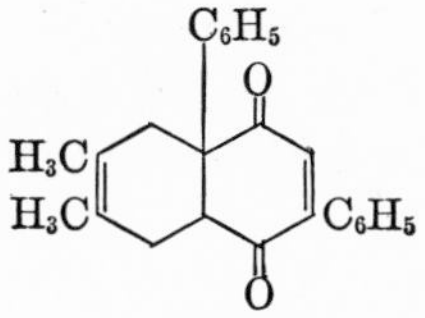 XLVIII 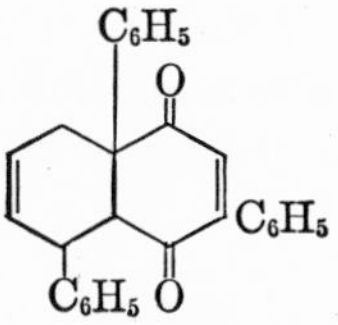 XLIX

ω-Carboxypropyl- and ω-carboxyamyl-p-benzoquinone react with butadiene to form the expected products L and LI.[37] The most striking feature of these reactions is the large diene:quinone ratio employed; 30:1 with the carboxypropyl- and 10:1 with the carboxyamyl-quinone.

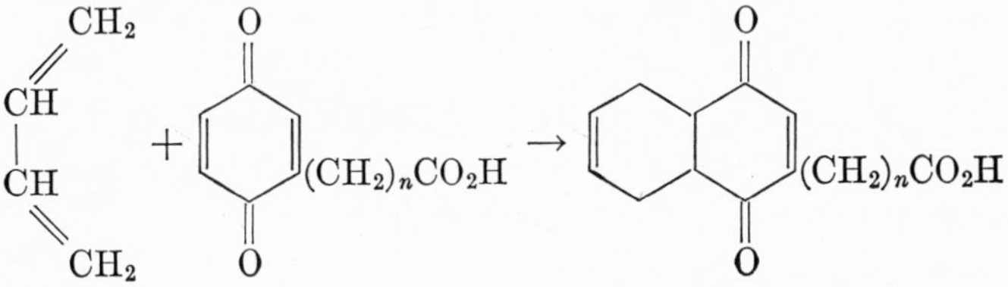

L $n = 3(86\%)$
LI $n = 5(75\%)$

Chloro-p-benzoquinone reacts with 2,3-dimethylbutadiene [38] and with 2-chlorobutadiene,[1] yielding the expected products LII and LIII. 2,3-Dichloro-1,4-benzoquinone reacts similarly with butadiene and with 2,3-dimethylbutadiene, yielding LIV and LV.[38] Diene additions to

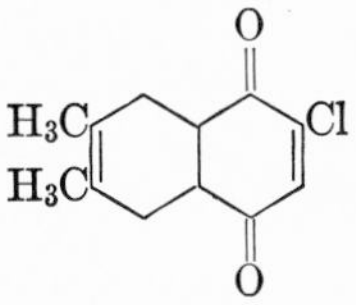

LII 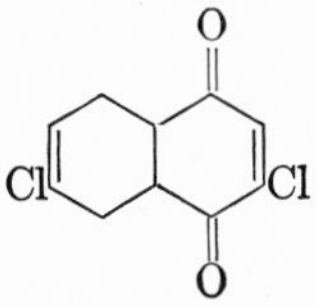 LIII 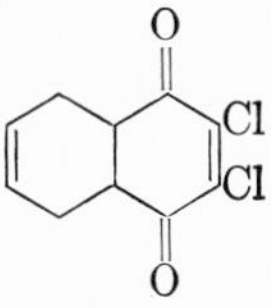 LIV 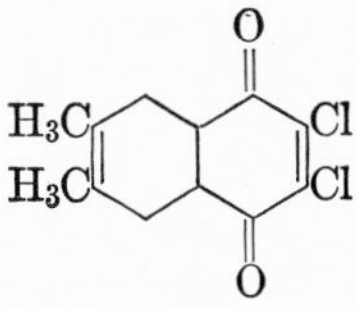 LV

tetrachloro-p-benzoquinone are accompanied by the loss of a molecule of chlorine and lead to dichloro adducts. Tetrachloro-p-benzoquinone and cyclopentadiene give a 1:1 adduct of unknown structure; [14,39] with anthracene LVI is obtained.[25] 10-Methylene-9-anthrone and tetra-

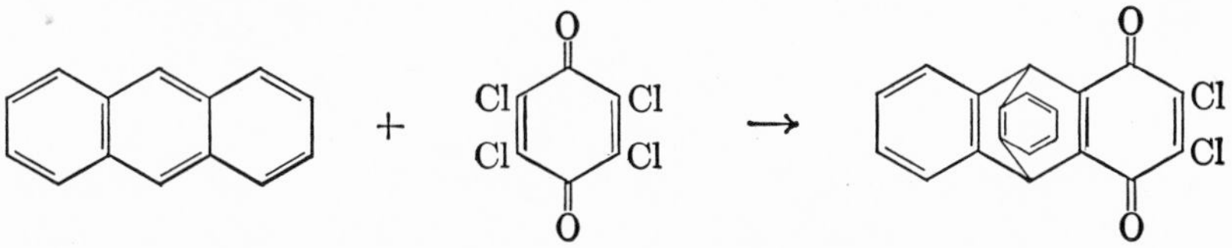

LVI

[37] Fieser, Gates, and Kilmer, *J. Am. Chem. Soc.*, **62**, 2966 (1940).
[38] I.G. Farbenind. A.-G., Fr. pat. 677,296 [*C.A.*, **24**, 3118 (1930)].
[39] Wassermann, Fr. pat. 838,454 [*C.A.*, **33**, 7818 (1939)].

chloro-p-benzoquinone in xylene give the dichloro compound LVII.   In nitrobenzene two moles of diene add, and the adduct LVIII or LVIIIA is halogen free.[40]   5,8-Dihydro-1,4-naphthoquinone and 5,6,7,8-tetra-

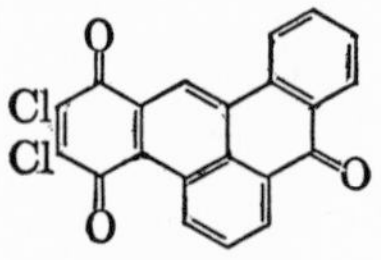

LVII 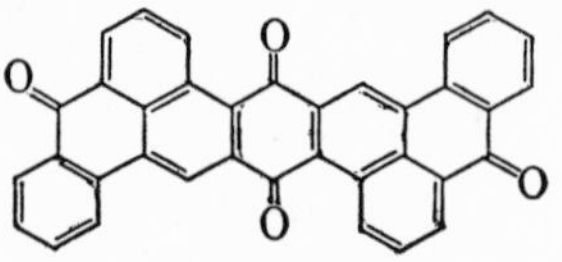   LVIII 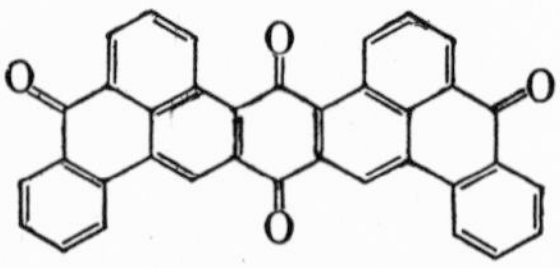   LVIIIA

hydro-1,4-naphthoquinone react with butadiene in the expected manner, yielding LIX and LX.[38, 41]

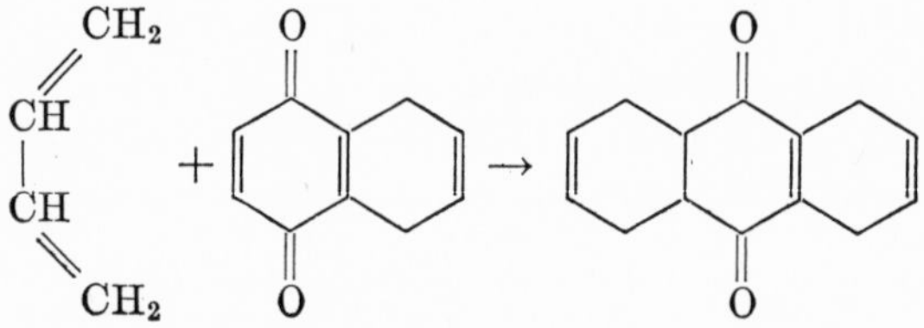

LIX

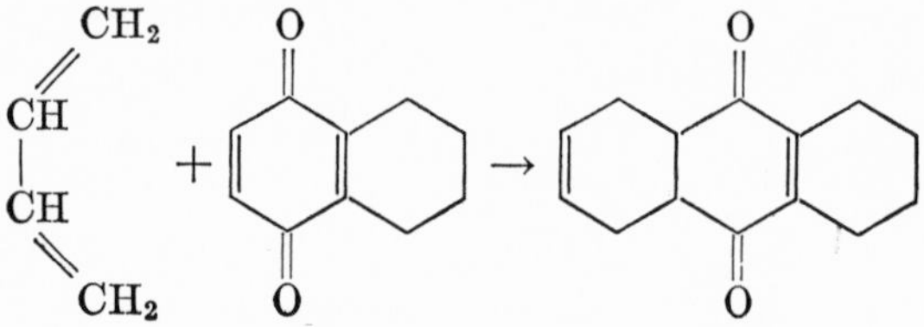

LX

Diene Additions to o-Quinones (Table IV)

Relatively few o-quinones have been utilized in Diels-Alder additions. In all the reactions for which data are available, the ratio of diene to quinone employed has been quite large (2.5:1 to 34:1).   Most of these reactions were carried out in ethanol or in chloroform.

o-Benzoquinone and cyclopentadiene give a 1:1 adduct of unknown constitution while tetramethyl-o-benzoquinone and cyclopentadiene react to form the *endo*methylene adduct LXI in 63% yield.[42]   2,3-Dimethylbutadiene and 3,7-dimethyl-1,2-naphthoquinone yield the angular methyl derivative LXII.[43, 44]

[40] Clar, *Ber.*, **69**, 1686 (1936).
[41] I.G. Farbenind. A.-G., Brit. pat. 327,128 [*C.A.*, **24**, 5045 (1930)].
[42] Smith and Hac, *J. Am. Chem. Soc.*, **58**, 229 (1936).
[43] Fieser and Seligman, *J. Am. Chem. Soc.*, **56**, 2690 (1934).
[44] Fieser and Dunn, *J. Am. Chem. Soc.*, **59**, 1021 (1937).

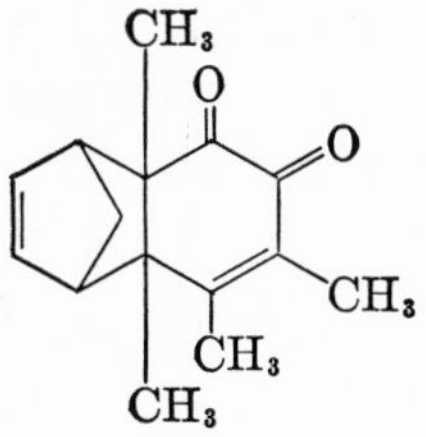

LXI 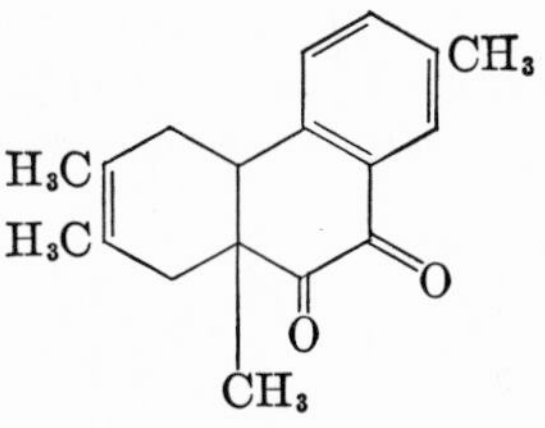   LXII

Several chloro- and bromo-1,2-naphthoquinones participate in Diels-Alder additions. With the exception of LXIII, the product from 2,3-dimethylbutadiene and 3,4-dichloro-1,2-naphthoquinone,[45] all the adducts are unstable. The adduct LXIV from 2,3-dimethylbutadiene and 3-chloro-1,2-naphthoquinone decomposes in a few hours when kept in a vacuum. When warmed with ethanolic sodium acetate it yields 2,3-dimethyl-9,10-phenanthraquinone (LXV) quantitatively.[45] The adduct

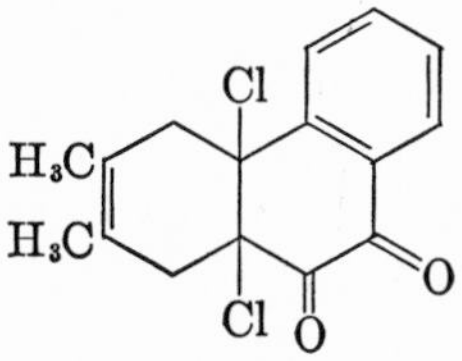

LXIII 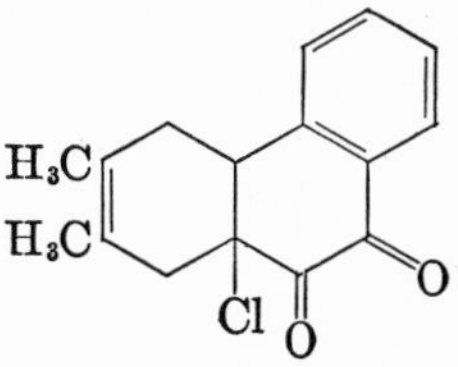   LXIV 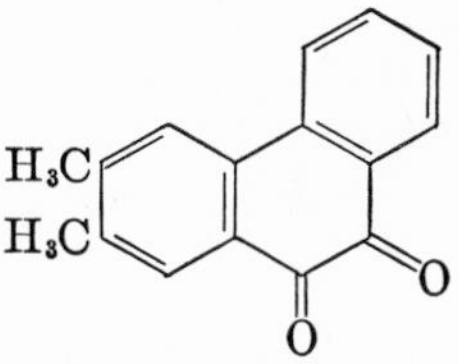   LXV

LXVI cannot be isolated from the reaction of 4-chloro-1,2-naphthoquinone and 2,3-dimethylbutadiene, but the reaction mixture yields 2,3-dimethyl-9,10-phenanthraquinone (LXV) on standing in air.[45] 6-Bromo-1,2-naphthoquinone and 2,3-dimethylbutadiene yield the nearly pure adduct LXVII which undergoes dehydrogenation on recrystallization to yield LXVIII.[45]

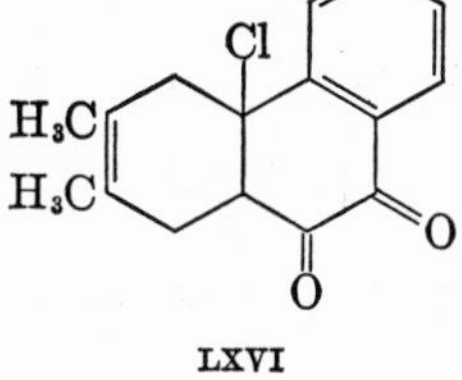

LXVI 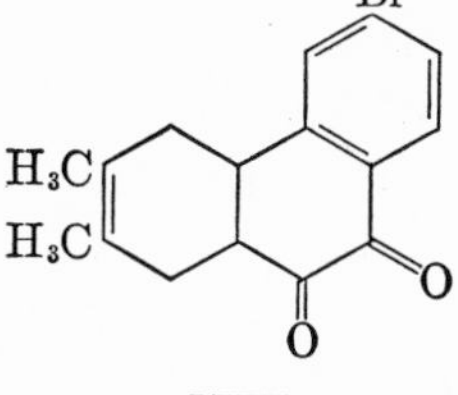   LXVII 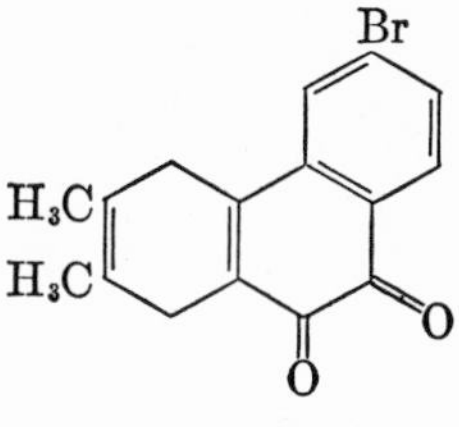   LXVIII

1,2-Phenanthraquinone with 2,3-dimethylbutadiene yields the tetracyclic product LXIX, which is also obtained from the same diene and

[45] Fieser and Dunn, *J. Am. Chem. Soc.*, **59**, 1016 (1937).

3-bromo-1,2-phenanthraquinone.[46]   2-Bromo-3,4-phenanthraquinone
and 2,3-dimethylbutadiene yield an oil which on oxidation with chromic
acid gives the quinone LXX in 90% yield.[46]

LXIX   LXX

Diene Additions to 1,4-Naphthoquinone (Table V)

A large variety of dienes add to 1,4-naphthoquinone. The addition
is limited to the double bond in the 2,3-position, and as a result only
1:1 adducts have been reported.

Butadiene adds to 1,4-naphthoquinone to yield the diketohydro-
anthracene (LXXI).[16,47,48]   2,3-Dimethylbutadiene in ethanol or in the
absence of a solvent gives the expected product LXXII; in nitrobenzene
the 9,10-anthraquinone is obtained.[11]   1-Chlorobutadiene does not
react with 1,4-naphthoquinone,[49] but 2-chlorobutadiene yields LXXIII
although considerable amounts of starting materials are recovered.[50]
2-Bromobutadiene and 1,4-naphthoquinone react in similar fashion.[51]

LXXI   LXXII   LXXIII

The 3-chloro- derivatives of pentadiene, 1,3-hexadiene, 1,3-octadiene,
and 1,3-hendecadiene yield 9,10-anthraquinones after aeration of the
adducts.[52]   2,3-Dimethoxybutadiene and 1,4-naphthoquinone react, and

[46] Fieser and Dunn, J. Am. Chem. Soc., **59**, 1024 (1937).
[47] I.G. Farbenind. A.-G., Swiss pat. 143,259 (Chem. Zentr., **1931**, I, 2937).
[48] Diels and Alder, Ann., **460**, 110 (1928).
[49] Coffman and Carothers, J. Am. Chem. Soc., **55**, 2043 (1933); Berchet and Carothers, ibid., **55**, 2004 (1933).
[50] Carothers, Williams, Collins, and Kirby, J. Am. Chem. Soc., **53**, 4206 (1931).
[51] Carothers, Collins, and Kirby, J. Am. Chem. Soc., **55**, 788 (1933).
[52] Jacobson and Carothers, J. Am. Chem. Soc., **55**, 1626 (1933).

the adduct, which has not been isolated, yields 2,3-dimethoxy-9,10-anthraquinone when treated with sodium hypochlorite.[53]

Cyclopentadiene and 1,3-cyclohexadiene add to 1,4-naphthoquinone giving LXXIV [14] and LXXV.[16] The *endo*methylene adduct LXXIV is unstable and gives 1,4-naphthohydroquinone diacetate with acetic anhydride. Air and ethanolic alkali dehydrogenate the *endo*ethylene adduct LXXV to LXXVI, which decomposes to ethylene and anthraquinone at 150°.[16] α-Chlorovinylcyclohexene and 1,4-naphthoquinone

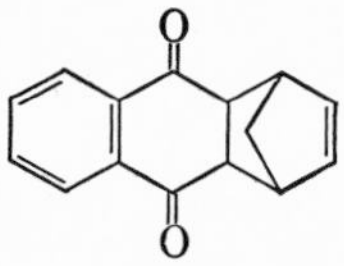

LXXIV 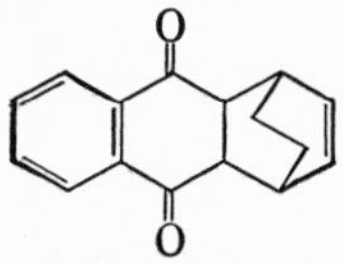   LXXV 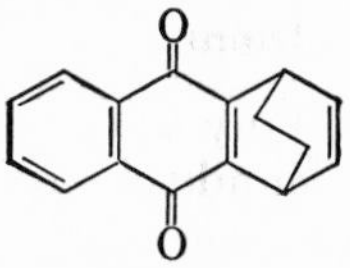   LXXVI

yield LXXVII, which can be partially dehydrogenated to yield LXXVIII.[54]

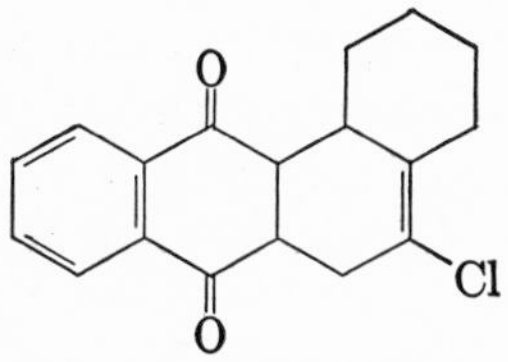

LXXVII 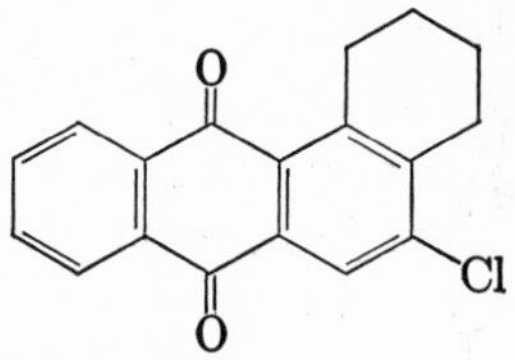   LXXVIII

1,1'-Bicyclopentenyl and 1,1'-bicyclohexenyl react with 1,4-naphtho-quinone yielding the pentacyclic products II [3] and LXXIX.[19] Cyclo-

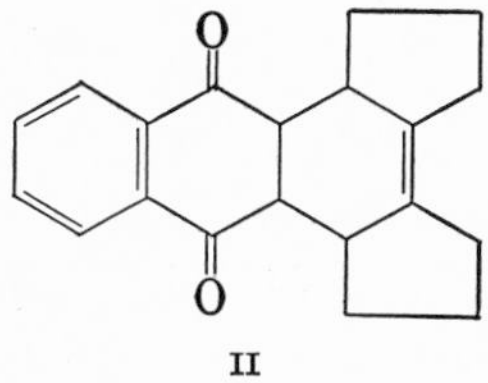

II

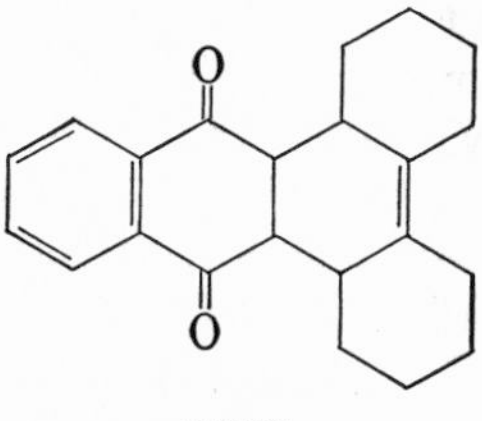

LXXIX

octatetraene and 7,8-dichlorobicyclo-[0.4.2]-octa-2,4-diene react with 1,4-naphthoquinone yielding the complex adducts LXXX and LXXXI.[21] 10-Methylene-9-anthrone and 1,4-naphthoquinone give LXXXII.[40, 55]

[53] Johnson, Jobling, and Bodamer, *J. Am. Chem. Soc.*, **63**, 131 (1941).
[54] Carothers and Coffman, *J. Am. Chem. Soc.*, **54**, 4071 (1932).
[55] I.G. Farbenind. A.-G., Ger. pat. 591,496 [*C.A.*, **28**, 2366 (1934)].

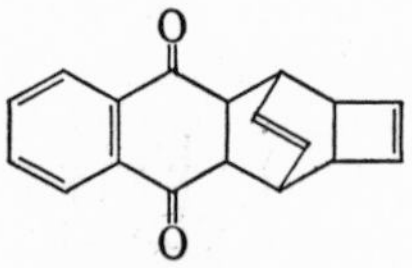

LXXX 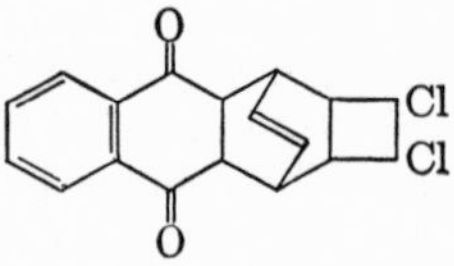   LXXXI 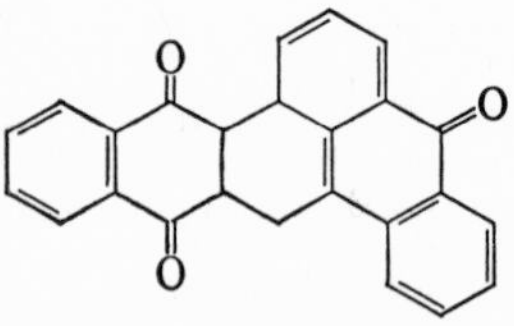   LXXXII

Tetraphenylcyclopentadienone (cyclone) and 3,4-(1,8-naphthylene)-2,5-diphenylcyclopentadienone do not react with 1,4-naphthoquinone.[56]

Diene Additions to Substituted 1,4-Naphthoquinones (Table VI)

Many substituted 1,4-naphthoquinones have been employed in Diels-Alder additions. Temperatures necessary for reaction are usually above 100°, and in all reactions solvents are employed.

2,6-Dimethyl-1,4-naphthoquinone and 2,3-dimethylbutadiene give a solid adduct LXXXIII; the reaction between 2,3-dimethyl-1,4-naphthoquinone and the same diene proceeds more slowly and yields an impure liquid.[43] 2-Chloro-1,4-naphthoquinone and butadiene give a 9,10-diketo-1,4-dihydroanthracene; with 2-methylbutadiene a 9,10-anthraquinone is the product.[57] 2,3-Dimethylbutadiene reacts with 2,3-dichloro-1,4-naphthoquinone and with 2,3-dichloro-5-nitro-1,4-naphthoquinone yielding LXXXIV and LXXXV.[57]

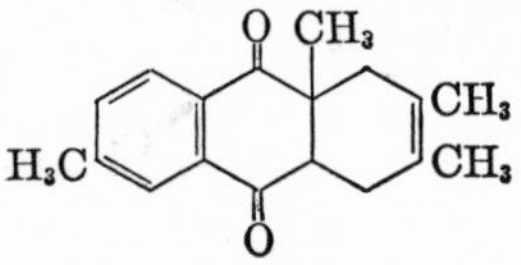

LXXXIII 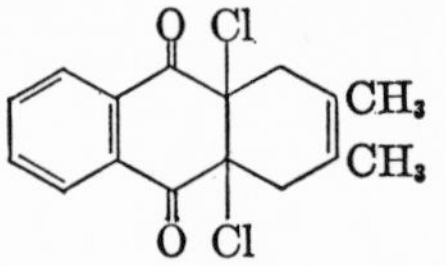   LXXXIV 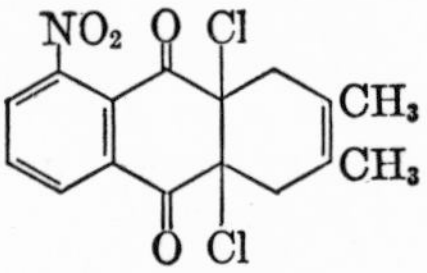   LXXXV

That 2-hydroxy-1,4-naphthoquinone reacts with 2,3-dimethylbutadiene is shown by the isolation of 2,3-dimethylanthraquinone after suitable treatment of the reaction product.[30] 5,8-Dihydroxy-1,4-naphthoquinone reacts with butadiene and 2,3-dimethylbutadiene yielding LXXXVI and LXXXVII.[57] 5,8-Diacetoxy-, 5,6,8-trihydroxy-, and

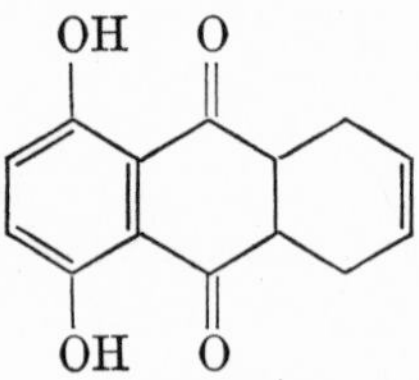

LXXXVI 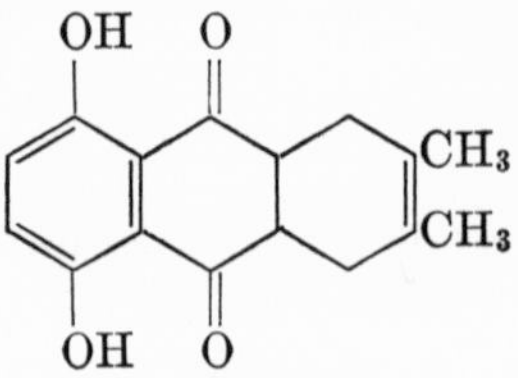   LXXXVII

[56] Arbuzov, Abramov, and Devyatov, *J. Gen. Chem. U.S.S.R.*, **9**, 1559 (1939) [*C.A.*, **34**, 2839 (1940)].
[57] I.G. Farbenind. A.-G., Brit. pat. 320,375 [*C.A.*, **24**, 2757 (1930)].

5,6,8-triacetoxy-1,4-naphthoquinone react with the simpler dienes giving the expected products (Table VI, p. 186). 5,6,11,12-Naphthacenediquinone reacts with butadiene and with 2,3-dimethylbutadiene to yield the complex adducts LXXXVIII and LXXXIX.[58]

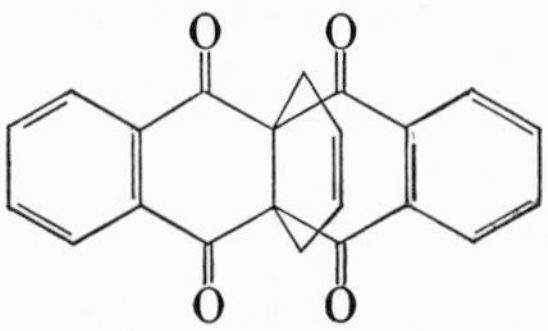

LXXXVIII 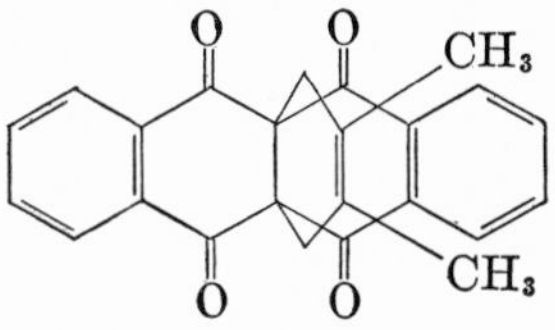   LXXXIX

Diene Additions to Cyclenones Other than Quinones (Table VII)

Many conjugated cyclenones have been used in Diels-Alder additions to yield a variety of fused-ring ketones or diketones. Generally the cyclenones require temperatures above 100° and longer periods of heating than the quinones.

Cyclopenten-3-one and butadiene react slowly yielding the bicyclic adduct XC in addition to some resinous material.[59]   1-Methylcyclo-

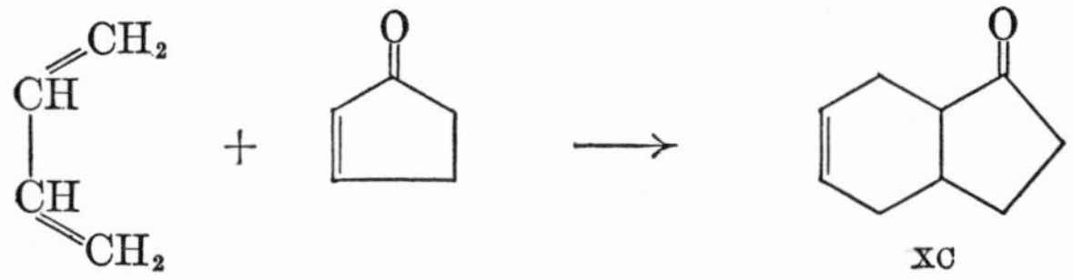

XC

penten-5-one and 2,3-dimethylbutadiene give the angular methyl product XCI in 52% yield.[60] This cyclenone also reacts with 1-vinylcyclohexene giving a 75% yield of an angular methyl derivative formulated as XCII or XCIIA.[60] 4a-Methyl-4-vinyl-1,2,4a,5,8,8a-hexahydronaph-

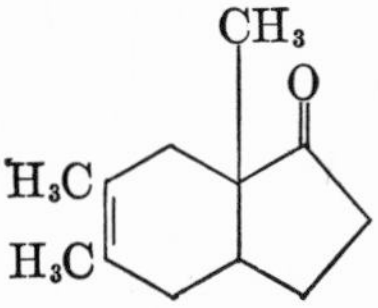

XCI 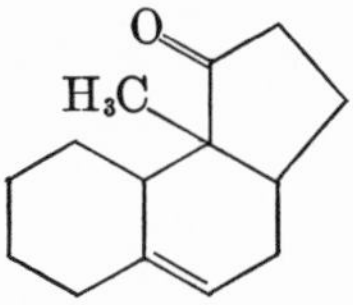   XCII 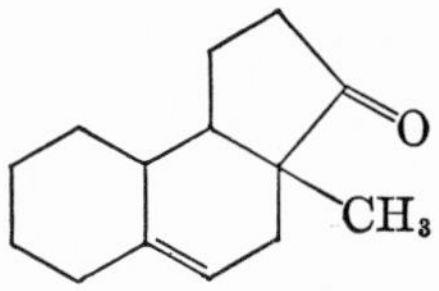   XCIIA

thalene and 1-methylcyclopenten-5-one give a product whose structure has not been established but whose elementary composition corresponds

---

[58] Fieser and Dunn, *J. Am. Chem. Soc.*, **58**, 1054 (1936).
[59] Dane and Eder, *Ann.*, **539**, 207 (1939).
[60] Bockemüller, U. S. pat. 2,179,809 [*C.A.*, **34**, 1823 (1940)].

to that of XCIII or XCIIIA.[61] 1-Methylcyclopentene-4,5-dione and

XCIII   XCIIIA

butadiene yield the angular methyl product XCIV,[62] while this cyclenone
and 6-methoxy-1-vinyl-3,4-dihydronaphthalene give a 15,16- or a 16,17-
diketosteroid which has been formulated as IV.[5, 6] The structure of this
product is uncertain (see p. 139).   4,4-Dibromocyclopentene-3,5-dione

XCIV   IV

and butadiene give XCV in unspecified yield, while the same dione and
6-methoxy-1-vinyl-3,4-dihydronaphthalene give a 16,16-dibromo-15,17-
diketosteroid XCVI.[59]

XCV   XCVI

   Butadiene and 2,3-dimethylbutadiene react with cyclohexen-3-one
giving the octalones XCVII and XCVIII in 11 and 20% yields.[63] Com-
bination of this cyclenone with 1-methyl-2-vinylcyclohexene followed

[61] Gaddis and Butz, J. Am. Chem. Soc., **69**, 1203 (1947).
[62] Dane, Schmitt, and Rautenstrauch, Ann., **532**, 29 (1937); Dane, U. S. pat. 2,230,233
[C.A., **35**, 3037 (1941)].
[63] Bartlett and Woods, J. Am. Chem. Soc., **62**, 2933 (1940).

by treatment with 2,4-dinitrophenylhydrazine yields what may be the 2,4-dinitrophenylhydrazone of XCIX or XCIXA.[64]   Cyclohexadiene

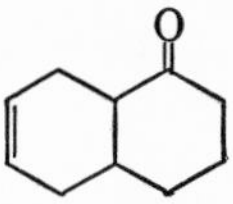

XCVII 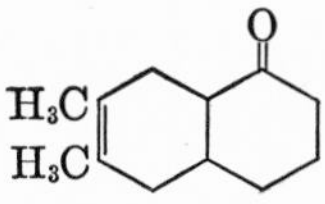   XCVIII 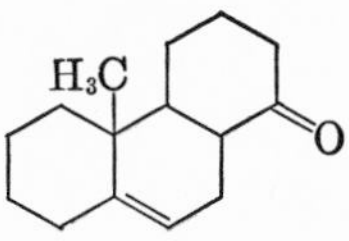   XCIX 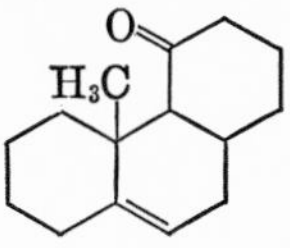   XCIXA

fails to react with cyclohexen-3-one.[65]   Butadiene and 1,3,5-hexatriene do not react with 1-methylcyclohexen-3-one.[66]   However, butadiene and 1-methylcyclohexen-6-one react to form C.[67]

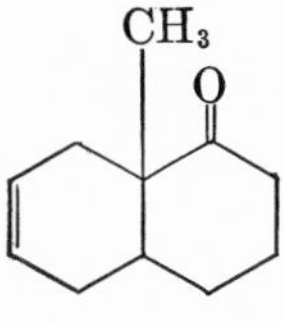

C

  The 1:1 adducts obtained from p-benzoquinone and a variety of dienes (discussed on pages 140–143) can add a second mole of diene.   A typical example is the diketotetrahydronaphthalene (from p-benzo-quinone and butadiene) which reacts with butadiene,[38] 2,3-dimethyl-butadiene,[38, 41] cyclopentadiene,[8] and 1,3-cyclohexadiene [8] to yield the expected adducts.   The 1:1 adduct from p-benzoquinone and cyclo-

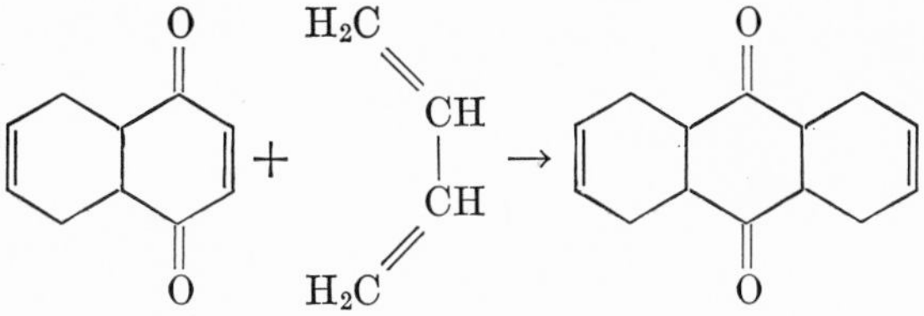

pentadiene (XI) reacts with cyclopentadiene and 1,3-cyclohexadiene giving XII [39] and XIV.[8]   The 1:1 adduct (XIX) from p-benzoquinone

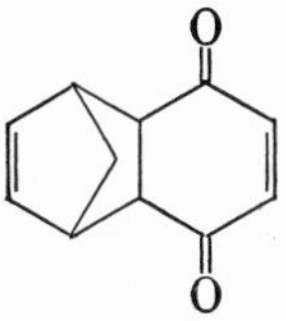

XI 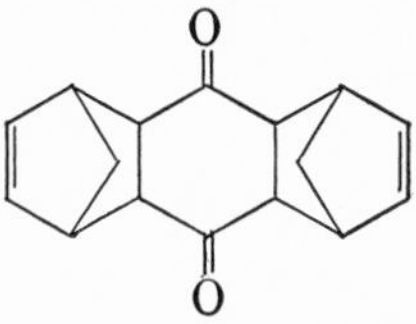   XII 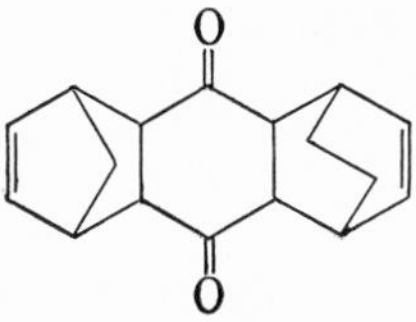   XIV

[64] Meggy and Robinson, *Nature*, **140**, 282 (1937).
[65] Whitmore and Pedlow, *J. Am. Chem. Soc.*, **63**, 758 (1941).
[66] Robinson and Walker, *J. Chem. Soc.*, **1935**, 1530.
[67] Nudenberg and Butz, *J. Am. Chem. Soc.*, **65**, 1436 (1943).

and 1,1'-bicyclopentenyl reacts with 1,1'-bicyclopentenyl and 1,1'-bicyclohexenyl to give the heptacyclic products XXI [3, 20] and CI.[3]

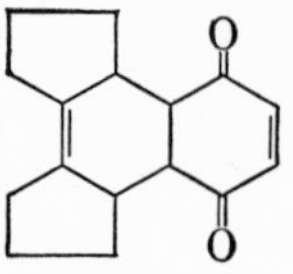

XIX 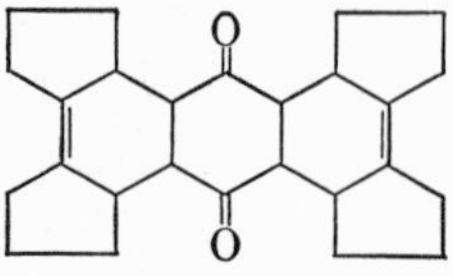   XXI 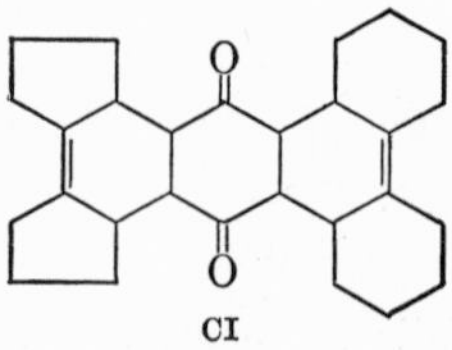   CI

Similarly XX, from p-benzoquinone and 1,1'-bicyclohexenyl, gives XXII on reaction with this diene.[3, 19]

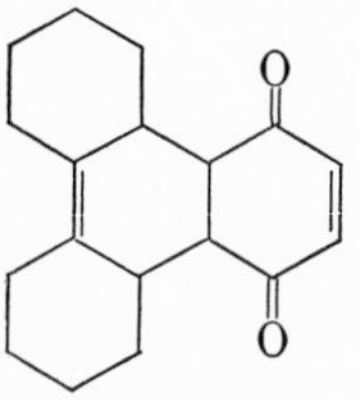

XX 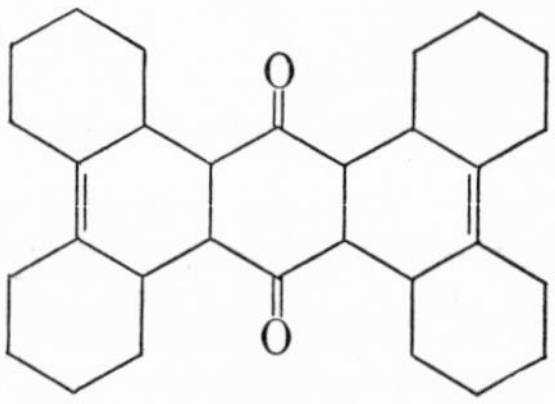   XXII

Tetrachlorocyclopentadienone and 3,4-diphenylcyclopentadienone [68] dimerize to products of unknown structure; 1,4-dimethyl-2,3-diphenylcyclopentadienone dimerizes by a Diels-Alder addition to give CII.[69]

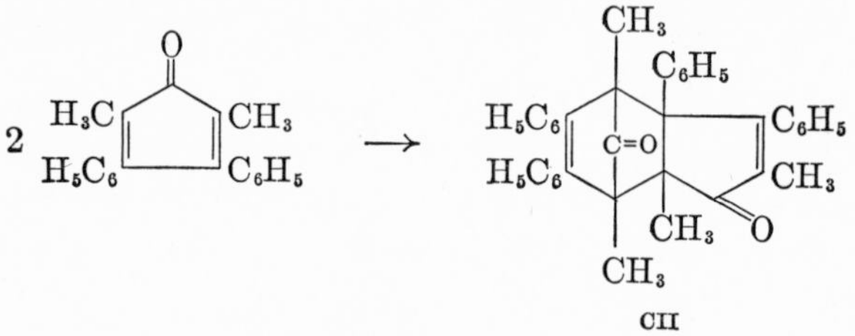

CII

Coumarin and 2,3-dimethylbutadiene react to form CIII.[70]

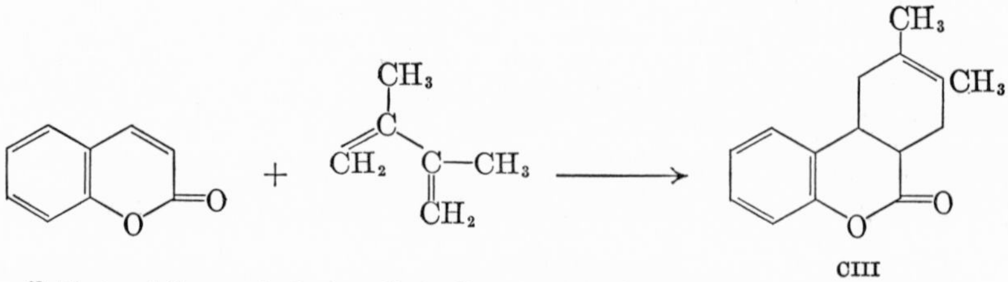

CIII

[68] Allen and Spanagel, J. Am. Chem. Soc., **55**, 3773 (1933).
[69] Allen and Van Allan, J. Am. Chem. Soc., **64**, 1260 (1942).
[70] Adams, McPhee, Carlin, and Wicks, J. Am. Chem. Soc., **65**, 356 (1943).

OTHER METHODS FOR THE SYNTHESIS OF FUSED-RING KETONES

In a review of the synthesis of alicyclic compounds,[71] Linstead divided the methods into seven groups: (1) reduction of an aromatic compound; (2) cyclization of a diolefin (preformed, or potential as in cyclodehydration of an olefin alcohol); (3) cyclization of an aromatic olefin; (4) the Diels-Alder synthesis; (5) cyclodehydration of a diketone or a keto ester; (6) formation of a cyclic ketone from a monocarboxylic acid or derivative thereof; and (7) formation of a cyclic ketone from a dicarboxylic acid. More recent reviews are concerned with the formation of cyclic ketones by intramolecular acylation,[72] by ester condensation,[73] and by the Mannich reaction.[74] All these methods can be used for the synthesis of fused-ring ketones; some of them yield the ketones directly.

Valuable modifications, extensions, and applications of the methods have been reported by Bachmann,[75] Linstead,[76] Robinson,[77] Johnson,[78] and Wilds.[79] An intramolecular cyclization method, novel in its employment of 1,5-dien-3-ynes, has been discovered and developed by Marvel.[30]

Except for quinones, other methods are not available for the preparation of the diketones and polyketones which have been obtained by cyclenone-diene addition. But only a few monoketones have been prepared by cyclenone-diene addition, and cyclane-1,3-diones have usually been prepared by cyclization of esters [81] and reduction of phenols.[82]

EXPERIMENTAL CONDITIONS AND PROCEDURES

The details of experimental conditions are recorded for many of the reactions in Tables I–VII. Numerous variations of the conditions have been employed, but few studies of the effect of changes in conditions upon yield in particular reactions have been made. Standard conditions, which will give good yields from many pairs of reactants, consist

[71] Linstead, *Ann. Repts. Chem. Soc. London*, **33**, 312 (1936).
[72] Johnson, *Org. Reactions*, **2**, 114 (1944).
[73] Hauser and Hudson, *Org. Reactions*, **1**, 266 (1942).
[74] Blicke, *Org. Reactions*, **1**, 303 (1942).
[75] Bachmann and co-workers, *J. Am. Chem. Soc.*, **66**, 553 (1944), and earlier papers.
[76] Linstead and co-workers, *J. Am. Chem. Soc.*, **64**, 1985 (1942), and earlier papers.
[77] Robinson and co-workers, *J. Chem. Soc.*, **1944**, 503, and earlier papers.
[78] Johnson and co-workers, *J. Am. Chem. Soc.*, **66**, 218 (1944), and earlier papers.
[79] Wilds and co-workers, *J. Am. Chem. Soc.*, **66**, 1688 (1944), and earlier papers.
[80] Marvel and co-workers, *J. Org. Chem.*, **7**, 88 (1942), and earlier papers; Linstead and Doering, *J. Am. Chem. Soc.*, **64**, 1996 (1942).
[81] Chuang, Ma, and Tien, *Ber.*, **68**, 1946 (1935); Chuang and Tien, *Ber.*, **69**, 25 (1936); Linstead and Millidge, *J. Chem. Soc.*, **1936**, 478.
[82] Hoffmann-La Roche and Co., Ger. pats. 606,857 [*C.A.*, **29**, 3692 (1935)] and 614,195 [*C.A.*, **29**, 5995 (1935)]; Thiele and Jaeger, *Ber.*, **34**, 2841 (1901).

of *temperatures* between 90° and 110°, a *reaction time* of twenty-four hours, and, as the *solvent*, benzene, ethanol, or excess diene.

The addition of 5,6,8-triacetoxy-1,4-naphthoquinone to 2,3-dimethyl-butadiene in ethanol precisely exemplifies the conditions taken as standard. Naphthoquinones with fewer substituents in the benzenoid ring react completely within much shorter periods.[45] The most reactive of the series (Table VI), the 5-hydroxy derivative, gave 95% of adduct in twenty minutes.

Some quinone additions require longer periods at 100°. 2,5-Dimethyl-1,4-benzoquinone in ethanol gave a higher yield after seventy-two hours than after twenty-seven. The yield was still higher at seventy-two hours in benzene. Such a difference in favor of benzene as against ethanol has not been observed in any other reaction.

The standard conditions are adequate for the addition of some quinones with a methyl group at the reacting double bond. An example is 2-methyl-8-hydroxy-1,4-naphthoquinone. With the variation of dioxane as solvent, 2-hydroxy-3,5-dimethyl-1,4-benzoquinone reacts under these conditions.

For the preparation of 2-cyclene-1,4-diones without substituents at carbons 2 or 3, a lower temperature must be used and an excess of diene avoided. A temperature of 35–40° in organic solvents or in aqueous emulsion is suitable (Table I). At higher temperatures the cyclenedione reacts with another mole of diene. Thus the diketodiethanohydro-anthracene XV, p. 142, is obtained in theoretical yield by refluxing *p*-benzoquinone and cyclohexadiene (80–85°) for twenty-four hours.

ι Monoketones definitely require a higher temperature. Methylcyclo-penten-5-one and vinylcyclohexene at 170° for sixteen hours give only 52% of the adduct; at 205° for twenty-four hours the yield is 75%. An excess of the ketone (Table VII) may be essential.

The conditions taken as standard are probably as vigorous as can be tolerated in the preparation of 2-cyclene-1,4-diones which lack an angular substituent at carbon 5 or the other angular carbon atom. Otherwise, rearrangement to a 1,4-hydroquinone will take place.

A longer period (fifty hours) was used for additions to methylcyclopen-tene-4,5-dione in dioxane (Table VII). The group —COCR=CHCO—, where R is methyl, ω-carboxypropyl, or ω-carboxyamyl in cyclohex-enediones which are not quinones, does not react with butadiene in benzene at 70° within six hours. In the preparation of some diketo-hexahydronaphthalenes containing this group (Tables II and III) it is standard practice to heat in the presence of an excess of diene. The —COC(C_6H_5)=CHCO— group in these cyclohexenediones does not react in one hour at 100° when the compound is dissolved in 2,3-dimethylbutadiene, but this group in 2,5-diphenyl-1,4-benzoquinone does react with 2,3-dimethylbutadiene in boiling ethanol (six days, 79%). The selection of solvent is important with certain unstable quinones. It is sometimes necessary to keep all the quinone dissolved during the reaction to prevent decomposition of suspended particles which initiates decomposition throughout the mixture. For this reason ethanol may be preferred to benzene. The addition of a few drops of acetic acid to the ethanol has been found advisable.[57] However, additions of 3- and 4-halo-1,2-naphthoquinones cannot be carried out successfully in ethanol.

There is evidence that p-benzoquinone and cyclopentadiene react more rapidly in certain solvents than in others (fast in benzene or ethanol, slow in carbon bisulfide, carbon tetrachloride, or n-hexane) (Table I). This reaction proceeds five times as fast, for a given activation energy, in nitrobenzene as it does in benzene.[83] No application of such information to preparative work seems yet to have been made.

No careful study of the relative reactivities of various dienes is available. Some of the data suggest that 1-substituted and 1,4-disubstituted butadienes react more slowly than others. For the addition of toluquinone to pentadiene forty hours was allowed, as compared with six for the addition of butadiene (Table II).

Preparations from unstable dienes can be carried out to advantage in aqueous dispersion. Effective withdrawal of heat of reaction is attained in the presence of the water. Polymerization inhibitors, such as copper and its salts, phenols, or amines, may also be added.

Occasionally the determination of ultraviolet absorption spectra may be useful in distinguishing a hydroquinone from a cyclenedione. Curves for typical hydroquinones [84] and cyclenediones [85] are available for comparison. The spectra may be valuable in detecting products of side reaction as well as rearrangement products. Although 1,6-addition of a 1,3-diene to a p-quinone to give a 1,4-hydroquinone monoether does not appear to be an interfering reaction in most quinone-diene syntheses, highly hindered quinones might react in this way.[86] Diisopropenylacetylene reacts with 1 mole of tetrachloro-p-benzoquinone to give a crystalline compound whose ultraviolet absorption is almost identical with that of tetrachlorohydroquinone.[87] The structure of the adduct from cyclopentadiene and tetrachloro-p-benzoquinone has never been demonstrated.[87]

[83] Hinshelwood, *J. Chem. Soc.*, **1938**, 236.
[84] Schjanberg, *Svensk Kem. Tid.*, **52**, 185 (1940) [*C.A.*, **34**, 7742 (1940)].
[85] Bastron, Davis, and Butz, *J. Org. Chem.*, **8**, 515 (1943).
[86] Criegee, *Ber.*, **69**, 2758 (1936).
[87] Butz, Gaddis, and Butz, *J. Am. Chem. Soc.*, **69**, 924 (1947).

Addition of a Diene to p-Benzoquinone; Preparation of 6-Chloro-1,4-diketo-1,4,4a,5,8,8a-hexahydronaphthalene.[1] To an emulsion of 112.5 parts of 2-chlorobutadiene in 500 parts of water containing 10 parts of an emulsifier made from 40 moles of ethylene oxide and 1 mole of castor oil is added 137.5 parts of p-benzoquinone. The mixture is stirred in the dark at 40° for twelve hours, cooled to 4°, and filtered. The adduct, which melts at 95° and is obtained in a 95% yield, is extraordinarily sensitive to light.

Addition of a Diene to a Substituted p-Benzoquinone; Preparation of 5,7,8-Triketo-6,10-dimethyl-2-octalin (XLII, p. 146).[5, 32] Half a gram of 2-hydroxy-3,5-dimethyl-1,4-benzoquinone, 4 ml. of butadiene, and 4 ml. of dioxane are heated at 110° for twenty hours in a sealed tube. The original yellowish red color changes to a bright yellow. After evaporation of the dioxane in vacuum, the residue crystallizes completely. Recrystallization from ether-petroleum ether gives a theoretical yield of colorless trione, m.p. 120°. Purification by high-vacuum sublimation at 110° is also possible. Similarly prepared triones which are not so easily purified can be obtained from the reaction mixtures by diluting with ether, extracting with aqueous sodium hydroxide, precipitating the trione from the water solutions of its sodium salt with dilute sulfuric acid, extracting with ether, and evaporating the ether after washing and drying.

Addition of a Diene to 1,4-Naphthoquinone; Preparation of 6,7-Dimethyl-9,10-diketo-5,8,8a,9,10,10a-hexahydroanthracene and 2,3-Dimethylanthraquinone. Excellent directions for the addition of 2,3-dimethylbutadiene to 1,4-naphthoquinone and subsequent dehydrogenation of the 1:1 adduct to 2,3-dimethylanthraquinone have been published in *Organic Syntheses*.[88]

Addition of a Diene to a 1,2-Naphthoquinone; Preparation of 10a-Chloro-2,3-dimethyl-9,10-diketo-1,4,4a,9,10,10a-hexahydro-9,10-phenanthraquinone (LXIV, p. 149) and 2,3-Dimethyl-9,10-phenanthraquinone (LXV, p. 149).[45] A mixture of 4 g. of 3-chloro-1,2-naphthoquinone, 8 ml. of 2,3-dimethylbutadiene, and 40 ml. of purified chloroform (shaken with concentrated sulfuric acid, then washed with water, dried, and distilled) is sealed in a tube and heated in a steam bath with exclusion of light. The tube is shaken vigorously until all solid material has dissolved, for it is generally found that solid particles of a quinone tend to suffer decomposition and initiate the destruction of material in solution. The red color of the solution soon begins to fade and in fifty minutes has changed to yellow. After one hour the solution is cooled and shaken with Norit for ten minutes at room temperature, and the

[88] Allen and Bell, *Org. Syntheses*, **22**, 37 (1942).

solvent is distilled from the filtered solution in vacuum, the temperature being kept below 60°. The resulting viscous oil can be preserved for some time as such or in ethereal solution without decomposing. Crystalline material is obtained by cooling an ethereal solution in a bath of solid carbon dioxide and adding petroleum ether, and with seed available the crystalline compound is obtained easily. Recrystallized from ether-petroleum ether, the adduct forms glistening, lemon-yellow needles, m.p. 87–88°; yield, 4 g. (70%).

The pure diketone adduct, suspended in ethanol or ether, when shaken with air, soon changes to an orange powder, which is crystallized from glacial acetic acid to give orange plates of 2,3-dimethyl-9,10-phenanthraquinone, m.p. 242–243° (cor.); yield, 87%. Warming the oily or crystalline diketone adduct with ethanolic sodium acetate solution gives 2,3-dimethyl-9,10-phenanthraquinone; yield, 100%.

To obtain satisfactory results in this diene addition, it is essential to prepare the quinone in a high state of purity and to employ pure chloroform or tetrachloroethane. Ethanol has a deleterious effect; even the small quantity present in commercial chloroform brings about extensive decomposition.

Addition of a Diene to a 1,2-Phenanthraquinone; Preparation of 6,7-Dimethyl-3,4-benzo-9,10-phenanthraquinone (LXIX, p. 150).[46] One gram of 3-bromo-1,2-phenanthraquinone and 6 ml. of 2,3-dimethylbutadiene are heated in 70 ml. of purified chloroform (see the preceding preparation) in a steam bath for three hours. The oil remaining after removal of the solvents is treated in 6 ml. of glacial acetic acid with 2 g. of chromic anhydride in 20 ml. of 80% acetic acid with gentle warming. By gradually adding water to the solution and scratching, 6,7-dimethyl-3,4-benzo-9,10-phenanthraquinone is caused to separate in a microcrystalline condition; yield, 79%. Recrystallization from ethanol yields lustrous, fiery-red plates, m.p. 194–195°.

SURVEY OF DIELS-ALDER DIENE-CYCLENONE ADDITIONS

In the tables are listed examples of diene additions to cyclenones which have been reported through 1946. The list may not be complete, as the reaction is often used merely to show the presence of a conjugated diene and such examples may have escaped notice.

Many of the adducts formed in these reactions are derivatives of complex polycyclic systems, and their structural formulas are so bulky that their use would expand the tables unduly. Their names also are cumbersome and have the additional disadvantage that most chemists are not familiar with them. We have therefore been forced to adopt the following expedient: Before each table is listed a group of structural formulas with their corresponding symbols. For example, 1,4-diketo-1,4,4a,5,8,8a-hexahydronaphthalene has the symbol A.

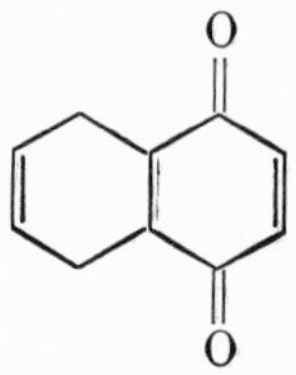

A

When this diketohexahydronaphthalene or its substitution product is formed and its structure established, the symbol A is used in the column under "Products." Although A actually refers only to the 1:1 adduct from butadiene and p-benzoquinone, the reader can easily work out the positions of the substituents when other dienes or p-benzoquinones are used and the reaction follows a normal course. Thus, the product from 2,3-dimethylbutadiene and p-benzoquinone has the symbol A which here denotes the 6,7-dimethyl derivative shown below.

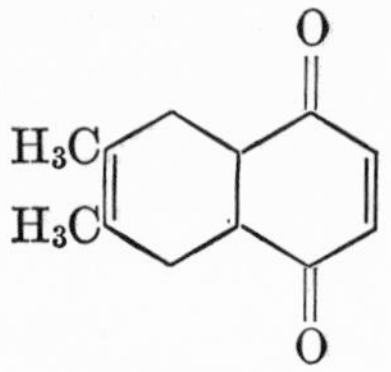

Since the structures of typical adducts have been adequately demonstrated, the products from analogous pairs of reactants are assumed to have analogous structures and are so entered in the tables, even though the structure of the particular compound was not proved. For reactions where the structure of the product has not been established but where a given structure is probable, the symbol is preceded by "probably." Where isomeric adducts are possible, the positions of the substituents will be identified by means of footnotes if these positions have been established.

The letter "t." in the column under "Temperature, °C" means that the reaction was carried out in a sealed tube.

In the column under "Yield," a dash (—) means that the yield was not recorded but does not necessarily mean that it was low. A "nearly quantitative" yield is entered as 100%. The yields usually refer to purified compounds, but there are some exceptions.

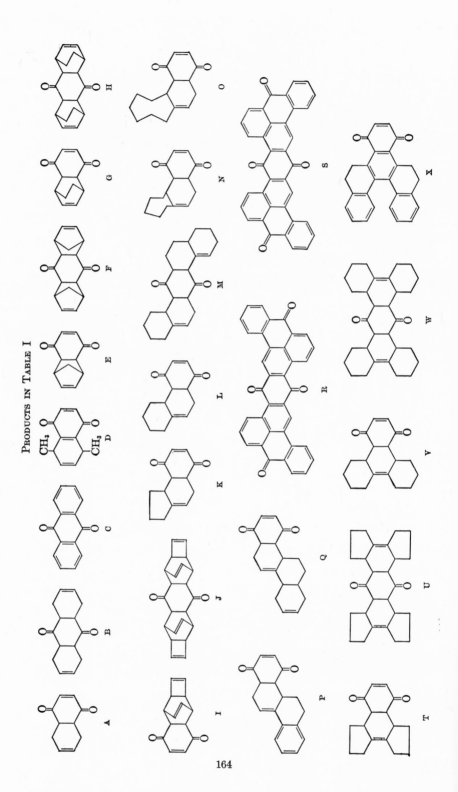

PRODUCTS IN TABLE I—*Continued*

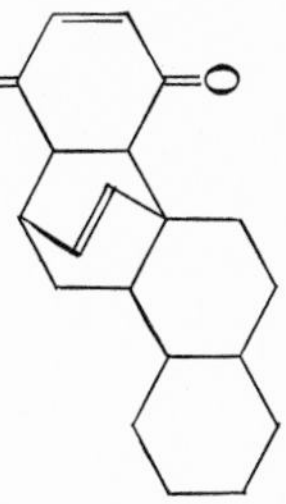

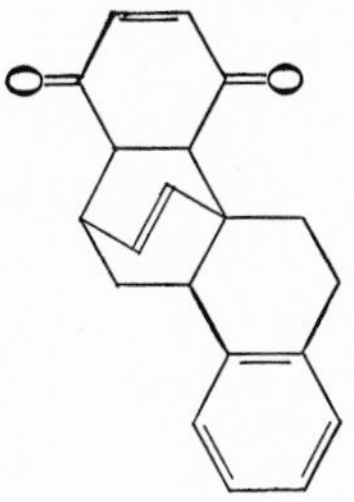

Z

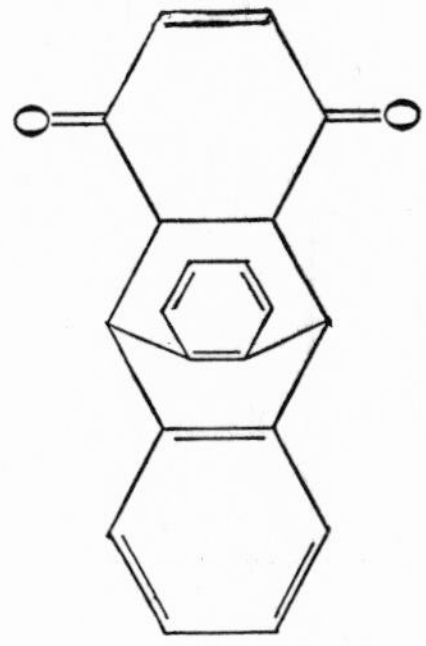

Y

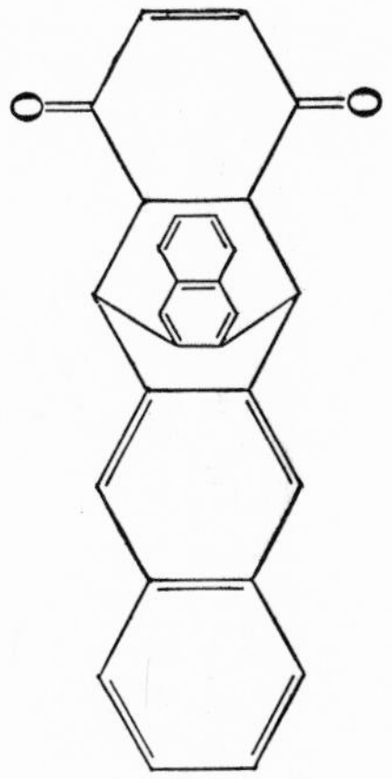

BB

AA

TABLE I

DIENE ADDITIONS TO p-BENZOQUINONE

1,3-Diene	Solvent	Ratio of Diene to Quinone	Temperature, °C.	Hours	Product *	Yield %	Reference †
Butadiene	Benzene	1.1	35	3	A	100	2
Butadiene	Water	1	50	12	A	80	1
Butadiene	—	1.8	65		A		89, 38
Butadiene	Benzene	>2	100	24	B		8
Butadiene	None	3	100t.	3	C‡		90
Pentadiene	C6H5NO2	2	130t.	7	A	16	91
2-Methylbutadiene	—	1	50t.		A		89, 38
2-Methylbutadiene	Ethanol	3	100	12	B§		16
2,4-Hexadiene	Ethanol	1	75t.	6	A		91
2,4-Hexadiene	Pyridine and C6H5NO2	2	125t.	12	D	16	91
2,4-Hexadiene	C6H5NO2	1	140t.	6	A	35	91
2,4-Hexadiene	(n-C4H9)2O	1	125-140t.	24	None	0	91
2-Methylpentadiene	—	—	—		B‖		92
2,3-Dimethylbutadiene	Water	1	40	12	A	100	1
2,3-Dimethylbutadiene	—	1	30t.		A		89, 38
2,3-Dimethylbutadiene	—	2.3	Reflux	1	B		93
2,3-Dimethylbutadiene	Ethanol	2	97t.	5	B	60	10
2,3-Dimethylbutadiene	C6H5NO2	2.3	150t.		C		11
3,4-Dimethyl-2,4-hexadiene	None	—	145 ¶	8	B**	49	20
2-Chlorobutadiene	Water	1	40	12	A	95	1

Diene	Solvent		Temperature		Product		Ref.
1-Phenylbutadiene	Xylene	2	Reflux	6	A and B ††	—	12
1-Phenylbutadiene	$C_6H_5NO_2$	2	200	3	C ‡‡	39	13
4-Phenylpentadiene	None	—	105	2	$C_{28}H_{20}O_2$	—	94
4-(2',4'-Dimethylphenyl)-pentadiene	Benzene	—	110	3	$C_{30}H_{24}O_2$	—	94
1,4-Diphenylbutadiene	None	1	—	5 §§	C	40	12
1,4-Diphenylbutadiene	$C_6H_5NO_2$	2	Reflux	—	C	60	13
2,3-Diphenylbutadiene	Benzene	1.4	100	18	A	37	95
1-Acetoxybutadiene	—	—	—	—	—	—	96
Cyclopentadiene	Ethanol	1	5	>1	E	65	14
Cyclopentadiene	CCl_4	1	40	8	E	98	15
Cyclopentadiene	Benzene	1	40	3	E	97	15
Cyclopentadiene	Ethanol	1	40	3	E	93	15
Cyclopentadiene	n-Hexane	1	40	6	E	97	15
Cyclopentadiene	CS_2	1	40	20	E	96	15
Cyclopentadiene	C_2H_5OH or C_6H_6	2	<Room temperature	—	F	100	14
Cyclohexadiene	None	3.1	Reflux	0.25	G	—	97
Cyclohexadiene	Benzene	3.4	Room temperature	48	G	—	16
Cyclohexadiene	None	5	Reflux	24	H	100	8
α-Terpinene (70%)	Ethanol	0.4	Reflux	2	G	29	98
α-Terpinene (94%)	Acetone	1	Reflux	2	Quinhydrone m.p. 170°	—	98

* See pp. 164–165 for explanation of symbols in this column.
† References 89–133 are listed on p. 192.
‡ From the adduct by aeration in alkaline solution.
§ Both isomers.
‖ One isomer; structure unknown.
¶ Previous reaction at 30–80°.
** Mixture of isomers.
†† Considered to be the 1,5-diphenyl isomer because of the high melting point of the anthraquinone to which it was dehydrogenated.
‡‡ The 1,5-diphenyl isomer.
§§ At slightly reduced pressure. The reaction was violent; the temperature was not measured.

TABLE I—*Continued*

DIENE ADDITIONS TO *p*-BENZOQUINONE

1,3-Diene	Solvent	Ratio of Diene to Quinone	Temperature, °C	Hours	Product *	Yield %	Reference †
α-Phellandrene	Ethanol	1	Reflux	1.5	G	—	16
Cycloöctatetraene	Xylene	—	140	—	I and J	—	21
1-Vinylcyclopentene	—	—	—	—	K	—	99
1-Vinylcyclohexene	Methanol	1.5	Reflux	2 ‡	L	—	17
1-Vinylcyclohexene	Tetralin	2.2	Reflux	0.2	M	10	17
1-Vinylcyclohexene	—	—	—	—	L	—	99
1-Vinylcycloheptene	—	—	—	—	N	—	99
1-Vinylcycloöctene	—	—	—	—	O	—	99
4-Vinyl-1,2-dihydronaphthalene	Cyclohexane	—	100	—	P	—	23
7-Methoxy-4-ethynyl-1,2-dihydronaphthalene	Cyclohexane	—	Room temperature	>48	None	0	23
7-Methoxy-4-vinyl-1,2-dihydronaphthalene	Cyclohexane	1	Room temperature	36	P	—	23
4a-Methyl-1-vinyl-1,2,4a,5,8,8a-hexahydronaphthalene	Benzene	—	50	24	Q	—	24
10-Methylene-9-anthrone	C$_6$H$_5$NO$_2$	0.52	Reflux	—	R or S	—	40
10-Methylene-9-anthrone	Acetic acid	—	Reflux	§	— =	—	55
Styrene	None ¶	4	—	0.75	Quinol and C$_{22}$H$_{12}$O$_2$**	—	100
β-(1-Cyclohexenyl)naphthalene	—	—	—	—	C$_{22}$H$_{16}$**	—	101
1,1'-Bicyclopentenyl	Methanol	1	Reflux	1	T	—	3

Diene	Solvent		Temperature		Product*	Yield	Ref.†
1,1'-Bicyclopentenyl	Butanol	—	Reflux	5	U	54	20
1,1'-Bicyclohexenyl	Ethanol	1	Reflux	5	V	—	3
1,1'-Bicyclohexenyl	—	—	To reflux	—	W	—	3
1,1'-Bicyclohexenyl	Butanol	2	Reflux	8	W	58.5	20
1,1'-Bicyclohexenyl	None	5	140	5	W	41	19
1,1'-Bicyclohexenyl	None	—	100	5	V††	86	18
Biphenyl	—	—	200	3	—	0	102
3,3',4,4'-Tetrahydro-1,1'-binaphthyl	None	0.1	150	3	X‡‡	80	18
1-Pimaric acid	Benzene	—	Room temperature	48	Y	—	103
Thebaine	Benzene	—	Reflux	0.2	Z	—	104
Anthracene	Xylene	1	Reflux	0.75	AA	93	25
2,3,6,7-Dibenzanthracene-9,10-diyl	None	1	Reflux	—	BB	—	25, 105
α-Methylfuran	—	—	—	—	None	0	106
2-Methylene-2,5-dihydrofuran	Benzene	—	Room temperature	12	$C_{17}H_{14}O_3$§§	2.1 g.	106
2-Methylene-2,5-dihydrofuran	None	—	Room temperature	48	$C_{17}H_{14}O_3$§§	96	106
Phencyclone[3,4-(2,2'-xenylene)-2,5-diphenylcyclopentadienone]	$C_6H_5NO_2$	2	100	2	1:2 Adduct	50	56
1,3-Diphenylisobenzofuran	Ether	—	−10	—	1:1 Adduct	—	107
1,3-Diphenylisobenzofuran	Ethanol	—	Reflux	2	1:2 Adduct	—	108
Isosafrole	—	—	—	—	—	0	109

* See pp. 164–165 for explanation of symbols in this column.
† References 89–133 are listed on p. 192.
‡ Stood overnight previously at room temperature.
§ Heating continued one-half hour after precipitation of red material ceases.
‖ Two products of undetermined structures.
¶ One-half gram of trichloroacetic acid added.
** Structure unknown.
†† Two isomers; structures unknown.
‡‡ A stable red crystalline compound apparently formed by the addition of 2 moles of quinone to 1 mole of 2-methylene-2,3-dihydrofuran.
§§ No addition when diene in excess or when dissolved in boiling benzene or xylene.

PRODUCTS IN TABLE II

TABLE II

DIENE ADDITIONS TO METHYL-p-BENZOQUINONES

p-Benzoquinone	1,3-Diene	Solvent	Ratio of Diene to Quinone	Temperature °C	Hours	Product *	Yield %	Reference †
Methyl-	Butadiene	Benzene	4	110	5	A	2.4 g.‡	27
Methyl-	Butadiene	Benzene	1.9	70	6	A	84	26
Methyl-	Pentadiene	Dioxane	1.3	70	40	A §	44	28
Methyl-	2,3-Dimethylbutadiene	Benzene	2.5	Reflux	4	A ‖	—	29
Methyl-	2,3-Dimethylbutadiene	None	2.5	110	1	A ‖	—	29
Methyl-	2,3-Dimethylbutadiene	None	2.5	170	—	CC ‖	93	29
Methyl-	2,3-Diethoxybutadiene	None	1.2	Reflux	36	DD	17	53
Methyl-	10-Methylene-9-anthrone	Acetic acid	5	Reflux	—	—	—	55
2,3-Dimethyl-	2,3-Dimethoxybutadiene	None	0.5	140	36	DD	82	110
2,3-Dimethyl-	2,3-Dimethylbutadiene	Ethanol	3	Reflux	8	A	80	26
2,3-Dimethyl-	Butadiene	Ethanol	5	100	62	A ¶	75	30
2,5-Dimethyl-	Butadiene	Benzene	—	110	5	None	0	27
2,5-Dimethyl-	Butadiene	Benzene	4	170	10	B	10	4
2,5-Dimethyl-	2,3-Dimethylbutadiene	Ethanol	4	100	27	A ¶	66	30
2,5-Dimethyl-	2,3-Dimethylbutadiene	Ethanol	4	100	72	A ¶	77	30
2,5-Dimethyl-	2,3-Dimethylbutadiene	Benzene	4	100	72	A ¶	85	30
2,5-Dimethyl-	1,3,5-Hexatriene	Ethanol	1.5	103	26	A ¶	57	35
2,5-Dimethyl-	Cyclohexadiene	Ethanol	1.5	80–104	72	G	1	7
2,5-Dimethyl-	2,3-Dimethylbutadiene	C_6H_6 + C_2H_5OH	4	100	87	A	82	30

* See p. 170 for explanation of symbols used in this column.

† References 89–133 are listed on p. 192.

‡ Erroneous; the theoretical yield is 1.75 g.

§ Both the 2,5- and 2,8-dimethyl isomers.

‖ The 2,6,7-trimethyl isomer.

¶ A liquid.

TABLE II—Continued
DIENE ADDITIONS TO METHYL-p-BENZOQUINONES

p-Benzoquinone	1,3-Diene	Solvent	Ratio of Diene to Quinone	Temperature °C	Hours	Product *	Yield %	Reference †
2-Isopropyl-5-methyl-	Pentadiene	Ethanol	—	100	112	A ‡	75.5	30
2-Isopropyl-5-methyl-	2,3-Dimethylbutadiene	Ethanol	3	100	>24	A ‡	—	30, 43
2-Acetoxy-5-methyl-	Butadiene	Ethanol	2	75	68	A §	25	32
2-Acetoxy-5-methyl-	2,3-Dimethylbutadiene	Ethanol	1.5	95	14t.	A ‖	42	33
2-Acetoxy-5-methyl-	1,3,5-Hexatriene	Ethanol	3	74	39t.	A ¶	45	33
2-Acetoxy-5-methyl-	1,3,5-Hexatriene	Ethanol	3	73	39t.	A **	21	33
2-Acetoxy-5-methyl-	1,3,5-Hexatriene	Ethanol	3	97	16t.	A ††	6	33
2-Acetoxy-5-methyl-	Cyclohexadiene	Ethanol	2.3	65	65t.	G ‡‡	55	33
2-Carbomethoxy-5-methyl-	Butadiene	Benzene	4	100	16	A §§	77	34
2-Carbomethoxy-6-methyl-	Butadiene	Benzene	2	100	66	A §§	78	34
2-Methoxy-5-methyl-	Butadiene	Ethanol	4.2	100	65	A ‖‖	75	7
2-Hydroxy-3,5-dimethyl-	Butadiene	Dioxane	15	110	20t.	A ¶¶	100	5
2-Hydroxy-3,5-dimethyl-	7-Methoxy-4-vinyl-1,2-dihydronaphthalene	Dioxane	—	120	15t.	EE or FF ***	—	5
Tetramethyl-	1,3,5-Hexatriene	Ethanol	2	100	43t.	None	0	35
Tetramethyl-	1,3,5-Hexatriene	Benzene	1.2	150	65	Duroquinol	—	35
Tetramethyl-	1,3,5-Hexatriene	Benzene	1.5	204	3	Duroquinol	42	35

* See p. 170 for explanation of symbols used in this column.
† References 89–133 are listed on p. 192.
‡ A liquid.
§ Isolated as the free enol from the angular methyl product.
‖ The 5-acetoxy-2,7,8-trimethyl isomer.
¶ The angular acetate.
** Possibly the 2-hydroxy-5-methyl-9-vinyl isomer.
†† An enol acetate.

‡‡ Three compounds obtained. Yields of crystalline substances: angular acetate, 55%; stereoisomeric angular acetate, 6%; enol (2-hydroxy-5-methyl derivative), 1%.
§§ The angular carboxylate.
‖‖ The 3-hydroxy-2,10-dimethyl isomer.
¶¶ The 3-hydroxy-2,10-dimethyl isomer.
*** The 3-hydroxy-2,14-dimethyl isomer.

DIENE SYNTHESIS III

173

PRODUCTS IN TABLE III

TABLE III

Diene Additions to Substituted p-Benzoquinones Other than Methyl-p-Benzoquinones

p-Benzoquinone	1,3-Diene	Solvent	Ratio of Diene to Quinone	Temperature, °C	Hours	Product *	Yield %	Reference †
Phenyl-	2,3-Dimethylbutadiene	None	5.5	100	1	A ‡	82	29
Phenyl-	Cyclopentadiene	Benzene	1	Reflux	2	A ‡	18	29
Phenyl-	1,1'-Bicyclohexenyl	None	0.9	120–150	4	V ‡	—	19
Phenyl-	1,1'-Bicyclohexenyl	$C_6H_5NO_2$	0.9	Reflux	4	GG	—	19
2,3-Diallyl-	2,3-Dimethylbutadiene	—	—	—	—	DD §	—	111
ω-Carboxypropyl-	Butadiene	Benzene	30	70	8	A ‖	86	37
ω-Carboxyamyl-	Butadiene	Benzene	10	70	6	A ‖	75	37
Chloro-	2,3-Dimethylbutadiene	—	—	60	—	A ¶	—	38
Chloro-	2-Chlorobutadiene	Water	1	40	12	A **	—	1
2,3-Dichloro-	Butadiene	—	—	100	—	A ††	—	38
2,3-Dichloro-	2,3-Dimethylbutadiene	—	—	Room temperature	—	A ‡‡	—	38
Tetrachloro-	Cyclopentadiene	Benzene	2	Room temperature	336	$C_{11}H_6O_2Cl_4$	—	14
Tetrachloro-	Cyclopentadiene	Benzene §§	—	29	24	$C_{11}H_6O_2Cl_4$	72	39
Tetrachloro-	Anthracene	Xylene or acetic acid	1	Reflux	—	HH	—	25
Tetrachloro-	Anthracene	None	1	260	0.5	HH	—	25
Tetrachloro-	Pentacene-9,10-diyl	Xylene	1	Reflux	—	— ‖‖	—	25, 105
Tetrachloro-	10-Methylene-9-anthrone	Xylene	0.9	Reflux	—	II	—	40

					Time to distil to 10 ml.	R or S		
Tetrachloro-	10-Methylene-9-anthrone	C₆H₅NO₂	0.5	Reflux	—	Contains chlorine	—	40
Trichloro-	10-Methylene-9-anthrone	Acetic acid	5	Reflux	—	—	—	55
AA *	10-Methylene-9-anthrone	Xylene	0.3	Reflux	1	JJ	100	40
AA *	Anthracene	Xylene	0.8	Reflux	1	1:1 Adduct	90	25
5,6,7,8-Tetrahydro-1,4-naphthoquinone	Butadiene	None	2	80t.	—	KK	—	38, 41
5,8-Dihydro-1,4-naphthoquinone	Butadiene	None	2	80t.	—	LL	—	38, 41
2,5-Diphenyl-	Butadiene	Ethanol	—	90	96	A	77	36
2,5-Diphenyl-	2,3-Dimethylbutadiene	Ethanol	—	Reflux	144	A	79	36
2,5-Diphenyl-	1-Phenylbutadiene	Ethanol	—	Reflux	24	A ¶¶	89	36
2,5-Diphenyl-	1-Phenyl-1,3-pentadiene	—	—	—	—	Mixture	—	36
1-Keto-2,3-diphenylin-dene-4,7-quinone	Cyclopentadiene	Benzene	2	Reflux	—	The 3a, 7a-adduct	73	112

* See p. 173 for explanation of the symbols in this column.
† References 89–133 are listed on p. 192.
‡ The 2-phenyl isomer.
§ The adduct was isomerized to a hydroquinone which was oxidized by chromic acid to 2,3-diallyl-6,7-dimethyl-1,4-naphthoquinone.
|| Probably the 2-carboxyalkyl isomer.
¶ Probably the 2-chloro-6,7-dimethyl isomer.
** The 2,7-dichloro isomer.
†† Probably the 2,3-dichloro isomer.
‡‡ The 2,3-dichloro-6,7-dimethyl isomer.
§§ Trace of trichloroacetic acid added.
||| Normal adduct plus by-product.
¶¶ Formulated without evidence as the 2,5,9-triphenyl derivative.

PRODUCTS IN TABLE IV

TABLE IV

DIENE ADDITIONS TO o-QUINONES

Quinone	1,3-Diene	Solvent	Ratio of Diene to Quinone	Temperature °C	Hours	Product *	Yield %	Reference †
o-Benzo-	Cyclopentadiene	—	—	—	—	—	—	42
Tetramethyl-o-benzo-	Cyclopentadiene	95% ethanol	2.5	Reflux	4	MM	63	42
1,2-Naphtho-	l-Pimaric acid (crude)	—	—	—	—	—	—	114
1,2-Naphtho-	10-Methylene-9-anthrone	Acetic acid	—	Reflux	—	—‡	—	55
1,2-Naphtho-	?	—	—	—	—	—§	—	113
3,7-Dimethyl-1,2-naphtho-	2,3-Dimethylbutadiene	Ethanol	5	100	>24	NN	93	44
3,7-Dimethyl-1,2-naphtho-	2,3-Dimethylbutadiene	Ethanol	—	Heated	66	NN	83	30
4-Benzyl-1,2-naphtho-	2,3-Dimethylbutadiene	Ethanol	—	100	72	NN	0.5 g. crude	115
4-Dicarbethoxymethyl-1,2-naphtho-	2,3-Dimethylbutadiene	Ethanol	—	100	120	NN	—	115
3-Bromo-1,2-naphtho-	2,3-Dimethylbutadiene	CHCl₃	3.5	100	2	OO ‖	76	45

* See p. 176 for explanation of symbols in this column.
† References 89–133 are listed on p. 192.
‡ Constitution unknown.
§ Addition occurs.
‖ By dehydrogenation of the oily adduct with chromic acid in acetic acid.

TABLE IV—*Continued*

DIENE ADDITIONS TO *o*-QUINONES

Quinone	1,3-Diene	Solvent	Ratio of Diene to Quinone	Temperature °C	Hours	Product *	Yield %	Reference †
6-Bromo-1,2-naphtho-	2,3-Dimethylbutadiene	—	—	—	—	NN	45	45
3-Chloro-1,2-naphtho-	2,3-Dimethylbutadiene	CHCl₃	3.5	100t.	1	NN ‡	70	45
4-Chloro-1,2-naphtho-	2,3-Dimethylbutadiene	CHCl₃	3.5	100	72	OO §	15	45
3,4-Dichloro-1,2-naphtho-	2,3-Dimethylbutadiene	CHCl₃	5	100	60	NN	24	45
2,3-Dimethyl-1,4-dihydro-9,10-phenanthra-	2,3-Dimethylbutadiene	CHCl₃	4.5	100 ‖	2	1:1 Adduct	36	46
1,2-Phenanthra-	2,3-Dimethylbutadiene	CHCl₃	34	—	48	PP	29	46
3-Bromo-1,2-phenanthra-	2,3-Dimethylbutadiene	CHCl₃	15	—	3	PP	79	46
2-Bromo-3,4-phenanthra-	2,3-Dimethylbutadiene	CHCl₃	10	100	2	QQ ¶	90	46
3-Bromo-1,2-phenanthra-	Butadiene	CHCl₃	13	—	5	PP	65	46

* See p. 176 for explanation of the symbols in this column.
† References 89–133 are listed on p. 192.
‡ Is unstable; when warmed with ethanolic sodium acetate, gives a quantitative yield of 2,3-dimethyl-9,10-phenanthraquinone.
§ By oxidation of the crude adduct on standing in air.
‖ With exposure to sunlight.
¶ By dehydrogenation of the crude adduct with chromic acid in aqueous acetic acid.

PRODUCTS IN TABLE V

TABLE V

DIENE ADDITIONS TO 1,4-NAPHTHOQUINONE

1,3-Diene	Solvent	Ratio of Diene to Quinone	Temperature °C.	Hours	Product *	Yield %	Reference †
Butadiene	Ethanol	1.2	100	3	RR	—	16, 48
Butadiene	Benzene	1.2	70	2.5	RR	—	47
2-Methylbutadiene	Ethanol	1.5	100	4	RR	—	16
2-Methylbutadiene	Ethanol	2.3	80	8	C‡	100	57
2,3-Dimethylbutadiene	Ethanol	—	70	—	RR	—	57
2,3-Dimethylbutadiene	Ethanol	—	Reflux	5	RR	96	88
2,3-Dimethylbutadiene	None	2.3	Reflux	1	RR	—	88
2,3-Dimethylbutadiene	$C_6H_5NO_2$	—	—	—	C	—	11
2-Methylpentadiene	Ethanol	4	Reflux	2	RR	—	16, 47
2,4-Dimethylpentadiene	None	5	Reflux	6	RR	—	16
2,4-Dimethylpentadiene	None	—	Reflux	8	RR	—	116
2-t-Butyl-4-methylpentadiene	Dioxane	—	110	24	RR	62	116
2,5-Dimethyl-2,4-hexadiene	—	—	—	—	—	13	116
3,6-Diethyl-3,5-octadiene	—	—	—	—	—	0	116
Myrcene	Dioxane	—	Reflux	12	RR	64	116
1,3,5-Hexatriene	Ethanol	1.5	50	6	RR §	100	118
2,5-Dimethyl-1,3,5-hexatriene	—	—	—	—	No reaction	—	117
2,6-Dimethyl-2,4,6-octatriene	—	—	—	—	RR ‖	—	119
1-Chlorobutadiene	—	—	—	—	No reaction	—	49

Diene	Solvent		Temperature	Time	Product		Ref.
2-Chlorobutadiene	Benzene	2.4	Reflux + room temperature	3 + 16	RR ¶	—	50
2-Bromobutadiene	Benzene	2	Room temperature + reflux	48 + 1	RR	28	51
3-Chloropentadiene	—		100	2	C**		52
3-Chloro-1,3-hexadiene	—		100	2	C**		52
3-Chloro-1,3-octadiene	—		100	2	C**		52
3-Chloro-1,3-hendecadiene	—		100	2	C**		52
2,3-Dichlorobutadiene	None		—	—	No reaction		49
2-Chloro-3-methylbutadiene	None		100	0.5	RR		54
2-Chloro-3-methylpentadiene	—		100	1	RR		54
1,3,4,6-Tetrachloro-2,4-hexadiene	None		—	—	No reaction		49
2-Acetoxybutadiene	—		100	1.5	C††		120
1-Acetoxybutadiene	—		—	—	—		6
2-Ethoxybutadiene	Benzene		Reflux	6	C**		121
1-Hydroxybutadiene (crotonaldehyde)	Benzene + piperidine		—	—	C		122
2-Chloro-1-hydroxybutadiene	Benzene + piperidine		—	—	C		122
1-Hydroxy-2-methylbutadiene	Benzene + piperidine		—	—	C		122
2,3-Dimethoxybutadiene	Benzene	1	Reflux	8	C‡‡	40	53

* See p. 179 for explanation of symbols in this column.
† References 89–133 are listed on p. 192.
‡ By aeration of the crude adduct in boiling 5% potassium hydroxide.
§ A liquid.
‖ Converted to 9,10-diketo-1,1-dimethyl-4-(α-methylpropenyl)-1,4-dihydroanthracene by aeration in potassium hydroxide solution.
¶ Not entirely pure.
** Adduct aerated in alkaline solution without isolation.
†† The crude crystalline adduct was oxidized in alkaline solution.
‡‡ A solution of the adduct in ethanol was dehydrogenated with aqueous sodium hypochlorite.

TABLE V—*Continued*

DIENE ADDITIONS TO 1,4-NAPHTHOQUINONE

1,3-Diene	Solvent	Ratio of Diene to Quinone	Temperature °C.	Hours	Product *	Yield %	Reference †
2,3-Diethoxybutadiene	Benzene	—	Reflux	6	C ‡	—	53
1-Phenylbutadiene	None	—	—	—	C	—	16
1-Phenylbutadiene	C₆H₅NO₂	1.2	180	5 §	C	47	13
1,4-Diphenylbutadiene	None	—	160	10	C	—	12
1,4-Diphenylbutadiene	C₆H₅NO₂	1.7	Reflux	2	C	70	13
2,3-Diphenylbutadiene	Xylene	1	Reflux	2.5	RR	74	95
Cyclopentadiene	Benzene	—	5	—	SS	—	14
Cyclohexadiene	None	3.3	Reflux	2	TT	—	16
Cyclohexadiene	None	3.75	Reflux	—	TT	—	123
Cyclohexadiene	Ethanol	1.5	50	6t.	TT	70	118
α-Phellandrene	Ethanol	—	Reflux	2	TT	—	16
Cycloöctatetraene	—	—	>100	—	UU	—	21
7,8-Dichlorobicyclo[0.4.2]octa-2,4-diene	—	—	—	—	VV	—	21
1-Vinylcyclopentene	—	—	—	—	1:1 Adduct	—	99
1-Vinylcyclohexene	—	—	—	—	1:1 Adduct	—	99
1-Vinylcycloheptene	—	—	—	—	1:1 Adduct	—	99
1-Vinylcycloöctene	—	—	—	—	1:1 Adduct	—	99
α-Chlorovinylcyclohexene	None	—	100	0.33	WW	—	54
Isosafrole	—	—	—	—	—	0	109

4a-Methyl-4-vinyl-1,2,4a,5,8,8a-hexahydronaphthalene	None	2	110	0.75	1:1 Adduct	—	67
1,1'-Bicyclopentenyl	Ethanol	—	Reflux	1	XX	—	3
1,1'-Bicyclohexenyl	None	—	To reflux	—	YY	—	3
1,1'-Bicyclohexenyl	—	—	150t.	3	—||	—	19
1,1'-Bicyclohexenyl	None	5	100	2	YY	100	18
3,4,3',4'-Tetrahydro-1,1'-binaphthyl	—	0.5	130	3	1:1 Adduct	50	18
10-Methylene-9-anthrone	Ethanol	—	Reflux	—	ZZ	—	55
10-Methylene-9-anthrone	$C_6H_5NO_2$	1	Reflux	—	ZZ	—	40
1-Chloro-10-methylene-9-anthrone	Acetic acid	—	Reflux	—	Chloro derivative of ZZ	—	55
2,5-Diphenyl-3,4-(2,2'-xenylene)cyclopentadienone (phencyclone)	$C_6H_5NO_2$	—	100	4	1:1 Adduct ¶	73	56, 130
Tetraphenylcyclopentadienone (cyclone) **	Ethanol	—	180t.	—	None	0	56
Tetraphenylcyclopentadienone **	Toluene	—	220t.	—	None	0	56
Tetraphenylcyclopentadienone **	$C_6H_5NO_2$	—	160–200	2	None	0	56
1,3-Diphenylisobenzofuran	Xylene	1	Reflux	—	1:1 Adduct	79	124
1,3-Diphenylisobenzofuran	None	—	Room temperature	—	1:1 Adduct	90	125
1-Penten-3-yne	None	>1	100t.	2	None	0	126

* See p. 179 for explanation of symbols in this column.
† References 89–133 are listed on p. 192.
‡ The crude adduct was aerated in sodium hydroxide solution.
§ Minutes.
|| 1,4-Naphthohydroquinone; a diketodecahydrodibenzanthracene and a diketodecahydrodibenzanthracene (probably 1,2,3,4-dibutano-9,10-anthraquinone) were isolated.
¶ Converted to 1,4-diphenyl-2,3-(2,2'-xenylene)-9,10-anthraquinone by air and ethanolic alkali, nitrobenzene, or chromic acid.
** Acecyclone, 3,4-(1,8 naphthylene)-2,5-diphenylcyclopentadienone, gave similar results.

PRODUCTS IN TABLE VI

TABLE VI

DIENE ADDITIONS TO SUBSTITUTED 1,4-NAPHTHOQUINONES

1,4-Naphthoquinone	1,3-Diene	Solvent	Ratio of Diene to Quinone	Temperature °C.	Hours	Product *	Yield %	Reference †
2-Methyl-	—	Ethanol	6	100	>24	RR ‡	—	43
2,3-Dimethyl-	2,3-Dimethylbutadiene	Ethanol	5	100	100	RR ‡	—	43
2,6-Dimethyl-	2,3-Dimethylbutadiene	Ethanol	5	100	>24	RR	100	43
2,6-Dimethyl-	Pentadiene	Ethanol	—	100	96	RR ‡	45	30
2-Chloro-	Butadiene	—	—	125	—	9,10-Diketo-1,4-dihydro-anthracene	—	57
2-Chloro-	2-Methylbutadiene	—	—	120t.	5	C	—	57
2-Chloro	2,3-Dimethylbutadiene	Ethanol	—	105t.	5	C	—	57
2-Chloro-	10-Methylene-9-anthrone	Sodium acetate-acetic acid (1:10)	—	Reflux	—	ZZ	—	55
2,3-Dichloro-	2,3-Dimethylbutadiene	—	—	—	—	RR §	—	57
2,3-Dichloro-	10-Methylene-9-anthrone	Sodium acetate-acetic acid (1:10)	—	Reflux	—	ZZ	—	55

* See p. 184 for explanation of symbols in this column.
† References 89–133 are listed on p. 192.
‡ A liquid.
§ Converted to 2,3-dimethyl-9,10-anthraquinone by heating with ethanolic potassium hydroxide.

TABLE VI—*Continued*

DIENE ADDITIONS TO SUBSTITUTED 1,4-NAPHTHOQUINONES

1,4-Naphthoquinone	1,3-Diene	Solvent	Ratio of Diene to Quinone	Temperature °C.	Hours	Product *	Yield %	Reference †
2,3-Dichloro-	10-Methylene-9-anthrone	$C_6H_5NO_2$	—	Reflux	—	ZZ	—	40
5-Amino-	2,3-Dimethylbutadiene	Ethanol	—	Reflux	2	RR	—	57
2,3-Dichloro-5-nitro-	Butadiene	—	—	130	2	1-Amino-9,10-anthraquinone ‡	—	57
2,3-Dichloro-5-nitro-	2,3-Dimethylbutadiene	—	—	—	—	RR	74.5	57
5,6,11,12-Naphthacenediquinone	Butadiene	—	—	—	—	1:1 Adduct	—	58
5,6,11,12-Naphthacenediquinone	2,3-Dimethylbutadiene	Acetic acid	—	100	5	1:1 Adduct	87	58
2-Hydroxy-	2,3-Dimethylbutadiene	Ethanol	—	100	22	C §	70	30
2-Methoxy-	2,3-Dimethylbutadiene	Ethanol	—	100	66	C §	80	30
5-Hydroxy-	Butadiene	Ethanol	10	100	0.5	RR	94	45
5-Hydroxy-	2,3-Dimethylbutadiene	Ethanol	6	100	0.33	RR	95	45
5-Acetoxy-	2,3-Dimethylbutadiene	Ethanol	6	100	0.5	RR	94	45
5,8-Dihydroxy-	2,3-Dimethylbutadiene	Ethanol	17.5	100	6	RR	83	45
5,8-Diacetoxy-	2,3-Dimethylbutadiene	Ethanol	40	100	3	RR	92	45
{2,5,8-Trihydroxy- {5,6,8-Trihydroxy-	2,3-Dimethylbutadiene	Ethanol	15	100	60	RR ‖	33	45

Product	Diene	Solvent						Reference[†]
5,6,8-Triacetoxy-	2,3-Dimethylbutadiene	Ethanol	53	100	27	RR	70	45
2-Methyl-8-hydroxy-	2,3-Dimethylbutadiene	Ethanol	6.4	100	19	RR	84	45
5,8-Dihydroxy-	Butadiene	Benzene	1	100	6	RR ¶	—	57
5,8-Dihydroxy-	2,3-Dimethylbutadiene	Benzene	1	100	6	RR ¶	—	57
5,8-Dihydroxy-	2,3-Dimethylbutadiene	—	—	65	—	RR	43	127
5,8-Dihydroxy-	Pentadiene	$C_6H_5NO_2$	—	130t.	20	C	74	128, 129
5,8-Dihydroxy-	2,4-Hexadiene	$C_6H_5NO_2$	—	170t.	2	C	20.5	128, 129
5,8-Dihydroxy-	2,6-Dimethyl-1,3,5-heptatriene	Ethanol + CO_2	—	90t.	8	RR **	—	128, 129
5,8-Dihydroxy	2,6-Dimethyl-1,3,5-heptatriene	Benzene	—	80	12	RR **	9	129
5,8-Dihydroxy-	Phencyclone	—	—	—	—	1:1 Adduct	—	130
5,8-Diacetoxy-	Pentadiene	Ethanol	—	100	5	RR	—	131
5,8-Diacetoxy-	2-Methylbutadiene	Ethanol	—	100	5	RR	—	131
5,8-Diacetoxy-	1,1'-Bicyclohexenyl	Toluene	1	Reflux	2.5	YY	—	3
5,8-Dihydroxy-6-(1'-methoxy-4'-methyl-3'-pentenyl) [alkannin methyl ether]	2,3-Dimethylbutadiene	Ethanol	—	Reflux	2	1:1 Adduct ††	—	132

* See p. 184 for explanation of symbols in this column.
† References 89–133 are listed on p. 192.
‡ By treatment with potassium hydroxide, sodium hydrosulfite, and air.
§ From the adduct after aeration in ethanolic potassium hydroxide.
‖ The isomer to be expected from 5,6,8-trihydroxy-1,4-naphthoquinone.
¶ Not purified.
** Probable structure.
†† Aeration in ethanolic potassium hydroxide gave the anthraquinone, $C_{22}H_{20}O_4$, resulting from dehydrogenation and elimination of methanol.

COMPLEX CYCLENONES IN TABLE VII *

* Many of the 1:1 adducts from *p*-benzoquinone and a variety of dienes can add a second mole of diene. Because of the complexity of their names, the original symbols by which they were identified in Table I are used for their designation in the column labeled "Cyclenones."

PRODUCTS IN TABLE VII

TABLE VII
DIENE ADDITIONS TO CYCLENONES OTHER THAN QUINONES

Cyclenone	1,3-Diene	Solvent	Ratio of Diene to Cyclenone	Temperature °C.	Hours	Product*	Yield %	Reference†
Cyclopenten-3-one	Butadiene	Dioxane	3	120–160	40	AAA‡	—	59
Cyclopenten-3-one	6-Methoxy-1-vinyl-3,4-dihydronaphthalene	Dioxane	1.1	120	40t.	BBB	—	59
1-Methylcyclopenten-5-one	2,3-Dimethylbutadiene	CO_2	0.9	200t.	15	AAA‡	—	60
1-Methylcyclopenten-5-one	Vinylcyclohexene	N_2	0.2	170t.	16	CCC‡‡	52	60
1-Methylcyclopenten-5-one	Vinylcyclohexene	N_2	0.3	205t.	24	CCC‡‡	75	60
1-Methylcyclopenten-5-one	1-Vinyl-3,4-dihydronaphthalene	N_2	0.18	160t.	22	BBB‡‡	—	60
1-Methylcyclopenten-5-one	4a-Methyl-4-vinyl-1,2,4a,5,8,8a-hexahydronaphthalene	None	10	200	48	Dimethyl-steradienone	—	61
1-Methylcyclopentene-4,5-dione	Butadiene	Dioxane	13	130	40	DDD	—	62
1-Methylcyclopentene-4,5-dione	Butadiene	Dioxane	1.8	130	40	DDD	—	62
1-Methylcyclopentene-4,5-dione	6-Methoxy-1-vinyl-3,4-dihydronaphthalene	Dioxane	2	115	50	EEE	30 (crude)	5, 6
4,4-Dibromocyclopentene-3,5-dione	Butadiene	Dioxane	5	115	24	FFF	—	59
4,4-Dibromocyclopentene-3,5-dione	6-Methoxy-1-vinyl-3,4-dihydronaphthalene	Dioxane	5	115	24	GGG	12	59
Cyclohexen-3-one	Butadiene	None	2.3	190	72	An octalone	11	63
Cyclohexen-3-one	2,3-Dimethylbutadiene	None	1.5	200	72	An octalone	20	63
Cyclohexen-3-one	1-Methyl-2-vinylcyclohexene	—	—	—	—	$C_{15}H_{22}O$ §	—	64
Cyclohexen-3-one	Cyclohexadiene	None	2.5	Reflux	22	None	0	65
1-Methylcyclohexen-3-one	Butadiene	—	—	—	—	None	0	66

Diene	Reactant	Solvent	Ratio	Temp.	Time	Product	Yield, %	References
1-Methylcyclohexen-3-one	1,3,5-Hexatriene	—	—	—	—	None	0	66
1-Methylcyclohexen-6-one	Butadiene	—	—	—	—	An octalone	—	67
1-Methylcyclohexen-6-one	Butadiene	None	0.4	200	38	A 9-methyl-octalone-1	25	133
2,3-Dimethylindone	1,1'-Bicyclohexenyl	Toluene	—	200	8	HHH	—	19
A¶	Butadiene	None	—	100	—	B	—	38
A	2,3-Dimethylbutadiene	None	—	100	—	B	—	38, 41
A	Cyclopentadiene	—	6	Reflux	24	III	—	8
A	Cyclohexadiene	None	7	Reflux	24	JJJ	—	8
E	Cyclohexadiene	None	1	25	23	KKK	83	8
E	Cyclopentadiene	Benzene	—	—	—	F	—	39
K	1-Vinylcyclopentene	—	—	—	—	1:1 Adduct	—	99
L	1-Vinylcyclohexene	—	—	—	—	1:1 Adduct	—	99
N	1-Vinylcycloheptene	—	—	—	—	1:1 Adduct	—	99
O	1-Vinylcyclooctene	None	1.8	Reflux	30 seconds	1:1 Adduct	10	3
T	1,1'-Bicyclopentenyl	Butanol	—	Reflux	5	U	54	20
T	1,1'-Bicyclopentenyl	None	1.2	Reflux	30 seconds	U	—	3
T	1,1'-Bicyclohexenyl	—	—	—	—	1:1 Adduct	41–58.5	3, 19, 20
V	1,1'-Bicyclohexenyl	—	—	—	—	1:1 Adduct	—	68
Tetrachlorocyclopenta-dienone	Tetrachlorocyclopentadienone	—	—	—	—	Dimer	—	68
3,4-Diphenylcyclopenta-dienone	3,4-Diphenylcyclopentadienone	—	—	—	—	Dimer	—	68
1,4-Dimethyl-2,3-diphenyl-cyclopentadienone	1,4-Dimethyl-2,3-diphenylcyclopentadienone	—	—	—	—	LLL	—	69
Coumarin	2,3-Dimethylbutadiene	Xylene	2.1	260	40	MMM	22	70

* See p. 189 for explanation of symbols in this column.
† References 89–133 are listed on p. 192.
‡ A liquid.
§ Probably XCIX or XCIXA p. 155.
¶ See p. 188 for explanation of symbols in this column.

192 ORGANIC REACTIONS

REFERENCES FOR TABLES

[89] I.G. Farbenind. A.-G., Brit. pat. 324,661 [C.A., **24**, 3801 (1930)].

[90] I.G. Farbenind. A.-G., Ger. pat. 494,433 [C.A., **24**, 2757 (1930)].

[91] Arbuzov and Spekterman, Trans. Kirov Inst. Chem. Tech. Kazan, No. 8, 21 (1940) [C.A., **35**, 2498 (1941)].

[92] I.G. Farbenind. A.-G., Swiss pats. 143,259 through 143,264 (Chem. Zentr., **1931**, I, 2937).

[93] I.G. Farbenind. A.-G., Swiss pat. 143,262 [Chem. Zentr., **1931**, I, 2937].

[94] Lehmann, Ber., **71**, 1874 (1938).

[95] Allen, Elliot, and Bell, Can. J. Research, **17B**, 75 (1935).

[96] I.G. Farbenind. A.-G., Ger. pat. 739,438 [C.A., **39**, 2079 (1945)].

[97] I.G. Farbenind. A.-G., Swiss pat. 143,260 [Chem. Zentr., **1931**, I, 2937].

[98] Gascoigne, J. Proc. Roy. Soc. N. S. Wales, **74**, 353 (1941) [C.A., **35**, 2878 (1941)].

[99] Backer and van der Bij, Rec. trav. chim., **62**, 561 (1943).

[100] Kern and Feuerstein, J. prakt. Chem., [2] **158**, 186 (1941).

[101] Bergmann and Bergmann, J. Am. Chem. Soc., **62**, 1699 (1940).

[102] Arbuzov, Salmina, and Shapshinskaya, Trans. Butlerov Inst. Chem. Technol. Kazan, No. 2, 9 (1934) [C.A., **29**, 3672 (1935)].

[103] Ruzicka and Kaufmann, Helv. Chim. Acta, **24**, 1425 (1941).

[104] Schöpf, von Gottberg, and Petri, Ann., **536**, 216 (1938).

[105] Clar and John, Ber., **63**, 2967 (1930).

[106] Kishner, J. Gen. Chem. U.S.S.R., **3**, 198 (1933) [C.A., **28**, 1696 (1934)].

[107] Barnett, J. Chem. Soc., **1935**, 1326.

[108] Allen and Gates, J. Am. Chem. Soc., **65**, 1502 (1943).

[109] Hudson and Robinson, J. Chem. Soc., **1941**, 715.

[110] Adams and Wicks, J. Am. Chem. Soc., **66**, 1315 (1944).

[111] Fieser, Bowen, Campbell, Fry, and Gates, J. Am. Chem. Soc., **61**, 1926 (1939).

[112] Koelsch and Prill, J. Am. Chem. Soc., **67**, 1296 (1945).

[113] Alder, in Abderhalden, Handbuch der biologischen Arbeitsmethoden, Urban und Schwarzenberg, Berlin, 1933, Abt. I, Teil 2, Heft 9, p. 3112.

[114] Arbuzov, J. Gen. Chem. U.S.S.R., **12**, 343 (1942) [C.A., **37**, 3099 (1943)].

[115] Fieser and Bradsher, J. Am. Chem. Soc., **61**, 417 (1939).

[116] Fieser and Wieghard, J. Am. Chem. Soc., **62**, 153 (1940).

[117] Johnson and Johnson, J. Am. Chem. Soc., **62**, 2619 (1940).

[118] Butz, Butz, and Gaddis, J. Org. Chem., **5**, 171 (1940).

[119] Arbuzov, Ber., **67**, 563 (1934).

[120] Werntz, J. Am. Chem. Soc., **57**, 204 (1935).

[121] Dykstra, J. Am. Chem. Soc., **57**, 2255 (1935).

[122] I.G. Farbenind. A.-G., Ger. pat. 63,322: cited by Alder, Die Chemie, **56**, 53 (1942).

[123] I.G. Farbenind. A.-G., Swiss pat. 143,261 [Chem. Zentr., **1931**, I, 2937].

[124] Bergmann, J. Chem. Soc., **1938**, 1147.

[125] Dufraisse and Compagnon, Compt. rend., **207**, 585 (1938).

[126] Sargent, Buchman, and Farquhar, J. Am. Chem. Soc., **64**, 2692 (1942).

[127] I.G. Farbenind. A.-G., Swiss pat. 143,264 [Chem. Zentr., **1931**, I, 2937].

[128] Arbuzov and Nikanorov, J. Gen. Chem. U.S.S.R., **10**, 649 (1940) [C.A., **34**, 7896 (1940)].

[129] Arbuzov and Nikanorov, Trans. Kirov Inst. Chem. Technol. Kazan, No. 8, 16 (1940).

[130] Dilthey and Leonhard, Ber., **73**, 430 (1940).

[131] Dieterle, Salomon, and Nosseck, Ber., **64**, 2086 (1931).

[132] Raudnitz and Stein, Ber., **68**, 1479 (1935).

[133] Gaddis and Butz, J. Am. Chem. Soc., **69**, 117 (1947).

CHAPTER 4

PREPARATION OF AROMATIC FLUORINE COMPOUNDS FROM DIAZONIUM FLUOBORATES

THE SCHIEMANN REACTION

Arthur Roe

University of North Carolina

CONTENTS

193

INTRODUCTION

An excellent method for the introduction of fluorine into the aromatic nucleus, described by Balz and Schiemann [1] in 1927, has been extensively developed since that time by Schiemann. The method involves two steps: first, the preparation and isolation of a dry diazonium fluoborate; and second, the controlled decomposition of this salt by heat to yield an aromatic fluoride, nitrogen, and boron trifluoride.

$$C_6H_5NH_2 + HNO_2 + BF_4^- \longrightarrow C_6H_5N_2BF_4 + H_2O + OH^- \quad (1)$$

$$C_6H_5N_2BF_4 \xrightarrow{\text{Heat}} C_6H_5F + N_2 + BF_3 \quad (2)$$

The phenomenon which makes possible the Schiemann reaction is the remarkable stability of the dry diazonium fluoborates (sometimes called diazonium borofluorides). These salts, almost alone among the diazonium salts, are quite stable and insensitive to shock, and many can be handled safely in quantities of several kilograms. Most of them have definite decomposition temperatures, and the rates of decomposition, with few exceptions, are easily controlled. The over-all yields in general are satisfactory. No special apparatus is required, and the inorganic fluoborates necessary as intermediates may be purchased or easily prepared.

The first diazonium fluoborates were prepared in 1913 by Bart,[2] who made benzenediazonium fluoborate, as well as p-chloro-, p-nitro-, and p-ethoxy-benzenediazonium fluoborate. He noted the great stability of these compounds and claimed them to be useful as intermediates in preparing therapeutic agents and dyes; he did not prepare aromatic fluorides from them, however. No further report appeared until 1924 when Wilke-Dorfurt [3] isolated two diazonium fluoborates and noted that they were less explosive than the diazonium perchlorates. In 1926

[1] Balz and Schiemann, Ber., 60, 1186 (1927).
[2] Bart, Ger. pat. 281,055 [C.A., 9, 1830 (1915)].
[3] Wilke-Dorfurt, Z. angew. Chem., 37, 712 (1924).

Funk and Binder [4] published a study of the salts of fluoboric acid; they isolated benzenediazonium fluoborate and recorded some of its properties. Wilke-Dorfurt and Balz [5] in 1927 also isolated benzenediazonium fluoborate and reported the decomposition point of the salt to be 100°. Later the same year the paper of Balz and Schiemann [1] appeared, showing that aromatic fluorides could be prepared in excellent yield by the decomposition of these dry diazonium fluoborates.

The Schiemann reaction may be carried out on a wide variety of amines, and over-all yields as high as 70% are not uncommon. Polynuclear aromatic compounds as well as benzene may be used; fluorine has been introduced into naphthalene, phenanthrene, anthracene, biphenyl, fluorene, and benzanthrone by this method. It has been shown that fluoropyridines and fluoroquinolines may be prepared in this manner.

The simultaneous introduction of two fluorine atoms by the use of a bis-diazonium fluoborate has been successful in several instances, although the yields are low unless the two diazonium groups are situated on different benzene rings.

$$H_2N\text{—}\bigcirc\text{—}NH_2 \rightarrow F\text{—}\bigcirc\text{—}F \qquad (27\%)$$

$$H_2N\text{—}\bigcirc\text{—}\bigcirc\text{—}NH_2 \rightarrow F\text{—}\bigcirc\text{—}\bigcirc\text{—}F \qquad (80\%)$$

The effect on the Schiemann reaction of other groups present in the ring is discussed in detail later in the sections "Preparation of Diazonium Fluoborates" and "Decomposition of Diazonium Fluoborates." At this point it need only be noted that the chief effect which other groups may have on the preparation of the intermediate diazonium fluoborate is to render the molecule more soluble, thus lowering the yield. The rate of decomposition of a diazonium fluoborate and the yield of fluoride obtained from it are profoundly affected by the presence of certain groups. Nitro groups generally cause unruly decomposition, and low yields of nitrofluorides result; other groups, such as alkoxy and amino, also lower the yield of fluoride obtained.

Diazonium fluoborates are occasionally used to introduce groups other than fluorine into an aromatic ring. For example, the diazonium fluoborate group may be replaced by the acetoxyl group,[6,7] the nitro

[4] Funk and Binder, Z. anorg. allgem. Chem., 159, 121 (1926).
[5] Wilke-Dorfurt and Balz, Ber., 60, 115 (1927).
[6] Smith and Haller, J. Am. Chem. Soc., 61, 143 (1939).
[7] Haller and Schaffer, J. Am. Chem. Soc., 55, 4954 (1933).

group,[8] the nitrile group,[9] and a hydrogen atom;[10,11] an apparently unsuccessful effort has been made to replace it by a methoxyl group.[12] Diazonium fluoborates may also be used in the preparation of aromatic derivatives of arsenic,[13] mercury,[14,15] and copper.[16,17]

MECHANISM OF THE REACTION

The mechanism of the decomposition of the diazonium fluoborates is not known with certainty, nor is the reason for the unusual stability of these salts fully understood. Schiemann [1,18] proposed that the stability of these salts was due to the linking of an unstable diazonium cation with the complex fluoborate anion, the breaking down of the fluoborate complex to boron trifluoride and fluoride ion requiring approximately the same amount of energy as is given off by the decomposition of the cation. The amount of energy required was calculated by De Boer and Van Liempt [19] to be about 70 kilocalories on the basis of the following equation.

$$BF_3 \text{ (gas)} + F^- \text{ (gas)} \rightarrow BF_4^- \text{ (gas)} + 70 \text{ kcal.}$$

There are three possible mechanisms for the decomposition of the diazonium fluoborates; they are shown diagrammatically below. In

$$[Ar:N{\equiv}N:]^+ \quad [:\ddot{F}:BF_3]^- \xrightarrow{\text{Heat}}$$

1. Carbonium ion: $Ar^+ + N_2 + [:\ddot{F}:BF_3]^-$ (A)

$$Ar^+ + [:\ddot{F}:BF_3]^- \rightarrow Ar:\ddot{F}: + BF_3 \quad \text{(B)}$$

2. Free radical: $Ar\cdot + N_2 + BF_3 + \cdot\ddot{F}:$ (A)

$$Ar\cdot + \cdot\ddot{F}: \rightarrow Ar:\ddot{F}: \quad \text{(B)}$$

3. Rearrangement:
$$\begin{bmatrix} Ar \rightarrow :N{\equiv}N: \\ \quad\nwarrow \\ :\ddot{F}: \\ \uparrow \\ \ddot{B}F_3 \end{bmatrix} \rightarrow Ar:\ddot{F}: + N_2 + BF_3$$

[8] Starkey, *Org. Syntheses, Coll. Vol.* **2**, 225 (1943).
[9] Ruggli and Caspar, *Helv. Chim. Acta,* **18**, 1414 (1935).
[10] Leslie and Turner, *J. Chem. Soc.,* **1933**, 1590.
[11] Schmelkes and Rubin, *J. Am. Chem. Soc.,* **66**, 1631 (1944).
[12] Smith, Elisberg, and Sherrill, *J. Am. Chem. Soc.,* **68**, 1301 (1946).
[13] Ruddy, Starkey, and Hartung, *J. Am. Chem. Soc.,* **64**, 828 (1942).
[14] Dunker and Starkey, *J. Am. Chem. Soc.,* **61**, 3005 (1939).
[15] Dunker, Starkey, and Jenkins, *J. Am. Chem. Soc.,* **58**, 2308 (1936).
[16] Bolth, Whaley, and Starkey, *J. Am. Chem. Soc.,* **65**, 1456 (1943).
[17] Whaley and Starkey, *J. Am. Chem. Soc.,* **68**, 793 (1946).
[18] Schiemann, *Chem. Ztg.,* **52**, 754 (1928).
[19] De Boer and Van Liempt, *Rec. trav. chim.,* **46**, 130 (1927).

order to make the formulas less complex, only those electrons immediately involved are represented; Ar represents any aromatic radical.

Hodgson, Birtwell, and Walker [20] propose mechanism 2, while Bell [21] favors a mechanism like 1, although he calls it a "free radical" mechanism. Such evidence as there is does not make it possible to distinguish among these various possibilities. Bell conducted an interesting experiment to determine whether two "obstacle" amino groups in an optically active biphenyl molecule could be replaced by other groups without loss of optical activity. He reported that *levo*-2,2'-diamino-6,6'-dimethylbiphenyl could be transformed into optically active 2,2'-diiodo-6,6'-dimethylbiphenyl by a diazonium reaction. The replacement of the amino groups by fluorine was also successful, but the optical activity of the product was so slight that Bell stated "the result was not regarded as unambiguous."

This evidence indicates that the replacement of the diazonium group by iodine and fluorine takes place by different mechanisms; this might be anticipated, as the one replacement occurs in cold aqueous solution and the other in the dry state at an elevated temperature. Racemization during the Schiemann reaction might be expected to take place with either mechanism 1 or 2, although it would be less likely with 3. Much work has been done on the mechanism of the decomposition of the diazonium salts in general,* but little has been done directly with the fluoborates.

One related question upon which it is interesting to speculate is the connection between the relatively high stability of the diazonium fluoborates containing the nitro group (as evidenced by their high decomposition temperatures, which are as a group higher than those of any other substituted diazonium fluoborates; see Tables I, II, and III) and the uniformly low yields of nitrofluorides and high yields of tarry by-products obtained by the pyrolysis of these diazonium fluoborates.

Two possibilities suggest themselves. First, the known electron-attracting power of the nitro group may lessen the electron density around the diazonium group, thereby increasing its positive charge and

---

* For leading references see Waters, *J. Chem. Soc.*, **1942**, 266, also reference 20.

[20] Hodgson, Birtwell, and Walker, *J. Chem. Soc.*, **1941**, 770.

[21] Bell, *J. Chem. Soc.*, **1934**, 835.

increasing its electrostatic attraction for the fluoborate ion. This would tend to raise the decomposition point; why such a situation should lower the yield of the product on decomposition is not clear.

A second possibility (suggested in a private communication by Professor O. K. Rice) is that a coördinate bond could be formed between the fluoborate ion and the nitro group existing in one of its resonance forms. Such a situation would be expected to interfere with either mechanism

$$\left[\begin{array}{c} :\overset{..}{O}: \\ :N:::\overset{+}{N}:Ar:\overset{..}{N}::\overset{..}{O}: \\ \overset{..}{F}:BF_3{}^- \end{array} \right] \rightleftharpoons \left[\begin{array}{c} :\overset{..}{O}: \\ :N:::\overset{+}{N}:Ar:\overset{..}{N}:\overset{..}{O}: \\ \overset{..}{F}:BF_3{}^- \end{array} \right] \rightarrow \begin{array}{c} :\overset{..}{O}: \\ :N:::\overset{+}{N}:Ar:\overset{..}{N}:\overset{..}{O}:^- \\ :\overset{..}{F}: \\ BF_3 \end{array}$$

1 or 2, both of which require the presence of the $BF_4{}^-$ ion close to the carbonium ion or free radical. Longer life of either the ion or radical postulated in mechanisms 1 and 2 would be expected from the above equation and would lead to increased polymerization and tar formation.

PREPARATION OF DIAZONIUM FLUOBORATES

Effect of Structure on the Yield of Diazonium Fluoborate

In general, any aromatic amine which can be diazotized will form a diazonium fluoborate, and yields above 90% are frequent. The yield reported is often of unpurified material, however, and may be high owing to coprecipitation of sodium fluoborate; a large excess of sodium fluoborate is sometimes used to obtain maximum yields, and some reported yields are over 100% for this reason.

The most important effect other groups in the ring may have upon the yield is that of increasing the solubility of the salt, thereby decreasing the yield. In a series of isomers, regardless of the nature of the second group, the *ortho* diazonium salt is usually the most soluble, hence is isolated in the lowest yield. The *para* isomer is usually formed in the highest amount, although the *meta* isomer is often formed in about the same yield.

Certain groups, such as carboxyl and hydroxyl, tend to increase the solubility, and the transformation of these groups into esters and ethers improves the yield of the diazonium fluoborate. This is illustrated by the following facts. In an attempt to prepare the diazonium fluoborates from the three aminophenols, only the *meta* isomer was isolated, and this in less than 50% yield.[22] Starting with the phenetidines, however,

[22] Bennett, Brooks, and Glasstone, *J. Chem. Soc.*, **1935**, 1821.

the diazonium fluoborates were isolated in the following yields: *ortho*, 69%; *meta*, 75%; *para*, 87%.[13] The fluorophenetoles obtained may be converted to fluorophenols in good yields. The three anisidines were used with similar results. Again, the highest yield reported for the preparation of the diazonium fluoborate from *o*-aminobenzoic acid was 46%,[13] whereas the yield from the corresponding ethyl ester was 80%.[23]

No other generalizations concerning the effect of specific substituents on the yield of diazonium fluoborates can be made; the yield is also affected by the method of diazotization and the source of the fluoborate ion, as discussed in the next sections.

An interesting side reaction that may occur during the diazotization should be mentioned here. Willstaedt and Scheiber [24] attempted to prepare 1-nitro-2-fluoronaphthalene and found that their product would not undergo reduction to 1-amino-2-fluoronaphthalene; they attributed this to a powerful *"ortho* effect" exerted by the neighboring fluorine atom.

NO$_2$ NO$_2$ NO$_2$

naphthalene-NH$_2$ → naphthalene-N$_2$BF$_4$ → naphthalene-F

Schiemann and Ley [25] demonstrated that this was definitely not an *ortho* effect and showed that the reason for the non-reducibility of Willstaedt's nitro group was that no nitro group was present in the molecule. During the diazotization the nitro group was replaced by a chlorine atom; the final product was, therefore, 1-chloro-2-fluoronaphthalene. This replacement of a nitro group during diazotization has been observed before.[26]

NO$_2$ Cl Cl

naphthalene-NH$_2$ $\xrightarrow[\substack{\text{NaNO}_2,\ \text{then}\\ \text{HBF}_4}]{\text{Concd. HCl}}$ naphthalene-N$_2$BF$_4$ → naphthalene-F

Methods of Preparation

In preparing diazonium fluoborates the volume of solution is kept as small as possible to reduce loss of product, since the salts are slightly soluble even in cold water. The salts must be thoroughly dried, as unruly decomposition and lowered yields result from the pyrolysis of a moist product. Sometimes the fluoborates undergo spontaneous de-

[23] Bergmann, Engel, and Sandor, *Z. physik. Chem.*, **10B**, 106 (1930).
[24] Willstaedt and Scheiber, *Ber.*, **67**, 466 (1934).
[25] Schiemann and Ley, *Ber.*, **69**, 960 (1936).
[26] Morgan, *J. Chem. Soc.*, **81**, 1376 (1902).

composition if a tightly packed moist salt is allowed to stand. Rapid drying is advantageous; this can be achieved by spreading the salt rather thinly on porous paper (supported on a screen or wire netting so that air can circulate freely underneath) and placing near a hood. Direct sunlight is reported to cause decomposition of fluoborates.[27] Occasionally some diazonium fluoborates will decompose while drying; m-methoxybenzenediazonium fluoborate is quite unstable,[28, 29, 30] and o-methylbenzenediazonium fluoborate sometimes gives trouble in this way. Diazonium fluoborates of certain heterocyclic compounds are likewise unstable.[31, 32]

There are two general methods of preparing these salts. The first method involves the diazotization of the amine in the usual manner, followed by addition of the fluoborate ion in the form of fluoboric acid or some derivative. In the second method the amine is diazotized in the presence of the fluoborate ion, and the diazonium fluoborate precipitates continuously as the diazotization proceeds. Various modifications of these procedures are described in detail below.

I. Diazotization Followed by Addition of Fluoborate Ion

DIAZOTIZING AGENT	SOURCE OF FLUOBORATE ION
A. Nitrous acid	Fluoboric acid
B. Nitrous acid	Sodium fluoborate
C. Nitrous acid	Ammonium fluoborate
D. Amyl nitrite	Fluoboric acid
E. Nitrosylsulfuric acid	Fluoboric acid
F. Nitrous acid in presence of hydrofluoric acid	Boron trifluoride

Methods IA, B, and C. The most common procedure in following the first method consists in diazotizing as usual with sodium nitrite and hydrochloric acid,* and adding a cold aqueous solution of fluoboric acid, sodium fluoborate, or ammonium fluoborate to the clear diazonium solution (filtered if necessary). A precipitate forms immediately and is allowed to stand at 0° or lower for at least half an hour to ensure complete precipitation. The precipitate is then filtered, washed with cold water (or cold sodium fluoborate solution or fluoboric acid), sucked as

* Bradlow and VanderWerf (private communication) report that considerable time may be saved when diazotizing large quantities by adding solid sodium nitrite in small portions to a vigorously stirred solution which is kept below 0° by the addition of Dry Ice.

[27] Schiemann, J. prakt. Chem., [2] 140, 97 (1934).
[28] Becker and Adams, J. Am. Chem. Soc., 54, 2973 (1932).
[29] Schiemann, Z. physik. Chem., A156, 397 (1931).
[30] Bradlow and VanderWerf, J. Am. Chem. Soc., 70, 654 (1948).
[31] Roe and Hawkins, J. Am. Chem. Soc., 69, 2443 (1947).
[32] Roe and Hawkins, New York Meeting A.C.S., 1947, Abstracts, p. 36L.

dry as possible on the filter, then sometimes washed with cold alcohol, dioxane, or ether. Many fluoborates are appreciably soluble in alcohol or dioxane, however, so caution in washing is necessary. If a clear diazonium solution is used and the precipitate dried rapidly as described above, washing with organic solvents is unnecessary. Drying the salt in a desiccator is usually not required. Many fluoborates are sufficiently stable to be recrystallized from acetone, and some may be recrystallized from water; in this way very pure salts can be prepared if needed.

It is advisable to filter the solution (or extract it with ether) before addition of the fluoborate ion in order to remove by-products formed during the diazotization; the presence of these by-products in the diazonium fluoborate is undesirable and lowers the yield of final product. The formation of these by-products—chiefly phenols and coupling products—seems to be decreased when the diazotization is carried out in the presence of the fluoborate ion, as in method II.

Meigs [33] states that the yields are lowered when fluoborate ion is added to the diazonium chloride in strongly acid solution because of the increased solubility of the diazonium fluoborate in such a solution; it is recommended that the solution contain less than 1 mole of hydrogen ion per liter at the time the fluoborate is added. Sodium fluoborate rather than fluoboric acid is recommended as a source of the fluoborate ion. Support for this recommendation was obtained by adding four different precipitants to four identical solutions each containing 0.1 mole of benzenediazonium chloride. The results are shown below.

PRECIPITANT (IN SOLUTION)	HYDROGEN ION IN MOLES PER LITER AT END	YIELD %
1. 0.11 mole HBF_4	1.96	67
2. 0.11 mole 50% HBF_4 50% $NaBF_4$	1.09	78.1
3. 0.11 mole 25% HBF_4 75% $NaBF_4$	0.67	80.1
4. 0.11 mole $NaBF_4$	0.26	84.3

Dippy and Williams [34] reported similar findings in the preparation of o-fluorobenzoic acid: o-carbethoxybenzenediazonium fluoborate was prepared by the addition of fluoboric acid to the diazonium chloride; an excess of acid lowered the yield appreciably.

Finger and Reed [35] carried out parallel experiments using both sodium and ammonium fluoborate as the source of fluoborate ion; they found

[33] Meigs, U. S. pat. 1,916,327 [C.A., 27, 4539 (1933)].
[34] Dippy and Williams, J. Chem. Soc., 1934, 1466.
[35] Finger and Reed, Trans. Illinois State Acad. Sci., 33, No. 2, 108 (1940) [C.A., 35, 2480 (1941)].

that in most experiments the two salts gave practically identical results. Sodium fluoborate is more soluble than the ammonium salt, and a larger volume of water is therefore necessary if the latter is used.

Method ID. von Braun and Rudolph [36] used amyl nitrite followed by the addition of 2 moles of fluoboric acid in the preparation of 2-nitro-6-methylbenzenediazonium fluoborate from the amine in 50% yield. This method was also used by Willstaedt and Scheiber [24] in the preparation of 1-benzeneazo-2-naphthalenediazonium fluoborate in 31% yield from the amine.

Method IE. Nitrosylsulfuric acid was used as the diazotizing agent in the preparation of the diazonium sulfate of Bz-1-aminobenzanthrone by Lüttringhaus and Neresheimer; [37] the slightly soluble diazonium sulfate was dissolved in warm water and converted quantitatively to the fluoborate by addition of fluoboric acid.

Method IF. The use of boron trifluoride in the preparation of the diazonium fluoborates is described by Meigs.[33] The diazotization is carried out in the presence of hydrofluoric acid, then gaseous boron trifluoride is led into the solution until precipitation of the diazonium fluoborate is complete.

An excellent method of analyzing diazonium fluoborates by decomposing them in sulfuric acid and measuring the nitrogen evolved has been reported by Schiemann and Pillarsky.[38]

EXPERIMENTAL PROCEDURES METHOD I. Almost any diazonium fluoborate may be prepared by any of the procedures in this or the next section. The preparation of benzenediazonium fluoborate,[39] p-carbethoxybenzenediazonium fluoborate,[40] and 4,4'-biphenyl-bis-diazonium fluoborate [41] by method I is described in *Organic Syntheses*; the preparation of p-nitrobenzenediazonium fluoborate by method II is also described there.[8] All the experimental procedures in this chapter have been checked by the author.

Preparation of Reagents. Fluoboric acid and sodium and ammonium fluoborate are available commercially. The preparation of the first two is briefly described.

Fluoboric acid may be prepared by dissolving 1 mole of boric acid slowly with cooling in approximately 4 moles of 40–48% hydrofluoric acid. The mixing should be done in a wax-lined or rubber beaker, and the temperature should be kept below 25° to prevent melting of the

[36] von Braun and Rudolph, *Ber.*, **64**, 2465 (1931).
[37] Lüttringhaus and Neresheimer, *Ann.*, **473**, 259 (1929).
[38] Schiemann and Pillarsky, *Ber.*, **62**, 3035 (1929).
[39] Flood, *Org. Syntheses, Coll. Vol.* **2**, 295 (1943).
[40] Schiemann and Winkelmüller, *Org. Syntheses, Coll. Vol.* **2**, 299 (1943).
[41] Schiemann and Winkelmüller, *Org. Syntheses, Coll. Vol.* **2**, 188 (1943).

wax by the heat of reaction. Stirring may be done with a lead or rubber rod.

Sodium fluoborate [42] may be prepared by adding 333 g. of powdered boric acid to 1338 ml. of concentrated hydrochloric acid. To this mixture 900 g. of sodium fluoride is added slowly with shaking and cooling. The mixture is allowed to stand for two hours and filtered. About 1465 ml. of solution is obtained, containing 5.38 moles of sodium fluoborate.

p-Bromobenzenediazonium Fluoborate. To a mixture of 62 ml. (0.75 mole) of concentrated hydrochloric acid and an equal amount of water is added 43 g. (0.25 mole) of *p*-bromoaniline. The mixture is cooled to 0°, and a cold solution of 17.3 g. (0.25 mole) of sodium nitrite is added slowly, the temperature being kept near 0°; Dry Ice added in small portions to the solution is helpful in controlling the temperature. The diazotized solution is filtered if necessary through a cold sintered-glass filter; a cold solution of 35 g. (0.34 mole) of ammonium fluoborate in 120 ml. of water is added with vigorous stirring. The light-green precipitate is stirred at 0° for at least half an hour, filtered, and washed with 25 ml. of cold 5% ammonium fluoborate solution, 30 ml. of ice-cold methanol, and several 50-ml. portions of ether, the precipitate being sucked as dry as possible after each washing. The salt is dried by spreading it thinly on porous paper supported on a screen or wire netting allowing air circulation underneath. The yield is 48–55 g. (71–82%).

m-Nitrobenzenediazonium Fluoborate. This compound may be prepared by following the above directions, using 34.6 g. (0.25 mole) of *m*-nitroaniline. A solution of 35 g. of either sodium fluoborate or ammonium fluoborate in water may be used as a precipitant, or, if preferred, 48 ml. of cold 42% fluoboric acid (0.3 mole). The precipitate is treated as described above. The yield is 53–57 g. (90–97%).

β-Naphthalenediazonium Fluoborate. This salt may be prepared by the method described for *p*-bromobenzenediazonium fluoborate, using 35.8 g. (0.25 mole) of *β*-naphthylamine. Dioxane may be substituted for methanol for washing the precipitate. The yield is 55–60 g. (90–97%).

m-Toluenediazonium Fluoborate. The apparatus is placed in a good hood. A wax-coated beaker is placed in an ice-salt bath; 41 ml. of concentrated hydrochloric acid and 12 g. of 48% hydrofluoric acid are placed in the beaker, and 26.8 g. (0.25 mole) of freshly distilled *m*-toluidine is added. The solution is diazotized with a cold solution of 17.3 g. of sodium nitrite, the temperature being kept at about 0°; a wax-coated or lead stirrer is used. When all the sodium nitrite has been added, boron trifluoride from a cylinder is introduced until precipitation of the

[42] Suter, Lawson, and Smith, *J. Am. Chem. Soc.*, **61**, 161 (1939).

diazonium fluoborate is complete. Efficient stirring and cooling are essential during the addition of the boron trifluoride; Dry Ice added to the solution helps control the temperature. The precipitate is washed with 50 ml. of ice water and 50 ml. of iced methanol, followed by several washings with ether; it is then dried as described above. The yield is 39–43 g. (76–84%). This is the least convenient of any of the procedures for the preparation of a diazonium fluoborate on a laboratory scale.

II. Diazotization in the Presence of Fluoborate Ion

Source of the fluoborate ion:

A. Fluoboric acid.
B. Sodium fluoborate.
C. Ammonium fluoborate.
D. Nitrosyl fluoborate.

Excellent yields are obtained by diazotizing in the presence of fluoborate ion. Fluoboric acid may be the only acid present, acting both as acid and source of fluoborate ion. Sodium and ammonium fluoborates are used in conjunction with an acid (usually hydrochloric), as is nitrosyl fluoborate, although the last serves as diazotizing agent as well as a source of fluoborate ion.

The insoluble diazonium fluoborate separates from the solution as it is formed; side reactions such as phenol formation and coupling are held to the minimum. Temperature control is not so critical in this procedure; the temperature may in some cases rise to 30° during the diazotization with no ill effect.[33] There are certain disadvantages, however; a continuously thickening precipitate is formed as the reaction proceeds; efficient stirring overcomes this difficulty. The fumes of fluoboric acid are corrosive and obnoxious, and fluoboric acid has been known to eat its way out of the wax-lined bottles in which it is stored. The yields of diazonium fluoborates produced by this method are usually as good as and sometimes better than the yields by method I; it is claimed [17] that a cleaner and more easily purified salt results from method II.

Method IIA. Starkey [8] prepared *p*-nitrobenzenediazonium fluoborate in 95–99% yield from *p*-nitroaniline with fluoboric acid as the only acid present. Aniline, *o*-, *m*-, and *p*-chloroaniline, ethyl *p*-aminobenzoate, *p*-aminoacetophenone, and other amines have been converted to the diazonium fluoborates by this method in better yield than by other methods.[13] These are but a few examples of the preparation of diazonium fluoborates by diazotization in the presence of fluoboric acid.

The tetrazotization of diamines is also carried out with good yields this way; Ruggli and Caspar [9] report the preparation of 1,4-benzene-bis-diazonium fluoborate from p-phenylenediamine in 78% yield, varying the method slightly by adding a mixture of the amine and sodium nitrite slowly to a cold solution of fluoboric acid. The corresponding meta derivative is formed in an unspecified lower yield. They also prepared 1,5-dimethyl-2,4-benzene-bis-diazonium fluoborate quantitatively by this method.

Methods IIB and C. Parts [43] diazotized β-naphthylamine in the presence of sodium fluoborate to prepare the diazonium fluoborate in unspecified yield. Both sodium and ammonium fluoborates are now available commercially, and there is no reason why they could not be used in the preparation of diazonium fluoborates in this way.

Method IID. Voznesenkii and Kurskii [44] prepared benzenediazonium fluoborate in 90% yield from aniline hydrochloride and nitrosyl fluoborate. The latter reagent was prepared from fluoboric acid and nitrogen dioxide in good yield.

EXPERIMENTAL PROCEDURES METHOD II. The preparation of p-nitrobenzenediazonium fluoborate is described in *Organic Syntheses*.[8] Any amine which can be diazotized, including diamines, may be transformed into the diazonium fluoborate by this method.

p-Methoxybenzenediazonium Fluoborate. To 100 ml. of 42% fluoboric acid (0.625 mole) diluted with 100 ml. of water is added 30.8 g. of p-anisidine (0.25 mole); the solution is cooled in an ice bath. A solution of 17.3 g. of sodium nitrite (0.25 mole) in 35 ml. of water is added slowly, the temperature being kept at about 10°. The gradually thickening precipitate requires vigorous stirring toward the end of the reaction. The mixture is cooled to 0° and filtered. The precipitate is washed with 40 ml. of cold 5% fluoboric acid, 50 ml. of ice-cold methanol, and several 50-ml. portions of ether, and dried overnight as described in Method I. The yield is 52–54 g. (94–98%).

Instead of fluoboric acid, 51 ml. of concentrated hydrochloric acid, 100 ml. of water, and 35 g. of either sodium or ammonium fluoborate may be used. The procedure is identical with the above, and the yield is about the same.

4,4'-Biphenyl-bis-diazonium Fluoborate. This salt may be prepared by the same procedure as described above, using 46 g. (0.25 mole) of benzidine and 240 ml. of 42% fluoboric acid. If desired, 64.4 g. (0.25 mole) of benzidine dihydrochloride may be added to 91 ml. (0.57

[43] Parts, Z. physik. Chem., **10B**, 264 (1930).
[44] Voznesenkii and Kurskii, J. Gen. Chem. U.S.S.R., **8**, 524 (1938) [C.A., **32**, 8379 (1938)].

mole) of fluoboric acid and 250 ml. of water; this is then diazotized as above. The yield is 80–86 g. (93–100%).

3-*Pyridinediazonium Fluoborate*.[31] Twelve and a half grams of 3-aminopyridine is dissolved in a mixture of 50 ml. of 40% fluoboric acid and 100 ml. of 95% ethanol. The solution is cooled to 0°, and a stream of ethyl nitrite [45] is passed in until precipitation of the diazonium fluoborate is complete. Fifty milliliters of cold ether is added to complete the precipitation, and the mixture is filtered while cold and washed once with cold ether and then once with cold petroleum ether. The precipitate must not be allowed to become dry at any time, for this diazonium salt when dry will undergo violent spontaneous decomposition. The salt is dampened with petroleum ether and transferred to a beaker containing 50 ml. of ice-cold high-boiling petroleum ether.

DECOMPOSITION OF DIAZONIUM FLUOBORATES

Effect of Structure on the Decomposition of Diazonium Fluoborates

$$C_6H_5N_2BF_4 \xrightarrow{\text{Heat}} C_6H_5F + N_2 + BF_3$$

The decomposition of diazonium fluoborates usually proceeds smoothly, and the average yield from all types of compounds is in the neighborhood of 65%. There is no great variation in the yield of *ortho*, *meta*, and *para* isomers formed by the decomposition of substituted diazonium fluoborates, although in general the *ortho* isomer is formed in the smallest amount. Polynuclear aromatic compounds decompose smoothly and produce the fluorine compounds in good yields. Of the few heterocyclic diazonium fluoborates known, some decompose spontaneously, while others are quite stable and decompose evenly, producing good yields of the fluoride. Decomposition of substances containing two diazonium fluoborate groups occurs smoothly and in surprisingly good yield if the groups are on different rings of a polynuclear molecule; otherwise the yields are low.

Diazonium fluoborates of otherwise unsubstituted aromatic molecules give the best yield of fluorides; however, the presence of halogen and alkyl groups on the molecule does not seriously interfere with the yield. Compounds with an ether linkage decompose smoothly but the yields are somewhat lowered, most of them being between 40% and 60%. The presence of ester, carboxyl, amino, nitro, and hydroxyl groups also lowers the yield, the effect increasing roughly in the order named. The above statements are generalizations, and some individual exceptions may be found.

[45] Semon and Damerell, *Org. Syntheses, Coll. Vol.* **2**, 204 (1943).

Highly substituted molecules do not necessarily give poor yields, as evidenced by the 74% yield of 2-bromo-3-methoxy-4,6-dimethylfluorobenzene obtained by the decomposition of the corresponding diazonium fluoborate.[28]

$$
\begin{array}{ccc}
& N_2BF_4 & & & F \\
Br\!\!-\!\!\bigcirc\!\!-CH_3 & \xrightarrow{\text{Heat}} & Br\!\!-\!\!\bigcirc\!\!-CH_3 \\
CH_3O & & CH_3O \\
& CH_3 & & & CH_3
\end{array}
$$

The compounds whose decomposition is most troublesome and difficult to control are those containing the nitro group. The decomposition of these compounds is tempestuous and unruly, and special methods are required for handling them, as outlined in a later section. The yields of fluoronitro compounds are, with few exceptions, low; the preparation of 2-fluoro-6-nitrotoluene in 63% yield from the corresponding diazonium fluoborate[46] and the preparation of fluoronitromesitylene in an over-all yield of 65–68% from the amine[47] are the best yields of nitrofluoro compounds yet reported. The following list serves to illustrate the generalizations in the previous paragraphs by showing the yields obtained by the decomposition of a few simple *ortho-* and *para-*substituted benzenediazonium fluoborates; in every case the best reported yield is given. (References are to be found in the larger tables at the end of the chapter and are not repeated here.)

Ortho SUBSTITUENT	YIELD FLUORIDE %	Para SUBSTITUENT	YIELD FLUORIDE %
H—	100	H—	100
CH₃—	90	CH₃—	97
C₂H₅O₂C—	87	C₂H₅O₂C—	90
Cl—	85	Br—	75
Br—	81	CH₃O—	67
I—	70	F—	62
CH₃O—	67	O₂N—	58
CH₃O₂C—	53	C₂H₅O—	53
C₂H₅O—	36	(C₂H₅)₂N—	20
F—	30	(CH₃)₂N—	17
HO₂C—	19		
O₂N—	19		

The statement has been made [27] that the yield of fluoride is somewhat dependent upon the decomposition temperature of the diazonium fluo-

---

[46] Lock, *Ber.*, **69**, 2253 (1936).

[47] Finger and co-workers, Atlantic City Meeting A.C.S., 1946, *Abstracts*, p. 13M.

borate, lower temperatures producing better yields. This statement is qualitatively true for unsubstituted hydrocarbons and those already containing one or more fluorine atoms; for other types of diazonium fluoborates the relationship does not hold very well. The two reactions which follow illustrate this statement.

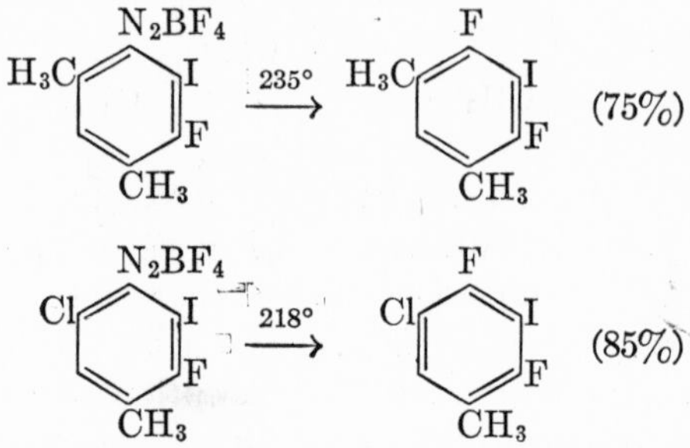

$$H_3C \overset{N_2BF_4}{\underset{CH_3}{\bigcirc}} I \quad \overset{235°}{\longrightarrow} \quad H_3C \overset{F}{\underset{CH_3}{\bigcirc}} I \quad (75\%)$$

$$Cl \overset{N_2BF_4}{\underset{CH_3}{\bigcirc}} I \quad \overset{218°}{\longrightarrow} \quad Cl \overset{F}{\underset{CH_3}{\bigcirc}} I \quad (85\%)$$

The decomposition temperature of 2-iodo-3-fluoro-4,6-dimethylbenzenediazonium fluoborate (235°) is the highest reported in the literature.

Side Reactions during Decomposition

The diazonium fluoborate must be thoroughly dry before being decomposed. The presence of moisture sometimes makes the decomposition uncontrollable and always markedly lowers the yield; phenols and tars are formed instead of the desired product. However, perfectly dry

$$C_6H_5N_2BF_4 + H_2O \xrightarrow{Heat} C_6H_5OH + HF + N_2 + BF_3 + tar$$

fluoborates sometimes form tar and resinous material on decomposition. The ability of boron trifluoride to bring about condensations and polymerizations is well known, and this action is probably responsible in large measure for the formation of these products of high molecular weight. The decomposition of molecules containing the nitro group always results in the formation of a large amount of tarry material of unknown nature.

The boron trifluoride evolved during the decomposition may cause splitting of ester groups present on the molecule. Schiemann [27] and Bergmann, Engel, and Sandor [23] report that some o-fluorobenzoic acid is formed directly during the decomposition of o-carbethoxybenzenediazonium fluoborate.

$$\overset{CO_2C_2H_5}{\underset{N_2BF_4}{\bigcirc}} \xrightarrow{Heat} \overset{CO_2C_2H_5}{\underset{F}{\bigcirc}} + \overset{CO_2H}{\underset{F}{\bigcirc}}$$

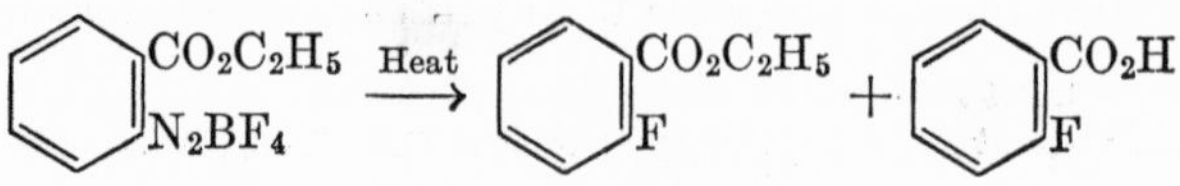

The substitution of hydrogen for the diazonium fluoborate radical during pyrolysis was reported by Niemann, Benson, and Mead [48] (also private communication from Dr. Niemann). They prepared methyl 3,5-difluoro-4-methoxybenzoate from 2-methoxy-3-fluoro-5-carbomethoxybenzenediazonium fluoborate, obtaining at the same time some methyl 3-fluoro-4-methoxybenzoate. Never more than one-fifth as much monofluoro as difluoro compound was formed, and the yield of the crude ester mixture was only about 35%. A somewhat similar

result was reported by Schmelkes and Rubin.[11] They prepared 2-fluoro-4-nitrotoluene and found that, if all the methanol used in washing the diazonium fluoborate was not carefully removed, partial deamination with formation of 4-nitrotoluene occurred on pyrolysis of the salt. Of interest in connection with the two results reported above is the work of Leslie and Turner,[10] who obtained a 78% yield of 2-nitro-3'-bromobiphenyl from 2-nitro-3'-bromo-4,4'-biphenyl-*bis*-diazonium fluoborate by warming it with ethanolic sulfuric acid.

Apparatus for Decomposing Diazonium Fluoborates

Large amounts of boron trifluoride and nitrogen are evolved during the reaction; wide tubing should be used for all connections. The apparatus should be arranged so that these gases may be led to a good hood; often a trap to catch the boron trifluoride is included. The boron trifluoride may be taken up in water, alkali, or a suspension of sodium fluoride in water; the latter procedure is recommended as a satisfactory method of preserving the gas for future use, as sodium fluoborate is formed.[33]

The apparatus depends on the method of decomposition chosen and upon the volatility of the product. The flask in which the decomposition is carried out should never be more than half full of the salt. If the product is relatively non-volatile, as are many of the biphenyl derivatives, a short air condenser attached to the decomposition flask will suffice.[49] Another satisfactory method of decomposing compounds of this type is to carry out the decomposition in a large distilling flask, the side arm

[48] Niemann, Benson, and Mead, *J. Am. Chem. Soc.*, **63**, 2204 (1941).
[49] Shaw and Turner, *J. Chem. Soc.*, **1932**, 509.

of which leads to another distilling flask acting as a receiver; the receiver may be cooled with running water if necessary.[41] More volatile products, such as the fluorotoluenes, will distil during the decomposition, and an efficient cooling system consisting of a condenser, cooled receiving flask, and an ice trap must be provided. Some compounds, such as the fluorobenzotrifluorides, are still more volatile, and special brine or Dry Ice traps are necessary.[50, 51]

Methods of Decomposing Diazonium Fluoborates

The pyrolysis is carried out by heating the *dry* diazonium fluoborate gently near its surface until decomposition commences. Often no more heat is required, the decomposition continuing spontaneously; sometimes heat must be applied intermittently. Occasionally the reaction becomes too violent and the flask must be cooled with water or by rubbing it with ice. After most of the salt has decomposed, the flask is heated strongly to ensure complete decomposition of the salt.

Most decompositions go smoothly, and large quantities of material may be handled safely.[39] Compounds containing the nitro group are an outstanding exception; they usually decompose suddenly and with considerable violence. Usually they are mixed with three to five times their weight of a diluent, such as sand, barium sulfate, or sodium fluoride,[52] and decomposed in small quantities—5 g. to 25 g. at a time. Carrying out the decomposition at a reduced pressure often helps control the reaction.

The diazonium fluoborates may be decomposed in the following ways:

A. By heating the salt gently with a free flame in a flask fitted with a suitable condensing system to collect the product.

B. Same as A, the decomposition being carried out under reduced pressure.

C. By placing the salt in a flask and keeping it for some time at a temperature 10–20° below its decomposition temperature.[53, 54]

D. By adding the salt little by little to a flask whose temperature is at or above the decomposition temperature of the salt.[53, 54]

E. By mixing a few grams of the salt with three or four times its weight of a diluent such as sand, barium sulfate, or sodium fluoride, and decomposing the mixture according to one of the above methods.[14, 38, 52]

[50] Aelony, *J. Am. Chem. Soc.*, **56**, 2063 (1934).

[51] Finger and Reed, *J. Am. Chem. Soc.*, **66**, 1972 (1944).

[52] Roe and Fleishmann, *J. Am. Chem. Soc.*, **69**, 509 (1947).

[53] Cannoni de Degiorgi and Zappi, *Anales asoc. quím. argentina*, **28**, 72 (1940) [*C. A.*, **34**, 6593 (1940)].

[54] Kleiderer and Adams, *J. Am. Chem. Soc.*, **55**, 4219 (1933).

F. By suspending the salt in an indifferent solvent such as petroleum ether, toluene, biphenyl, or quinoline, and heating.[27, 31, 55, 56]

Method A is the one most often employed, although Method F is used occasionally. The other techniques are used chiefly for carrying out the decomposition of diazonium fluoborates containing the nitro group.

Experimental Procedures

The amount of diazonium fluoborates used in the following examples is the amount prepared in the previous experimental section. In every preparation except that of m-nitrofluorobenzene, much larger quantities may be used safely.

m-Fluorotoluene. Forty grams of dry m-toluenediazonium fluoborate is placed in a 500-ml. round-bottomed flask connected by a wide tube through a condenser to two 500-ml. Erlenmeyer flasks in series cooled in ice-salt mixtures. The last flask is fitted with a tube leading to a good hood or to an absorption flask containing ice and water, soda solution, or a suspension of sodium fluoride to absorb the voluminous fumes of boron trifluoride evolved; the outlet tube from the last flask should lead to a hood. The salt is heated gently with a free flame at a point near the surface until decomposition commences as evidenced by the evolution of white fumes; the flame is then removed. Gentle heating is continued only if necessary to keep the decomposition going; at the end of the decomposition the flask is heated vigorously until no more fumes are evolved. The fluorotoluene may be removed completely from the decomposition flask by further heating and the application of slight suction; another satisfactory procedure is to return all the fluorotoluene to the reaction flask, add water to dissolve the boron trifluoride and hydrogen fluoride, and steam-distil. In either procedure the fluorotoluene is dissolved in 150 ml. of ether, washed first with dilute sodium hydroxide, then with water, and dried over calcium chloride. After removal of the ether the product boils at 114–115°; yield, 19 g. (89%).

p-Fluoroanisole. A 500-ml. round-bottomed flask is connected by a wide tube through a condenser to a cooled 250-ml. distilling flask, the side arm of which leads to a hood or trap as described above. The dry p-methoxybenzenediazonium fluoborate (54 g.) is placed in the decomposition flask, and the decomposition is carried out as described above. The small amount of product in the receiving flask is returned to the decomposition flask and steam-distilled. The distillate is extracted with 100 ml. of ether; the ether solution is washed with 50 ml. of 10%

[55] Goldberg, Ordas, and Carsch, J. Am. Chem. Soc., **69**, 260 (1947).
[56] Zenitz and Hartung, J. Org. Chem., **11**, 444 (1946).

sodium hydroxide solution, followed by water, and dried over calcium chloride. After removal of the ether on the steam bath the product boils at 156–157°; yield, about 16 g. (52%).

p-Bromofluorobenzene. The dry *p*-bromobenzenediazonium fluoborate (50 g.) is placed in the decomposition flask of an apparatus similar to that described above for the preparation of *p*-fluoroanisole. The decomposition of the salt and the working up of the product are carried out as described for *p*-fluoroanisole. The product boils at 150–151°; yield, 25 g. (77%).

β-Fluoronaphthalene. The apparatus consists of a 500-ml. distilling flask whose side arm leads to another distilling flask of the same size which is cooled with running water. The side arm of the receiving flask leads to a good hood or a trap as described above. The dry β-naphthalenediazonium fluoborate (55 g.) is placed in the decomposition flask and heated gently until decomposition starts; further gentle heating may be necessary from time to time. Some of the white powdery product is collected in the receiving flask; at the conclusion of the decomposition the product is steam-distilled. The product melts at 60°, and the yield is about 27 g. (81%).

4,4′-Difluorobiphenyl. The apparatus is identical with that described for β-fluoronaphthalene; 80 g. of dry 4,4′-biphenyl-*bis*-diazonium fluoborate is placed in the decomposition flask, and the decomposition is carried out as described for β-fluoronaphthalene. The product is steam-distilled; yield, 36 g. (82%). A second steam distillation is sometimes necessary to obtain a pure product, m.p. 90°.

m-Fluoronitrobenzene. The apparatus consists of a 250-ml. flask connected by a wide bent tube through a water-cooled condenser to a second 250-ml. flask acting as a receiver. The side arm of the flask leads to a good hood or a trap as previously described. An intimate mixture of 13 g. of *m*-nitrobenzenediazonium fluoborate and 36 g. of clean dry sand (or barium sulfate or sodium fluoride) is placed in the reaction flask and heated cautiously until decomposition starts. Intermittent heating is necessary to complete the reaction. The products of four such decompositions are combined in a 1-l. flask and steam-distilled. The product is taken up in 100 ml. of ether, washed with 25 ml. of 5% sodium hydroxide then twice with 25 ml. of water, and dried over anhydrous potassium carbonate. After removal of the ether on a steam bath the product distils at 53–54°/1–2 mm.; the yield is 16 g. (54%). It is possible to decompose as much as 25 g. of the salt at a time, although the yields are sometimes smaller with larger quantities.

3-Fluoropyridine. The 3-pyridinediazonium fluoborate,* covered with at least 50 ml. of cold high-boiling petroleum ether, is allowed to warm slowly until decomposition starts; the temperature is kept below 25°, however, as the decomposition is uncontrollable above this temperature. After decomposition is complete, 5 ml. of concentrated hydrochloric acid is added to ensure salt formation, and the solvent is removed under reduced pressure. The residue is made alkaline with sodium hydroxide solution, the solution being kept cold during the process. The solution is then distilled; solid sodium hydroxide is added to the distillate, whereupon an oil separates. The oil, after drying over sodium hydroxide, distils at 105–107°/752 mm.; the yield is 6.4 g. (50% from the amine). The use of ether to extract the product is impractical because of the difficulty in separating the ether from the product.

OTHER METHODS OF PREPARING AROMATIC FLUORIDES

During World War II a vast amount of research was done on the preparation of organic fluorine compounds; few aromatic fluorocarbons were prepared, however. Perfluoro alicyclic compounds (such as dodecafluorocyclohexane) were prepared by direct fluorination of aromatic hydrocarbons in the presence of a catalyst consisting of copper coated with the fluorides of silver [57] and by fluorination with cobalt trifluoride,[58] silver difluoride,[59] and other metallic fluorides.[60] All compounds prepared by any of these methods are fully saturated. The preparation of two aromatic fluorides—hexafluorobenzene and octafluorotoluene—has been accomplished; [61] the method is illustrated in the accompanying

$$C_6Cl_6 \xrightarrow{BrF_3} C_6Br_2Cl_4F_6 \xrightarrow{SbF_5} C_6BrCl_4F_7 \xrightarrow{Zn} C_6F_6$$

equation. No simple hydrogen-containing aromatic fluorine compounds have been prepared by any of the above methods.

Much work had been done on direct fluorination before the war, and it had been found that direct fluorination of aromatic compounds is difficult because of the extreme activity of this halogen; instead of undergoing fluorination many compounds are decomposed, polymerized,

* 3-Pyridinediazonium fluoborate undergoes violent spontaneous decomposition when dry. Consequently the material, prepared as described on p. 206 and covered with petroleum ether, is used directly without drying and weighing.

[57] Cady, Grosse, Barber, Burger, and Sheldon, *Ind. Eng. Chem.*, **39**, 290 (1947).
[58] Fowler and co-workers, *Ind. Eng. Chem.*, **39**, 292 (1947).
[59] McBee and Bechtol, *Ind. Eng. Chem.*, **39**, 380 (1947).
[60] Fowler and co-workers, *Ind. Eng. Chem.*, **39**, 343 (1947).
[61] McBee, Lindgren, and Ligett, *Ind. Eng. Chem.*, **39**, 378 (1947).

or transformed into saturated cyclic fluorides by the action of fluorine.[62-69] Few well-defined products have been reported, though several patents covering this field have been issued, a few of which are noted here.[70-75] A method of preparing aromatic fluorine compounds that has had considerable success is the decomposition of diazonium salts in hydrogen fluoride, aqueous or anhydrous.[76-79]　The first aromatic fluorine com-

$$C_6H_5N_2Cl + HF(\text{excess}) \longrightarrow C_6H_5F + N_2 + HCl$$

$$C_6H_5NH_2 \xrightarrow[\text{NaNO}_2 \text{ (solid)}]{\text{HF (anhydrous)}} C_6H_5N_2F \rightarrow C_6H_5F$$

pound prepared, p-fluorobenzoic acid, was made this way by Schmitt and von Gehren [80,81] in 1870. This method has the disadvantage of requiring special apparatus capable of handling hydrofluoric acid. Yields are often excellent, however, and a few compounds for which the Schiemann reaction would not work have been made this way; one of these is 2-iodo-3-fluorobenzoic acid.[82]

The method devised by Wallach [83,84] has had limited usefulness. It consists of isolating a diazonium piperidide and decomposing it with aqueous hydrogen fluoride. The intermediates, in contrast to the diazonium fluoroborates, are unstable and difficult to purify, and they can be handled safely only in small quantities; the yields are generally low. This method has not been much used since the development of the Schiemann reaction in 1927.

[62] Bancroft and Whearty, *Proc. Natl. Acad. Sci. U.S.*, **17**, 183 (1931).
[63] Bigelow and Pearson, *J. Am. Chem. Soc.*, **56**, 2773 (1934).
[64] Bigelow, Pearson, Cook, and Miller, *J. Am. Chem. Soc.*, **55**, 4614 (1933).
[65] Bockemüller, *Ann.*, **506**, 20 (1933).
[66] Fredenhagen and Cadenbach, *Ber.*, **67**, 928 (1934).
[67] Fukuhara and Bigelow, *J. Am. Chem. Soc.*, **60**, 427 (1938).
[68] Fukuhara and Bigelow, *J. Am. Chem. Soc.*, **63**, 2792 (1941).
[69] Whearty, *J. Phys. Chem.*, **35**, 3121 (1931).
[70] Calcott, U. S. pat. 2,227,628 [*C.A.*, **35**, 2738 (1941)].
[71] Calcott and Benning, U. S. pat. 2,013,030 [*C.A.*, **29**, 6900 (1935)].
[72] Daudt and Parmelee, U. S. pat. 2,013,035 [*C.A.*, **29**, 6900 (1935)].
[73] E. I. du Pont de Nemours and Co., Fr. pat. 761,946 [*C.A.*, **28**, 4430 (1934)].
[74] E. I. du Pont de Nemours and Co., Ger. pat. 671,087 [*C.A.*, **33**, 3396 (1939)].
[75] Fichter, *J. Soc. Chem. Ind.*, **48**, 354 (1929).
[76] Holleman and Beckman, *Rec. trav. chim.*, **23**, 225 (1904).
[77] Holleman and Slothouwer, *Verhandel. Koninkl. Nederland. Akad. Wetenschap.*, **19**, 497 (1911) [*C.A.*, **5**, 1905 (1911)].
[78] Osswald and Scherer, Ger. pat. 600,706 [*C.A.*, **28**, 7260 (1934)].
[79] Swarts, *Bull. acad. roy. Belg.*, **1913**, 241 [*C.A.*, **8**, 680 (1914)].
[80] Schmitt and von Gehren, *J. prakt. Chem.*, [2] **1**, 394 (1870).
[81] Paterno, *Gazz. chim. ital.*, **11**, 90 (1881).
[82] Stanley, McMahon, and Adams, *J. Am. Chem. Soc.*, **55**, 706 (1933).
[83] Wallach, *Ann.*, **235**, 255 (1886).
[84] Wallach and Heusler, *Ann.*, **243**, 219 (1888).

Lange and Müller [85] report the preparation of 4,4'-difluorobiphenyl in low yield by heating the aryl-*bis*-diazonium fluophosphate, and Wiley [86] has prepared *p*-fluorobenzoic acid in low yield by the pyrolysis of *p*-carbethoxybenzenediazonium fluosilicate.

A few miscellaneous fluorinating agents such as lead tetrafluoride,[87] *p*-tolyl iodofluoride,[88, 89] and others have been tried with but slight success.

TABLES OF COMPOUNDS PREPARED BY THE SCHIEMANN REACTION

The compounds which have been prepared by means of the Schiemann reaction are listed in five tables under the following headings:

    I. Benzene Derivatives.
    II. Naphthalene Derivatives.
    III. Biphenyl and Other Polynuclear Hydrocarbon Derivatives.
    IV. Heterocyclic Derivatives.
    V. Compounds with Two Fluorine Atoms Simultaneously Introduced.

Within each table the compounds are listed according to the groups they contain in the following sequence:

Fluorine only	Acids
Other halogens	Esters
Trifluoromethyl groups	Amines, anilides, and azo compounds
Alkyl groups	Ketones
Phenols	Tetracovalent sulfur compounds
Ethers	Nitro groups

The "principle of latest position" has been utilized; a molecule containing more than one of the above groups will be listed with the group which is lowest on the list. For example, 2-fluoro-4-nitrotoluene will be found among the nitro compounds, and 2-fluoro-4-bromoanisole is listed with the ethers.

Included are formulas of several fluoro compounds that have not been prepared by this method. They are present either because their preparation was unsuccessfully attempted or because the intermediate diazonium fluoborate was prepared and used for some reaction other than the Schiemann reaction.

[85] Lange and Müller, *Ber.*, **63**, 1058 (1930).
[86] Wiley, U. S. pat. 2,423,359 [*C.A.*, **41**, 6284 (1947)].
[87] Dimroth and Bockemüller, *Ber.*, **64**, 516 (1931).
[88] Bockemüller, *Ber.*, **64**, 522 (1931).
[89] Garvey, Hadley, and Allen, *J. Am. Chem. Soc.*, **59**, 1827 (1937).

There are two columns of references, one for the preparation of the diazonium fluoborates and the other for the preparation of the fluorine compounds from the diazonium fluoborates. This arrangement has been adopted because, as explained above, a diazonium fluoborate has sometimes been prepared but not used in the Schiemann reaction, and also because the best yield in the preparation of a certain diazonium fluoborate is sometimes reported in one paper and the best yield of fluoride obtained by the decomposition of the same fluoborate is reported in another paper.

The entire range of yields reported for each compound is given in the tables. Thus 56–78% means that 56% and 78% are the lowest and highest yields reported. No more than four references for any one compound have been given; if there were more than four references, the four giving the best yields are reported.

The literature has been covered through *Chemical Abstracts* for 1946, although some 1947 articles are included.

TABLE I

BENZENE DERIVATIVES

Compound	$\overset{5\quad 6}{\underset{3\quad 2}{4\langle\ \rangle}}N_2BF_4$	Diazonium Fluoborate Decomposition Temperature °C.	Yield %	Reference *	RN₂BF₄ → RF Yield %	Reference *
		Compounds Containing Fluorine Only				
Fluorobenzene		100, 121	58–97	15, 33, 44, 90	51–100	1, 33, 39, 44
o-Difluorobenzene	2—F	159	45	23, 38	30	23, 38
m-Difluorobenzene	†				†	
p-Difluorobenzene	4—F	154.5	64	38	62 †	38, 91
1,2,4-Trifluorobenzene	2—F, 4—F	145	42	27	17	27
1,2,4-Trifluorobenzene	2—F, 5—F	150	29	27	55, 58 ‡	27, 91
1,2,4,5-Tetrafluorobenzene	2—F, 4—F, 5—F	—	—	91	—	91
		Compounds Containing Other Halogens				
o-Bromofluorobenzene	2—Br	156	50	23	81, 37 §	23, 92
m-Bromofluorobenzene	3—Br	141, 145	86–95	6, 29	78, 50 §	29, 92
p-Bromofluorobenzene	4—Br	133	64	92, 93	75, 52 §	92, 93
3,5-Dibromofluorobenzene	3—Br, 5—Br	126	72	53	55	53
o-Chlorofluorobenzene	2—Cl	171	90–98	13, 23, 90	85	23
m-Chlorofluorobenzene	3—Cl	140, 157	91–97	7, 46, 90	68, 60 §	46, 94
p-Chlorofluorobenzene	4—Cl	—	90	2, 13, 95	—	95
2,4-Dichlorofluorobenzene	2—Cl, 4—Cl	—	—	96	—	96
3,5-Dichlorofluorobenzene	3—Cl, 5—Cl	170–80	77	97	48	97
2,4,6-Trichlorofluorobenzene	2—Cl, 4—Cl, 6—Cl	187	75	94	80	94
o-Iodofluorobenzene	2—I	89, 109	75–80	23, 27	44–70	23, 27
m-Iodofluorobenzene	3—I	104, 134	81–98	6, 27	68	27
		Compounds Containing Trifluoromethyl Groups				
m-Fluorotrifluoromethylbenzene	3—CF₃	140	79–87	50, 98	82–92	50, 98
2,5-Difluorotrifluoromethylbenzene	2—CF₃, 4—F	—	85	51	67	51
3,5-Difluorotrifluoromethylbenzene	3—CF₃, 5—F	—	94	51	—	51
2,3,5-Trifluorotrifluoromethylbenzene	2—F, 3—CF₃, 5—F	—	—	99	—	99
2-Fluoro-5-bromotrifluoromethylbenzene	2—CF₃, 4—Br	—	79	100	86	100

* References 90–142 are on p. 228.
† See Table V.
‡ 58% from p-nitroaniline.
§ Over-all yield from amine.

TABLE I—Continued

BENZENE DERIVATIVES

Compound	5 6 4⟨ ⟩N₂BF₄ 3 2	Diazonium Fluoborate			RN₂BF₄ → RF	
		Decomposition Temperature °C.	Yield %	Reference *	Yield %	Reference *
Compounds Containing Alkyl Groups						
o-Fluorotoluene	2—CH₃	106	59–90	13, 35, 101, 102	90	101, 102
m-Fluorotoluene	3—CH₃	108	79–90	13, 101, 103	87, 87 §	101, 103
p-Fluorotoluene	4—CH₃	110	67–90	1, 13, 90	97, 70 §	1, 14
2,5-Difluorotoluene	2—CH₃, 4—F	114	62	101	80	101
2,6-Difluorotoluene	2—CH₃, 3—F	—	—	46	50 †· §	46
2,4-Dimethylfluorobenzene	2—CH₃, 4—CH₃	108	31–47	1, 103	66–100	1, 103
3,5-Dimethylfluorobenzene	3—CH₃, 5—CH₃	88	98	104	56 §	104
1,3-Difluoro-4,6-dimethylbenzene	†· ‖				†· ‖	
2,4,6-Trimethylfluorobenzene	2—CH₃, 4—CH₃, 6—CH₃	—	—	105	—	105
Difluoromesitylene	2—CH₃, 4—CH₃, 6—CH₃, 3—F	—	—	47	86 ¶	47
Trifluoromesitylene	2—CH₃, 4—CH₃, 6—CH₃, 3—F, 5—F	—	—	47	26 **	47
2,6-Dimethyl-4-tert-butylfluorobenzene	2—CH₃, 4—t-C₄H₉, 6—CH₃	—	—	103	70 §	103
2,4-Dimethyl-6-bromofluorobenzene	2—CH₃, 4—CH₃, 6—Br	161	60	106	Quantitative	106
2-Chloro-4-fluorotoluene	3—Cl, 4—CH₃	125	—	107	71 §	107
2-Chloro-6-fluorotoluene	2—CH₃, 3—Cl	141	80–91	46, 108	58–81	46, 108
3-Iodo-4-fluorotoluene	2—I, 4—CH₃	110	70	109	70	109
1,3-Difluoro-2-iodo-4-chloro-6-methylbenzene	2—I, 3—F, 4—CH₃, 6—Cl	218	65	54	85	54
1,3-Difluoro-2-iodo-4,6-dimethylbenzene	2—I, 3—F, 4—CH₃, 6—CH₃	235	65	54	75	54
Phenols and Ethers						
o-Fluorophenol	2—OH	—	—	22	††	22
m-Fluorophenol	3—OH	—	—	22	50 §	22
p-Fluorophenol	4—OH	—	—	22	††	22
o-Fluoroanisole	2—OCH₃	125	52–91	22, 48, 111	54–67, 64 §	29, 48, 110
m-Fluoroanisole	3—OCH₃	68	76–82 ‡‡	28, 29, 30	42–64	28, 29
p-Fluoroanisole	4—OCH₃	139	85	22, 29	67, 47 §	22, 29
2,4-Difluoroanisole	3—F, 4—OCH₃	98	60	110	81	110

* References 90–142 are on p. 228.
† See Table V.
§ Over-all yield from amine.
‖ Preparation not attempted.
¶ Over-all from fluoromesidine.
** Over-all yield from mesitylene.
†† Preparation attempted and failed.
‡‡ This diazonium fluoborate, because of its low decomposition point, is likely to decompose spontaneously.

TABLE I—*Continued*

BENZENE DERIVATIVES

Compound	4⟨5 6 / 3 2⟩N₂BF₄	Diazonium Fluoborate			RN₂BF₄ → RF	
		Decomposition Temperature °C.	Yield %	Reference *	Yield %	Reference *
2,6-Difluoroanisole	2—OCH₃, 3—F	—	85	48	56	48
3,4-Dimethoxyfluorobenzene	3—OCH₃, 4—OCH₃	123	76	112	‖	—
2-Fluoro-4-bromoanisole	2—OCH₃, 5—Br	156	92	113	54	113
2-Fluoro-4-methylanisole	2—OCH₃, 5—CH₃	120	82	29	48	29
2-Fluoro-6-methylanisole	2—OCH₃, 3—CH₃	88	68	114	62	114
2,6-Difluoro-4-methylanisole	†				†	
2-Bromo-3-fluoro-4,6-dimethylanisole	2—Br, 3—OCH₃, 4—CH₃, 6—CH₃	105	70	28	52 §	28
o-Fluorophenetole	2—OC₂H₅	105, 135	65–69	29, 110	35–36	29, 110
m-Fluorophenetole	3—OC₂H₅	70	75 ‡‡	29	47	29
p-Fluorophenetole	4—OC₂H₅	105	46–87	13, 29, 90	35–53	29, 42
2,4-Difluorophenetole	3—F, 4—OC₂H₅	82	17–37	110, 115	0–44	110, 115
4-Fluorodiphenyl ether	4—OC₆H₅	81–3	83	116	67	116
4,4′-Difluorodiphenyl ether	†				†	
3-Fluoro-4-methoxydiphenyl ether	2—OCH₃, 5—OC₆H₅	145	Quantitative	114	Slight	114

Acids and Esters

o-Fluorobenzoic acid	2—CO₂H	125	0–46	13, 15, 34, 102	19	34
m-Fluorobenzoic acid	3—CO₂H	155	31	34	16	34
p-Fluorobenzoic acid	4—CO₂H	—	76–84	13, 15	††	34
3,4-Difluorobenzoic acid	2—F, 5—CO₂H	185	77	14	‖	—
2-Iodo-3-fluorobenzoic acid	2—I, 3—CO₂H	—	—	82	††	82
2-Hydroxy-5-fluorobenzoic acid	3—CO₂H, 4—OH	—	75–85	15	‖	—
p-Fluorophenylacetic acid	4—CH₂CO₂H	—	Poor	34	††	34
Methyl o-fluorobenzoate	2—CO₂CH₃	102	66	117	53	117
Ethyl o-fluorobenzoate	2—CO₂C₂H₅	105, 118	56–90	23, 27	60–87	23, 27
Ethyl p-fluorobenzoate	4—CO₂C₂H₅	93	75–94	13, 40, 90	90	40
Methyl 3-fluoro-4-methoxybenzoate	2—OCH₃, 5—CO₂CH₃	—	88	48	56	48
Methyl 3,5-difluoro-4-methoxybenzoate	2—OCH₃, 3—F, 5—CO₂CH₃	—	89	48, 111	28–35	48, 111
Diethyl 4-fluorophthalate	3—CO₂C₂H₅, 4—CO₂C₂H₅	125	98	118	50	118
Ethyl p-fluorophenylacetate	4—CH₂CO₂C₂H₅	—	Poor	34	††	34

* References 90–142 are on p. 228.
† See Table V.
§ Over-all yield from amine.
‖ Preparation not attempted.
†† Preparation attempted and failed.
‡‡ This diazonium fluoborate, because of its low decomposition point, is likely to decompose spontaneously.

TABLE I—*Continued*

BENZENE DERIVATIVES

Compound	$\overset{5\quad 6}{\underset{3\quad 2}{4\langle\rangle}}N_2BF_4$	Decomposition Temperature °C.	Yield %	Reference *	Yield %	Reference *
			Diazonium Fluoborate		**$RN_2BF_4 \rightarrow RF$**	
Amines, Anilides, and Azo Compounds						
p-Fluorodimethylaniline	4—N(CH₃)₂	151	56–61	119, 120	17	119
p-Fluorodiethylaniline	4—N(C₂H₅)₂	113	83	119, 120	20	119
p-Fluoroacetanilide	4—NHCOCH₃	135	84	7	—	30
p-Fluorophenyldiphenylamine	4—N(C₆H₅)₂	162	—	120	‖	—
4-Fluoroazobenzene	4—N=N—C₆H₅	145	92	90, 116	16 §	116
Ketones						
m-Fluoroacetophenone	3—COCH₃	83	—	121	—	121
p-Fluoroacetophenone	4—COCH₃	—	90	13	‖	—
o-Fluoropropiophenone	2—COC₂H₅	81–2	79	56	47 §	56
m-Fluoropropiophenone	3—COC₂H₅	97–8	88	56	68 §	56
4-Fluorobenzophenone	4—COC₆H₅	115	90	116	40 §	116
4,4'-Difluorobenzophenone	†				†	
Tetracovalent Sulfur Compounds						
4-Fluorobenzenesulfonic acid	4—SO₃H	—	80	15	‖	—
3-Fluoro-4-hydroxybenzenesulfonic acid	2—OH, 5—SO₃H	Soluble	—	15	‖	—
4-Fluorobenzenesulfonamide	4—SO₂NH₂	—	—	17	‖	—
4,4'-Difluorodiphenylsulfone	†· ††				†· ††	
Nitro Compounds						
o-Nitrofluorobenzene	2—NO₂	135	63–92	8, 13, 14, 22	10–19	1, 14, 22, 38
m-Nitrofluorobenzene	3—NO₂	170, 178	79–99	13, 14, 22, 90	43–54	14, 22, 28, 38
p-Nitrofluorobenzene	4—NO₂	156	80–100	1, 8, 14, 123	40–58 50–60 §	22, 38, 91, 122
3,4-Dinitrofluorobenzene	3—NO₂, 4—NO₂	161	69	53	24	53
3,5-Dinitrofluorobenzene	3—NO₂, 5—NO₂	203	57	124, 125	15	124, 125

* References 90–142 are on p. 228.
† See Table V.
§ Over-all yield from amine.
‖ Preparation not attempted.
†† Preparation attempted and failed.

TABLE I—*Continued*

BENZENE DERIVATIVES

Compound	$\overset{5\quad6}{\underset{3\quad2}{\underset{4}{\bigcirc}}}N_2BF_4$	Decomposition Temperature °C.	Yield %	Reference *	Yield %	Reference *
					$RN_2BF_4 \rightarrow RF$	
3-Nitro-4-bromofluoro-benzene	3—NO$_2$, 4—Br	200	—	49	30 §	49
3-Nitro-5-chlorofluoro-benzene	3—NO$_2$, 5—Cl	190–5	76	97	—	97
3-Trifluoromethyl-4-nitro-fluorobenzene	3—CF$_3$, 4—NO$_2$	—	94	51	41	51
3-Trifluoromethyl-5-nitro-fluorobenzene	3—CF$_3$, 5—NO$_2$	—	88	51	49	51
2-Methyl-3-nitrofluoro-benzene	2—CH$_3$, 3—NO$_2$	118	80	46	63	46
2-Methyl-4-nitrofluoro-benzene	2—CH$_3$, 4—NO$_2$	—	—	11	60 §	11
2-Methyl-6-nitrofluoro-benzene	2—CH$_3$, 6—NO$_2$	143	50	36	20–23	36
3-Nitro-2,4,6-trimethyl-fluorobenzene	3—NO$_2$, 2—CH$_3$, 4—CH$_3$, 6—CH$_3$	—	—	47	50–60 §	47
2,4-Dimethyl-5-nitrofluoro-benzene	2—CH$_3$, 4—CH$_3$, 5—NO$_2$	130	53	28	53	28
2-Methyl-4-chloro-5-nitro-fluorobenzene	2—CH$_3$, 4—Cl, 5—NO$_2$	153	61	54	50	54
2-Bromo-3-nitro-4,6-di-methylfluorobenzene	2—Br, 3—NO$_2$, 4—CH$_3$, 6—CH$_3$	195	67	106	45	106
2-Fluoro-4-nitroanisole	2—OCH$_3$, 5—NO$_2$	173	70–85	126, 127	10–14	126, 127
3-Fluoro-5-nitroanisole	3—OCH$_3$, 5—NO$_2$	150	93	128, 129	36	128
2,6-Difluoro-4-nitroanisole	2—OCH$_3$, 3—F, 5—NO$_2$	—	60	111	10 †	111
2-Fluoro-4-nitrophenetole	2—OC$_2$H$_5$, 5—NO$_2$	179	90	127	6	127
3-Fluoro-5-nitrophenetole	3—OC$_2$H$_5$, 5—NO$_2$	110	64	125, 129	31	125, 129
4-Fluoro-4'-nitrodiphenyl sulfone	4—(p-SO$_2$C$_6$H$_4$NO$_2$)	145	Quantitative	30	63	30

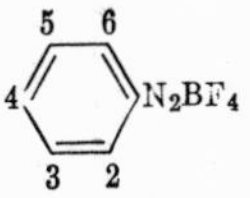

* References 90–142 are on p. 228.
† See Table V.
§ Over-all yield from amine.

TABLE II

NAPHTHALENE DERIVATIVES

Compound	Diazonium Fluoborate				RN₂BF₄ → RF	
	(structure: naphthalene numbered 8,1,2,3,4,5,6,7)	Decomposition Temperature °C.	Yield %	Reference *	Yield %	Reference *
1-Fluoronaphthalene	1—N₂BF₄	113	62–91	1, 35, 90, 130	60–98	1, 43, 130
2-Fluoronaphthalene	2—N₂BF₄	108, 116	90–97	33, 130, 131	69–Quantitative	33, 43, 130, 131
1,4-Difluoronaphthalene	1—N₂BF₄, 4—F	163	47	130	37	130
1,5-Difluoronaphthalene	†				†	
1,8-Difluoronaphthalene	†, ‡				†, ‡	
1-Bromo-2-fluoronaphthalene	1—Br, 2—N₂BF₄	98	—	131	23 §	131
1-Fluoro-4-bromonaphthalene	1—N₂BF₄, 4—Br	152	97	130	66	130
1-Chloro-2-fluoronaphthalene	1—Cl, 2—N₂BF₄‖	166	80	25; see 24	90	25
1-Fluoro-8-chloronaphthalene	1—N₂BF₄, 8—Cl	106	80	132	50	132
1-Fluoro-2-methylnaphthalene	1—N₂BF₄, 2—CH₃	150	—	24	—	24
1-Benzeneazo-2-fluoronaphthalene	1—N₂C₆H₅, 2—N₂BF₄	158	31	24	Slight	24
1-Fluoro-4-naphthalenesulfonic acid	1—N₂BF₄ 4—SO₃H	—	—	130	¶	130
1-Nitro-2-fluoronaphthalene	1—NO₂, 2—N₂BF₄	—	—	—	¶	24, 25
1-Nitro-8-fluoronaphthalene	1—N₂BF₄, 8—NO₂	124	—	24	¶	24

* References 90–142 are on p. 228.
† See Table V.
‡ Preparation not attempted.
§ Over-all yield from amine.
‖ From 1-nitro-2-aminonaphthalene; see p. 199.
¶ Preparation attempted and failed.

TABLE III

BIPHENYL AND OTHER POLYNUCLEAR HYDROCARBON DERIVATIVES

Compound	$3'\ 2'\quad 2\ 3$ / $4'$⟨⟩⟨⟩4 / $5'\ 6'\quad 6\ 5$	Decomposition Temperature °C.	Yield %	Reference *	Yield %	Reference *
		Diazonium Fluoborate			$RN_2BF_4 \to RF$	
2-Fluorobiphenyl	2—N$_2$BF$_4$	81	85	133	89	52, 133
3-Fluorobiphenyl	3—N$_2$BF$_4$	91	85	133	60 †	133, 134
4-Fluorobiphenyl	4—N$_2$BF$_4$	116	88–94	15, 90, 133	82 †	52, 133
2,2'-Difluorobiphenyl	‡				‡	
3,3'-Difluorobiphenyl	‡				‡	
4,4'-Difluorobiphenyl	‡				‡	
2,4,4'-Trifluorobiphenyl §	2—N$_2$BF$_4$, 4—F, 4'—F	88	95	135, 136, 137	85	135, 136, 137
2,4,4',5-Tetrafluorobiphenyl ‖	2—N$_2$BF$_4$, 4—F, 4'—F, 5—F	102	83	133, 137	91	133, 137
2,2',4,4',5-Pentafluorobiphenyl	‡, ¶				‡, ¶	
4-Fluoro-4'-bromobiphenyl	4—N$_2$BF$_4$, 4'—Br	<100	Quantitative	138	57	138
2-Fluoro-4,4'-dimethylbiphenyl	2—N$_2$BF$_4$, 4—CH$_3$, 4'—CH$_3$	<100	74	139	91	139
2,2'-Difluoro-4,4'-dimethylbiphenyl	2—N$_2$BF$_4$, 2'—F, 4—CH$_3$, 4'—CH$_3$	100	90	139	83 ‡	139
2,2'-Difluoro-6,6'-dimethylbiphenyl	‡				‡	
3,3'-Dimethyl-4,4'-difluorobiphenyl	‡				‡	
3,3'-Dimethyl-4,4',6-trifluorobiphenyl	2—N$_2$BF$_4$, 4—F, 4'—F, 5—CH$_3$, 5'—CH$_3$	93	52	140	52	140
2-Nitro-2'-fluorobiphenyl	2—N$_2$BF$_4$, 2'—NO$_2$	87	95	52	13	52
4-Nitro-4'-fluorobiphenyl	4—N$_2$BF$_4$, 4'—NO$_2$	130	—	133	15 †	138
2-Nitro-4,4'-difluorobiphenyl	‡				‡	
2-Nitro-3'-bromo-4,4'-difluorobiphenyl	‡, **				‡, **	
2,2'-Dinitro-4,4'-difluorobiphenyl	‡				‡	
3,3'-Dimethyl-4,4'-difluoro-6-nitrobiphenyl	‡				‡	

* References 90–142 are on p. 228.
† Over-all yield from amine.
‡ See Table V.
§ Prepared and erroneously reported as 3,4,4'-trifluorobiphenyl in ref. 136.
‖ Prepared and erroneously reported as 3,4,4'-5-tetrafluorobiphenyl in ref. 133.
¶ Preparation attempted and failed.
** Preparation not attempted.

TABLE III—*Continued*

BIPHENYL AND OTHER POLYNUCLEAR HYDROCARBON DERIVATIVES

Compound	Diazonium Fluoborate				$RN_2BF_4 \rightarrow RF$	
	Formula	Decomposition Temperature °C.	Yield %	Reference *	Yield %	Reference *
Miscellaneous Polynuclear Hydrocarbon Derivatives						
2-Fluorofluorene		145	76	141	—	141
9-Fluorophenanthrene		—	—	55	30–42	55
2-Fluorofluorenone		160	—	141	50 †	141
2-Fluoroanthraquinone		—	68	116	60	116
Bz-1-Fluorobenzanthrone		150	Quant.	37	63	37

* References 90–142 are on p. 228.
† Over-all yield from amine.

THE SCHIEMANN REACTION

225

TABLE IV

Heterocyclic Fluorine Compounds

Pyridine Derivatives

Compound	Diazonium Fluoborate				RN₂BF₄ → RF	
	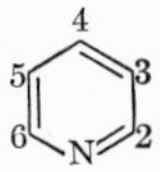	Decomposition Temperature °C.	Yield %	Reference *	Yield %	Reference *
2-Fluoropyridine	2—N₂BF₄	<0	—	31	34 †	31
3-Fluoropyridine	3—N₂BF₄	15 ‡	—	31	50 †	31
4-Fluoropyridine	§			31	§	31
2,6-Difluoropyridine	§, ‖				§, ‖	

Quinoline Derivatives

Compound	Diazonium Fluoborate				RN₂BF₄ → RF	
	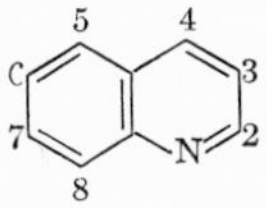	Decomposition Temperature °C.	Yield %	Reference *	Yield %	Reference *
2-Fluoroquinoline	2—N₂BF₄	<0	—	32	28 †	32
4-Fluoroquinoline	§	10	—	32	§	32
5-Fluoroquinoline	5—N₂BF₄	95	94	32	59 †	32
6-Fluoroquinoline	6—N₂BF₄	90–100	96	32	57 †	32
7-Fluoroquinoline	7—N₂BF₄	123	100	32	27 †	32
8-Fluoroquinoline	8—N₂BF₄	133	74	32	24 †	32
5-Fluoro-6-methoxyquinoline	5—N₂BF₄, 6—OCH₃	—	83	142	§	142

Quinazolone Derivative

Compound	Diazonium Fluoborate				RN₂BF₄ → RF	
6-Fluoro-4-quinazolone	4—Quinazolone-6—diazonium fluoborate	—	Almost quantitative	12	¶	12

* References 90–142 are on p. 228.
† Over-all yield from the amine.
‡ This diazonium fluoborate decomposes spontaneously when dry.
§ Preparation attempted and failed.
‖ See Table V.
¶ Preparation not attempted.

TABLE V

Compounds with Two Fluorine Atoms Simultaneously Introduced

Compound	bis-Diazonium Fluoborate	Decomposition Temperature, °C.	Yield %	Reference *	Yield %	Reference *
		bis-Diazonium Fluoborate			$R(N_2BF_4)_2 \rightarrow RF_2$	
m-Difluorobenzene	N_2BF_4 / N_2BF_4	206	88	9, 38	31 †	38
p-Difluorobenzene	F_4BN_2 — N_2BF_4	186	78–82	9, 38	27 †, ‡	38
2,6-Difluorotoluene	CH_3; F_4BN_2 — N_2BF_4	—	—	46	Slight ‡	46
1,5-Difluoro-2,4-dimethylbenzene	H_3C CH_3; F_4BN_2 — N_2BF_4	—	Quantitative	9	§	—
2,6-Difluoro-4-methylanisole	OCH_3; F_4BN_2 — N_2BF_4; CH_3	—	48	110	Slight	110
4,4'-Difluorodiphenyl ether	$\left(F_4BN_2 \right)_2 O$	—	63	116	10 †	116
4,4'-Difluorobenzophenone	$\left(F_4BN_2 \right)_2 C{=}O$	82	98	116	20 †	116
4,4'-Difluorodiphenyl sulfone	$\left(F_4BN_2 \right)_2 SO_2$	—	—	30	¶	30
2,6-Difluoro-4-nitroanisole	N_2BF_4; O_2N — OCH_3; N_2BF_4	—	52	111	Slight ‡	111
1,5-Difluoronaphthalene	N_2BF_4 / N_2BF_4	184, 190	92	130, 131	54	130, 131
1,8-Difluoronaphthalene	F_4BN_2 N_2BF_4	—	67	9	§	—
2,2'-Difluorobiphenyl	F_4BN_2 N_2BF_4	133	84	140	70	140

* References 90–142 are on p. 228.
† Over-all yield from amine.
‡ See Table I.

§ Preparation not attempted.
¶ Preparation attempted and failed.

TABLE V—*Continued*

COMPOUNDS WITH TWO FLUORINE ATOMS SIMULTANEOUSLY INTRODUCED

Compound	bis-Diazonium Fluoborate				R(N₂BF₄)₂ → RF₂	
	bis-Diazonium Fluoborate	Decomposition Temperature,°C.	Yield %	Reference *	Yield %	Reference *
3,3′-Difluorobiphenyl	F₄BN₂ ... N₂BF₄	106	98	140	50	140
4,4′-Difluorobiphenyl	F₄BN₂ ... N₂BF₄	135, 157	64–95	33, 35, 41, 136	Low-quantitative 80 †	33, 41, 49, 136
2,2′,4,4′,5-Pentafluorobiphenyl	F₄BN₂ F ... F N₂BF₄	—	¶	140	¶	140
2,2′-Difluoro-4,4′-dimethylbiphenyl **	F₄BN₂ N₂BF₄ ... H₃C CH₃	—	—	139	—	139
2,2′-Difluoro-6,6′-dimethylbiphenyl	CH₃ CH₃ ... F₄BN₂ N₂BF₄	<100	96	21	>17	21
3,3′-Dimethyl-4,4′-difluorobiphenyl	H₃C CH₃ ... F₄BN₂ N₂BF₄	125	—	135	64 †	135
2-Nitro-4,4′-difluorobiphenyl	NO₂ ... F₄BN₂ N₂BF₄	128	95	135 137	10	135, 137
2-Nitro-3′-bromo-4,4′-difluorobiphenyl	NO₂ Br ... F₄BN₂ N₂BF₄	—	>78	10	§	—
2,2′-Dinitro-4,4′-difluorobiphenyl	NO₂ NO₂ ... F₄BN₂ N₂BF₄	<200	—	49	19 †	49
3,3′-Dimethyl-4,4′-difluoro-6-nitrobiphenyl	CH₃ CH₃ ... F₄BN₂ N₂BF₄ NO₂	98	98	135	10	135
2,6-Difluoropyridine	F₄BN₂ N N₂BF₄	—	—	104	¶	104

* References 90–142 are on p. 228.
† Over-all yield from amine.
§ Preparation not attempted.

¶ Preparation attempted and failed.
** See Table III.

REFERENCES FOR TABLES

[90] Starkey, *J. Am. Chem. Soc.*, **59**, 1479 (1937).

[91] Finger and co-workers, Atlantic City Meeting A.C.S., 1946, *Abstracts*, p. 14M; also private communication.

[92] Kharasch, *J. Org. Chem.*, **3**, 347 (1938).

[93] Schiemann and Pillarsky, *Ber.*, **64**, 1340 (1931).

[94] Booth, Elsey, and Burchfield, *J. Am. Chem. Soc.*, **57**, 2064 (1935).

[95] Allen and Sugden, *J. Chem. Soc.*, **1932**, 760.

[96] van de Lande, *Rec. trav. chim.*, **51**, 98 (1932).

[97] Cannoni de Degiorgi and Zappi, *Anales asoc. quim. argentina*, **26**, 41 (1938) [*C.A.*, **33**, 152 (1939)].

[98] Booth, Elsey, and Burchfield, *J. Am. Chem. Soc.*, **57**, 2066 (1935).

[99] Finger and Williams, Chicago Meeting A.C.S., 1946, *Abstracts*, p. 57M.

[100] Bachman and Lewis, *J. Am. Chem. Soc.*, **69**, 2022 (1947).

[101] Schiemann, *Ber.*, **62**, 1794 (1929).

[102] Kailan and Antropp, *Monatsh.*, **52**, 297 (1929).

[103] Darzens and Levy, *Compt. rend.*, **199**, 959 (1934).

[104] Roe, unpublished results.

[105] Brown, de Bruyne, and Gross, *J. Am. Chem. Soc.*, **56**, 1291 (1934).

[106] Kleiderer and Adams, *J. Am. Chem. Soc.*, **53**, 1575 (1931).

[107] Magidson and Travin, *J. Gen. Chem. U.S.S.R.*, **11**, 243 (1941) [*C.A.*, **35**, 7965 (1941)].

[108] Willstaedt, *Ber.*, **64**, 2688 (1931).

[109] Stoughton and Adams, *J. Am. Chem. Soc.*, **54**, 4426 (1932).

[110] Schiemann and Seyhan, *Ber.*, **70**, 2396 (1937).

[111] English, Mead, and Niemann, *J. Am. Chem. Soc.*, **62**, 350 (1940).

[112] Smith and Haller, *J. Am. Chem. Soc.*, **56**, 237 (1934).

[113] Schiemann, Winkelmüller, Baesler, and Ley, *J. prakt. Chem.*, [2] **143**, 18 (1935).

[114] Schiemann and Winkelmüller, *J. prakt. Chem.*, [2] **135**, 101 (1932).

[115] Seyhan, Esmer, and Schiemann, *Ber.*, **72**, 365 (1939).

[116] Roe and Miller, unpublished results.

[117] Bergmann and Bondi, *Ber.*, **64**, 1455 (1931).

[118] Blicke and Smith, *J. Am. Chem. Soc.*, **51**, 1865 (1929).

[119] Schiemann and Winkelmüller, *Ber.*, **66**, 727 (1933).

[120] Stollé and Gunzert, *J. prakt. Chem.*, [2] **139**, 141 (1934).

[121] Evans, Morgan, and Watson, *J. Chem. Soc.*, **1935**, 1167.

[122] Bergmann, Engel, and Sandor, *Z. physik. Chem.*, **10B**, 397 (1930).

[123] Hager and Starkey, *J. Am. Pharm. Assoc.*, **30**, 65 (1941).

[124] Cannoni de Degiorgi, *Anales asoc. quim. argentina*, **23**, 4 (1935) [*C.A.*, **29**, 7297 (1935)].

[125] Cannoni de Degiorgi and Zappi, *Anales asoc. quim. argentina*, **24**, 119 (1936) [*C.A.*, **31**, 4657 (1937)].

[126] Niemann, Mead, and Benson, *J. Am. Chem. Soc.*, **63**, 609 (1941).

[127] Schiemann and Miau, *Ber.*, **66**, 1179 (1933).

[128] Cannoni de Degiorgi, *Anales asoc. quim. argentina*, **24**, 1 (1936) [*C.A.*, **30**, 8181 (1936)].

[129] Cannoni de Degiorgi and Zappi, *Bull. soc. chim. France*, [5] **4**, 1636 (1937).

[130] Schiemann, Gueffroy, and Winkelmüller, *Ann.*, **487**, 270 (1931).

[131] Nakata, *Ber.*, **64**, 2059 (1931).

[132] Bergmann and Hirshberg, *J. Chem. Soc.*, **1936**, 331.

[133] Schiemann and Roselius, *Ber.*, **62**, 1805 (1929).

[134] Renoll, *J. Am. Chem. Soc.*, **68**, 1159 (1946).

[135] Schiemann and Roselius, *Ber.*, **64**, 1332 (1931).

[136] Schiemann and Bolstad, *Ber.*, **61**, 1403 (1928).

[137] Le Fèvre and Turner, *J. Chem. Soc.*, **1930**, 1158.

[138] Marler and Turner, *J. Chem. Soc.*, **1931**, 1359.

[139] Marler and Turner, *J. Chem. Soc.*, **1937**, 266.

[140] Schiemann and Roselius, *Ber.*, **65**, 737 (1932).

[141] Bergmann, Hoffmann, and Winter, *Ber.*, **66**, 46 (1933).

[142] Elderfield and co-workers, *J. Am. Chem. Soc.*, **68**, 1584 (1946).

CHAPTER 5

THE FRIEDEL AND CRAFTS REACTION WITH ALIPHATIC DIBASIC ACID ANHYDRIDES

Ernst Berliner

Bryn Mawr College

CONTENTS

229

INTRODUCTION

The Friedel and Crafts reaction between an aliphatic dibasic acid anhydride and an aromatic compound results in the formation of an aroyl fatty acid with the aroyl group situated at the last carbon atom of the aliphatic chain. Since the lowest known dibasic anhydride is succinic anhydride, the number of methylene groups between the carboxyl group

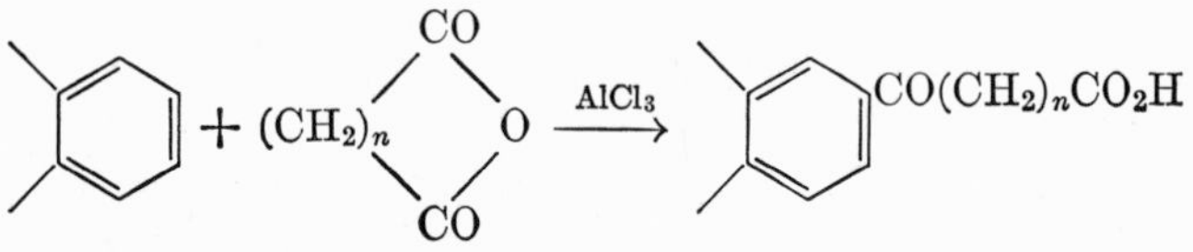

$$\text{} + (CH_2)_n \begin{array}{c} CO \\ \diagup \quad \diagdown \\ \quad \quad O \\ \diagdown \quad \diagup \\ CO \end{array} \xrightarrow{AlCl_3} \text{} CO(CH_2)_nCO_2H$$

and the carbonyl group cannot be less than two. β-Aroylpropionic acids are therefore the lowest members of the series that can be prepared by the general reaction. Acids such as benzoylformic and benzoylacetic acid are not accessible by this procedure, and their synthesis is beyond the scope of this discussion. When maleic anhydride (or a substituted maleic anhydride) is used instead of the saturated anhydride, a β-benzoylacrylic acid is obtained. Burcker introduced the reaction in

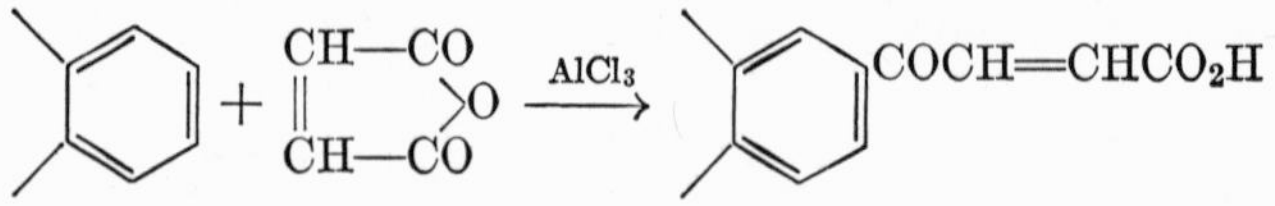

$$\text{} + \begin{array}{c} CH—CO \\ \| \quad \quad \diagdown \\ \quad \quad O \\ CH—CO \end{array} \xrightarrow{AlCl_3} \text{} COCH=CHCO_2H$$

1882, when he condensed succinic anhydride with benzene in the presence of aluminum chloride and obtained β-benzoylpropionic acid in small yield.[1] In the same year von Pechmann prepared β-benzoylacrylic acid by using maleic anhydride instead of succinic anhydride.[2] A more detailed description of both reactions was given some years later by Gabriel and Colman.[3] Since that time the general reaction has been extended to include substituted succinic and maleic anhydrides, glutaric anhydride, and the polymeric anhydrides of higher dibasic acids such as adipic or sebacic acid. Of all anhydrides utilized in the reaction, succinic anhydride has been employed the most extensively and its reactions with aromatic hydrocarbons, their derivatives, and hetero-cyclic compounds have been studied the most thoroughly.

The impetus for the elaboration and extensive use of the succinic anhydride synthesis came from the discovery that the β-aroylpropionic acids, obtained from the reaction, constitute very important interme-diates in the synthesis of aromatic hydrocarbons. The keto acids can easily be reduced by the Clemmensen reduction;[4] the reduced acids can be converted into cyclic ketones,[5] which in turn can be converted into polycyclic hydroaromatic and aromatic compounds by standard pro-cedures. Through the use of substituted succinic anhydrides the corre-

$$\text{COCH}_2\text{CH}_2\text{CO}_2\text{H} \longrightarrow \text{CH}_2\text{CH}_2\text{CH}_2\text{CO}_2\text{H} \longrightarrow$$

sponding substituted hydrocarbons become available, and further modi-fications are possible through a Grignard reaction on one or both of the keto groups. The general scheme of synthesis is sometimes known as the Haworth reaction because Haworth was the first to use it ex-tensively,[6] although isolated examples of the reaction had been known before.[7,8] The search for properly substituted β-aroylpropionic acids

[1] Burcker, Ann. chim., [5] **26**, 435 (1882).

[2] von Pechmann, Ber., **15**, 881 (1882).

[3] Gabriel and Colman, Ber., **32**, 395 (1899).

[4] Martin, Organic Reactions, I, 155, Wiley, New York, 1942.

[5] Johnson, Organic Reactions, II, 114, Wiley, New York, 1944.

[6] Haworth, J. Chem. Soc., **1932**, 1125. See also references 9–11.

[7] Krollpfeiffer and Schäfer, Ber., **56**, 620 (1923).

[8] Farbwerke vorm. Meister Lucius and Brüning, Ger. pat. 376,635 (Chem. Zentr., **1924**, I, 966); I.G. Farbenind. A.-G., Fr. pat. 636,065 [C.A., **22**, 4537 (1928)]; Swiss pat. 131,959 (Chem. Zentr., **1930**, I, 1539); Gruene, U. S. pat. 1,759,111 [C.A., **24**, 3654 (1930)].

led to the preparation of many new acids, to an improved technique, and to a greater knowledge of the reaction. In this way many new hydrocarbons have been synthesized by Haworth, Fieser, and others, and the structures of many natural products elucidated.[9, 10, 11] Since so much more is known at the present time about the reaction with succinic anhydride than with all the other anhydrides, the following discussion is primarily concerned with this reagent; the others will be included in special sections.

MECHANISM

According to the work of Noller and Adams [12] and the investigations of Groggins and Nagel,[13] the Friedel and Crafts reaction with an anhydride proceeds with a maximum yield when two moles of aluminum chloride are used per mole of anhydride. According to Groggins and Nagel one mole of catalyst brings about the fission of the anhydride with the formation of the aluminum chloride salt of one carboxyl group and the formation of the acid chloride from the second carboxyl group.[14] The second mole of aluminum chloride functions as the catalyst as in a typical Friedel and Crafts acylation. In harmony with these views and the present theories of aromatic substitution the reaction can therefore be visualized as proceeding through the complex I, which attacks the

$$
\begin{array}{ccc}
& & O \\
& & \diagup\!\!\diagup \\
CH_2CO & & CH_2C\!\!-\!\!OAlCl_2 \\
| \quad >\!\!O + 2AlCl_3 \rightarrow & & | \\
CH_2CO & & CH_2C^+AlCl_4^- \\
& & \diagdown\!\!\diagdown \\
& & O \\
& & I
\end{array}
$$

aromatic ring by virtue of the electrophilic center on the acyl ion. The preferential fission of unsymmetrical anhydrides can be explained if the assumption is made that the electron-seeking aluminum chloride opens the anhydride toward the carboxyl group that has the higher electron density. The effect of substitution is not great with methylsuccinic anhydride but is pronounced with the para-substituted phenyl-

---

[9] Fieser, Chemistry of Natural Products Related to Phenanthrene, 2nd ed., pp. 71–75, Reinhold Publishing Corp., New York, 1937.

[10] Linstead, Ann. Repts. on Progress Chem. (Chem. Soc. London), 33, 336 (1936).

[11] Springall, Ann. Repts. on Progress Chem. (Chem. Soc. London), 36, 301 (1939).

[12] Noller and Adams, J. Am. Chem. Soc., 46, 1889 (1924).

[13] Groggins and Nagel, Ind. Eng. Chem., 26, 1313 (1934); Groggins, Unit Processes in Organic Synthesis, 3rd ed., p. 761–762, McGraw-Hill Book Co., New York, 1947.

[14] Evidence for the formation of such a complex is presented by Saboor, J. Chem. Soc. 1945, 922.

succinic anhydrides listed on p. 245, which are cleaved in accordance with the character of the substituents. The dual nature of the phenyl group could account for the formation of both acids in equal amounts

$$\text{R--CH--C=O} \atop \underset{\text{CH}_2\text{--C=O}}{\overset{\diagdown \text{O}}{|}} + \text{2AlCl}_3 \longrightarrow \overset{\overset{\text{O}}{\diagup}}{\underset{\text{CH}_2\text{C}^+ \ \text{AlCl}_4^-}{\underset{\diagdown \text{O}}{\overset{|}{\text{RCHC--OAlCl}_2}}}} \xrightarrow{\text{C}_6\text{H}_6} \underset{\text{CH}_2\text{COC}_6\text{H}_5}{\overset{|}{\text{RCHCO}_2\text{AlCl}_2}}$$

when phenylsuccinic anhydride is condensed with benzene.[15] Nitrobenzene, when employed as a solvent, accentuates preferential cleavage in one direction,[16, 17] which may be due to the solvent power of nitrobenzene or to its greater ionizing power.[14, 18] Other mechanisms for the reaction of unsymmetrical anhydrides have been advanced.[6, 14, 16, 18]

SCOPE AND LIMITATIONS

The reaction between an anhydride and an aromatic compound in the presence of anhydrous aluminum chloride is a Friedel and Crafts reaction; it is therefore applicable to all those aromatic compounds on which that type of reaction can be carried out, i.e., aromatic hydrocarbons, their halogen derivatives, phenols and phenolic ethers, and many heterocyclic compounds. Recently the successful condensation of succinic anhydride and acetanilide has been reported.[19] Compounds having nitro, carboxyl, carbonyl, and similar deactivating groups which impede the Friedel and Crafts reaction cannot be utilized. If the deactivating group is removed from the aromatic ring by a few methylene groups, the reaction becomes possible, as has been shown for ethyl β-phenylpropionate or β-phenylpropionitrile.[20, 21]

The yields in succinoylations are usually fair or good (between 50% and 100%), although some much lower yields have been reported, particularly with substituted succinic anhydrides or with halogenated benzene derivatives, which of all compounds have been studied least. Only a few reactions have failed completely or failed to yield the expected product. Guaiacol and hydroquinone monomethyl ether are reported not

[15] Ali, Desai, Hunter, and Muhammad, *J. Chem. Soc.*, **1937**, 1013.
[16] Desai and Wali, *Proc. Indian Acad. Sci.*, **6A**, 135 (1937) [*C.A.*, **32**, 508 (1938)].
[17] Wali, Khalil, Bhatia, and Ahmad, *Proc. Indian Acad. Sci.*, **14A**, 139 (1941) [*C.A.*, **36**, 1598 (1942)].
[18] Rothstein and Saboor, *J. Chem. Soc.*, **1943**, 425.
[19] English, Clapp, Cole, and Krapcho, *J. Am. Chem. Soc.*, **67**, 2263 (1945).
[20] Borsche and Sinn, *Ann.*, **553**, 260 (1942).
[21] See also Fieser and Heymann, *J. Am. Chem. Soc.*, **63**, 2333 (1941), for the reaction between phthalic anhydride and γ-phenylbutyric acid.

to react with succinic anhydride under a variety of different conditions in nitrobenzene, tetrachloroethane, or carbon disulfide as the solvent.[22], * At elevated temperatures demethylation of phenolic ethers often occurs.[23, 24, 25] Pyrogallol trimethyl ether yields β-(2-hydroxy-3,4-dimethoxybenzoyl)propionic acid in all solvents that have been employed;[26, 27, 28] when, however, the organic layer is separated from the aqueous acidic layer before steam distillation, a small amount of the undemethylated acid is obtained.[28a] 9,10-Dihydroanthracene with succinic anhydride and aluminum chloride in nitrobenzene solution undergoes substitution in the aliphatic 9-position [29] instead of the 2-

position as expected by analogy with the behavior of tetralin. A small amount of the same acid was also obtained from anthracene directly when benzene was used as solvent.[30] With a large excess of catalyst substitution occurred in the 2-position only.[21] p-Di-tert-butylbenzene reacts with succinic anhydride in carbon disulfide with elimination of one tert-butyl group; β-(p-tert-butylbenzoyl)propionic acid is formed together with a small amount of an unidentified acid.[31]

Types of Compounds Condensed with Succinic Anhydride

Hydrocarbons. A great number of methylated benzenes have been successfully condensed with succinic anhydride. Toluene, the three xylenes, mesitylene, the tetramethylbenzenes, and pentamethylbenzene can be converted into the corresponding methylated β-aroylpropionic

* Guaiacol and succinic anhydride have been shown to react in a mixture of tetrachloroethane and nitrobenzene to form β-(4-hydroxy-3-methoxybenzoyl)propionic acid in low yield. Holmes and Trevoy, Can. J. Research, 22, 109 (1944).
[22] Dalal and Nargund, J. Indian Chem. Soc., 14, 406 (1937).
[23] Perkin and Robinson, J. Chem. Soc., 93, 489 (1908).
[24] Hill, Short, and Stromberg, J. Chem. Soc., 1937, 937.
[25] Rice, J. Am. Chem. Soc., 50, 229 (1928).
[26] Bargellini and Giua, Gazz. chim. ital., 42, I, 197 (1912).
[27] Dalal, Bokil, and Nargund, J. Univ. Bombay, 8, Pt. 3, 203 (1939) [C.A., 34, 2821 (1940)].
[28] Mitter and De, J. Indian Chem. Soc., 16, 35 (1939).
[28a] Manske and Holmes, J. Am. Chem. Soc., 67, 95 (1945).
[29] Cook, Robinson, and Roe, J. Chem. Soc., 1939, 266.
[30] Berliner, unpublished results.
[31] Price, Shafer, Huber, and Bernstein, J. Org. Chem., 7, 517 (1942).

acids in good yields.[7, 32, 33] Alkylated benzene derivatives having alkyl groups larger than methyl that have been employed as starting materials in the reaction include ethylbenzene,[7, 32, 34] cumene,[32, 33] p-cymene,[32] o-ethyltoluene,[32] tert-butylbenzene,[35] and tert-amylbenzene.[36] Migration or isomerization of larger groups, which often accompanies Friedel and Crafts reactions,[37] has not been observed in succinoylations; but compounds such as n-propyl- or n-butyl-benzene, with which such isomerizations might be expected to take place, have not been studied extensively. n-Propylbenzene has been converted to β-(4-n-propylbenzoyl)propionic acid without isomerization of the n-propyl group.[37a]

Naphthalene and its alkyl derivatives have been the most thoroughly studied of all the polynuclear hydrocarbons, and a great number of phenanthrene derivatives have been synthesized through the appropriate β-naphthoylpropionic acid.[38, 39, 40] Phenanthrene,[41, 42] anthracene,[21, 39, 43, 44] pyrene,[45, 46, 47] retene,[48, 49] and chrysene [50, 51] condense fairly readily with succinic anhydride, as do also some methyl derivatives of phenanthrene.[52, 53, 54] Partially hydrogenated aromatic compounds and

[32] Muhr, Ber., 28, 3215 (1895).
[33] Barnett and Sanders, J. Chem. Soc., 1933, 434.
[34] Levy, Ann. chim., [11] 9, 5 (1938).
[35] Fieser and Price, J. Am. Chem. Soc., 58, 1838 (1936).
[36] (a) Fieser, Berliner, Bondhus, Chang, Dauben, Ettlinger, Fawaz, Fields, Heidelberger, Heymann, Vaughan, Wilson, Wilson, Mao-i Wu, and (b) Leffler, Hamlin, Matson, Moore, Moore, and Zaugg, J. Am. Chem. Soc., 70, 3174, 3197 (1948).
[37] Thomas, Anhydrous Aluminum Chloride in Organic Chemistry, p. 94, Reinhold Publishing Corp., New York, 1941. Haworth, Letsky, and Mavin (ref. 112 below) condensed succinic anhydride with the hydrocarbon obtained from naphthalene and n-propyl bromide in the presence of aluminum chloride. The resulting keto acid was not identical with β-(6-isopropyl-2-naphthoyl)propionic acid and was probably β-(6-n-propyl-2-naphthoyl)propionic acid; i.e., the succinoylation proceeded without isomerization.
[37a] Smith and Chien-Pen Lo, J. Am. Chem. Soc., 70, 2209 (1948).
[38] Haworth et al., J. Chem. Soc., 1932, 1125, 1784, 2248, 2720.
[39] Fieser and Peters, J. Am. Chem. Soc., 54, 4347 (1932).
[40] Bachmann and Struve, J. Org. Chem., 4, 472 (1939).
[41] Haworth and Mavin, J. Chem. Soc., 1933, 1012.
[42] Bachmann and Bradbury, J. Org. Chem., 2, 175 (1937–1938)
[43] Cook and Robinson, J. Chem. Soc., 1938, 505.
[44] Bergmann and Weizmann, J. Chem. Soc., 1938, 1243.
[45] Cook, Hewett, and Hieger, J. Chem. Soc., 1933, 395.
[46] Fieser and Fieser, J. Am. Chem. Soc., 57, 782 (1935).
[47] Winterstein, Vetter, and Schön, Ber., 68, 1079 (1935).
[48] Adelson and Bogert, J. Am. Chem. Soc., 59, 1776 (1937); Cassaday and Bogert, ibid., 63, 703 (1941).
[49] Fieser and Clapp, J. Am. Chem. Soc., 63, 319 (1941).
[50] Beyer, Ber., 71, 915 (1938).
[51] Cook and Graham, J. Chem. Soc., 1944, 329
[52] Bachmann and Edgerton, J. Am. Chem. Soc., 62, 2550 (1940).
[53] Bachmann and Cortes, J. Am. Chem. Soc., 65, 1329 (1943).
[54] Fieser and Cason, J. Am. Chem. Soc., 62, 1293 (1940).

compounds having aliphatic rings that have been employed in succinoylations include hydrindene,[55, 56, 57] fluorene,[58] acenaphthene,[39] tetralin,[7, 59] as well as partially hydrogenated anthracene,[21, 29] phenanthrene,[60] retene,[49] pyrene,[45] and acephenanthrene.[61] Reaction with these compounds often proceeds with higher yields than with the fully aromatic compounds and leads to a single product (compare p. 239). Among the bicyclic compounds that have been employed are biphenyl,[62, 63] diphenylmethane,[29, 36] and phenylcyclohexane.[36, 64] All four halogenated benzenes [36, 65, 66, 67] and o-chlorotoluene [36] have been converted into the corresponding p-halobenzoylpropionic acids, but no halogen derivatives of polynuclear hydrocarbons or of compounds having more than one halogen atom have been tried.[68]

Phenolic Ethers and Free Phenols. Phenolic ethers, which undergo the succinoylation reaction particularly readily, have been extensively studied. The compounds utilized include anisole,[26, 69, 70, 71] many ethers of phenol with alkyl groups larger than methyl,[3, 72, 73] all three cresol methyl ethers,[74, 75] and a number of derivatives of anisole with more and larger alkyl groups,[76-79] as well as o-chloroanisole and o-chlorophenetole.[80] The α- and β-methoxynaphthalenes have been readily converted into the

[55] Fieser and Seligman, *J. Am. Chem. Soc.*, **59**, 883 (1937).

[56] Sengupta, *J. Indian Chem. Soc.*, **16**, 89 (1939).

[57] McQuillin and Robinson, *J. Chem. Soc.*, **1941**, 586.

[58] Koelsch, *J. Am. Chem. Soc.*, **55**, 3885 (1933).

[59] Newman and Zahn, *J. Am. Chem. Soc.*, **65**, 1097 (1943).

[60] See p. 240.

[61] Fieser and Peters, *J. Am. Chem. Soc.*, **54**, 4373 (1932).

[62] Weizmann, Bergmann, and Bograchow, *Chemistry & Industry*, **59**, 402 (1940).

[63] Hey and Wilkinson, *J. Chem. Soc.*, **1940**, 1030.

[64] Buu-Hoi, Cagniant, and Metzner, *Bull. soc. chim. France*, **11**, 127 (1944).

[65] Skraup and Schwamberger, *Ann.*, **462**, 135 (1928).

[66] Fieser and Seligman, *J. Am. Chem. Soc.*, **60**, 170 (1938).

[67] Chovin, *Ann. chim.*, [11] **9**, 447 (1938).

[68] Haworth and Mavin, *J. Chem. Soc.*, **1932**, 2720, reported that the condensation of 4-bromo-1-methylnaphthalene with succinic anhydride seemed unpromising.

[69] Poppenberg, *Ber.*, **34**, 3257 (1901).

[70] Hahn, *J. Am. Chem. Soc.*, **38**, 1517 (1916).

[71] Fieser and Hershberg, *J. Am. Chem. Soc.*, **58**, 2314 (1936).

[72] Rice, *J. Am. Chem. Soc.*, **46**, 2319 (1924).

[73] Trivedi and Nargund, *J. Univ. Bombay*, **11**, Pt. 3, 127 (1942) [*C.A.*, **37**, 2005 (1943)].

[74] Rosenmund and Schapiro, *Arch. Pharm.*, **272**, 313 (1934) [*C.A.*, **28**, 4046 (1934)].

[75] Desai and Wali, *Proc. Indian Acad. Sci.*, **6A**, 144 (1937) [*C.A.*, **32**, 509 (1938)].

[76] Fieser and Lothrop, *J. Am. Chem. Soc.*, **58**, 2050 (1936).

[77] Harland and Robertson, *J. Chem. Soc.*, **1939**, 937.

[78] Cocker, *J. Chem. Soc.*, **1946**, 36.

[79] Soloveva and Preobrazhenskii, *J. Gen. Chem. U.S.S.R.*, **15**, 60 (1945) [*C.A.*, **40**, 1820 (1946)].

[80] Nguyen-Hoan and Buu-Hoi, *Compt. rend.*, **224**, 1228 (1947).

succinoylated products in good yields,[39, 71, 81-86] as have also the dimethyl ethers of the three dihydric phenols,[22, 23, 26, 28, 71] the trimethyl ether of pyrogallol,[26, 27, 28] and hydroxyhydroquinone.[26] 1,5- and 2,6-Dimethoxynaphthalene react smoothly with succinic anhydride with the formation of the corresponding dimethoxy-β-naphthoylpropionic acids.[24, 87] Free phenols, such as phenol itself,[28, 88, 89] the cresols,[88] resorcinol,[90] and orcinol,[90] are succinoylated only under more drastic conditions at elevated temperatures, and mixtures are often obtained. The failure of guaiacol and the monomethyl ether of hydroquinone to undergo reaction has already been mentioned,[22] as has also the partial demethylation of methyl ethers which are sometimes split by aluminum chloride. Diphenyl ether [36, 91, 92, 93] and diphenyl sulfide [93a] afford the corresponding acids in almost quantitative yields.

Heterocyclic Compounds. Thiophene,[94] dimethylthiophene,[95] benzo-[96] and dibenzo-thiophene,[97] and thiochroman [98] are sulfur-containing heterocyclic compounds that have been condensed with succinic anhydride. Diphenylene oxide [99, 100, 101] reacts with succinic anhydride as expected, but carbazole and its N-methyl derivative react with two moles of the anhydride; the mono acid has not been isolated.[102, 103] N-Acetylphenothiazine, however, yields a mono acid on succinoylation.[104]

[81] Ruzicka and Waldmann, *Helv. Chim. Acta*, **15**, 907 (1932).

[82] Bachmann and Holmes, *J. Am. Chem. Soc.*, **62**, 2752 (1940).

[83] Bachmann and Morin, *J. Am. Chem. Soc.*, **66**, 553 (1944).

[84] Hill, Short, and Higginbottom, *J. Chem. Soc.*, **1936**, 317.

[84a] Bachmann and Horton, *J. Am. Chem. Soc.*, **69**, 58 (1947).

[85] Short, Stromberg, and Wiles, *J. Chem. Soc.*, **1936**, 319.

[86] Desai and Wali, *J. Univ. Bombay*, **5**, Pt. 2, 73 (1936) [*C.A.*, **31**, 3038 (1937)].

[87] Fieser and Hershberg, *J. Am. Chem. Soc.*, **58**, 2382 (1936).

[88] Raval, Bokil, and Nargund, *J. Univ. Bombay*, **7**, Pt. 3, 184 (1938) [*C.A.*, **33**, 3779 (1939)].

[89] Fieser, Gates, and Kilmer, *J. Am. Chem. Soc.*, **62**, 2968 (1940).

[90] Desai and Shroff, *J. Univ. Bombay*, **10**, Pt. 3, 97 (1941) [*C.A.*, **36**, 3795 (1942)].

[91] Kipper, *Ber.*, **38**, 2490 (1905).

[92] Rice, *J. Am. Chem. Soc.*, **48**, 269 (1926).

[93] Huang-Minlon, *J. Am. Chem. Soc.*, **68**, 2487 (1946).

[93a] Fieser, Moser, and Paulshock, unpublished results.

[94] Fieser and Kenelly, *J. Am. Chem. Soc.*, **57**, 1611 (1935).

[95] Steinkopf, Poulsson, and Herdey, *Ann.*, **536**, 128 (1938).

[96] Buu-Hoi and Cagniant, *Ber.*, **76**, 1269 (1943).

[97] Gilman and Jacoby, *J. Org. Chem.*, **3**, 108 (1938).

[98] Cagniant and Deluzarche, *Compt. rend.*, **223**, 1012 (1946).

[99] Mayer and Krieger, *Ber.*, **55**, 1659 (1922). The authors also mention an acid obtained from succinic anhydride and tetrahydrodiphenylene oxide, but they give no details.

[100] Mosettig and Robinson, *J. Am. Chem. Soc.*, **57**, 902 (1935).

[101] Gilman, Parker, Bailie, and Brown, *J. Am. Chem. Soc.*, **61**, 2836 (1939).

[102] Mitchell and Plant, *J. Chem. Soc.*, **1936**, 1295.

[103] Rejnowski and Suszko, *Arch. Chem. i Farm. Warsaw*, **3**, 135 (1937) (*Chem. Zentr.*, **1937**, II, 3748).

[104] Baltzly, Harfenist, and Webb, *J. Am. Chem. Soc.*, **68**, 2673 (1946).

Orientation of Entering Groups

The position at which substitution occurs in the aromatic ring is determined by the group already present and can be predicted from the rules governing aromatic substitution. The course of the reaction, however, appears to be subject to some steric hindrance, as is generally true with Friedel and Crafts reactions. Succinic anhydride is relatively large and avoids in most instances the *ortho* position; hence reaction occurs at the *para* position if possible. Otherwise *ortho* substitution occurs without great difficulty. Thus only the *para* isomer is formed in the succinoylation of toluene or ethylbenzene,[7, 32, 34] which in other substitution reactions are invariably attacked in both the *ortho* and *para* positions. On the other hand, *p*-xylene and mesitylene are necessarily substituted *ortho* to a methyl group.[32, 33] The halogenated benzenes likewise are only attacked in the *para* positions.[36, 65, 66, 67] The succinoylation of phenols is exceptional in that *ortho* substitution predominates. Whereas anisole, phenetole,[3, 69–72] and higher alkyl ethers of phenol are substituted exclusively in the position *para* to the alkoxyl group, phenol and succinic anhydride furnish a mixture of *ortho* and *para* isomers in which the *ortho* predominates.[28, 88, 89]

Two isomeric acids are also formed in the reaction of succinic anhydride with *o*- and *m*-cresol, but *p*-cresol is attacked only in the position *ortho* to the hydroxyl group.[88] When the methyl ethers of the cresols are employed as starting materials, the anhydride always attaches itself to the position that corresponds to the stronger directing influences of the methoxyl group.[74, 75] This is also true for higher alkylated derivatives of anisole, such as compounds II and III, which are always substituted *para* to the methoxyl group.[77, 79] *o*-Chlorotoluene is succinoylated in

II   III

the *para* position to the chlorine atom.[36] Although few disubstituted derivatives of the above type have been investigated, succinoylations may always be expected to follow the course of the Friedel and Crafts acylation, possibly with still more stress on unhindered positions. If additional isomers of the above compounds are formed, the amounts are so small that they have escaped detection.

Diphenyl ether and diphenyl sulfide are succinoylated in almost quantitative yields in the *para* positions,[36, 91, 92, 93a] and only the formation of one isomer is reported in the reactions with biphenyl,[62, 63] diphenylmethane,[29, 36] and phenylcyclohexane.[36, 64] 4-Methoxybiphenyl, however, furnishes both the 4' and the 3 derivatives.[105]

In the succinoylation of polynuclear hydrocarbons two isomeric acids are often produced, but separation can usually be effected quite easily. Naphthalene is substituted in both the 1- (36%) and 2- (47%) positions, and the isomers can readily be separated by virtue of the greater solubility of the 1-acid.[6, 39] Anthracene also affords two isomeric acids, but the 1-acid is formed to a much smaller extent.[44] Phenanthrene forms predominantly the 3-acid, with a small amount of the 2-acid.[41, 42] The isolation of the predominant acid from both anthracene and phenanthrene offers no difficulties. The reaction between pyrene and succinic anhydride results in the formation of the 1-acid in almost quantitative yield,[45, 46, 47] and chrysene yields predominantly the 2-acid with a small amount of an isomer.[50, 51] Partially hydrogenated aromatic compounds are often employed as starting materials to avoid polysubstitution or to effect substitution in a position different from the one attacked in the parent hydrocarbon. In addition, the yields with these compounds are generally higher than with the fully aromatic compounds. For instance, tetralin is substituted exclusively in the 2-position,[7, 59] whereas naphthalene yields a mixture of the 1- and 2-acids.[6, 39, 40] Retene is substituted in position 3 in 58.5% yield; dihydroretene affords the 2-acid in 80% yield.[48, 49] Hydrogenated phenanthrene derivatives have been employed quite extensively, and dehydrogenation to the fully aromatic acids offers no difficulties. The formulas on page 240 illustrate the different points of attack on the hydrogenated phenanthrene nucleus.[40, 41, 42, 106–111] Pyrene and hexahydropyrene are likewise substituted in two different positions.[45] Hydrindene and fluorene yield only one substitution product;[55-58] but two acids are obtained from acenaphthene, predominantly the 3-acid, which can easily be obtained in a very pure state.[39]

When the naphthalene ring is substituted by an alkyl or a methoxyl group, only one acid is usually isolated. 1-Methyl- and 1-ethyl-naphthalene are substituted exclusively in the 4-position,[40, 68] while 2-methyl-

[105] Fieser and Bradsher, *J. Am. Chem. Soc.*, **58**, 1738 (1936).

[106] 1,2,3,4-Tetrahydrophenanthrene: Bachmann and Struve, ref. 40, and Bachmann and Struve, *J. Org. Chem.*, **5**, 416 (1940).

[107] 1,2,3,4,9,10,11,12-Octahydrophenanthrene: Cook and Haslewood, *J. Chem. Soc.*, **1935**, 767.

[108] 1,2,3,4,5,6,7,8-Octahydrophenanthrene: van de Kamp, Burger, and Mosettig, *J. Am. Chem. Soc.*, **60**, 1321 (1938).

[109] 9,10-Dihydrophenanthrene: Burger and Mosettig, *J. Am. Chem. Soc.*, **59**, 1302 (1937).

[110] 9,10-Dihydrophenanthrene: Fieser and Johnson, *J. Am. Chem. Soc.*, **61**, 168, 1647 (1939).

[111] 9,10-Dihydro-4,5-methylenephenanthrene: Fieser and Cason, *J. Am. Chem. Soc.*, **62**, 1293 (1940).

ORIENTATION IN THE SUCCINOYLATION OF THE PHENANTHRENE NUCLEUS

naphthalene, and in general 2-alkylnaphthalenes, react predominantly, but not exclusively, in position 6.[35, 39, 112, 113, 114] Only one acid is formed in reactions with succinic anhydride and 2,3-dimethyl- [115] and 2,7-dimethyl-naphthalene.[39] When methoxyl groups are situated in positions 1 or 2 of the naphthalene ring, the anhydride attaches itself predomi-

R(OR)

R(OR)

nantly to positions 4 or 6 (the latter in nitrobenzene solution) just as it does in the methylnaphthalenes,[39, 71, 81, 85] and only one isomer is formed from 1,5- and 2,6-dimethoxynaphthalene.[24, 87] The stronger directive influence of the methoxyl group is borne out in the succinoylations of 1-methoxy-7-methyl-,[81] 1-methyl-2-methoxy-,[84] and 2-methyl-6-methoxy-naphthalene,[116] which are all substituted in the positions corresponding to the stronger influence of the methoxyl group. 3-Methylphenanthrene yields only the 6-acid on treatment with succinic anhydride,[53] but the

OCH3

H3C

CH3

OCH3

CH3

CH3O

4-methylphenanthrene affords a small amount of the 1-isomer in addition to the 6-acid.[52] The few heterocyclic compounds that have been succinoylated are substituted in the expected positions.

Often the solvent or the reaction temperature affects the position of substitution or the ratio of isomers. When nitrobenzene is used as solvent, positions that are ordinarily subject to steric inhibition are usually avoided. This may be due to the formation of a bulky complex of nitrobenzene, aluminum chloride, and the anhydride, which finds an easier reaction path in a less blocked position.[117] Bromination, nitration,

[112] Haworth, Letsky, and Mavin, J. Chem. Soc., **1932**, 1784.
[113] Bachmann, Cronyn, and Struve, J. Org. Chem., **12**, 596 (1947).
[114] The 6-acid is probably the easiest to isolate. Orcutt and Bogert, J. Am. Chem. Soc., **63**, 127 (1941), isolated 56% of the 6-acid and 38% of the more soluble 5-acid from the reaction between 2-methylnaphthalene and succinic anhydride. A mixture from which only the 6-acid was isolated in pure form is also obtained from 2-isopropylnaphthalene (ref. 112).
[115] Haworth and Bolam, J. Chem. Soc., **1932**, 2248.
[116] Royer, Ann. chim., [12], I, 395 (1946); Royer and Buu-Hoi, Compt. rend., **222**, 746 (1946).
[117] Fieser, Chemistry of Natural Products Related to Phenanthrene, 2nd ed., p. 74, Reinhold Publishing Corp., New York, 1937.

and other reactions with naphthalene take place in the 1-position, whereas succinoylation of naphthalene in nitrobenzene solution yields appreciable amounts of the 2-isomer. Acetylation takes place in the 2-position when nitrobenzene is employed as solvent, but predominantly in the 1-position in carbon disulfide,[118] which does not form a complex with aluminum chloride. The predominant formation of the 6-isomer in succinoylations of 2-alkylnaphthalenes appears to occur for the same reasons. 2-Methoxynaphthalene affords 9 parts of the 6-acid and 1 part of the 1-acid when the reaction is conducted in nitrobenzene. One group of workers has reported the formation of the 1-acid [84] when carbon disulfide is used as solvent, while another group has reported the formation of the 8-acid.[84a] Benzene as a solvent is similar to carbon disulfide and unlike nitrobenzene. Two different acids are obtained in the succinoylation of chrysene, depending upon the solvent (nitrobenzene or benzene).[50, 51] The use of higher temperatures increases the amount of the isomer that is produced to the smaller extent at low temperatures, as is always true in aromatic substitution reactions. Acenaphthene yields 87% of the 3-acid and 5% of the 1-acid at −15°, but at higher temperature more of the 1-acid is formed and the products become more difficult to purify.[39, 119]

Substituted Succinic Anhydrides

The reaction between an aromatic compound and a monosubstituted succinic anhydride can proceed in two directions and result in the formation of two isomeric acids. Thus benzene and methylsuccinic anhydride can furnish α-methyl-β-benzoylpropionic acid (IV) and β-methyl-β-benzoylpropionic acid (V). Although many investigators isolated only

$$
\text{C}_6\text{H}_6 +
\begin{array}{l}
\text{CH}_2\text{CO} \\
\quad\quad\quad\text{>O} \\
\text{CH--CO} \\
\quad| \\
\text{CH}_3
\end{array}
\xrightarrow{\text{AlCl}_3}
\underset{\substack{|\\ \text{CH}_3 \\ \text{IV}}}{\text{C}_6\text{H}_5\text{COCH}_2\text{CHCO}_2\text{H}} +
\underset{\substack{|\\ \text{CH}_3 \\ \text{V}}}{\text{C}_6\text{H}_5\text{COCHCH}_2\text{CO}_2\text{H}}
$$

the α-methyl acid (IV),[7, 120, 121] both isomers are actually produced.[122] The β-methyl acid is more difficult to isolate because it is formed to a

[118] Thomas, *Anhydrous Aluminum Chloride in Organic Chemistry*, pp. 271–272, Reinhold Publishing Corp., New York, 1941.
[119] Fieser, *Org. Syntheses*, **20**, 1 (1940).
[120] Klobb, *Bull. soc. chim. France*, [3] **23**, 511 (1900).
[121] Oppenheim, *Ber.*, **34**, 4227 (1901).
[122] Mayer and Stamm, *Ber.*, **56**, 1424 (1923).

much smaller extent and is more soluble. The reaction between methyl-succinic anhydride and toluene also produces both possible isomers.[122]

Naphthalene and methylsuccinic anhydride react to form two acids in which the acid chains are attached to the 1- and 2-positions of the naphthalene ring, respectively. Both acids correspond to type IV, with the methyl group farthest removed from the carbonyl group.[6] The formation of the two other isomers (type V) is not reported. The preferential formation of the isomer in which the methyl group is directed away from the aromatic ring appears to be the rule with polynuclear hydrocarbons. Phenanthrene yields two acids of type IV with methyl-succinic anhydride through substitution in positions 2 and 3.[123] The 1- and 2-methylnaphthalenes are substituted in positions 4 and 6, respectively,[115, 124] to form two acids, which also belong to the α-methyl type (IV). When pyrene is condensed with methylsuccinic anhydride, the same type acid is obtained.[47, 125] It is possible that a very small amount of the other isomer (type V) is formed, but for all practical purposes polynuclear hydrocarbons and methylsuccinic anhydride produce only the corresponding α-methyl-β-aroylpropionic acids.

Substituted α-methyl-β-aroylpropionic acids (type IV) are also formed predominantly in the reaction between methylsuccinic anhydride and phenolic ethers or phenols. Anisole forms exclusively α-methyl-β-anisoylpropionic acid,[126] and the three cresol methyl ethers are also reported to yield only the α-methyl acids.[127] Veratrole, however, reacts with methylsuccinic anhydride to form both the α-methyl and β-methyl acids.[128, 129] Small amounts of the isomeric β-methyl-β-aroylpropionic acids are also formed in the methylsuccinoylation of resorcinol di-methyl ether and pyrogallol trimethyl ether, but the main product in both reactions is the α-acid.[126] Anisole has been condensed with mono-substituted succinic anhydrides in which the alkyl substituents varied from methyl to n-hexadecyl; only the α-alkyl-β-benzoylpropionic acid (type IV) was isolated.[130] Phenol is substituted in the 2-position, and the methyl group is again situated away from the benzene ring.[126]

[123] Cook and Haslewood, *J. Chem. Soc.*, **1934**, 428.
[124] Haworth, Mavin, and Sheldrick, *J. Chem. Soc.*, **1934**, 454.
[125] Bachmann and Carmack, *J. Am. Chem. Soc.*, **63**, 2494 (1941). See also Fieser and Hershberg, *J. Am. Chem. Soc.*, **60**, 1658 (1938), regarding the structure of this acid.
[126] Mitter and De, *J. Indian Chem. Soc.*, **16**, 199 (1939).
[127] Bhatt and Nargund, *J. Univ. Bombay*, **11**, Pt. 3, 131 (1942) [*C.A.*, **37**, 2000 (1943)].
[128] Borsche and Niemann, *Ann.*, **502**, 264 (1933).
[129] Robertson and Water, *J. Chem. Soc.*, **1933**, 83.
[130] Mehta, Bokil, and Nargund, *J. Univ. Bombay*, **12A**, Pt. 3, 64 (1943) [*C.A.*, **38**, 2328 (1944)].

$$OCH_3 \qquad + \qquad \begin{matrix} CH_2CO \\ | \qquad \rangle O \\ RCH-CO \end{matrix} \qquad \xrightarrow{AlCl_3} \qquad OCH_3$$

$$COCH_2CHCO_2H$$
$$|$$
$$R$$

With phenylsuccinic anhydride or substituted phenylsuccinic anhydrides the ratio of isomeric α-phenyl and β-phenyl acids depends on the solvent. In the reaction between phenylsuccinic anhydride and benzene only β-phenyl-β-benzoylpropionic acid (VII) was isolated at first,[131] but it was later shown that both acids (VI and VII) are formed in almost equal amounts when excess benzene is used as solvent.[15] When the reaction is carried out in nitrobenzene, 89% of the α-phenyl acid (VI)

$$C_6H_6 + \begin{matrix} CH_2CO \\ | \qquad \rangle O \\ CH-CO \\ | \\ C_6H_5 \end{matrix} \xrightarrow{AlCl_3} C_6H_5COCH_2CHCO_2H + C_6H_5COCHCH_2CO_2H$$

$$\underset{VI}{\overset{|}{C_6H_5}} \qquad\qquad \underset{VII}{\overset{|}{C_6H_5}}$$

is produced and only 11% of the isomer.[17] With toluene instead of benzene as reactant and diluent the acid corresponding to VII is formed to the extent of 77%, but in nitrobenzene solution the amounts are reversed and an 83% yield of α-phenyl-β-p-toluoylpropionic acid (type VI) is obtained. The effect of nitrobenzene on the ratio of isomeric acids formed when differently substituted phenylsuccinic anhydrides are condensed with benzene or toluene has been studied extensively with the results shown in Table I.[17] Depending on the nature of the substituent in the p-position of the phenyl group, nitrobenzene seems to favor preferential formation of one isomer (see p. 233). The large amounts of acids of type VII obtained in some reactions seem to exclude steric hindrance as a factor determining the direction in which fission of the monosubstituted succinic anhydride occurs.

Mixtures of the two acids corresponding to VI and VII are also obtained when o- or m-cresyl methyl ether is condensed with o-methoxyphenylsuccinic anhydride,[132] whereas p-methoxyphenylsuccinic anhydride forms only the α-isomer with the same two ethers.[133] The latter anhydride also forms only one isomer with the dimethyl ethers of the

[131] Anschütz, Hahn, and Walter, Ann., **354**, 150 (1907).

[132] Mehta, Bokil, and Nargund, J. Univ. Bombay, **10**, Pt. 5, 137 (1942) [C.A., **37**, 622 (1943)].

[133] Dalal, Bokil, and Nargund, J. Univ. Bombay, **8**, Pt. 3, 190 (1939) [C.A., **34**, 2819 (1940)].

TABLE I

REACTION BETWEEN SUBSTITUTED PHENYLSUCCINIC ANHYDRIDES AND BENZENE
OR TOLUENE [17]

A. *Without a Solvent*

Substituent in Succinic Anhydride	Aromatic Compound	Yield	
		α-Acid %	β-Acid %
Phenyl	Benzene	48	52
p-Nitrophenyl	Benzene	45	55
p-Methoxyphenyl	Benzene	Predominant	
p-Chlorophenyl	Benzene	46	54
Phenyl	Toluene	23	77
p-Nitrophenyl	Toluene	20	80
p-Methoxyphenyl	Toluene	82	18

B. *Nitrobenzene as Solvent*

Phenyl	Benzene	89	11
p-Nitrophenyl	Benzene	5	95
p-Methoxyphenyl	Benzene	Predominant	
p-Chlorophenyl	Benzene		Predominant
Phenyl	Toluene	83	17
p-Nitrophenyl	Toluene	33	67
p-Methoxyphenyl	Toluene	Predominant	

three dihydric phenols.[134]   Only the α-isomer is formed in the condensation of veratrole with phenylsuccinic anhydride,[135] but biphenyl reacts with phenylsuccinic anhydride with the formation of the β-acid as the principal reaction product.[136]

Unsymmetrically substituted succinic anhydrides having two substituents on the same carbon atom, such as α,α-dimethyl- or α,α-diethyl-succinic anhydride, invariably react so as to form the α,α-dialkyl-β-aroylpropionic acid as the sole product.   This has been demonstrated in

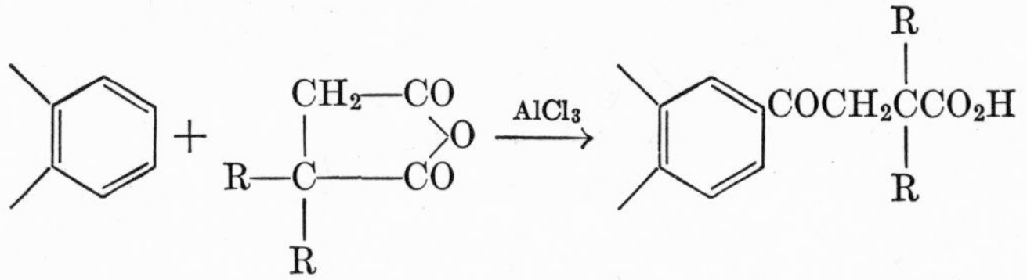

[134] Savkar, Bokil, and Nargund, *J. Univ. Bombay*, **8**, Pt. 3, 198 (1939) [*C.A.*, **34**, 2820 (1940)].   Guaiacol and hydroquinone monomethyl ether do not react with p-methoxy-phenylsuccinic anhydride.   For the failure of these compounds to react with succinic anhydride see ref. 22.   p-Methoxyphenylsuccinic anhydride was at first reported not to react very smoothly with veratrole.   See Robinson and Walker, *J. Chem. Soc.*, **1935**, 1530.

[135] Robinson and Young, *J. Chem. Soc.*, **1935**, 1414.

[136] Price and Tomisek, *J. Am. Chem. Soc.*, **65**, 439 (1943).

the reaction of α,α-dimethylsuccinic anhydride with benzene,[14, 16, 18, 137, 138] toluene,[138] naphthalene,[139] α-methylnaphthalene,[139] and hydrindene [56] and also in the condensation of α,α-diethylsuccinic anhydride with benzene.[138] With naphthalene two acids are produced (1- and 2-position), but fission of the anhydride always occurs in such a way that the *gem*-dialkyl group is farthest away from the aromatic ring.[139] The same generalization also holds for the reaction between benzene or naphthalene and α-methyl-α-ethylsuccinic anhydride.[137, 140] Certain more complex anhydrides, such

$$
\begin{array}{ccc}
\text{CH}_2\text{CH}_2 & \text{CH}_2\text{CH}_2 & \text{COCH}_2\text{CCO}_2\text{H} \\
\mid \quad\quad \text{C}\!-\!\text{CO} & \diagup \quad\quad \text{C}\!-\!\text{CO} & \text{CH}_2 \quad \text{CH}_2 \\
\diagup\ \mid\quad \rangle\!\text{O} & \text{CH}_2 \quad\quad \diagup\ \mid\quad \rangle\!\text{O} & \mid \qquad \mid \\
\text{CH}_2\text{CH}_2\ \ \text{CH}_2\!-\!\text{CO} & \text{CH}_2\text{CH}_2 \quad \text{CH}_2\!-\!\text{CO} & \text{CH}_2\!-\!\text{CH}_2 \\
\text{VIII} & \text{IX} & \text{X}
\end{array}
$$

as VIII and IX, which can be considered unsymmetrically substituted succinic anhydrides, have been condensed with benzene, toluene, ethylbenzene, hydrindene, naphthalene, and methylnaphthalene.[14, 16, 141, 142, 143] All the acids obtained are of type X, with the cyclic substituent away from the aromatic ring.

The reactions between α,β-dimethylsuccinic anhydride and benzene,[18] and α,β-diethylsuccinic anhydride and anisole,[144] give the corresponding α,β-dialkylaroylpropionic acids in 86% and 91% yield, respectively. The formation of stereoisomers has not been observed; *cis*- and *trans*-dimethylsuccinic anhydride yield the same acid when condensed with veratrole.[145] In the reaction between trimethylsuccinic anhydride and benzene, α,α,β-trimethylbenzoylpropionic acid is obtained in good yield,[18] but tetramethylsuccinic anhydride cannot be used in the preparation of keto acids.[18] Carbon monoxide is evolved during the reaction, and the product obtained is in all probability $\alpha,\alpha,\beta,\beta$-tetramethyl-$\beta$-phenylpropionic acid (XI). Tetramethylsuccinic anhydride reacts

[137] Clemo and Dickenson, *J. Chem. Soc.*, **1937**, 255.

[138] Sengupta, *J. prakt. Chem.*, [2] **151**, 82 (1938).

[139] Sengupta, *J. prakt. Chem.*, [2] **152**, 9 (1939).

[140] Barker and Clemo, *J. Chem. Soc.*, **1940**, 1277.

[141] Sengupta, *J. Indian Chem. Soc.*, **16**, 349 (1939).

[142] Sengupta, *J. Indian Chem. Soc.*, **17**, 101 (1940); *Current Sci.*, **5**, 295 (1936) [*C.A.*, **31**, 2587 (1937)].

[143] Sengupta, *J. Indian Chem. Soc.*, **17**, 183 (1940); *Science and Culture*, **3**, 56 (1937) [*C.A.*, **31**, 7868 (1937)].

[144] Baker, *J. Am. Chem. Soc.*, **65**, 1572 (1943).

[145] Haworth and Mavin, *J. Chem. Soc.*, **1932**, 1485.

similarly with toluene. Reactions with loss of carbon monoxide are general with anhydrides of tertiary carboxylic acids.[146, 147]

$$C_6H_6 + \begin{matrix} (CH_3)_2C-CO \\ | \quad \quad >O \\ (CH_3)_2C-CO \end{matrix} \xrightarrow{AlCl_3} \begin{matrix} CH_3 \quad CH_3 \\ | \quad \quad | \\ C_6H_5C \quad \quad CCO_2H \\ | \quad \quad | \\ CH_3 \quad CH_3 \end{matrix}$$

XI

Glutaric Anhydride and Substituted Glutaric Anhydrides

Only a few reactions between glutaric anhydride and an aromatic compound have been carried out. The products are γ-aroylbutyric acids, but the formation of a small amount of the corresponding diketone ($ArCOCH_2CH_2CH_2COAr$) has been observed in at least two reactions.[148, 149] The formation of diketones may be found to be more general if the reaction with glutaric anhydride is studied in more detail. From

$$\text{(ring)} + \begin{matrix} CH_2CO \\ | \quad \quad \\ CH_2 \quad \quad O \\ | \quad \quad \\ CH_2CO \end{matrix} \xrightarrow{AlCl_3} \text{(ring)}COCH_2CH_2CH_2CO_2H$$

the scanty data that are available the yield in the reaction between glutaric anhydride and an aromatic compound appears to be lower than in the corresponding reaction with succinic anhydride. The reaction between glutaric anhydride and acenaphthene in nitrobenzene solution is described as particularly poor, by contrast with the condensation with succinic anhydride.[39] Benzene,[15, 148] toluene,[149] anisole,[36, 150, 151] phenetole,[150, 152] chlorobenzene,[30] veratrole,[153] thiophene,[154] tetralin,[36] pyrogallol trimethyl ether,[155] and acenaphthene[39] have been converted into the respective γ-aroylbutyric acids. The point of attack on the aromatic ring is the same as with the lower homolog.

Some β,β-dialkylglutaric anhydrides have been successfully condensed with benzene, but β-phenylglutaric anhydride did not react in the ex-

[146] Laughlin and Whitmore, *J. Am. Chem. Soc.*, **54**, 4462 (1932).
[147] Whitmore and Crooks, *J. Am. Chem. Soc.*, **60**, 2078 (1938).
[148] Borsche and Sinn, *Ann.*, **538**, 283 (1939).
[149] Carter, Simonsen, and Williams, *J. Chem. Soc.*, **1940**, 451.
[150] Plant and Tomlinson, *J. Chem. Soc.*, **1935**, 856.
[151] van der Zanden, *Rec. trav. chim.*, **57**, 242 (1938).
[152] van der Zanden, *Rec. trav. chim.*, **58**, 181 (1939).
[153] Haworth and Atkinson, *J. Chem. Soc.*, **1938**, 797.
[154] Cagniant and Deluzarche, *Compt. rend.*, **222**, 1301 (1946).
[155] Haworth, Moore, and Pauson, *J. Chem. Soc.*, **1948**, 1045.

pected manner; instead it formed ketohydrindene-3-acetic acid by an internal condensation.[15, 156] Camphoric anhydride, which can be considered to be a completely alkylated glutaric anhydride like tetramethylsuccinic anhydride, loses carbon monoxide when treated with aluminum chloride.[157, 158, 159] However, camphoric anhydride with toluene [160] or anisole [160] yields the corresponding aroylcamphoric acid (XII or XIII).

$$\underset{\textbf{XII}}{\begin{array}{c}CH_3\\ \\H_3CCCH_3 \quad CO\text{—}\langle \ \rangle\text{R}\\ \\CO_2H\end{array}} \qquad \underset{\textbf{XIII}}{\begin{array}{c}CH_3\\ \\H_3CCCH_3 \quad CO_2H\\ \\CO\text{—}\langle \ \rangle\text{R}\end{array}}$$

$$\underset{\textbf{XIV}}{\begin{array}{c}CH_2CH_2 \quad CH_2CO\\ \diagdown C \diagdown \quad O\\ CH_2CH_2 \quad CH_2CO\end{array}} \qquad \underset{\textbf{XV}}{\begin{array}{c}CH_2CH_2 \quad CH_2CO\\ CH_2 \diagdown C \diagdown \quad O\\ CH_2CH_2 \quad CH_2CO\end{array}}$$

The disubstituted glutaric anhydrides XIV and XV, on treatment with benzene or toluene in the presence of aluminum chloride, furnish the expected acids.[15]

Polymeric Anhydrides of Higher Dibasic Acids

The polymeric anhydrides of adipic and sebacic acid can be employed in the Friedel and Crafts synthesis of keto acids.[161] With benzene as reactant and solvent, ω-benzoylvaleric and ω-benzoylpelargonic acid are obtained in 75 and 78% yields, respectively. The reaction does not yield an aroylaliphatic acid exclusively but follows the course outlined in the equation to furnish dibasic acid and diketone as well. The yields

$$C_6H_6 + [\text{—}CO(CH_2)_nCO_2\text{—}]_x \xrightarrow{AlCl_3} \frac{x}{2} C_6H_5CO(CH_2)_nCO_2H +$$

$$\frac{x}{4} C_6H_5CO(CH_2)_nCOC_6H_5 + \frac{x}{4} HO_2C(CH_2)_nCO_2H$$

---

[156] Internal cyclization of phenylethylsuccinic anhydride could not be effected, Bergs, *Ber.*, **63**, 1294 (1930), but benzylsuccinic anhydrides cyclize readily under the influence of aluminum chloride with the formation of 1-tetralone-3-carboxylic acids. Haworth, Jones, and Way, *J. Chem. Soc.*, **1943**, 10.

[157] Lees and Perkin, *J. Chem. Soc.*, **79**, 356 (1901).

[158] Perkin and Yates, *J. Chem. Soc.*, **79**, 1373 (1901).

[159] Burcker, *Bull. soc. chim. France*, [3] **4**, 112 (1890); [3] **13**, 901 (1895).

[160] Eykman, *Chem. Weekblad*, **4**, 727 (1907) (*Chem. Zentr.*, **1907**, II, 2046).

[161] Hill, *J. Am. Chem. Soc.*, **54**, 4105 (1932).

quoted are based on this equation. In the above reactions the yields of diketones are 85% and 86%, respectively. Although only a few examples have been recorded, this reaction should be applicable to many other aromatic compounds as well as to anhydrides of other dibasic acids. Anisole and phenetole have been condensed with the polymeric anhydride of adipic acid.[162] The reaction between thiophene and the polymeric anhydrides of adipic, suberic, azelaic, and sebacic acid results in the formation of the respective thenoyl fatty acids in 3.8%, —%,[163] 24.5%, and 8.3% yield.[164] Yields of 0%, 29.8%, 27%, and 21.2% of the diketones were secured.[164] All the yields are based on the equation above. These yields are fairly low, and, in spite of the fact that the polymeric anhydrides are easily prepared, the Friedel and Crafts reaction with the ester acid chlorides of the acids might often be preferable. (See Table II, p. 253.)

Maleic Anhydride and Substituted Maleic Anhydrides

The interest in β-aroylacrylic acids, obtained from maleic anhydride and an aromatic compound in the presence of aluminum chloride, has not been so great as that in the β-aroylpropionic acids. Such interest as there has been has centered chiefly around the stereochemistry of the acids [165-169] and the structure of the so-called "Pechmann dyes," colored substances obtained when benzoylacrylic acids are heated with dehydrating agents.[2, 67, 170] Benzoylacrylic acids have been utilized as starting materials in a synthesis of anthraquinone derivatives.[171] The reaction between aromatic compounds and maleic anhydride has generally given lower yields and less pure products than the comparable reaction with succinic anhydride. Consequently many chemists have preferred to prepare the acrylic acids by elimination of hydrogen bromide from the

[162] Plant and Tomlinson, *J. Chem. Soc.*, **1935**, 1092.

[163] The product resulting from the reaction of suberic anhydride was not obtained in a solid state.

[164] Billman and Travis, *Proc. Indiana Acad. Sci.*, **54**, 101 (1945) [*C.A.*, **40**, 1826 (1946)].

[165] Benzoylacrylic acid, obtained by the general Friedel and Crafts reaction, has the *trans* configuration as a result of an isomerization brought about by the catalyst. By analogy, the same configuration might be expected whenever maleic anhydride itself is condensed with aromatic compounds. However, dibromomaleic anhydride forms the *cis* acid with benzene and mesitylene; and dimethylmaleic anhydride forms the *cis* acid with benzene and biphenyl, but the *trans* acid with mesitylene. See Lutz and co-workers, refs. 166-169.

[166] Lutz, *J. Am. Chem. Soc.*, **52**, 3405 (1930).

[167] Lutz and Taylor, *J. Am. Chem. Soc.*, **55**, 1168 (1933).

[168] Lutz and Taylor, *J. Am. Chem. Soc.*, **55**, 1593 (1933).

[169] Lutz and Couper, *J. Org. Chem.*, **6**, 77 (1941).

[170] Bogert and Ritter, *Proc. Natl. Acad. Sci. U.S.*, **10**, 363 (1924).

[171] Fieser and Fieser, *J. Am. Chem. Soc.*, **57**, 1679 (1935).

corresponding bromopropionic acids, which can be readily obtained by direct bromination of the propionic acids.[39, 172-175] More careful study of the reaction between maleic anhydride and alkylated benzenes [171] and certain phenolic ethers [176] has led to purer products in better yield. An extension of these studies to reactions of maleic anhydride with other aromatic compounds has resulted in comparable improvements.[176a]

A reasonably large number of aromatic compounds have been condensed with maleic anhydride. Substitution occurs generally in the expected position with the formation of only one isomer. From the reaction between maleic anhydride and naphthalene two acids have been isolated (substitution in the 1- and the 2-positions).[177] Anthracene, in contrast to its behavior on succinoylation, is reported to form the 9-acid,[178] but no proof of structure is given. The reaction between maleic anhydride and polynuclear hydrocarbons in nitrobenzene solution has been reported to give particularly poor results, despite contrary claims in the patent literature.[39] Acenaphthene forms the corresponding acid in only 32% yield, whereas in succinoylation a yield of about 85% is easily secured. No product could be isolated when naphthalene was used with nitrobenzene as solvent.

In the early investigations of the reaction between the alkylbenzenes and maleic anhydride, the alkylbenzenes were used both as reactant and solvent and the yields of pure products were very low.[179, 180] More recent work has shown that alkylbenzenes can readily be condensed with maleic anhydride in 60–70% yields in tetrachloroethane solution.[171] Good yields are obtained in the reaction of maleic anhydride with the cresol methyl ethers, veratrole, and hydroquinone dimethyl ether when nitrobenzene is employed as the solvent.[176] Reaction in carbon disulfide gives lower yields. Diphenyl ether also reacts with maleic anhydride,[181] as does anisole,[171, 176] phenetole,[72, 179] and phenol itself.[177] Resorcinol dimethyl ether, however, forms the expected acid (XVI) only to a small extent.[182] The main product of the reaction is a substituted succinic anhydride (XVII) formed by addition of resorcinol dimethyl ether to

[172] Bougault, Ann. chim., [8] 15, 498 (1908).
[173] Kohler and Engelbrecht, J. Am. Chem. Soc., 41, 764 (1919).
[174] Rice, J. Am. Chem. Soc., 45, 222 (1923).
[175] Rice, J. Am. Chem. Soc., 46, 214 (1924).
[176] Dave and Nargund, J. Univ. Bombay, 7, Pt. 3, 191 (1938) [C.A., 33, 3779 (1939)].
[176a] Papa, Schwenk, Villani, and Klingsberg, J. Am. Chem. Soc., 70, 3356 (1948).
[177] Bogert and Ritter, J. Am. Chem. Soc., 47, 526 (1925).
[178] Oddy, J. Am. Chem. Soc., 45, 2156 (1923).
[179] Kozniewski and Marchlewski, Bull. Acad. Sci. Cracow, 81 (1906) (Chem. Zentr., 1906, II, 1189).
[180] Kozak, Bull. Acad. Sci. Cracow, 407 (1906) (Chem. Zentr., 1907, I, 1788).
[181] Rice, J. Am. Chem. Soc., 48, 269 (1926).
[182] Rice, J. Am. Chem. Soc., 53, 3153 (1931).

maleic anhydride.   The anhydride (XVII) is partly hydrolyzed to the substituted succinic acid (XVIII). A fourth product is the acid XIX, formed by addition of the ether to the acrylic acid XVI.   A similar

$$\begin{array}{ccccc}
\text{COCH=CHCO}_2\text{H} & \text{CH}_2\text{—CO} & \text{CH}_2\text{CO}_2\text{H} & \text{COCH}_2\text{CHCO}_2\text{H} \\
\text{XVI} & \text{XVII} & \text{XVIII} & \text{XIX}
\end{array}$$

addition has been observed with maleic anhydride and benzene in the presence of excess aluminum chloride.[183]   The product, α-phenyl-β-

$$C_6H_6 + \begin{matrix}\text{CHCO}\\ \| \quad \rangle O \\ \text{CHCO}\end{matrix} \xrightarrow{\text{AlCl}_3} C_6H_5\text{COCH=CHCO}_2\text{H} \xrightarrow{C_6H_6} \underset{\underset{C_6H_5}{|}}{C_6H_5\text{COCH}_2\text{CHCO}_2\text{H}}$$
$$\text{XX}$$

benzoylpropionic acid (XX), is also obtained when benzene is condensed with β-benzoylacrylic acid in the presence of aluminum chloride. Toluene behaves similarly.

The reaction with methylmaleic anhydride and benzene, like the corresponding reaction with methylsuccinic anhydride, was first reported to yield only one isomer.[2,177]   Actually both α-methyl- and β-methyl-benzoylacrylic acid are formed.[122,184]   Two acids are also obtained from

$$C_6H_6 + \begin{matrix}\text{CH—CO}\\ \| \quad \rangle O \\ \underset{\underset{\text{CH}_3}{|}}{\text{C—CO}}\end{matrix} \xrightarrow{\text{AlCl}_3} C_6H_5\text{COCH=}\underset{\underset{\text{CH}_3}{|}}{\text{CCO}_2\text{H}} + C_6H_5\text{CO}\underset{\underset{\text{CH}_3}{|}}{\text{C=}}\text{CHCO}_2\text{H}$$

the reaction between bromomaleic anhydride and benzene.[185]   Dimethyl-maleic anhydride has been successfully condensed with benzene,[168] mesitylene,[168] biphenyl,[169] and bromobenzene,[169] while dibromomaleic anhydride has been condensed with benzene and mesitylene.[166]   Maleic anhydride reacts with hydroquinone, hydroquinone methyl ethers, or their substituted derivatives in a sodium chloride-aluminum chloride

[183] Pummerer and Buchta, *Ber.*, **69**, 1005 (1936).

[184] The stereochemical configuration of the acids from methylmaleic anhydride and benzene is not known. However, with bromobenzene, instead of benzene, the resulting β-methyl-β-p-bromobenzoylacrylic acid has the *cis* configuration, whereas the α-methyl-β-p-bromobenzoylacrylic acid is *trans*. See ref. 167.

[185] Rice, *J. Am. Chem. Soc.*, **52**, 2094 (1930).

melt at temperatures above 200° with the formation of naphtha-zarins.[186,187] The reaction has been used extensively, but a detailed description is beyond the scope of this chapter.

Other Synthetic Methods

In addition to the synthesis from an aromatic hydrocarbon, succinic anhydride or a substituted succinic anhydride, and aluminum chloride, β-aroylpropionic acids can be prepared by two other methods: the Grignard reaction between succinic anhydride or a substituted succinic anhydride and an arylmagnesium halide,[188] and the stepwise elaboration of the side chain in an alkyl aryl ketone.

The first method suffers from the disadvantage that the yields are generally low, although satisfactory yields have been obtained with dimethylsuccinic anhydride.[189] The advantage of this method is that

$$C_6H_5MgBr + \begin{matrix} CH_2CO \\ | \quad\quad >O \\ CH_2CO \end{matrix} \xrightarrow{HX} C_6H_5COCH_2CH_2CO_2H$$

the point of attachment of the side chain is determined by the location of the halogen in the aryl halide; this permits the succinic acid side chain to be attached to positions that may not be available through the direct Friedel and Crafts synthesis.

The second method usually starts with a methyl aryl ketone, which is brominated and then condensed with sodium malonic ester. Hydrolysis and decarboxylation furnish the aroylpropionic acid. This method is obviously more laborious than the Friedel and Crafts reaction, but it

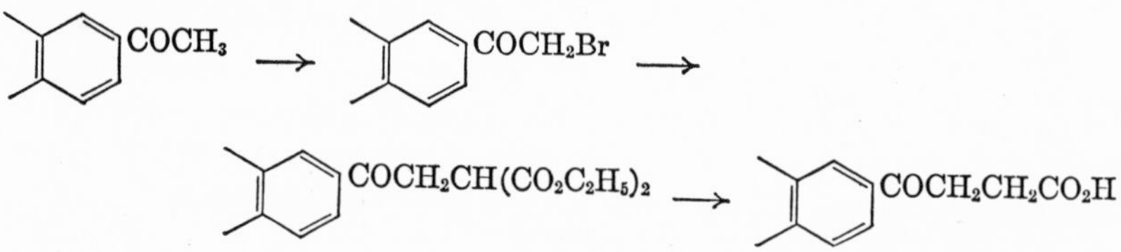

has been used frequently where acetylation and succinoylation do not occur at the same position in an aromatic nucleus or for the proof of structure of acids obtained by succinoylation. If an aryl ethyl ketone is

[186] Zahn and Ochwat, *Ann.*, **462**, 72 (1928).

[187] Thomas, *Anhydrous Aluminum Chloride in Organic Chemistry*, pp. 581–582, Reinhold Publishing Corp., New York, 1941.

[188] Weizmann, Blum-Bergmann, and Bergmann, *J. Chem. Soc.*, **1935**, 1370; Weizmann and Pickles, *Proc. Roy. Soc. London*, **20**, 201 (1904); Komppa and Rohrmann, *Ann.*, **509**, 259 (1934).

[189] Fieser and Daudt, *J. Am. Chem. Soc.*, **63**, 782 (1941).

used, β-methyl-β-aroylpropionic acids (which are less accessible by direct succinoylation) can be obtained. If methylmalonic ester is used, α-methyl-β-aroylpropionic acids can be prepared.

The reaction between an aromatic hydrocarbon and succinoyl dichloride or the ester acid chloride of succinic acid has been used only in single instances for the preparation of β-aroylpropionic acids.[190, 191] However, the ester acid chlorides of the higher homologs of succinic acid seem superior to the corresponding polymeric anhydrides for the synthesis of ω-aroylaliphatic acids such as XXI, where $n > 2$.[36, 191a] The

$$C_6H_6 + (CH_2)_n \overset{COCl}{\underset{CO_2C_2H_5}{\diagup}} \quad \xrightarrow[\text{hydrolysis}]{2AlCl_3, \text{ then}} \quad C_6H_5CO(CH_2)_nCO_2H$$

XXI

ester acid chlorides are prepared easily,[191a, 192] and the final products are obtained in much better yields and greater purity. The more direct preparation of the polymeric anhydrides is offset by the fact that only one-half of the available anhydride is converted into the keto acid, which

TABLE II

COMPARISON OF ESTER ACID CHLORIDES WITH ACID ANHYDRIDES IN THE PREPARATION OF ω-AROYLALIPHATIC ACIDS

Aromatic Compound	Ester Acid Chloride	Yield %	Reference	Anhydride	Yield %	Reference
Anisole	Glutaric	93.5	191a	Glutaric	85	36
Thiophene	Glutaric	75	154	Glutaric	39.4	154
Tetralin	Glutaric	71	36	Glutaric	43	36
Benzene	Adipic	55, 78	36, 191a	Polyadipic	75	161
Anisole	Adipic	66, 95	36, 191a	Polyadipic	43	162
Thiophene	Adipic	37.6, 70 *	36, 191a	Polyadipic	3.8 †	164
Benzene	Sebacic	80	36, 191a	Polysebacic	78	161
Thiophene	Sebacic	25, 66 *	36, 191a	Polysebacic	8.3 †	164

* Stannic chloride was used as the condensing agent; with aluminum chloride the yields were between 30% and 40%.
† Stannic chloride was used as the condensing agent.

[190] Claus, Ber., **20**, 1374 (1887).
[191] Fager, J. Am. Chem. Soc., **67**, 2217 (1945).
[191a] Papa, Schwenk, and Hankin, J. Am. Chem. Soc., **69**, 3018 (1947).
[192] Org. Syntheses, Coll. Vol. **2**, 276 (1943); Org. Syntheses, **25**, 19, 71 (1945).

makes the procedure less suitable for larger-scale preparations. For small-scale preparations, and when one of the reactants, e.g., benzene, can be used as solvent, the quicker preparation through the polymeric anhydrides has its advantages. Table II supports the statement that better yields are obtained with the ester acid chlorides than with the polymeric anhydrides or with glutaric anhydride.

The same acids that are now accessible through the use of either the polymeric anhydrides or the ester acid chlorides were previously obtained only as by-products in the reaction of the aromatic compounds with the acid dichlorides [193, 194] or through stepwise elaboration of the side chain by standard procedures.

The alternative method for the preparation of β-benzoylacrylic acids was mentioned earlier. This method starts with the β-benzoylpropionic acids obtained from succinic anhydride and an aromatic compound.

Bromination, followed by elimination of hydrobromic acid, usually gives the unsaturated acid in good yield, and many investigators have prepared β-aroylacrylic acids by this method rather than by the Friedel and Crafts reaction with maleic anhydride.[39, 172-175]

EXPERIMENTAL CONDITIONS

The usual precautions of a Friedel and Crafts reaction must be observed, particularly with regard to the anhydrous conditions of catalyst and reactants.[195] Solvents should be of good grade, and benzene should be sulfur free. Finely divided aluminum chloride is preferable to coarsely ground material (lumps), although very finely powdered material may lead to too rapid a reaction, often undesirable with sensitive compounds. When a solvent is used in which aluminum chloride is soluble (nitrobenzene or tetrachloroethane), the particle size is not of too great importance, but large lumps should always be avoided.

The permissible variations in carrying out the reaction include the solvent, the temperature, the reaction time, and the order of addition

[193] Etaix, Ann. chim., [7] 9, 391 (1896).

[194] Borsche, Ber., 52, 2079 (1919).

[195] Thomas, Anhydrous Aluminum Chloride in Organic Chemistry, pp. 867 ff., Reinhold Publishing Corp., New York, 1941.

of reagents. Of these the choice of the proper solvent is probably the most important, because this often determines the yield and the purity of the product and in some reactions also the point of substitution. The usual solvents are carbon disulfide, benzene, nitrobenzene, and *sym*-tetrachloroethane. If the compound to be substituted is readily available and cheap, such as benzene or toluene, it can be used in excess as solvent. The use in excess of more highly substituted liquid alkyl-benzenes or phenolic ethers is not recommended although it has been reported. The early investigators appear to have employed carbon disulfide or benzene in preference to other solvents, but these solvents have been replaced most advantageously by nitrobenzene, tetrachloro-ethane, or a mixture of the two.

Aluminum chloride has a definite destructive action on many poly-nuclear aromatic hydrocarbons, their phenolic ethers, and some hetero-cyclic compounds such as thiophene.[196] Nitrobenzene and tetrachloro-ethane both dissolve aluminum chloride and form complexes with it; the catalytic activity and the destructiveness of the catalyst are de-creased by complex formation with the solvent.[196, 196a] Carbon disulfide, benzene, and ligroin do not dissolve aluminum chloride to any appre-ciable extent, and the compound to be substituted is exposed to the destructive influence of the catalyst throughout most of the reaction (unless the compound itself, for example chlorobenzene, forms a complex with aluminum chloride). It follows then that for sensitive compounds, and all polynuclear hydrocarbons belong to this group, nitrobenzene or tetrachloroethane should be employed as solvents.

Carbon disulfide may be used with compounds such as the halo-benzenes that contain deactivating groups. Prolonged heating is then necessary. But the yields are usually not high, and if the halobenzenes are readily available it is probably preferable to use them in excess without a diluent. When comparisons were made to determine the effect of different solvents, carbon disulfide was usually found to result in the lowest yield. Nitrobenzene does not appear to be a good solvent for succinoylation of halogenated benzenes,[36, 66, 68] possibly because the catalytic activity of aluminum chloride in solution is too low.

Although nitrobenzene is the most adequate solvent for polynuclear hydrocarbons, alkylated benzenes are best succinoylated in *sym*-tetra-chloroethane solution.[33] This solvent proved to be more suitable than carbon disulfide, benzene, ligroin, or nitrobenzene, but was unsuitable for naphthalene. The yields usually range between 80% and 90%.

[196] Fieser, *Experiments in Organic Chemistry*, 2nd ed., p. 413, D. C. Heath and Co., Boston, 1941.
[196a] Thomas, *Anhydrous Aluminum Chloride in Organic Chemistry*, pp. 210–211, 873, Reinhold Publishing Corp., New York, 1941.

For phenolic ethers in both the benzene and naphthalene series, nitrobenzene and tetrachloroethane have been employed with good success. Usually nitrobenzene gives the higher yields, but sometimes this is reversed (see Table III). Benzene has also been used as solvent, but it is not so generally applicable as the other solvents mentioned. With carbon disulfide the yields are low throughout. Some of the results on the succinoylation of the methyl ethers of dihydric phenols are summarized in Table III.

TABLE III [22]

EFFECT OF THE SOLVENT ON THE YIELD OF β-AROYLPROPIONIC ACIDS FROM THE
DIMETHYL ETHERS OF THE DIHYDROXYBENZENES

| | Yield of β-Aroylpropionic Acid in | | |
| | Carbon Disulfide | sym-Tetra-chloro-ethane | Nitro-benzene |
Aromatic Compound	%	%	%
Resorcinol dimethyl ether	50	60	88
Catechol dimethyl ether	46	64	44
Hydroquinone dimethyl ether	40	45	70

The best solvent for the succinoylation of aromatic ethers, however, appears to be a mixture of tetrachloroethane (80%) and nitrobenzene (20%).[71] This mixture can be employed in large runs, where nitrobenzene has been found to have scme undesirable oxidative action; [24] yields of 80–90% and often more are usually secured.[197] A 95% yield of β-p-anisoylpropionic acid was obtained by several investigators with as much as three moles of anisole.[36, 198, 199] The mixed solvent is particularly useful for aromatic ethers containing a naphthyl group. The yields from the reaction of 1,5-dimethoxynaphthalene and succinic anhydride are summarized in Table IV. The mixed solvent has also proved useful in the succinoylation of compounds other than ethers, for example, ethylbenzene,[200] hydrindene,[55] diphenylene oxide,[101] and phenylcyclohexane.[36]

Benzene, which can be used as solvent only for those compounds that are more reactive than itself, is generally employed in all reactions where it is one of the reactants. In the reaction between dimethylmaleic

[197] Fieser and Hershberg, ref. 71, report that the acid from veratrole and succinic anhydride is formed in a yield of 46% in carbon disulfide, 73% in nitrobenzene, and 67% in the mixture of nitrobenzene and tetrachloroethane. The product obtained with the solvent mixture is purest. Haworth and Mavin, ref. 145, obtained an 85% yield using nitrobenzene. An 84% yield of the acid was later secured by Holmes and Mann, ref. 252, who employed the solvent mixture. See also ref. 275.

[198] Plimmer, Short, and Hill, J. Chem. Soc., 1938, 696.

[199] Price and Kaplan, J. Am. Chem. Soc., 66, 447 (1944).

[200] Baddar and Warren, J. Chem. Soc., 1939, 944.

TABLE IV

SUCCINOYLATION OF 1,5-DIMETHOXYNAPHTHALENE

Solvent	Yield %	Reference
Carbon disulfide	21	24
Tetrachloroethane	80 *	24
Nitrobenzene	85	24
Mixture of nitrobenzene and tetrachloroethane	93 †	87

* This reaction was run at 74°, and partial demethylation took place.
† When three equivalents of aluminum chloride were used the yield was 98%.

anhydride and benzene, however, better results were obtained when carbon disulfide was the diluent.[168] Although inferior to nitrobenzene and tetrachloroethane for reactions involving polynuclear hydrocarbons, benzene has been found to be an excellent solvent for certain benzene derivatives containing alicyclic rings, such as tetralin,[59] fluorene,[58] and also diphenyl ether and diphenyl sulfide,[36, 93a] but not hydrindene or acenaphthene.[30] Benzene is also the most suitable solvent for the succinoylation of retene and is superior to nitrobenzene.[48, 49]

Table V, summarizing the results in the literature, suggests the solvents which may be most advantageously employed for the succinoylation of several classes of compounds.

TABLE V

PREFERRED SOLVENTS FOR SUCCINOYLATION

Type of Compound to Be Succinoylated	Solvent
Benzene	Benzene
Alkylbenzenes	Tetrachloroethane
Phenols	Tetrachloroethane
Aromatic ethers	Nitrobenzene, tetrachloroethane, or, best, a mixture of the two
Halogenated benzenes	Carbon disulfide or excess reactant *
Benzene with alicyclic rings	Benzene
Polynuclear hydrocarbons	Nitrobenzene

* The use of excess reactant as solvent in the succinoylation of iodobenzene does not appear to be suitable.

For anhydrides other than succinic anhydride or its derivatives, the data are not sufficiently numerous to permit similar generalizations. The solvent of choice will probably be similar to the solvent used for succinoylations, but the nature of the anhydride and its reactivity will have to be taken into account. From the available information regarding the condensation with maleic anhydride it would appear that tetrachloroethane is the most suitable solvent for the reaction with alkylated benzene derivatives.[171] The claim in the patent literature that nitrobenzene is a good solvent for the reaction between maleic anhydride and polynuclear hydrocarbons could not be substantiated.[39] The three cresol methyl ethers, veratrole, and hydroquinone dimethyl ether have been condensed with maleic anhydride in very good yield in nitrobenzene solution. The yields in carbon disulfide were generally lower.[176]

The reaction time and reaction temperature will usually depend on the solvent employed and the compound to be substituted. Reactions in carbon disulfide are slow. However, the conveniently low boiling point of carbon disulfide makes it the solvent of choice where heating is required. It is necessary to heat reactions with the halobenzenes for twenty-four hours or more. Benzene is also used in conjunction with heating; it acts more vigorously because of its higher boiling point. Refluxing for one hour is usually sufficient with the alicyclic-aromatic compounds and diphenyl ether.

Of the two solvents that dissolve aluminum chloride, tetrachloroethane and nitrobenzene, the former gives the faster reaction. When employed for the succinoylation of alkylbenzenes, a one- or two-hour standing period at room temperature is usually sufficient. In reactions of polynuclear hydrocarbons and their ethers a low reaction temperature has to be maintained while the reagents are slowly mixed. Reactions in nitrobenzene are generally slow, and this fact, combined with the low temperature at which reaction has to be carried out, require prolonged standing. The usual procedure is to add the reagents slowly at ice-bath temperature or below and after a few hours at that temperature to let the reaction mixture come to room temperature by allowing the ice to melt. A total period of twenty-four hours' standing after mixing the reagents is usually sufficient, but in some reactions a period of several days results in a higher yield. The reaction between 1-methyl-2-methoxynaphthalene and succinic anhydride results in a 41% yield after forty hours, a 63% yield after three days, and a 78% yield after five days.[84] In the succinoylation of phenolic ethers using the tetrachloroethane-nitrobenzene mixture, three days' standing in the ice chest is recommended. With veratrole a 67% yield is secured when the low temperature is maintained for three days, but only 43% when the mixture is allowed to stand at room temperature for the same period of time.[71] Anisole need not be cooled during the long standing time.[201] When benzene is used as reactant and diluent, a short heating time

[201] Fieser and Desreux, *J. Am. Chem. Soc.*, **60**, 2255 (1938).

is usually necessary to compensate for the relative inertness of benzene.[202]

The order of addition of the reagents is not too important if the reaction is slow and the compound not sensitive to aluminum chloride. In all other cases, probably the majority, it is essential not to add the aluminum chloride alone to the compound to be substituted. It does not seem very important, however, whether the compound is added to the catalyst or vice versa. Haworth and collaborators conducted the reactions by adding slowly a mixture of the anhydride and the aromatic compound to the solution of aluminum chloride in nitrobenzene. Fieser and collaborators added the aluminum chloride through an addition tube to the solution of the other reagents. In some reactions the aluminum chloride can be dissolved in nitrobenzene and then added to the other reagents. One should also bear in mind that two moles of aluminum chloride is required for one mole of anhydride.[12, 13, 196] In the older literature, and also in some recent work, this ratio was not used. An excess of aluminum chloride does not seem necessary; in a few reactions higher yields are reported when more catalyst is used, in others the yields are lower. The relative ratio of succinic anhydride-aluminum chloride and the compound to be substituted depends on the compounds; when the reactant is used as solvent it will obviously be present in excess. Often reagents can be used in equivalent amounts. An excess of about 20% of succinic anhydride-aluminum chloride with regard to other reactants generally results in a higher yield than an excess of the latter.[39]

Apparatus and Isolation of Products

When the reaction does not require stirring, as is often the case when carbon disulfide or benzene is used as the solvent, an ordinary round-bottomed flask equipped with reflux condenser, calcium chloride tube, and gas-outlet tube is satisfactory. However, stirring is usually preferable even in a single-phase reaction because it provides faster mixing of the reagents and helps to eliminate the hydrogen chloride formed. A three-necked flask, equipped with a mercury-sealed stirrer, addition tube [203] (or dropping funnel), thermometer, and a gas-outlet tube, is the most suitable apparatus. When the reaction is allowed to stand for a longer period of time, stirring is usually discontinued a few hours after mixing the reagents.

[202] Too long standing may promote side reactions, and the continuous evolution of hydrogen chloride is not always a sign that the reaction is still progressing in the desired direction. See ref. 195.

[203] Fieser, *Experiments in Organic Chemistry*, 2nd ed., p. 311, D. C. Heath and Co., Boston, 1941.

The reaction mixture can be decomposed by the addition of ice and hydrochloric acid; but, as in all Friedel and Crafts reactions, it is better to pour the reaction mixture on ice and dilute hydrochloric acid in order to avoid local overheating or accumulation of too much hydrochloric acid.[196a] If the decomposition is to be followed by steam distillation, it is advisable to carry out the decomposition of the reaction complex in a large round-bottomed flask which can be used directly for the steam distillation.

Carbon disulfide and benzene possess the advantage that they can easily be removed from the reaction mixture. The reaction complex usually precipitates during the reaction when carbon disulfide is the solvent, and the carbon disulfide layer, containing the unreacted reagents, can be decanted before decomposition; the remaining solvent is removed on the steam bath after acidification. The usual procedure with the other solvents is to remove them by steam distillation and to dissolve the remaining product in sodium carbonate solution. This is an important step, because alumina is always left behind with the acid and stays with the neutral materials when the acid is extracted with carbonate. Sodium hydroxide is obviously not suitable for this purpose because it dissolves alumina.

Nitrobenzene is not very volatile with steam, and even with an efficient steam-distillation apparatus a few hours are required to remove it completely.[119, *] Small amounts of residual nitrobenzene tend to contaminate the final product and often cause it to separate as an oil after precipitation from the alkaline solution. It is good practice to filter the acid after the first steam distillation, or to decant the supernatant liquid if the acid is oily, return the acid to the original flask, add a solution of sodium carbonate, and continue the steam distillation.[119] The second distillation, which must be begun carefully to avoid frothing, removes the last traces of solvents while the acid goes into solution as its sodium salt, leaving only the alumina and neutral products undissolved. The acid does not dissolve easily in carbonate solution because it is occluded by alumina, and, if the second steam distillation is omitted, prolonged boiling is often necessary to dissolve all the acidic material.[204] The sodium carbonate solution is treated with charcoal while still warm and filtered, preferably with the help of some filtering aid, without which the alkaline solution filters very slowly owing to the suspended alumina. The solution should be placed in a large beaker, to prevent

---

* Holmes and Trevoy, *Can. J. Research*, **22**, 109 (1944), found that some demethylation of 3,4-dimethoxybenzoylpropionic acid took place during steam distillation. Demethylation could be suppressed by separating the organic from the aqueous-acidic layer before the steam distillation.

[204] Somerville and Allen, *Org. Syntheses, Coll. Vol.* **2**, 81 (1943).

loss during acidification, and should be cooled before adding dilute acid. Since almost all the acids are very slightly soluble in cold water, ice can be added to the solution. If the first crop of material precipitates as an oil it can be disregarded or worked up separately, but usually the acids solidify readily in the cold.

In place of the second steam distillation, the reaction mixture can be dissolved in ether and the acid extracted with carbonate, or the filtered alkaline solution can be extracted with ether to remove the remaining solvent. But if much solvent is still present the separation of the layers is often tedious. Some acids form difficultly soluble sodium salts; [39, 43–47, 111, 119] whenever this occurs isolation and crystallization of the sodium salt is the preferred method of purification.

EXPERIMENTAL PROCEDURES

Preparation of Anhydrides. Succinic anhydride is commercially available. It can be prepared from succinic acid by procedures described in *Organic Syntheses*.[205]

Glutaric anhydride can be prepared from glutaric acid by the methods just mentioned for succinic anhydride. Because of the low melting point of glutaric anhydride it is advisable to purify the product by vacuum distillation rather than crystallization.[205]

Methylsuccinic anhydride can be prepared by catalytic hydrogenation of citraconic anhydride.[206] The synthesis of citraconic anhydride from citric acid is described in *Organic Syntheses*.[207] A more convenient method for the preparation of methylsuccinic acid from ethyl crotonate has been described.[208]

dl-α,β-Dimethylsuccinic anhydride can be prepared from ethyl cyanoacetate and ethyl α-bromopropionate.[189, 209]

Phenylsuccinic anhydride is prepared by dehydration of phenylsuccinic acid,[135, 210] which is obtained from α-cyano-β-phenylacrylic acid.[211]

as-Dimethylsuccinic anhydride, *as*-methylethylsuccinic anhydride, and trimethylsuccinic anhydride can be synthesized by the method of Higson and Thorpe.[212]

Maleic anhydride is available commercially.

[205] *Org. Syntheses, Coll. Vol.* **2**, 560 (1943).
[206] Bergmann and Blum-Bergmann, *J. Am. Chem. Soc.*, **59**, 1573 (1937).
[207] *Org. Syntheses, Coll. Vol.* **2**, 368, 140 (1943).
[208] *Org. Syntheses*, **26**, 54 (1946).
[209] Bone and Sprankling, *J. Chem. Soc.*, **75**, 839 (1899).
[210] *Org. Syntheses, Coll. Vol.* **1**, 451 (1941).
[211] *Org. Syntheses, Coll. Vol.* **1**, 181 (1941).
[212] Higson and Thorpe, *J. Chem. Soc.*, **89**, 1455 (1906).

Polymeric anhydrides of higher dibasic acids can be prepared according to the directions on p. 263.

Preparation of β-Benzoylpropionic Acid. Detailed directions for this preparation, which illustrates the use of excess hydrocarbon as solvent, are given in *Organic Syntheses*.[204]

Preparation of β-(3-Acenaphthoyl)propionic Acid. Detailed directions are given in *Organic Syntheses*.[119, 213] "The procedure is a general one and may be used for the condensation of succinic anhydride with naphthalene and with the mono- and di-methylnaphthalenes, although in no other case are the purification and separation of isomers so easily accomplished."[119] This general method can also be employed for the succinoylation of higher polynuclear hydrocarbons.

Preparation of β-(p-Methoxybenzoyl)propionic Acid.[71] A solution of 43 g. (0.4 mole) of anisole and 42 g. (0.42 mole) of succinic anhydride in 400 ml. of tetrachloroethane and 100 ml. of nitrobenzene is stirred and cooled to 0–5° (thermometer in liquid), and 112 g. (0.84 mole) of aluminum chloride is added gradually, the temperature being kept at 0–5°. At the end of the addition (one to two hours) a clear solution is usually obtained. It is allowed to stand at 0–5° (packed in ice in the cold room) for three days, during which time a complex sometimes separates.[214] After ice and hydrochloric acid have been added and the solvents removed with steam, the product is either allowed to crystallize directly or it is dissolved in soda solution, and the solution is clarified with Norit and acidified. β-(p-Methoxybenzoyl)propionic acid is obtained as colorless needles, m.p. 146–147; 71 g. (85%).[215]

This is a general procedure for the succinoylation of ethers of mono- and di-hydric phenols and naphthols, and it illustrates the use of a mixture of tetrachloroethane and nitrobenzene as a solvent.

Preparation of β-(p-Phenoxybenzoyl)propionic Acid.[36, 93] To a solution of 170 g. (1.0 mole) of diphenyl ether in 500 ml. of dry, thiophene-free benzene, 100 g. (1.0 mole) of finely ground succinic anhydride is added. Two moles of aluminum chloride (266.6 g.) is added all at once, and, after the initial reaction has ceased, the mixture is refluxed on the steam bath for one hour. The reaction mixture is decomposed with ice and hydrochloric acid, and the solvent is removed with steam. The

---

[213] Anhydrous hydrogen fluoride has also been employed as a condensing agent in the succinoylation of acenaphthene. The yield is lower (49% of crude material), but the proportion of the two isomeric acids is approximately the same. Naphthalene does not react when hydrogen fluoride is used as the catalyst. Fieser and Hershberg, *J. Am. Chem. Soc.*, **61**, 1272 (1939).

[214] It is reported that the low temperature during the three days' standing is not required for the preparation of β-(p-methoxybenzoyl)propionic acid. See ref. 201.

[215] By the same procedure yields of 95% have been reported subsequently. Refs. 36, 198, 199.

crude acid is dissolved in sodium carbonate solution, the solution is filtered from aluminum oxide, and the filtrate is acidified. The yield of acid melting at 118–119° is 262–270 g. (97–100%).

Preparation of β-(p-Chlorobenzoyl)propionic Acid.[36] Fifty grams of chlorobenzene (0.44 mole) is dissolved in 200 ml. of carbon disulfide. Forty grams of succinic anhydride (0.4 mole) is added, followed by 110 g. of aluminum chloride (0.83 mole), and the mixture is refluxed on a water bath for twenty-four hours. The almost colorless carbon disulfide layer is then decanted, and the residue is treated with ice and hydrochloric acid. Any remaining solvent is removed by heating the mixture on the steam bath for a brief period. The crude acid is filtered, dissolved in soda solution, and clarified with charcoal. The yield of cream-colored acid, m.p. 132–133°, obtained on acidification is 34–42.5 g. (40–50%).[216]

The other halogenated β-benzoylpropionic acids can be prepared by similar methods.

Condensation of Alkylbenzenes with Succinic Anhydride.[33] Sixty grams of finely powdered aluminum chloride is slowly added to 20 g. of succinic anhydride (0.2 mole), 0.22 mole of the hydrocarbon, and 75 ml. of tetrachloroethane. Most reactions (p-xylene is an exception) are complete in two or three hours. The products are worked up as usual and, after being precipitated from soda solution, are sufficiently pure for most purposes. The yields range from 80% to 90%.

Preparation of γ-(p-Methoxybenzoyl)butyric Acid.[36] A mixture of 25 ml. (0.23 mole) of anisole, 50 ml. of nitrobenzene, and 25 ml. of tetrachloroethane is cooled in a three-necked flask equipped with stirrer, dropping funnel, and gas-outlet tube. Aluminum chloride (57 g., 0.43 mole) is added, and the solution is cooled to 0–5°. A solution of 23 g. (0.2 mole) of glutaric anhydride in 25 ml. of tetrachloroethane is added through the dropping funnel over a period of forty-five minutes. After twenty-four hours, during which time the mixture is allowed to come to room temperature, the reaction is worked up in the usual way. The acid, once crystallized from ethanol, melts at 139.5–140.5° and weighs 38 g. (85%).

Preparation of ω-Benzoylvaleric Acid.[161] One hundred and forty-six grams (1.0 mole) of adipic acid is refluxed with 400 ml. of acetic anhydride for six hours. The excess acetic anhydride and the acetic acid formed are removed by distillation in vacuum up to 120° (bath temperature). The resulting polyanhydride is dissolved in 400 ml. of warm, dry benzene, and this solution is added with stirring over a period of one

---

[216] This acid can also be prepared with excess chlorobenzene as the solvent. Refs. 65, 66, 67.

hour to 300 g. (2.25 moles) of aluminum chloride suspended in 1.5 l. of dry benzene contained in a three-necked 3-l. flask fitted with a reflux condenser and a mechanical stirrer.

The reaction mixture, after having been allowed to stand overnight, is decomposed with ice, and 250 ml. of concentrated hydrochloric acid is added. The benzene layer is separated and extracted with dilute aqueous sodium hydroxide. The alkaline solution is acidified, and the crystalline precipitate of ω-benzoylvaleric acid is filtered. The crude acid weighs 78 g. (75%). The product after crystallization from a benzene-petroleum ether mixture melts at 70–71°.

The extracted benzene is concentrated to a small volume and chilled; 56.5 g. (85%) of 1,4-dibenzoylbutane is obtained. The diketone after a single recrystallization from ethanol has a slightly pink color and melts at 105–106°.

TABULAR SURVEY OF FRIEDEL-CRAFTS REACTIONS WITH ALIPHATIC DIBASIC ACID ANHYDRIDES

In Tables VI–XV are summarized the reactions of the anhydrides of aliphatic dibasic acids with aromatic compounds reported prior to September 15, 1947. A few references available during 1948 have also been included. Some of the yields, particularly those recorded in the older literature, do not constitute the maximum yield but might be improved by choosing the right solvent and the right amount of catalyst. Whenever percentage yields are reported in the original paper they are quoted directly; all other yields have been computed from the available data and are based on the amount of anhydride. A dash indicates that the yield was not reported.

TABLE VI

REACTIONS OF SUCCINIC ANHYDRIDE WITH AROMATIC HYDROCARBONS AND HALOGEN
DERIVATIVES

Aromatic Compound	Product β-Aroylpropionic Acid	Solvent	Yield %	Reference *
Benzene	Benzoyl	Benzene	6–7	1
Benzene	Benzoyl	Benzene	36	3
Benzene	Benzoyl	Benzene	—	2, 7, 217
Benzene	Benzoyl	Benzene	75	173
Benzene	Benzoyl	Benzene	39	218
Benzene	Benzoyl	Benzene	56	65
Benzene	Benzoyl	Benzene	77–82	204
Benzene	Benzoyl	Benzene	92–95	219
Benzene	Benzoyl	CS_2	—	32
Fluorobenzene	4-Fluorobenzoyl	CS_2	27–33	36
Chlorobenzene	4-Chlorobenzoyl	Chlorobenzene	47	65
Chlorobenzene	4-Chlorobenzoyl	CS_2	40–50	36
Bromobenzene	4-Bromobenzoyl	Bromobenzene †	74	66, 279
Bromobenzene	4-Bromobenzoyl	Bromobenzene	27.5	67
Bromobenzene	4-Bromobenzoyl	CS_2	30–40; 56	36
Iodobenzene	4-Iodobenzoyl	CS_2	15–20	36
Iodobenzene	Mixture of benzoyl and 4-iodobenzoyl	Iodobenzene	13	283
Toluene	4-Toluyl	Toluene	—	7, 81, 217, 220, 221, 279
Toluene	4-Toluyl	Toluene	47; 71	222
Toluene	4-Toluyl	Toluene	94.5	223
Toluene	4-Toluyl	CS_2	—	32
Toluene	4-Toluyl	$CHCl_2CHCl_2$	80–90	33
Toluene	4-Toluyl	$C_6H_5NO_2$	90	279a
o-Chlorotoluene	4-Chloro-3-methylbenzoyl	CS_2	60	36
Ethylbenzene	4-Ethylbenzoyl	CS_2	68	36
Ethylbenzene	4-Ethylbenzoyl	Benzene	57	7
Ethylbenzene	4-Ethylbenzoyl	Benzene	80	34
Ethylbenzene	4-Ethylbenzoyl	$CHCl_2CHCl_2$	80	36
Ethylbenzene	4-Ethylbenzoyl	$CHCl_2CHCl_2$ + $C_6H_5NO_2$	80	200
Ethylbenzene	4-Ethylbenzoyl	Ethylbenzene	57	224
o-Xylene	3,4-Dimethylbenzoyl	CS_2	—	32
o-Xylene	3,4-Dimethylbenzoyl	$CHCl_2CHCl_2$	80–90	33
o-Xylene	3,4-Dimethylbenzoyl	$CHCl_2CHCl_2$	88	225
o-Xylene	3,4-Dimethylbenzoyl	$CHCl_2CHCl_2$	92.7 and 96.7	36
m-Xylene	2,4-Dimethylbenzoyl	CS_2	—	32
m-Xylene	2,4-Dimethylbenzoyl	Benzene	—	7
m-Xylene	2,4-Dimethylbenzoyl	$CHCl_2CHCl_2$	80–90	33
m-Xylene	2,4-Dimethylbenzoyl	$CHCl_2CHCl_2$	Almost quantitative	36
m-Xylene	2,4-Dimethylbenzoyl	$C_6H_5NO_2$	86–90	284
p-Xylene	2,5-Dimethylbenzoyl	CS_2	—	32, 81
p-Xylene	2,5-Dimethylbenzoyl	$CHCl_2CHCl_2$	80–90	33, 36
Mesitylene	2,4,6-Trimethylbenzoyl	CS_2	—	32, 226

* References 217–296 appear on pp. 288–289.
† Nitrobenzene is not a satisfactory solvent in this reaction.

TABLE VI—*Continued*

REACTIONS OF SUCCINIC ANHYDRIDE WITH AROMATIC HYDROCARBONS AND HALOGEN
DERIVATIVES

Aromatic Compound	Product β-Aroylpropionic Acid	Solvent	Yield %	Reference *
Mesitylene (*Continued*)	2,4,6-Trimethylbenzoyl	Mesitylene(?)	—	227
Mesitylene	2,4,6-Trimethylbenzoyl	$CHCl_2CHCl_2$	91	36
1,3,4-Trimethylbenzene	2,4,5-Trimethylbenzoyl	CS_2	—	32
n-Propylbenzene	4-n-Propylbenzoyl	$C_6H_5NO_2$	63	37a
Isopropylbenzene	4-Isopropylbenzoyl	CS_2	—	32
Isopropylbenzene	4-Isopropylbenzoyl	$CHCl_2CHCl_2$	80–90	33
Isopropylbenzene	4-Isopropylbenzoyl	$CHCl_2CHCl_2$ + $C_6H_5NO_2$	58	36
Isopropylbenzene	4-Isopropylbenzoyl	$C_6H_5NO_2$	59	37a
ɤ-Ethyltoluene	4-Methyl-3-ethylbenzoyl or 4-ethyl-3-methylbenzoyl	CS_2	—	32
Durene	2,3,5,6-Tetramethylbenzoyl	CS_2	—	32
p-Cymene	2-Methyl-5-isopropylbenzoyl	CS_2	—	32
p-Cymene	2-Methyl-5-isopropylbenzoyl	CS_2, benzene, or $CHCl_2CHCl_2$	Low †	36
p-Cymene	2-Methyl-5-isopropylbenzoyl	$C_6H_5NO_2$	70	285
tert-Butylbenzene	4-tert-Butylbenzoyl	CS_2	55	35
tert-Butylbenzene	4-tert-Butylbenzoyl	CS_2	—	36, 228
sec-Amylbenzene	sec-Amylbenzoyl	sec-Amylbenzene	—	272
tert-Amylbenzene	4-tert-Amylbenzoyl	CS_2	50	36
Pentamethylbenzene	Pentamethylbenzoyl	CS_2	—	32
sec-Octyltoluene	sec-Octyltoluyl	sec-Octyltoluene	—	272
Di-tert-butylbenzene	4-tert-Butylbenzoyl and an unidentified acid	CS_2	—	31
Hydrindene	5-Hydrindoyl	$CHCl_2CHCl_2$ + $C_6H_5NO_2$	97	55
Hydrindene	5-Hydrindoyl	$CHCl_2CHCl_2$ + $C_6H_5NO_2$	60	36
Hydrindene	5-Hydrindoyl	$C_6H_5NO_2$	42	56, 229
Hydrindene	5-Hydrindoyl	$C_6H_5NO_2$	37	57
Hydrindene	5-Hydrindoyl	Benzene	69, 79 ‡	30
Tetralin	2-Tetroyl	Benzene	52	7
Tetralin	2-Tetroyl	Benzene	76; 72.5	59, 36
Tetralin	2-Tetroyl	Benzene	Good yield	230
Tetralin	2-Tetroyl	$C_6H_5NO_2$	70	231
Naphthalene	Mixture of 1- and 2-naphthoyl §	CS_2	—	232

* References 217–296 appear on pp. 288–289.

† The product of all runs was of poor quality, possibly because of isomers present in commercial p-cymene. The best product was obtained when the reaction was run in a mixture of tetrachloroethane and nitrobenzene.

‡ The yield refers to a crude product; benzene is not a suitable solvent for the succinoylation of hydrindene.

§ Heat increased the proportion of the 2-isomer.

TABLE VI—Continued

REACTIONS OF SUCCINIC ANHYDRIDE WITH AROMATIC HYDROCARBONS AND HALOGEN
DERIVATIVES

Aromatic Compound	Product β-Aroylpropionic Acid	Solvent	Yield %	Reference *
Naphthalene (Continued)	Mixture of 1- and 2-naphthoyl	Benzene	—	7
Naphthalene	Mainly 2-naphthoyl	CS_2	6.8–7.8	233
Naphthalene	Mixture of 1- and 2-naphthoyl	$C_6H_5NO_2$	91	40, 238
Naphthalene	Mixture of 1- and 2-naphthoyl	$C_6H_5NO_2$	—	234, 238
Naphthalene	1-Naphthoyl and 2-naphthoyl	$C_6H_5NO_2$	35 29	6
Naphthalene	1-Naphthoyl and 2-naphthoyl	$C_6H_5NO_2$	36 47	39
1-Methylnaphthalene	1-Methyl-4-naphthoyl	$C_6H_5NO_2$	80	68
2-Methylnaphthalene	2-Methyl-6-naphthoyl	$C_6H_5NO_2$	79	112
2-Methylnaphthalene	2-Methyl-6-naphthoyl	$C_6H_5NO_2$	60–75	39
2-Methylnaphthalene	6-Methyl-2-naphthoyl and 6-methyl-1-naphthoyl	$C_6H_5NO_2$	56 38	114
1-Ethylnaphthalene	4-Ethyl-1-naphthoyl	$C_6H_5NO_2$	74	40
2-Ethylnaphthalene	6-Ethyl-2-naphthoyl	$CHCl_2CHCl_2$	66	113
2,3-Dimethylnaphthalene	6,7-Dimethyl-2-naphthoyl	$C_6H_5NO_2$	70	115, 235
2,7-Dimethylnaphthalene	2,7-Dimethyl-1-naphthoyl	$C_6H_5NO_2$	60–75	39
2-Isopropylnaphthalene	6-Isopropyl-2-naphthoyl	$C_6H_5NO_2$	28	112
2-n-Propylnaphthalene	6-n-Propyl-2-naphthoyl(?)	$C_6H_5NO_2$	—	37, 112
2-tert-Butylnaphthalene	6-tert-Butyl-2-naphthoyl	$C_6H_5NO_2$	37	35
1,2,3,4-Tetramethylnaphthalene	1,2,3,4-Tetramethyl-6-naphthoyl	$C_6H_5NO_2$	90	236
Phenylcyclohexane	4-Cyclohexylbenzoyl	$CHCl_2CHCl_2$ + $C_6H_5NO_2$	85	36
Phenylcyclohexane	4-Cyclohexylbenzoyl	$C_6H_5NO_2$	—	64
Biphenyl	4-Phenylbenzoyl	$C_6H_5NO_2$	90; 85	62, 36
Biphenyl	4-Phenylbenzoyl	$C_6H_5NO_2$	70	63
Acenaphthene	3-Acenaphthoyl and 1-acenaphthoyl	$C_6H_5NO_2$	78 † 15	39
Acenaphthene	3-Acenaphthoyl and 1-acenaphthoyl	$C_6H_5NO_2$	81 5	119
Acenaphthene	Mixture of 1- and 3-acenaphthoyl	Benzene	Poor	30
Diphenylmethane	4-Benzylbenzoyl	$C_6H_5NO_2$	—	29
Diphenylmethane	4-Benzylbenzoyl	$C_6H_5NO_2$	53.4	36
Fluorene	2-Fluoroyl	Benzene	75–86	58, 36
Fluorene	2-Fluoroyl	$C_6H_5NO_2$ or $CHCl_2CHCl_2$	80	241
Cyclohexane-1-spiro-hydrindene	5-(or 6-)Cyclohexane-1-spirohydrindoyl	$C_6H_5NO_2$	—	242
9,10-Dihydroanthracene	9-(9,10-Dihydroanthroyl)	$C_6H_5NO_2$	38	29
9,10-Dihydroanthracene	2-Anthroyl	$C_6H_5NO_2$	11	21
Anthracene	2-Anthroyl	$C_6H_5NO_2$	22	39, 21
Anthracene	2-Anthroyl	$C_6H_5NO_2$	18	43

* References 217–296 appear on pp. 288–289.
† These are the yields when the reaction is conducted at 0°; at −15° the yields are 87% and 5%, respectively.

TABLE VI—*Continued*

REACTIONS OF SUCCINIC ANHYDRIDE WITH AROMATIC HYDROCARBONS AND HALOGEN
DERIVATIVES

Aromatic Compound	Product β-Aroylpropionic Acid	Solvent	Yield %	Reference *
Anthracene (*Continued*)	1-Anthroyl and 2-anthroyl	$C_6H_5NO_2$	—	44
Anthracene	9-(9,10-Dihydro)anthroyl	Benzene	—	30
9,10-Dihydrophenanthrene	2-(9,10-Dihydrophen-anthroyl)	$C_6H_5NO_2$	98	109
9,10-Dihydrophenanthrene	2-(9,10-Dihydrophen-anthroyl)	$C_6H_5NO_2$	96	110, 237
1,2,3,4-Tetrahydrophen-anthrene	9-(1,2,3,4-Tetrahydro-phenanthroyl) and 7-(1,2,3,4-tetrahydro-phenanthroyl)	$C_6H_5NO_2$	78 5	40, 106, 36
1,2,3,4,5,6,7,8-Octahydro-phenanthrene	9-(1,2,3,4,5,6,7,8-Octa-hydrophenanthroyl)	CS_2	86	108
1,2,3,4,9,10,11,12-Octa-hydrophenanthrene	6-(1,2,3,4,9,10,11,12-Octa-hydrophenanthroyl)	$C_6H_5NO_2$	31	107
Phenanthrene	3-Phenanthroyl (and an isomer)	$C_6H_5NO_2$	60	41
Phenanthrene	3-Phenanthroyl and 2-phenanthroyl	$C_6H_5NO_2$	60(?) 5	42
4,5-Methylene-9,10-di-hydrophenanthrene	4,5-Methylene-9,10-di-hydro-2-phenanthroyl	$C_6H_5NO_2$	99	54
4,5-Methylenephenanthrene	4,5-Methylene-1-phenan-throyl	$C_6H_5NO_2$	45.4	54
4-Methyl-1,2,3,4-tetrahy-drophenanthrene	4-Methyl-1,2,3,4-tetrahy-dro-9-phenanthroyl †	$C_6H_5NO_2$	—	286
9-Methyl-1,2,3,4-tetrahy-drophenanthrene	9-Methyl-1,2,3,4-tetrahy-dro-7-phenanthroyl	$C_6H_5NO_2$	62	113
3-Methylphenanthrene	6-(3-Methylphenanthroyl)	$C_6H_5NO_2$	36.5	53
4-Methylphenanthrene	3-(5-Methylphenanthroyl) and some 1-(4-methyl-phenanthroyl)	$C_6H_5NO_2$	22	52
9,10-Dihydroretene	9,10-Dihydro-2-retoyl	$C_6H_5NO_2$	80	49
Retene	3-Retoyl	Benzene	58.5	48
Retene	3-Retoyl	$C_6H_5NO_2$	21	49
1,2,3,4-Tetrahydro-8,9-acephenanthrene	5-(1,2,3,4-Tetrahydro-8,9-acephenanthroyl)	$C_6H_5NO_2$	83	61
1,2,3,6,7,8-Hexahydro-pyrene	1,2,3,6,7,8-Hexahydro-4-pyrenoyl	$C_6H_5NO_2$	67.5	45
Pyrene	1-Pyrenoyl	$C_6H_5NO_2$	62	45
Pyrene	1-Pyrenoyl	$C_6H_5NO_2$	90–94	46
Pyrene	1-Pyrenoyl	$C_6H_5NO_2$	96	47
Pyrene	1-Pyrenoyl	$C_6H_5NO_2$	90	239
Chrysene	2-Chrysenoyl	Benzene	50–55	50, 240
Chrysene	4- or 5-Chrysenoyl ‡	$C_6H_5NO_2$	37 §	50
Chrysene	4- or 5-Chrysenoyl and some of the 2-isomer	$C_6H_5NO_2$	5.5, 9.1 ‖	51

* References 217–296 appear on pp. 288–289.
† No analysis was reported for this product.
‡ The author assumed this to be the 1-acid, but see ref. 51.
§ This yield refers to a crude product.
‖ This experiment was run at 30°; at 0° an inseparable mixture of acids was obtained.

TABLE VII

REACTIONS OF SUCCINIC ANHYDRIDE WITH PHENOLIC ETHERS

Ether	Product β-Aroylpropionic Acid	Solvent	Yield %	Reference *
Anisole	4-Anisoyl	Anisole	48–55	69
Anisole	4-Anisoyl	CS_2	—	26, 70
Anisole	4-Anisoyl	CS_2	65	175
Anisole	4-Anisoyl	Benzene	—	7
Anisole	4-Anisoyl	$CHCl_2CHCl_2$	80.5	28
Anisole	4-Anisoyl	$CHCl_2CHCl_2$	Almost quantitative	243
Anisole	4-Anisoyl	$C_6H_5NO_2$	Almost quantitative	244
Anisole	4-Anisoyl	$CHCl_2CHCl_2$ + $C_6H_5NO_2$	85	71
Anisole	4-Anisoyl	$CHCl_2CHCl_2$ + $C_6H_5NO_2$	90	201
Anisole	4-Anisoyl	$CHCl_2CHCl_2$ + $C_6H_5NO_2$	93.5	36
Anisole	4-Anisoyl	$CHCl_2CHCl_2$ + $C_6H_5NO_2$	95	198, 199
Anisole	4-Anisoyl	$C_6H_5NO_2$ †	75–85	287
Anisole	4-Anisoyl	$C_6H_5NO_2$	83	74, 274
Anisole	4-Anisoyl and 1,2-di(p-hydroxybenzoyl)ethane	$C_6H_5NO_2$	34.5 9.6	75
Anisole	4-Anisoyl	$CH_3CH_2CH_2NO_2$	86–90	288
o-Chloroanisole	4-Methoxy-3-chlorobenzoyl	?	—	80
Phenetole	4-Ethoxybenzoyl	Phenetole	45–63	3
Phenetole	4-Ethoxybenzoyl	Phenetole	59	72
Phenetole	4-Ethoxybenzoyl	$C_6H_5NO_2$	80–90	73, 274
o-Chlorophenetole	4-Ethoxy-3-chlorobenzoyl	?	—	80
n-Propyl phenyl ether ‡	4-n-Propoxybenzoyl	$C_6H_5NO_2$	80–90	73, 274
n-Butyl phenyl ether	4-n-Butoxybenzoyl	$C_6H_5NO_2$	80–90	73, 274
Isobutyl phenyl ether	4-Isobutoxybenzoyl	$C_6H_5NO_2$	80–90	73
Isoamyl phenyl ether	4-Isoamyloxybenzoyl	$C_6H_5NO_2$	80–90	73
n-Hexyl phenyl ether	4-n-Hexoxybenzoyl	$C_6H_5NO_2$	80–90	73
β-Phenoxyethoxyethyl chloride	(β-Chloroethoxyethoxy)benzoyl	CS_2	—	267
o-Cresyl methyl ether	4-Methoxy-3-methylbenzoyl	$C_6H_5NO_2$	74	74
o-Cresyl methyl ether	4-Methoxy-3-methylbenzoyl	$C_6H_5NO_2$	—	75, 274
o-Cresyl ethyl ether	4-Ethoxy-3-methylbenzoyl	$C_6H_5NO_2$	82	273
o-Cresyl n-propyl ether	4-n-Propoxy-3-methylbenzoyl	$C_6H_5NO_2$	88	273
o-Cresyl isopropyl ether	4-Isopropoxy-3-methylbenzoyl	$C_6H_5NO_2$	14	273
o-Cresyl n-butyl ether	4-n-Butoxy-3-methylbenzoyl	$C_6H_5NO_2$	86	273
o-Cresyl isobutyl ether	4-Isobutoxy-3-methylbenzoyl	$C_6H_5NO_2$	80	273
o-Cresyl isoamyl ether	4-Isoamyloxy-3-methylbenzoyl	$C_6H_5NO_2$	95	273
o-Cresyl n-hexyl ether	4-n-Hexoxy-3-methylbenzoyl	$C_6H_5NO_2$	65	273
o-Cresyl n-heptyl ether	4-n-Heptoxy-3-methylbenzoyl	$C_6H_5NO_2$	55	273
m-Cresyl methyl ether	4-Methoxy-2-methylbenzoyl	CS_2	—	245
m-Cresyl methyl ether	4-Methoxy-2-methylbenzoyl	$C_6H_5NO_2$	—	74, 75, 274

* References 217–296 are on pp. 288–289.
† In nitroethane the yield was slightly lower.
‡ Isopropyl phenyl ether did not react with succinic anhydride.

TABLE VII—Continued

REACTIONS OF SUCCINIC ANHYDRIDE WITH PHENOLIC ETHERS

Ether	Product β-Aroylpropionic Acid	Solvent	Yield %	Reference *
m-Cresyl methyl ether (Continued)	Mixture of equal amounts of 4-methoxy-2-methylbenzoyl and 4-hydroxy-2-methylbenzoyl	$C_6H_5NO_2$	—	191a
m-Cresyl ethyl ether	4-Ethoxy-2-methylbenzoyl	$C_6H_5NO_2$	65	273
m-Cresyl n-propyl ether †	4-n-Propoxy-2-methylbenzoyl	$C_6H_5NO_2$	95	273
m-Cresyl n-butyl ether	4-n-Butoxy-2-methylbenzoyl	$C_6H_5NO_2$	50	273
m-Cresyl isobutyl ether	4-Isobutoxy-2-methylbenzoyl	$C_6H_5NO_2$	40	273
m-Cresyl isoamyl ether	4-Isoamyloxy-2-methylbenzoyl	$C_6H_5NO_2$	90	273
m-Cresyl n-hexyl ether	4-n-Hexoxy-2-methylbenzoyl	$C_6H_5NO_2$	55	273
p-Cresyl methyl ether	2-Methoxy-5-methylbenzoyl	$C_6H_5NO_2$	—	74, 75, 274
p-Cresyl ethyl ether	2-Ethoxy-5-methylbenzoyl	$C_6H_5NO_2$	75	273
p-Cresyl n-propyl ether †	2-n-Propoxy-5-methylbenzoyl	$C_6H_5NO_2$	80	273
p-Cresyl n-butyl ether	2-n-Butoxy-5-methylbenzoyl	$C_6H_5NO_2$	75	273
p-Cresyl isobutyl ether	2-Isobutoxy-5-methylbenzoyl	$C_6H_5NO_2$	60	273
p-Cresyl isoamyl ether	2-Isoamyloxy-5-methylbenzoyl	$C_6H_5NO_2$	80	273
p-Cresyl n-hexyl ether	2-n-Hexoxy-5-methylbenzoyl	$C_6H_5NO_2$	60	273
2,3-Dimethylanisole	4-Methoxy-2,3-dimethylbenzoyl	Benzene	50	78
2,4-Dimethylanisole	2-Methoxy-3,5-dimethylbenzoyl	Benzene	24.5	246
2,5-Dimethylanisole	4-Methoxy-2,5-dimethylbenzoyl	Benzene	75	247
2,5-Dimethylanisole	4-Methoxy-2,5-dimethylbenzoyl	$CHCl_2CHCl_2$ + $C_6H_5NO_2$	86	76
2,6-Dimethylanisole	4-Methoxy-3,5-dimethylbenzoyl	Benzene	35	78
2-Methyl-5-ethylanisole	4-Methoxy-3-methyl-6-ethyl-benzoyl	$C_6H_5NO_2$	90	77
3-Methyl-6-ethylanisole	4-Methoxy-2-methyl-5-ethyl-benzoyl	$C_6H_5NO_2$	Quantitative	77
3-Methyl-6-isopropylanisole	4-Methoxy-2-methyl-5-isopropyl-benzoyl	$C_6H_5NO_2$	—	74
3-Methyl-6-isopropylanisole	4-Methoxy-2-methyl-5-isopropyl-benzoyl	$C_6H_5NO_2$	81.3	79
4-tert-Butylanisole	2-Methoxy-5-tert-butylbenzoyl	$C_6H_5NO_2$	Good	248
Veratrole	3,4-Dimethoxybenzoyl	$C_6H_5NO_2$	85	145, 295
Veratrole	3,4-Dimethoxybenzoyl	$C_6H_5NO_2$	44	22, 278
Veratrole	3,4-Dimethoxybenzoyl	$C_6H_5NO_2$	93	249
Veratrole	3,4-Dimethoxybenzoyl	$C_6H_5NO_2$	73	71
Veratrole	3,4-Dimethoxybenzoyl	$C_6H_5NO_2$	—	250, 251
Veratrole	3,4-Dimethoxybenzoyl	CS_2	—	26, 251
Veratrole	3,4-Dimethoxybenzoyl	CS_2	46	22, 71
Veratrole	3,4-Dimethoxybenzoyl	$CHCl_2CHCl_2$	Nearly quantitative	243
Veratrole	3,4-Dimethoxybenzoyl	$CHCl_2CHCl_2$	64	22
Veratrole	3,4-Dimethoxybenzoyl	$CHCl_2CHCl_2$ + $C_6H_5NO_2$	67	71
Veratrole	3,4-Dimethoxybenzoyl	$CHCl_2CHCl_2$ + $C_6H_5NO_2$	84	252

* References 217–296 are on pp. 288–289.
† The isopropyl ether did not react with succinic anhydride.

TABLE VII—*Continued*

REACTIONS OF SUCCINIC ANHYDRIDE WITH PHENOLIC ETHERS

Ether	Product β-Aroylpropionic Acid	Solvent	Yield %	Reference *
Veratrole (*Continued*)	3,4-Dimethoxybenzoyl and 3-methoxy-4-hydroxybenzoyl	$CHCl_2CHCl_2$ + $C_6H_5NO_2$	84.8;† 81	275, 296
Resorcinol dimethyl ether	2,4-Dimethoxybenzoyl	Resorcinol dimethyl ether	—	253
Resorcinol dimethyl ether	2,4-Dimethoxybenzoyl	CS_2	—	23, 26
Resorcinol dimethyl ether	2,4-Dimethoxybenzoyl	CS_2	65–75 ‡	25
Resorcinol dimethyl ether	2,4-Dimethoxybenzoyl	CS_2	50	22
Resorcinol dimethyl ether	2,4-Dimethoxybenzoyl	$CHCl_2CHCl_2$	60	22
Resorcinol dimethyl ether	2,4-Dimethoxybenzoyl, 2-hydroxy-4-methoxybenzoyl	$CHCl_2CHCl_2$	90 §	28
Resorcinol dimethyl ether	2-Hydroxy-4-methoxybenzoyl	$CHCl_2CHCl_2$	—	271
Resorcinol dimethyl ether	2,4-Dimethoxybenzoyl	$C_6H_5NO_2$	88	22
Resorcinol dimethyl ether	2-Hydroxy-4-methoxybenzoyl	Resorcinol dimethyl ether	—	23
Hydroquinone dimethyl ether	2,5-Dimethoxybenzoyl	CS_2	40; —	22; 26
Hydroquinone dimethyl ether	2,5-Dimethoxybenzoyl	$CHCl_2CHCl_2$	45	22
Hydroquinone dimethyl ether	2,5-Dimethoxybenzoyl	$C_6H_5NO_2$	70	22, 274, 278
Hydroquinone dimethyl ether	2,5-Dimethoxybenzoyl	$CHCl_2CHCl_2$ + $C_6H_5NO_2$	51.9	89, 36
Hydroquinone diethyl ether	2,5-Diethoxybenzoyl	$CHCl_2CHCl_2$ + $C_6H_5NO_2$	59, 62	36
Hydroquinone diethyl ether	2,5-Diethoxybenzoyl	$C_6H_5NO_2$	52.5	36
Orcinol dimethyl ether	2,4-Dimethoxy-6-methylbenzoyl	CS_2	40	27
Orcinol dimethyl ether	2,4-Dimethoxy-6-methylbenzoyl	$CHCl_2CHCl_2$	45	27
Orcinol dimethyl ether	2,4-Dimethoxy-6-methylbenzoyl	$C_6H_5NO_2$	60	27
Hydroxyhydroquinone trimethyl ether	2,4,5-Trimethoxybenzoyl	CS_2	—	26
Pyrogallol trimethyl ether	2-Hydroxy-3,4-dimethoxybenzoyl	CS_2	—	26
Pyrogallol trimethyl ether	2-Hydroxy-3,4-dimethoxybenzoyl	CS_2	20	27
Pyrogallol trimethyl ether	2-Hydroxy-3,4-dimethoxybenzoyl	$CHCl_2CHCl_2$	67	28
Pyrogallol trimethyl ether	2-Hydroxy-3,4-dimethoxybenzoyl	$CHCl_2CHCl_2$	60	27
Pyrogallol trimethyl ether	2-Hydroxy-3,4-dimethoxybenzoyl	$CHCl_2CHCl_2$	—	271
Pyrogallol trimethyl ether	2-Hydroxy-3,4-dimethoxybenzoyl	$CHCl_2CHCl_2$	31	28a
Pyrogallol trimethyl ether	2-Hydroxy-3,4-dimethoxybenzoyl	$C_6H_5NO_2$	45	27
Pyrogallol trimethyl ether	2-Hydroxy-3,4-dimethoxybenzoyl and 2,3,4-trimethoxybenzoyl ‖	$CHCl_2CHCl_2$ + $C_6H_5NO_2$	— 6.2	28a
1-Methoxy-5,6,7,8-tetrahydronaphthalene	5,6,7,8-Tetrahydro-4-methoxy-1-naphthoyl	$C_6H_5NO_2$	82	254

* References 217–296 are on pp. 288–289.

† The yield refers to the dimethoxy acid after methylation of the accompanying hydroxy acid. The yield of demethylated acid was as much as 23% in one run, but demethylation can be suppressed by separating the organic layer from the aqueous-acidic layer before steam distillation.

‡ Some demethylation took place.

§ The reaction was carried out at 50–60°. The yield refers to the total product.

‖ The reaction mixture was steam-distilled after the organic layer had been separated from the acidic aqueous layer. See also ref. 275.

TABLE VII—*Continued*

REACTIONS OF SUCCINIC ANHYDRIDE WITH PHENOLIC ETHERS

Ether	Product β-Aroylpropionic Acid	Solvent	Yield %	Reference *
6-Ethoxy-1,2,3,4-tetrahydro-naphthalene	1,2,3,4-Tetrahydro-6-ethoxy-7-naphthoyl and 1,2,3,4-tetrahydro-6-ethoxy-8-naphthoyl	$C_6H_5NO_2$	—	255
1-Methoxynaphthalene	4-Methoxy-1-naphthoyl	CS_2	—	81
1-Methoxynaphthalene	4-Methoxy-1-naphthoyl	CS_2	30–40	256
1-Methoxynaphthalene	4-Methoxy-1-naphthoyl	Petroleum ether	40	256
1-Methoxynaphthalene	4-Methoxy-1-naphthoyl	$CHCl_2CHCl_2$	98	71
1-Methoxynaphthalene	4-Methoxy-1-naphthoyl	$CHCl_2CHCl_2$	92	256
1-Methoxynaphthalene	4-Methoxy-1-naphthoyl	$C_6H_5NO_2$	92	256
1-Methoxynaphthalene	4-Methoxy-1-naphthoyl	$C_6H_5NO_2$	83	82
1-Methoxynaphthalene	4-Methoxy-1-naphthoyl	$C_6H_5NO_2$ †	—	86
2-Methoxynaphthalene	2-Methoxy-1-naphthoyl	CS_2	—	85, 86
2-Methoxynaphthalene	2-Methoxy-8-naphthoyl	CS_2	33.5 crude	84a
2-Methoxynaphthalene	2-Methoxy-6-naphthoyl	$C_6H_5NO_2$	60–75	39
2-Methoxynaphthalene	2-Methoxy-6-naphthoyl	$C_6H_5NO_2$	33 ‡	83
2-Methoxynaphthalene	2-Methoxy-6-naphthoyl	$C_6H_5NO_2$	—	86
2-Methoxynaphthalene	2-Methoxy-6-naphthoyl and 2-methoxy-1-naphthoyl	$C_6H_5NO_2$	9 parts 1 part §	85
2-Methoxynaphthalene	2-Methoxy-1-naphthoyl	(?)	—	274
1-Ethoxynaphthalene	4-Ethoxy-1-naphthoyl	CS_2	—	257
1-Methoxy-7-methylnaphthalene	1-Methoxy-7-methyl-4-naphthoyl	Benzene	—	81
1-Methoxy-7-isopropylnaphthalene	1-Methoxy-7-isopropyl-4-naphthoyl	Benzene or, better, $CHCl_2CHCl_2$	90	258
1-Methyl-2-methoxynaphthalene	1-Methyl-2-methoxy-6-naphthoyl	$C_6H_5NO_2$	78 ‖	84
2-Methoxy-6-methylnaphthalene	2-Methoxy-6-methyl-1-naphthoyl	$C_6H_5NO_2$	40	116
1,5-Dimethoxynaphthalene	4,8-Dimethoxy-1-naphthoyl	$CHCl_2CHCl_2$ + $C_6H_5NO_2$	93 ¶	87
1,5-Dimethoxynaphthalene	4,8-Dimethoxy-1-naphthoyl	CS_2	21	24
1,5-Dimethoxynaphthalene	4,8-Dimethoxy-1-naphthoyl	$C_6H_5NO_2$	85	24
1,5-Dimethoxynaphthalene	4-Hydroxy-8-methoxy-1-naphthoyl **	$CHCl_2CHCl_2$	80	24
2,6-Dimethoxynaphthalene	2,6-Dimethoxy-1-naphthoyl	$CHCl_2CHCl_2$ + $C_6H_5NO_2$	82	87
Diphenyl ether	4-Phenoxybenzoyl	CS_2	93	91
Diphenyl ether	4-Phenoxybenzoyl	CS_2	58	92
Diphenyl ether	4-Phenoxybenzoyl	Benzene	Almost quantitative	36
Diphenyl ether	4-Phenoxybenzoyl	Benzene	93	93
Diphenyl ether	4-Phenoxybenzoyl	$C_6H_5NO_2$	—	274
Diphenyl sulfide	4-Mercaptophenylbenzoyl	Benzene	94	93a
4-Methoxybiphenyl	4-Methoxy-4'-xenoyl, 4-methoxy-3-xenoyl	$C_6H_5NO_2$	24.5 60	105

* References 217–296 are on pp. 288–289.
† In carbon disulfide a small amount of 1-methoxy-4-dithiocarboxylic acid was obtained.
‡ A mixture was obtained and some of the acid was isolated as the ethyl ester.
§ The total yield of pure acids was 45%.
‖ This yield refers to a reaction time of five days; see p. 258.
¶ With three equivalents of aluminum chloride the yield was 98%.
** This was the reaction product when the reaction was conducted between 40° and 74°.

TABLE VIII

REACTIONS OF SUCCINIC ANHYDRIDE WITH PHENOLS

Phenol	Product β-Aroylpropionic Acid	Solvent	Yield %	Reference *
Phenol	2-Hydroxybenzoyl	$CHCl_2CHCl_2$	62	28, 243
Phenol	2-Hydroxybenzoyl, 4-hydroxybenzoyl	$CHCl_2CHCl_2$	30–35 2–3	88, 278
Phenol	2-Hydroxybenzoyl, 4-hydroxybenzoyl	$CHCl_2CHCl_2$	20 3	89
o-Cresol	2-Hydroxy-3-toluyl, 4-hydroxy-3-toluyl	$CHCl_2CHCl_2$	35–40 15–20	88
m-Cresol	2-Hydroxy-4-toluyl, 4-hydroxy-2-toluyl	$CHCl_2CHCl_2$	60–65 1–2	88, 278
p-Cresol	2-Hydroxy-5-toluyl	$CHCl_2CHCl_2$	40–45	88
Resorcinol	2,4-Dihydroxybenzoyl	$C_6H_5NO_2$	40	90, 280
Resorcinol	—			281
3,5-Dihydroxytoluene	2,6-Dihydroxy-4-methyl-benzoyl	$C_6H_5NO_2$	8	90
Hydroquinone	—	$\begin{cases} CS_2, C_6H_5NO_2, \\ CHCl_2CHCl_2 \end{cases}$		90
Guaiacol	—	$\begin{cases} CS_2, C_6H_5NO_2, \\ CHCl_2CHCl_2 \end{cases}$		22
Guaiacol	3-Methoxy-4-hydroxybenzoyl	$CHCl_2CHCl_2 +$ $C_6H_5NO_2$	Low	275
Resorcinol monomethyl ether	2-Hydroxy-4-methoxybenzoyl	CS_2	35	22, 280
Resorcinol monomethyl ether	2-Hydroxy-4-methoxybenzoyl	$CHCl_2CHCl_2$	40	22
Resorcinol monomethyl ether	2-Hydroxy-4-methoxybenzoyl	$C_6H_5NO_2$	40	22
Hydroquinone monomethyl ether	—	CS_2, $CHCl_2CHCl_2$, $C_6H_5NO_2$		22
Orcinol monomethyl ether	2-Methoxy-4-hydroxy-6-methylbenzoyl	$C_6H_5NO_2$	25	27
Phloroglucinol	—	$CHCl_2CHCl_2$, $C_6H_5NO_2$		90
1-Naphthol	—	$CHCl_2CHCl_2$, $C_6H_5NO_2$		90

* References 217–296 are on pp. 288–289.

TABLE IX

REACTIONS OF SUCCINIC ANHYDRIDE WITH HETEROCYCLES AND MISCELLANEOUS COMPOUNDS

Starting Compound	Product β-Aroylpropionic Acid	Solvent	Yield %	Reference *
Thiophene	2-Thenoyl	$C_6H_5NO_2$	54; 58.5	94; 164
Thiophene	2-Thenoyl	CS_2	21	94
2,5-Dimethylthiophene	2,5-Dimethyl-3-thenoyl	$C_6H_5NO_2$	—	95
Benzothiophene (thionaphthene)	3-Thionaphthoyl	$C_6H_5NO_2$	43	96
Thiochromane	6-Thiochromanoyl	$C_6H_5NO_2$	90	98
Dibenzothiophene	2-Dibenzothenoyl	$CHCl_2CHCl_2$ + $C_6H_5NO_2$	66	97
Dibenzothiophene	2-Dibenzothenoyl	$C_6H_5NO_2$	61.5	96
Diphenylene oxide	2-Dibenzofuroyl	?	—	99
Diphenylene oxide	2-Dibenzofuroyl	$C_6H_5NO_2$	93	100, 259
Diphenylene oxide	2-Dibenzofuroyl	$CHCl_2CHCl_2$ + $C_6H_5NO_2$	83	101
Diphenylene oxide	2-Dibenzofuroyl	Benzene	73, 90 †	36
Carbazole	Carbazole-3,6-bis-γ-ketobutyric acid (3,6-bis-carbazoyl)	$C_6H_5NO_2$	54	102
Carbazole	Carbazole-3,6-bis-γ-ketobutyric acid (3,6-bis-carbazoyl)	$C_6H_5NO_2$	91–94	103
N-Methylcarbazole	N-Methylcarbazole-3,6-bis-γ-keto-butyric acid	$C_6H_5NO_2$	—	102
1-Nitro-3-phenylpropane	4(?)-ω-Nitropropylbenzoyl	CS_2	26.5	20
Ethyl hydrocinnamate	4(?)-(-ω-Carbethoxyethyl)benzoyl	CS_2	29	20
1-Cyano-2-phenylethane	4-ω-Cyanoethylbenzoyl	CS_2	7.4	20
Benzyl cyanide	No reaction	CS_2		20
Phenothiazine	N-Phenothiazoyl	CS_2	50	104
N-Acetylphenothiazine	2-Phenothiazoyl ‡	CS_2	9	104
o-Phenyleneurea	3,4-Ureylenebenzoyl	$CHCl_2CHCl_2$	9	293
Acetanilide	4-Acetylaminobenzoyl	CS_2	50–60	19
o-Nitroanisole	4-Methoxy-3-nitrobenzoyl	$C_6H_5NO_2$	Low	19
1-Acetylamino-7-meth-oxynaphthalene	1-Acetylamino-7-methoxy-3-naph-thoyl	$C_6H_5NO_2$	84	289

* References 217–296 are on pp. 288–289.

† The 90% yield was obtained after refluxing for two hours.

‡ The primary product was probably the N-acetyl compound which was hydrolyzed during the isolation. The same compound was obtained in 58% yield with the ester acid chloride of succinic acid instead of the anhydride.

TABLE X

REACTIONS OF SUBSTITUTED SUCCINIC ANHYDRIDES

Aromatic Compound	Product β-Aroylpropionic Acid	Solvent	Yield %	Reference *
A. Methylsuccinic Anhydride				
Benzene	α-Methyl-β-benzoyl	Benzene	39	120
Benzene	α-Methyl-β-benzoyl	Benzene	60	121
Benzene	α-Methyl-β-benzoyl	Benzene	49.5	7
Benzene	α-Methyl-β-benzoyl	Benzene	—	270
Benzene	{ α-Methyl-β-benzoyl, β-methyl-β-benzoyl	Benzene	75 12	122
Toluene	{ α-Methyl-β-p-toluyl, β-methyl-β-p-toluyl	Toluene	40 † 57	122
Toluene	α-Methyl-β-p-toluyl	C₆H₅NO₂	86	284
p-Cymene	α-Methyl-β-(2-methyl-5-isopropyl)benzoyl	C₆H₅NO₂	60	285
Naphthalene	α-Methyl-β-1-naphthoyl and α-methyl-β-2-naphthoyl	C₆H₅NO₂	28 27	6
1-Methylnaphthalene	α-Methyl-β-(4-methyl-1-naphthoyl)	C₆H₅NO₂	75	124
2-Methylnaphthalene	α-Methyl-β-(6-methyl-2-naphthoyl)	C₆H₅NO₂	60	115
2-Isopropylnaphthalene	α-Methyl-β-(6-isopropyl-2-naphthoyl)	C₆H₅NO₂	21.5	276
Phenanthrene	{ α-Methyl-β-3-phenanthroyl, α-methyl-β-2-phenanthroyl	C₆H₅NO₂	30 3.3	123, 206
Pyrene	α-Methyl-β-1-pyrenoyl	C₆H₅NO₂	90	47, 125
Anisole	α-Methyl-β-p-anisoyl	C₆H₅NO₂	77	126
Anisole	α-Methyl-β-p-anisoyl	C₆H₅NO₂	50	130
o-Cresyl methyl ether	α-Methyl-β-(4-methoxy-3-toluyl)	C₆H₅NO₂ ‡	40	127
m-Cresyl methyl ether	α-Methyl-β-(4-methoxy-2-toluyl)	C₆H₅NO₂ ‡	20	127
p-Cresyl methyl ether	α-Methyl-β-(2-methoxy-5-toluyl)	C₆H₅NO₂ ‡	33	127
Veratrole	Mixture of α- and β-methyl-β-3,4-dimethoxy-benzoyl	C₆H₅NO₂	Quantitative	129
Veratrole	β-Methyl-β-3,4-dimethoxybenzoyl	C₆H₅NO₂	23.5 §	128
Resorcinol dimethyl ether	Mixture of α- and β-methyl-β-2,4-dimethoxy-benzoyl	C₆H₅NO₂	50	126
Pyrogallol trimethyl ether	{ α-Methyl-β-(2-hydroxy-3,4-dimethoxyben-zoyl) and β-methyl-β-(2-hydroxy-3,4-dimethoxyben-zoyl)	C₆H₅NO₂	10.2 ‖ 3.4	126
Phenol	α-Methyl-β-2-hydroxybenzoyl	CHCl₂CHCl₂	33	126
Thiophene	α-Methyl-β-2-thenoyl	C₆H₅NO₂	6.6	260
B. sym-Dimethylsuccinic Anhydride				
Benzene	α,β-Dimethyl-β-benzoyl	Benzene	86	18
Veratrole	α,β-Dimethyl-β-3,4-dimethoxybenzoyl	C₆H₅NO₂	39	145
Naphthalene	α,β-Dimethyl-β-(1-naphthoyl)	C₆H₅NO₂	17 ¶	189

* References 217–296 are on pp. 288–289.
† The total yield of acids was 77%.
‡ In carbon disulfide or tetrachloroethane the yields were much lower.
§ The reaction furnished a mixture of the α-methyl and β-methyl acids from which only the latter was isolated.
‖ The yield of the mixture before separation was 54%.
¶ The yield refers to a mixture of isomers.

TABLE X—*Continued*

REACTIONS OF SUBSTITUTED SUCCINIC ANHYDRIDES

Aromatic Compound	Product β-Aroylpropionic Acid	Solvent	Yield %	Reference *
	C. as-Dimethylsuccinic Anhydride			
Benzene	α,α-Dimethyl-β-benzoyl	Benzene	—	137
Benzene	α,α-Dimethyl-β-benzoyl	Benzene	93	16
Benzene	α,α-Dimethyl-β-benzoyl	Benzene	62	138
Benzene	α,α-Dimethyl-β-benzoyl	Benzene	80	18
Benzene	α,α-Dimethyl-β-benzoyl	$C_6H_5NO_2$	90	14
Toluene	α,α-Dimethyl-β-p-toluyl	Toluene	77.6	138
Hydrindene	α,α-Dimethyl-β-5-hydrindoyl	$C_6H_5NO_2$	21	56
Naphthalene	α,α-Dimethyl-β-1-naphthoyl, α,α-dimethyl-β-2-naphthoyl	$C_6H_5NO_2$	26 † 18	139
1-Methylnaphthalene	α,α-Dimethyl-β-(1-methyl-4-naphthoyl)	$C_6H_5NO_2$	72	139
	D. Trimethylsuccinic Anhydride			
Benzene	α,α,β-Trimethyl-β-benzoyl	Benzene	55, 85	18
	E. as-Methylethylsuccinic Anhydride			
Benzene	α-Methyl-α-ethyl-β-benzoyl	Benzene	—	137
Naphthalene	α-Methyl-α-ethyl-β-(1-naphthoyl)	$C_6H_5NO_2$	49	140
	F. sym-Diethylsuccinic Anhydride			
Anisole	α,β-Diethyl-β-p-anisoyl	Benzene	91	144
	G. as-Diethylsuccinic Anhydride			
Benzene	α,α-Diethyl-β-benzoyl	Benzene	63.3	138
	H. Tetramethylsuccinic Anhydride			
Benzene	α,α,β,β-Tetramethyl-β-phenylpropionic acid (?)	Benzene	70	18
Toluene	α,α,β,β-Tetramethyl-β-p-tolylpropionic acid (?)	Toluene	—	18

* References 217–296 are on pp. 288–289.
† The yield of the mixture was 60%.

TABLE X—*Continued*

REACTIONS OF SUBSTITUTED SUCCINIC ANHYDRIDES

Aromatic Compound	Substituent in Anhydride	Product β-Aroylpropionic Acid	Solvent	Yield %	Reference *

I. Mono-n-alkylsuccinic Anhydrides

Aromatic Compound	Substituent in Anhydride	Product β-Aroylpropionic Acid	Solvent	Yield %	Reference *
Anisole	Ethyl	α-Ethyl-β-p-anisoyl	$C_6H_5NO_2$	70	130
Anisole	Propyl	α-n-Propyl-β-p-anisoyl	$C_6H_5NO_2$	62	130
Anisole	Amyl	α-n-Amyl-β-p-anisoyl	$C_6H_5NO_2$	30	130
Anisole	Hexyl	α-n-Hexyl-β-p-anisoyl	$C_6H_5NO_2$	45	130
Anisole	Tetradecyl	α-n-Tetradecyl-β-p-anisoyl	$C_6H_5NO_2$	60	130
Anisole	Hexadecyl	α-n-Hexadecyl-β-p-anisoyl	$C_6H_5NO_2$	50	130
o-Cresyl methyl ether	Ethyl	α-Ethyl-β-(4-methoxy-3-methylbenzoyl)	$C_6H_5NO_2$	40	277
o-Cresyl methyl ether	Propyl	α-n-Propyl-β-(4-methoxy-3-methylbenzoyl)	$C_6H_5NO_2$	45	277
o-Cresyl methyl ether	Amyl	α-n-Amyl-β-(4-methoxy-3-methylbenzoyl)	$C_6H_5NO_2$	30	277

J. Aromatically Substituted Succinic Anhydrides

Aromatic Compound	Substituent in Anhydride	Product β-Aroylpropionic Acid	Solvent	Yield %	Reference *
Benzene	Phenyl	β-Phenyl-β-benzoyl	Benzene	—	131
Benzene	Phenyl	Equal mixture of α- and β-phenyl-β-benzoyl	Benzene	—	15
Benzene	Phenyl	Mixture of α- and β-phenyl-β-benzoyl	Benzene	65	14
Benzene	Phenyl	{ α-Phenyl-β-benzoyl, β-phenyl-β-benzoyl	Benzene	48 52	17
Benzene	Phenyl	{ α-Phenyl-β-benzoyl, β-phenyl-β-benzoyl	$C_6H_5NO_2$	89 11	17
Benzene	p-Nitrophenyl	{ α-p-Nitrophenyl-β-benzoyl, β-p-nitrophenyl-β-benzoyl	Benzene	45 55	17
Benzene	p-Nitrophenyl	{ α-p-Nitrophenyl-β-benzoyl, β-p-nitrophenyl-β-benzoyl	$C_6H_5NO_2$	5 95	17
Benzene	p-Methoxyphenyl	α-p-Methoxyphenyl-β-benzoyl	Benzene	Nearly quantitative	17
Benzene	p-Methoxyphenyl	α-p-Methoxyphenyl-β-benzoyl	$C_6H_5NO_2$	Nearly quantitative	17
Benzene	p-Chlorophenyl	{ α-p-Chlorophenyl-β-benzoyl, β-p-chlorophenyl-β-benzoyl	Benzene	46 54	17
Benzene	p-Chlorophenyl	β-p-Chlorophenyl-β-benzoyl	$C_6H_5NO_2$	Quant.	17
Toluene	Phenyl	{ α-Phenyl-β-p-toluyl, β-phenyl-β-p-toluyl	Toluene	20 † 33	16
Toluene	Phenyl	{ α-Phenyl-β-p-toluyl, β-phenyl-β-p-toluyl	Toluene	23 77	17
Toluene	Phenyl	{ α-Phenyl-β-p-toluyl, β-phenyl-β-p-toluyl	$C_6H_5NO_2$	46 ‡ 7.9	16

* References 217–296 are on pp. 288–289.
† The yield of the mixture was 69%.   ‡ The yield of the mixture was 71%.

TABLE X—*Continued*

REACTIONS OF SUBSTITUTED SUCCINIC ANHYDRIDES

Aromatic Compound	Substituent in Anhydride	Product β-Aroylpropionic Acid	Solvent	Yield %	Reference *
Toluene (*Continued*)	Phenyl	α-Phenyl-β-p-toluyl, β-phenyl-β-p-toluyl	$C_6H_5NO_2$	83 17	17
Toluene	p-Nitrophenyl	α-p-Nitrophenyl-β-p-toluyl, β-p-nitrophenyl-β-p-toluyl	Toluene	20 80	17
Toluene	p-Nitrophenyl	α-p-Nitrophenyl-β-p-toluyl, β-p-nitrophenyl-β-p-toluyl	$C_6H_5NO_2$	33 67	17
Toluene	p-Methoxyphenyl	α-p-Methoxyphenyl-β-p-toluyl, β-p-methoxyphenyl-β-p-toluyl	Toluene	82 18	17
Toluene	p-Methoxyphenyl	α-p-Methoxyphenyl-β-p-toluyl	$C_6H_5NO_2$	Preponderant	17
Biphenyl	Phenyl	β-Phenyl-β-p-phenylbenzoyl	CS_2	—	136
Anisole	o-Methoxyphenyl	α-o-Methoxyphenyl-β-p-anisoyl	$CHCl_2CHCl_2$ or $C_6H_5NO_2$	—	261
Anisole	p-Methoxyphenyl	α-p-Methoxyphenyl-β-p-anisoyl	CS_2	35	133
Anisole	p-Methoxyphenyl	α-p-Methoxyphenyl-β-p-anisoyl	$CHCl_2CHCl_2$	95 †	133
Anisole	p-Methoxyphenyl	α-p-Methoxyphenyl-β-p-anisoyl	$C_6H_5NO_2$	77	133
o-Cresyl methyl ether	o-Methoxyphenyl	α-o-Methoxyphenyl-β-(4-methoxy-3-methylbenzoyl), β-o-methoxyphenyl-β-(4-methoxy-3-methylbenzoyl)	$C_6H_5NO_4$	44 49	132
o-Cresyl methyl ether	o-Methoxyphenyl	α-o-Methoxyphenyl-β-(4-methoxy-3-methylbenzoyl), β-o-methoxyphenyl-β-(4-methoxy-3-methylbenzoyl)	$CHCl_2CHCl_2$	54 42	132
o-Cresyl methyl ether	p-Methoxyphenyl	α-p-Methoxyphenyl-β-(4-methoxy-3-methylbenzoyl)	CS_2	65	133
o-Cresyl methyl ether	p-Methoxyphenyl	α-p-Methoxyphenyl-β-(4-methoxy-3-methylbenzoyl)	$CHCl_2CHCl_2$	95	133
o-Cresyl methyl ether	p-Methoxyphenyl	α-p-Methoxyphenyl-β-(4-methoxy-3-methylbenzoyl)	$C_6H_5NO_2$	92	133
m-Cresyl methyl ether	o-Methoxyphenyl	α-o-Methoxyphenyl-β-(4-methoxy-2-methylbenzoyl), β-o-methoxyphenyl-β-(4-methoxy-2-methylbenzoyl)	$C_6H_5NO_2$	60 20	132
m-Cresyl methyl ether	o-Methoxyphenyl	α-o-Methoxyphenyl-β-(4-methoxy-2-methylbenzoyl), β-o-methoxyphenyl-β-(4-methoxy-2-methylbenzoyl)	$CHCl_2CHCl_2$	58 27	132
m-Cresyl methyl ether	p-Methoxyphenyl	α-p-Methoxyphenyl-β-(4-methoxy-2-methylbenzoyl)	CS_2	15	133
m-Cresyl methyl ether	p-Methoxyphenyl	α-p-Methoxyphenyl-β-(4-methoxy-2-methylbenzoyl)	$CHCl_2CHCl_2$	90	133
m-Cresyl methyl ether	p-Methoxyphenyl	α-p-Methoxyphenyl-β-(4-methoxy-2-methylbenzoyl)	$C_6H_5NO_2$	75	133
p-Cresyl methyl ether	p-Methoxyphenyl	α-p-Methoxyphenyl-β-(2-methoxy-5-methylbenzoyl)	CS_2	10	133

* References 217–296 are on pp. 288–289.
† Another isomer was formed in small amount.

TABLE X—*Continued*

REACTIONS OF SUBSTITUTED SUCCINIC ANHYDRIDES

Aromatic Compound	Substituent in Anhydride	Product β-Aroylpropionic Acid	Solvent	Yield %	Reference *
p-Cresyl methyl ether (Continued)	p-Methoxyphenyl	α-p-Methoxyphenyl-β-(2-methoxy-5-methylbenzoyl	$CHCl_2CHCl_2$	90	133
p-Cresyl methyl ether	p-Methoxyphenyl	α-p-Methoxyphenyl-β-(2-methoxy-5-methylbenzoyl)	$C_6H_5NO_2$ †	45	133
Veratrole	Phenyl	α-Phenyl-β-(3,4-dimethoxybenzoyl)	$C_6H_5NO_2$	84	135
Veratrole	o-Methoxyphenyl	α-o-Methoxyphenyl-β-(3,4-dimethoxybenzoyl)	$CHCl_2CHCl_2$ or $C_6H_5NO_2$	—	261
Veratrole	p-Methoxyphenyl	α-p-Methoxyphenyl-β-(3,4-dimethoxybenzoyl)	CS_2	—	134
Veratrole	p-Methoxyphenyl	α-p-Methoxyphenyl-β-(3,4-dimethoxybenzoyl)	$CHCl_2CHCl_2$	85	134
Veratrole	p-Methoxyphenyl	α-p-Methoxyphenyl-β-(3,4-dimethoxybenzoyl)	$C_6H_5NO_2$	64	134
Guaiacol	p-Methoxyphenyl	No reaction	CS_2, $CHCl_2CHCl_2$, $C_6H_5NO_2$		134
Resorcinol dimethyl ether	o-Methoxyphenyl	α-o-Methoxyphenyl-β-(2,4-dimethoxybenzoyl)	$CHCl_2CHCl_2$ or $C_6H_5NO_2$	—	261
Resorcinol dimethyl ether	p-Methoxyphenyl	α-p-Methoxyphenyl-β-(2,4-dimethoxybenzoyl)	CS_2	95	134
Resorcinol dimethyl ether	p-Methoxyphenyl	α-p-Methoxyphenyl-β-(2,4-dimethoxybenzoyl)	$CHCl_2CHCl_2$	43	134
Resorcinol dimethyl ether	p-Methoxyphenyl	α-p-Methoxyphenyl-β-(2,4-dimethoxybenzoyl)	$C_6H_5NO_2$	64	134
Resorcinol dimethyl ether	2,4-Dimethoxyphenyl	{ α-2,4-Dimethoxyphenyl-β-(2,4-dimethoxybenzoyl), β-2,4-dimethoxyphenyl-β-(2,4-dimethoxybenzoyl)	CS_2	60 ‡ 40	182
Resorcinol monomethyl ether	p-Methoxyphenyl	α-p-Methoxyphenyl-β-(2-hydroxy-4-methoxybenzoyl)	CS_2	21	134
Resorcinol monomethyl ether	p-Methoxyphenyl	α-p-Methoxyphenyl-β-(2-hydroxy-4-methoxybenzoyl)	$CHCl_2CHCl_2$	78	134
Resorcinol monomethyl ether	p-Methoxyphenyl	α-p-Methoxyphenyl-β-(2-hydroxy-4-methoxybenzoyl)	$C_6H_5NO_2$	69	134
Hydroquinone dimethyl ether	o-Methoxyphenyl	α-o-Methoxyphenyl-β-(2,5-dimethoxybenzoyl)	$CHCl_2CHCl_2$ or $C_6H_5NO_2$	—	261
Hydroquinone dimethyl ether	p-Methoxyphenyl	α-p-Methoxyphenyl-β-(2,5-dimethoxybenzoyl)	CS_2	—	134
Hydroquinone dimethyl ether	p-Methoxyphenyl	α-p-Methoxyphenyl-β-(2,5-dimethoxybenzoyl)	$CHCl_2CHCl_2$	14	134
Hydroquinone dimethyl ether	p-Methoxyphenyl	α-p-Methoxyphenyl-β-(2,5-dimethoxybenzoyl)	$C_6H_5NO_2$	29	134
Hydroquinone monomethyl ether	p-Methoxyphenyl	No reaction	CS_2, $CHCl_2CHCl_2$, $C_6H_5NO_2$		134

* References 217–296 are on pp. 288–289.
† In nitrobenzene 45% of an isomer was formed.
‡ The total yield of pure mixed product was 65%.

TABLE X—*Continued*

REACTIONS OF SUBSTITUTED SUCCINIC ANHYDRIDES

Aromatic Compound	Product β-Aroylpropionic Acid	Solvent	Yield %	Reference *

K. *Miscellaneous Substituted Succinic Anhydrides*

Cyclopentane-1-carboxy-1-acetic Acid Anhydride
(1,1-Spirocyclopentane Succinic Anhydride)

Benzene	α,α-Spirocyclopentane-β-benzoyl †	Benzene	60	262
Benzene	α,α-Spirocyclopentane-β-benzoyl	Benzene	—	14
Toluene	α,α-Spirocyclopentane-β-p-toluyl	Toluene	79	141
Ethylbenzene	α,α-Spirocyclopentane-β-p-ethylbenzoyl	CS$_2$	74	141
Hydrindene	α,α-Spirocyclopentane-β-5-hydrindoyl	C$_6$H$_5$NO$_2$	—	143
Naphthalene	α,α-Spirocyclopentane-β-1-naphthoyl and	C$_6$H$_5$NO$_2$	9.7	142
	α,α-spirocyclopentane-β-2-naphthoyl		3.7	
1-Methylnaphthalene	α,α-Spirocyclopentane-β-(4-methyl-1-naphthoyl)	C$_6$H$_5$NO$_2$	39	142

Cyclohexane-1-carboxy-1-acetic Acid Anhydride
(1,1-Spirocyclohexane Succinic Anhydride)

Benzene	α,α-Spirocyclohexane-β-benzoyl	Benzene	55	16
Benzene	α,α-Spirocyclohexane-β-benzoyl	Benzene	—	282
Benzene	α,α-Spirocyclohexane-β-benzoyl	C$_6$H$_5$NO$_2$	Poor	16
Toluene	α,α-Spirocyclohexane-β-p-toluyl	Toluene	85	16
Toluene	α,α-Spirocyclohexane-β-p-toluyl	Toluene(?)	—	282
Toluene	α,α-Spirocyclohexane-β-p-toluyl and	C$_6$H$_5$NO$_2$		16
	1,1-spirocyclohexane-1,2-di-p-toluylethane		20	
Ethylbenzene	α,α-Spirocyclohexane-β-p-ethylbenzoyl	Ethylbenzene(?)	—	282

3-Methylcyclopentane-1-carboxy-1-acetic Acid Anhydride
(1,1-(Spiro-3-methylcyclopentane)succinic Anhydride)

Benzene	α,α-Spiro-(3-methylcyclopentane)-β-benzoyl	Benzene	58	16
Benzene	α,α-Spiro-(3-methylcyclopentane)-β-benzoyl	C$_6$H$_5$NO$_2$	Poor	16
Toluene	α,α-Spiro-(3-methylcyclopentane)-β-p-toluyl	Toluene	78	16

Δ^{1,2}Cyclopentene-1,2-dicarboxylic Acid Anhydride

Naphthalene	Δ^{1,2}Cyclopentene-1-(1- and 2-naphthoyl)-2-carboxylic acid	C$_6$H$_5$NO$_2$	—	143

* References 217–296 are on pp. 288–289.
† This compound was first considered to be the β,β-isomer. See ref. 14.

TABLE X—*Continued*

REACTIONS OF SUBSTITUTED SUCCINIC ANHYDRIDES

Aromatic Compound	Product	Solvent	Yield %	Reference *
	cis-Hexahydrophthalic Anhydride			
Benzene	2-Benzoylcyclohexane-1-carboxylic acid	Benzene	90	263
	cis-3,6-Endomethylene-hexahydrophthalic Anhydride			
Benzene	3-Benzoylnorcamphane-2-carboxylic acid	Benzene	87	264
	Bromosuccinic Anhydride			
Benzene	α-Bromo-β-benzoylpropionic acid	Benzene	30	185
	Isodibromosuccinic Anhydride			
Benzene	Iso-α,β-dibromo-β-benzoylpropionic acid	Benzene	80–85	177
Benzene	Iso-α,β-dibromo-β-benzoylpropionic acid	Benzene	—	265

* References 217–296 are on pp. 288–289.

TABLE XI

REACTIONS OF GLUTARIC ANHYDRIDE

Aromatic Compound	Product γ-Aroylbutyric Acid	Solvent	Yield %	Reference *
Benzene	Benzoyl	Benzene	72	15
Benzene	Benzoyl	Benzene	80–85	204
Benzene	⎰Benzoyl, ⎱1,3-dibenzoylpropane	Benzene	24 18.5	148
Toluene	⎰p-Toluyl, ⎱1,3-di-p-toluylpropane	CHCl₂CHCl₂	69 15.2	149
Tetralin	2-Tetroyl	Benzene	43	36
Acenaphthene	3-Acenaphthoyl	C₆H₅NO₂	Poor	39
Anisole	4-Anisoyl	CS₂	—	150
Anisole	4-Anisoyl	Anisole	75	151
Anisole	4-Anisoyl	CHCl₂CHCl₂ + C₆H₅NO₂	85	36
Anisole	4-Anisoyl	CHCl₂CHCl₂ + C₆H₅NO₂	82	294
Phenetole	4-Ethoxybenzoyl	CS₂	—	150
Phenetole	4-Ethoxybenzoyl	Phenetole	64	152
Diphenyl ether	4-Phenoxybenzoyl	Benzene	84.5	93
Diphenyl ether	4-Phenoxybenzoyl	CS₂	Poor	93
Veratrole	3,4-Dimethoxybenzoyl	C₆H₅NO₂	45	153
Pyrogallol trimethyl ether	2,3,4-Trimethoxybenzoyl and a small amount of a γ-(hydroxydimethoxybenzoyl)butyric acid	C₆H₅NO₂	—	155
Chlorobenzene	p-Chlorobenzoyl	CS₂	Low	30
Thiophene	2-Thenoyl	C₆H₅NO₂	39.4	154
o-Phenyleneurea	3,4-Ureylenebenzoyl	CHCl₂CHCl₂	5	293

* References 217–296 are on pp. 288–289.

FRIEDEL AND CRAFTS REACTION 283

TABLE XII

REACTIONS OF SUBSTITUTED GLUTARIC ANHYDRIDES

Aromatic Compound	Substituent in Anhydride	Product γ-Aroylbutyric Acid	Solvent	Yield %	Reference *
Benzene	β,β-Dimethyl	β,β-Dimethyl-γ-benzoyl	Benzene	Quantitative	15
Benzene	β-Methyl-β-ethyl	β-Methyl-β-ethyl-γ-benzoyl	Benzene	—	15
Benzene	β-Phenyl	Ketohydrindene-3-acetic acid †	Benzene	—	15
Benzene	β,β-Spirocyclopentyl ‡	β,β-Spirocyclopentane-γ-benzoyl	Benzene	61	15
Benzene	β,β-Spirocyclohexyl §	β,β-Spirocyclohexane-γ-benzoyl	Benzene	—	15
Benzene	β,β-Spiro-(3-methylcyclopentyl)	β,β-Spiro-(3-methylcyclopentane)-γ-benzoyl	Benzene	—	15

Camphoric Anhydride

Benzene	1,1,2-Trimethyl-2-phenylcyclopentane-5-carboxylic acid ‖	Benzene	—	159
Toluene	1,1,2-Trimethyl-2(or 5)-toluylcyclopentane-5 (or 2)-carboxylic acid	Toluene	—	160
Anisole	1,1,2-Trimethyl-2 (or 5)-anisoylcyclopentane-5 (or 2)-carboxylic acid	Anisole	—	160

* References 217–296 are on pp. 288–289.
† This acid is formed by cyclization of the anhydride. See ref. 156.
‡ Formula XIV on p. 248.
§ Formula XV on p. 248.
‖ Phenylcamphoric acid. Carbon monoxide is lost in this reaction.

TABLE XIII

Reactions of Polymeric Acid Anhydrides *

Aromatic Compound	Product	Solvent	Yield %	Reference †

A. Polyadipic Anhydride

Aromatic Compound	Product	Solvent	Yield %	Reference †
Benzene	{ ω-Benzoylvaleric acid, 1,4-dibenzoylbutane	Benzene	75; 62 85	161, 36
n-Butylbenzene	ω-n-Butylbenzoylvaleric acid	n-Butylbenzene	—	272
sec-Butylnaphthalene	ω-sec-Butylnaphthoylvaleric acid	sec-Butyl- naphthalene	—	272
Anisole	{ ω-p-Anisoylvaleric acid, 1,4-di-p-anisoylbutane	CS_2	43 55	162
Anisole	{ ω-p-Anisoylvaleric acid, 1,4-di-p-anisoylbutane	$CHCl_2CHCl_2$ + $C_6H_5NO_2$	33 47	294
Phenetole	{ ω-p-Ethoxybenzoylvaleric acid, 1,4-di-p-ethoxybenzoylbutane	CS_2	—	162
Thiophene ‡	ω-2-Thenoylvaleric acid	Benzene	3.8	164

B. Polysuberic Anhydride

Aromatic Compound	Product	Solvent	Yield %	Reference †
Thiophene ‡	{ ω-2-Thenoylheptanoic acid, 1,6-di-2-thenoylhexane	Benzene	— 29.8	163, 164

C. Polyazelaic Anhydride

Aromatic Compound	Product	Solvent	Yield %	Reference †
Benzene	ω-Benzoyloctanoic acid	Benzene	25	30
Thiophene ‡	{ ω-2-Thenoyloctanoic acid, 1,7-di-2-thenoylheptane	Benzene	24.5 27	164

D. Polysebacic Anhydride

Aromatic Compound	Product	Solvent	Yield %	Reference †
Benzene	{ ω-Benzoylnonanoic acid, 1,8-dibenzoyloctane	Benzene	78 86	161
sec-Amylbenzene	ω-sec-Amylbenzoylnonanoic acid	sec-Amylbenzene	—	272
sec-Octyltoluene	ω-sec-Octyltoluylnonanoic acid	sec-Octyltoluene	—	272
Tetralin	ω-2-Tetroylnonanoic acid	$C_6H_5NO_2$	40 §	36
Thiophene ‡	{ ω-2-Thenoylnonanoic acid, 1,8-di-2-thenoyloctane	Benzene	8.3 21.2	164

* The yields are calculated on the basis of the equation on p. 248.
† References 217–296 are on pp. 288–289.
‡ Stannic chloride was used as the catalyst.
§ This yield refers to a crude product.

TABLE XIV

REACTIONS OF MALEIC ANHYDRIDE

Aromatic Compound	Product β-Aroylacrylic Acid	Solvent	Yield %	Reference *
Benzene	Benzoyl	Benzene	—	2, 174, 177, 183
Benzene	Benzoyl	Benzene	67 †	3
Benzene	Benzoyl	Benzene	About 55	179
Benzene	Benzoyl	Benzene	95	178
Benzene	Benzoyl	Benzene	91	176a
Benzene	α-Phenyl-β-benzoylpropionic acid ‡	Benzene	16	183
Chlorobenzene	4-Chlorobenzoyl	C6H5Cl	62	176a
Bromobenzene	4-Bromobenzoyl	C6H5Br	90	176a
Bromobenzene	4-Bromobenzoyl	CHBr2CHBr2	72	290
Bromobenzene	trans-β-(4-Bromobenzoyl)	CHCl2CHCl2	74	291
Iodobenzene	4-Iodobenzoyl	CHCl2CHCl2	10	176a
1,2-Dichlorobenzene	3,4-Dichlorobenzoyl	C6H4Cl2 (1,2)	56	176a
1,3-Dichlorobenzene	2,4-Dichlorobenzoyl	CHCl2CHCl2	17	176a
Toluene	p-Toluyl	Toluene	—	2
Toluene	p-Toluyl	Toluene	<50	179
Toluene	p-Toluyl	Toluene	77	178
Toluene	p-Toluyl	CHCl2CHCl2	70–75	171
Toluene	p-Toluyl	CHCl2CHCl2	65	176a
Toluene	α-p-Tolyl-β-(p-toluyl)propionic acid ‡	Toluene	18	183
o-Chlorotoluene	3-Methyl-4-chlorobenzoyl	CHCl2CHCl2	30	176a
p-Chlorotoluene	2-Chloro-5-methylbenzoyl	CHCl2CHCl2	39	176a
m-Xylene	2,4-Dimethylbenzoyl	m-Xylene	Approx. 25	179
m-Xylene	2,4-Dimethylbenzoyl	CHCl2CHCl2	41	171
m-Xylene	2,4-Dimethylbenzoyl	CHCl2CHCl2	91	176a
p-Xylene	2,5-Dimethylbenzoyl	CHCl2CHCl2	70–75	171
p-Xylene	2,5-Dimethylbenzoyl	CHCl2CHCl2	90	176a
Isopropylbenzene	4-Isopropylbenzoyl	CHCl2CHCl2	55	176a
Mesitylene	2,4,6-Trimethylbenzoyl	Mesitylene	—	179
Mesitylene	trans-β-(2,4,6-Trimethylbenzoyl)	CHCl2CHCl2	62.5	292
1,3,4-Trimethylbenzene	2,4,5-Trimethylbenzoyl	1,3,4-Trimethylbenzene	—	179
o-tert-Butyltoluene	4-(or 3)Methyl-3(or 4)-tert-butylbenzoyl	o-tert-Butyltoluene	—	180
p-tert-Butyltoluene	2-Methyl-5-tert-butylbenzoyl and 3-methyl-6-tert-butylbenzoyl	p-tert-Butyltoluene	—	180
sec-Amylbenzene	sec-Amylbenzoyl	sec-Amylbenzene	—	272
sec-Octylxylene	sec-Octylxyloyl	sec-Octylxylene	—	272
p-Di-tert-butylbenzene	p-tert-Butylbenzoyl	CS2	—	31
p-Di-tert-butylbenzene	2,5-Di-p-tert-butylbenzoyl	CHCl2CHCl2	48 §	176a
Phenylcyclohexane	4-Cyclohexylbenzoyl	CHCl2CHCl2	68	176a
Naphthalene	A mixture containing mainly 2-naphthoyl	Benzene ‖	—	178
Naphthalene	1-Naphthoyl and 2-naphthoyl	Benzene	40 ¶ 60	177
Tetralin	β-Tetralyl	CHCl2CHCl2	50	176a
Biphenyl	4-Phenylbenzoyl	Benzene	80	178
Acenaphthene	3-Acenaphthoyl	C6H5NO2	32	39

* References 217–296 are on pp. 288–289.
† The yield of pure acid was 50%.
‡ This acid was obtained only with an excess of aluminum chloride.
§ The product was isolated as the methyl ester.
‖ In nitrobenzene no product could be isolated; see ref. 39.
¶ The total yield of the mixture was 70–80%.

TABLE XIV—*Continued*

REACTIONS OF MALEIC ANHYDRIDE

Aromatic Compound	Product β-Aroylacrylic Acid	Solvent	Yield %	Reference *
Anthracene	9-Anthroyl †	Benzene	44	178
Anisole	4-Anisoyl	(?)	—	175
Anisole	4-Anisoyl	CHCl₂CHCl₂	27	171
Anisole	4-Anisoyl	CS₂	54	176
Anisole	4-Anisoyl	CHCl₂CHCl₂	70	176a
Phenetole	4-Ethoxybenzoyl	Phenetole	9–11	179
Phenetole	4-Ethoxybenzoyl	CS₂	61	266
Phenetole	4-Ethoxybenzoyl	CS₂	62	72
Phenetole	4-Ethoxybenzoyl	CHCl₂CHCl₂	60	176a
β-Phenoxyethoxyethyl chloride	(β-Chloroethoxyethoxy)benzoyl	CS₂	—	267
o-Cresyl methyl ether	3-Methyl-4-methoxybenzoyl	C₆H₅NO₂	100	176
m-Cresyl methyl ether	2-Methyl-4-methoxybenzoyl	C₆H₅NO₂	92	176
m-Cresyl methyl ether	2-Methyl-4-methoxybenzoyl	CS₂	—	245
p-Cresyl methyl ether	2-Methoxy-5-methylbenzoyl	CS₂	70	176
p-Cresyl methyl ether	2-Methoxy-5-methylbenzoyl	C₆H₅NO₂	82	176
2,4-Dimethylanisole	2-Methoxy-3,5-dimethylbenzoyl	Ligroin	8.8	246
2,5-Dimethylanisole	4-Methoxy-2,5-dimethylbenzoyl	Ligroin	38	247
Diphenyl ether	4-Phenoxybenzoyl	CS₂	25.5	181
1-Methoxynaphthalene	4-Methoxy-1-naphthoyl	C₆H₅NO₂	88	268
2-Methoxynaphthalene	2-Methoxy-1-naphthoyl ‡	C₆H₅NO₂	80	268
Veratrole	3,4-Dimethoxybenzoyl	CS₂	46	176
Veratrole	3,4-Dimethoxybenzoyl	C₆H₅NO₂	50	176
Resorcinol dimethyl ether	2,4-Dimethoxyphenylsuccinic anhydride,	CS₂	40	182
	2,4-dimethoxyphenylsuccinic acid,		4	
	2,4-dimethoxybenzoylacrylic acid,		4.6	
	α-(2,4-dimethoxyphenyl)-β-(2,4-di-methoxybenzoyl)propionic acid			
Hydroquinone dimethyl ether	2,5-Dimethoxybenzoyl	C₆H₅NO₂	—	176
Hydroquinone dimethyl ether	2,5-Dimethoxybenzoyl	CHCl₂CHCl₂	11	176a
Phenol	α-(p-Hydroxyphenyl)-β-(p-hydroxy-benzoyl)propionic acid §	Benzene	25	177
Phenol	4-Hydroxybenzoyl	CHCl₂CHCl₂	4	176a
m-Cresol	2-Methyl-4-hydroxybenzoyl	CHCl₂CHCl₂	25	176a
p-Cresol	2-Hydroxy-5-methylbenzoyl	CHCl₂CHCl₂	25	176a
3-Methyl-6-isopropylphenol	2-Methyl-4-hydroxy-5-isopropylbenzoyl	CHCl₂CHCl₂	13	176a
Thiophene	2-Thenoyl	CHCl₂CHCl₂	34	176a
2-Chlorothiophene	5-Chloro-2-thenoyl	CHCl₂CHCl₂	53	176a
Acetanilide	4-Acetaminobenzoyl	CS₂	85	176a

* References 217–296 are on pp 288–289.

† No proof for the position of attachment of the side chain was given.

‡ The acid was not obtained in analytically pure form.

§ The structure of this acid was established by Papa, Schwenk, Villani, and Klingsberg, ref. 176a.

TABLE XV

REACTIONS OF SUBSTITUTED MALEIC ANHYDRIDES

Aromatic Compound	Product β-Aroylacrylic Acid	Solvent	Yield %	Reference *
A. Methylmaleic Anhydride				
Benzene	β-Methyl-β-benzoyl	Benzene	—	2
Benzene	α-Methyl-β-benzoyl	Benzene	20	177
Benzene	{α-Methyl-β-benzoyl, β-methyl-β-benzoyl	Benzene	0.71 0.48	122
Toluene	{α-Methyl-β-p-toluyl, β-methyl-β-p-toluyl	Toluene	14 —	122
Mesitylene	trans-β-(2,4,6-Trimethylbenzoyl)-?-methyl- acrylic acid	CS₂	36	167
Bromobenzene	{cis-β-(4-Bromobenzoyl)crotonic acid, trans-α-methyl-β-(4-bromobenzoyl)acrylic acid	CS₂	47 2	167, 269
B. Dimethylmaleic Anhydride †				
Benzene	cis-α,β-Dimethylbenzoyl	CS₂‡	49	168
Mesitylene	trans-α,β-Dimethyl-β-(2,4,6-trimethylbenzoyl)	CS₂	61.5	168
Biphenyl	cis-α,β-Dimethyl-β-4-phenylbenzoyl	CS₂	50	169
Bromobenzene §	cis-α,β-Dimethyl-β-4-bromobenzoyl	CS₂	40	169
C. Bromomaleic Anhydride				
Benzene	{α-Bromo-β-benzoyl, β-bromo-β-benzoyl	Benzene	31.5 ‖ 8.5	185
D. Dibromomaleic Anhydride				
Benzene	cis-α,β-Dibromo-β-benzoyl	CS₂	63	166
Mesitylene	cis-α,β-Dibromo-β-(2,4,6-trimethylbenzoyl)	CS₂	79	166

* References 217–296 are on pp. 288–289.
† Methylpropylmaleic anhydride is reported to give very poor results in the condensation with aromatic compounds. Diphenylmaleic anhydride is reported not to react at all. See ref. 179.
‡ This reaction proceeds better in carbon disulfide than in benzene.
§ Aluminum bromide was used instead of aluminum chloride.
‖ The total yield of the mixture was 51%.

REFERENCES TO TABLES

[217] Borsche, *Ber.*, **47**, 1110 (1914).

[218] Kugel, *Ann.*, **299**, 50 (1898).

[219] Martin and Fieser, *Org. Syntheses, Coll. Vol.* **2**, 81, note 4 (1943).

[220] Burcker, *Bull. soc. chim. France*, [2] **49**, 449 (1888).

[221] Limpricht, *Ann.*, **312**, 110 (1900).

[222] Katzenellenbogen, *Ber.*, **34**, 3828 (1901).

[223] Fieser and Dunn, *J. Am. Chem. Soc.*, **58**, 575 (1936).

[224] Bachmann and Edgerton, *J. Am. Chem. Soc.*, **62**, 2219 (1940).

[225] Campbell and Soffer, *J. Am. Chem. Soc.*, **64**, 417 (1942).

[226] Meyer, *Ber.*, **28**, 1254 (1895).

[227] Allen, Normington, and Wilson, *Can. J. Research*, **11**, 382 (1934).

[228] Bromby, Peters, and Rowe, *J. Chem. Soc.*, **1943**, 144.

[229] Sengupta, *Current Sci. India*, **5**, 133 (1936) [*C.A.*, **31**, 5789 (1937)].

[230] Buu-Hoi, *Rev. sci.*, **80**, 319 (1942) [*C.A.*, **39**, 3276 (1945)].

[231] Orchin, *J. Am. Chem. Soc.*, **66**, 535 (1944).

[232] Giua, *Rend. soc. chim. ital.*, **9**, 239 (1912); *Ber.*, **47**, 2115 (1914).

[233] Borsche and Sauernheimer, *Ber.*, **47**, 1645 (1914).

[234] Drake and McVey, *J. Org. Chem.*, **4**, 466 (1939).

[235] Bograchow, *J. Am. Chem. Soc.*, **66**, 1613 (1944).

[236] Hewett, *J. Chem. Soc.*, **1940**, 293.

[237] Bachmann and Struve, *J. Org. Chem.*, **4**, 456 (1939).

[238] For a separation of the two isomeric acids see Newman, Taylor, Hodgson, and Garrett *J. Am. Chem. Soc.*, **69**, 1784 (1947).

[239] Vollmann, Becker, Corell, and Streeck, *Ann.*, **531**, 1 (1937).

[240] I.G. Farbenind. A.-G., Ger. pat. 652,912 (*Chem. Zentr.*, **1938**, I, 2064).

[241] Barnett, Goodway, and Watson, *Ber.*, **66**, 1876 (1933).

[242] Cook, Hewett, and Robinson, *J. Chem. Soc.*, **1939**, 168.

[243] Mitter and De, *J. Indian Chem. Soc.*, **12**, 747 (1935).

[244] Haworth and Sheldrick, *J. Chem. Soc.*, **1934**, 1950.

[245] Bentley, Gardner, and Weizmann, *J. Chem. Soc.*, **91**, 1626 (1907).

[246] Cocker and Lipman, *J. Chem. Soc.*, **1947**, 533.

[247] Clemo, Haworth, and Walton, *J. Chem. Soc.*, **1929**, 2368.

[248] Buu-Hoi and Cagniant, *Bull. soc. chim. France*, **11**, 349 (1944).

[249] Haq, Kapur, and Ray, *J. Chem. Soc.*, **1933**, 1088.

[250] Rafat Husain Siddiqui, *J. Indian Chem. Soc.*, **17**, 145 (1940).

[251] Chalmers and Lions, *J. Proc. Roy. Soc. N. S. Wales*, **67**, 178 (1933) (*Chem. Zentr.*, **1934**, I, 1979).

[252] Holmes and Mann, *J. Am. Chem. Soc.*, **69**, 2000 (1947).

[253] Hostmann, Dissertation, Rostock, 1895 (*Chem. Zentr.*, **1896**, II, 663).

[254] Bachmann and Ness, *J. Am. Chem. Soc.*, **64**, 536 (1942).

[255] Sergievskaya and Danilova, *J. Gen. Chem. U.S.S.R.*, **16**, 1077 (1946) [*C.A.*, **41**, 2719 (1947)].

[256] Dave and Nargund, *J. Indian Chem. Soc.*, **14**, 58 (1937).

[257] Giua, *Gazz. chim. ital.*, **47**, I, 89 (1917).

[258] Keimatsu, Ishiguro, and Sumi, *J. Pharm. Soc. Japan*, **56**, 588 (1936) (*Chem. Zentr.*, **1937**, I, 2188).

[259] Parker, *Iowa State Coll. J. Sci.*, **12**, 148 (1937) [*C.A.*, **32**, 2937 (1938)].

[260] Kitchen and Sandin, *J. Am. Chem. Soc.*, **67**, 1645 (1945).

[261] Savkar, Bokil, and Nargund, *J. Univ. Bombay*, **9**, Pt. 3, 150 (1940) [*C.A.*, **35**, 6946 (1941)].

[262] Sengupta, *J. Indian Chem. Soc.*, **11**, 389 (1934).

[263] Fieser and Novello, *J. Am. Chem. Soc.*, **64**, 802 (1942).

[264] Morgan, Tipson, Lowy, and Baldwin, *J. Am. Chem. Soc.*, **66**, 404 (1944).

265 Lutz, J. Am. Chem. Soc., **52**, 3423 (1930).
266 Eger, Dissertation, Heidelberg, 1897, quoted by Thomas, *Anhydrous Aluminum Chloride in Organic Chemistry*, p. 579, Reinhold Publishing Corp., New York, 1941.
267 Bruson and Eastes, U. S. pat. 2,132,675 [*C.A.*, **33**, 400 (1939)].
268 Dave, Bokil, and Nargund, J. Univ. Bombay, **10**, Pt. 3, 122 (1941) [*C.A.*, **36**, 3800 (1942)].
269 Lutz and Winne, J. Am. Chem. Soc., **56**, 445 (1934).
270 Sah and Brüll, Ber., **73**, 1430 (1940).
271 De, *Science and Culture*, **2**, 409 (1937) [*C.A.*, **31**, 3896 (1937)].
272 Bruson, Stein, and Robinson, U. S. pat. 1,962,478 (*Chem. Zentr.*, **1934**, II, 3683). The preparation of this acid is described in the patent, but no physical constants or analyses are reported.
273 Bhatt, Patel, and Nargund, J. Univ. Bombay, Sect. **A,15**, Pt. 3, 31 (1946) [*C.A.*, **41**, 6200 (1947)].
274 Shah and Phalnikar, J. Univ. Bombay, **13**, Pt. 3, 22 (1944) [*C.A.*, **39**, 2289 (1945)].
275 Holmes and Trevoy, Can. J. Research, **22B**, 109 (1944) [*C.A.*, **38**, 5505 (1944)].
276 Huebner and Jacobs, J. Biol. Chem., **169**, 211 (1947).
277 Mehta, Trivedi, Bokil, and Nargund, J. Univ. Bombay, **12A**, Pt. 5, 33 (1944) [*C.A.*, **38**, 4260 (1944)].
278 Trivedi and Nargund, J. Univ. Bombay, **10**, Pt. 3, 99 (1941) [*C.A.*, **36**, 3801 (1942)].
279 Walton, J. Chem. Soc., **1940**, 438.
279a Sukh Dev, J. Indian Chem. Soc., **25**, 315 (1948).
280 Desai and Figueredo, Proc. Indian Acad. Sci., **14A**, 605 (1941) [*C.A.*, **36**, 4812 (1942)].
281 Dalal and Nargund, J. Univ. Bombay, **7**, Pt. 3, 189 (1938) [*C.A.*, **33**, 3778 (1939)].
282 Sengupta, *Science and Culture*, **3**, 57 (1937) [*C.A.*, **31**, 7866 (1937)].
283 Strain, Plati, and Warren, J. Am. Chem. Soc., **64**, 1436 (1942).
284 Dev, J. Ind. Chem. Soc., **25**, 69 (1948).
285 Dev and Guha, J. Ind. Chem. Soc., **25**, 13 (1948).
286 Bachmann and Dice, J. Org. Chem., **12**, 877 (1947).
287 Dauben and Adams, J. Am. Chem. Soc., **70**, 1759 (1948).
288 Thomas and Nathan, J. Am. Chem. Soc., **70**, 331 (1948).
289 Miller and Morello, J. Am. Chem. Soc., **70**, 1900 (1948).
290 Kohler and Woodward, J. Am. Chem. Soc., **58**, 1933 (1936).
291 Lutz and Scott, J. Org. Chem., **13**, 284 (1948).
292 Lutz and Boyer, J. Am. Chem. Soc., **63**, 3189 (1941).
293 English, Clapp, Cole, Halverstadt, Lampen, and Roblin, J. Am. Chem. Soc., **67**, 295 (1945).
294 Pratt, Hoppe, and Archer, J. Org. Chem., **13**, 576 (1948).
295 Ghosh and Robinson, J. Chem. Soc., **1944**, 506.
296 Holmes and Stoik, Can. J. Research, **26B**, 396 (1948).

CHAPTER 6

THE GATTERMANN-KOCH REACTION

NATHAN N. CROUNSE *

The Hilton-Davis Chemical Company

CONTENTS

INTRODUCTION

The introduction of an aldehyde group into certain aromatic nuclei by means of carbon monoxide, hydrogen chloride, and an appropriate catalyst is known as the Gattermann-Koch reaction. The catalyst commonly used is aluminum chloride with cuprous chloride as a carrier. The carrier is not necessary when high pressures are used. The reaction was first reported in 1897 [1] and was discussed in detail a few years

---

* Present address, Institute of Medical Research, The Christ Hospital, Cincinnati, Ohio.
[1] Gattermann and Koch, *Ber.*, **30**, 1622 (1897).

later.[2] It has received little attention as a subject of academic study, but its application in the industrial field has been investigated. Gattermann discovered the reaction while attempting to extend the Friedel-Crafts reaction to the hypothetical formyl chloride. He pictured carbon monoxide as reacting with hydrogen chloride to yield formyl chloride which then condensed with benzene in the presence of aluminum chloride in the same manner as other acid chlorides. The cuprous chloride presumably serves to catalyze the formation of the formyl chloride.

$$CO + HCl \xrightarrow{\text{CuCl}} [HCOCl]$$

$$C_6H_6 + [HCOCl] \xrightarrow{\text{AlCl}_3} C_6H_5CHO + HCl$$

Gattermann did not isolate any intermediate compounds, and little evidence has since been offered to support Gattermann's proposed mechanisms. Hopff and co-workers [3] have described a complex compound, $HCOCl \cdot AlCl_3 \cdot CuCl$, formed by the reaction of aluminum chloride, cuprous chloride, hydrogen chloride, and carbon monoxide at 100 atmospheres. This complex reacts with toluene to give an unreported yield of p-tolualdehyde. However, the complex is not necessarily an intermediate in all Gattermann-Koch reactions, since formylation can be effected at high pressures without cuprous chloride.

SCOPE AND LIMITATIONS

The chief use of the Gattermann-Koch reaction appears to be the preparation in one step of benzaldehyde and the monoalkyl- and polyalkyl-benzaldehydes. The alkyl group in monoalkylbenzenes directs the aldehyde group almost exclusively to the *para* position.

Benzene furnishes benzaldehyde in yields up to 90%.[4] Among the monoalkylbenzenes, toluene, ethylbenzene,[1] *tert*-butylbenzene, *tert*-amylbenzene, cyclohexylbenzene, and (3-methylcyclohexyl)benzene have been converted to the corresponding p-alkylbenzaldehydes.[5] The only yields reported are 85% for p-tolualdehyde [4,6] and 15% for p-cyclohexylbenzaldehyde.[7] The formylation of isopropylbenzene is always accompanied by side reactions. Formylation at atmospheric pressure furnishes an unspecified yield of p-isopropylbenzaldehyde,[2] 2,4-diisopropylbenzal-

[2] Gattermann *Ann.*, **347**, 347 (1906).
[3] Hopff, Nenitzescu, Isacescu, and Cantuniari, *Ber.*, **69**, 2244 (1936).
[4] Gelsenkirchener Bergwerks A.G., Ger. pat. 403,489 [*Frdl.*, **14**, 435 (1925–26)].
[5] Meuly, Fr. pat. 820,545 [*C.A.*, **32**, 2955 (1938)].
[6] Boehringer & Söhne, Ger. pat. 281,212 [*C.A.*, **9**, 1830 (1915)].
[7] von Braun, Irmisch, and Nelles, *Ber.*, **66**, 1471 (1933).

dehyde,[8] a small amount of benzaldehyde, and a mixture of diisopropyl-benzenes, chiefly *meta* and *para*.[8a] Formylation at high pressures with an excess of carbon monoxide furnishes a 60% yield of *p*-isopropylbenz-aldehyde, together with benzaldehyde and 2,4-diisopropylbenzalde-hyde.[9]

The alkylation and dealkylation just described in the formylation of isopropylbenzene are again encountered when the Gattermann-Koch reaction is extended to the more highly alkylated benzenes. In addition the migration of an alkyl group sometimes occurs. These side reactions are unquestionably due to the aluminum chloride, for this reagent is known to bring about just such reactions with the polyalkylbenzenes. *o*-Xylene and *m*-xylene on formylation yield the expected products, 3,4-dimethylbenzaldehyde (58%) and 2,4-dimethylbenzaldehyde (45%), respectively.[2] *p*-Xylene, however, undergoes a shift of a methyl group to furnish 2,4-dimethylbenzaldehyde (45%).[2] At one time the formation of 2,5-dimethylbenzaldehyde from *p*-xylene was postulated, but this was later disproved.[10, 11, 12] *p*-Cymene furnishes a methylisopropylbenzalde-hyde of unknown orientation in unspecified yield.[8]

Mesitylene and pseudocumene yield 2,4,6-trimethylbenzaldehyde (80%) and 2,4,5-trimethylbenzaldehyde (56%), the normal products.[2] Diisopropyltoluene furnishes a methyldiisopropylbenzaldehyde in which the location of the aldehyde group is not known.[8] Triisopropylbenzene is dealkylated to yield a diisopropylbenzaldehyde.[8] Diisopropylxylene gives a dimethyldiisopropylbenzaldehyde of unknown orientation.[8] The orientation of the diisopropyltoluene, triisopropylbenzene, and diiso-propylxylene is not given in the patent covering this work.

Chlorobenzene[4] has been formylated at atmospheric pressure in nitrobenzene as a solvent to give a 70% yield of *p*-chlorobenzaldehyde, but there is no report of the extension of the reaction to bromobenzene, to iodobenzene, or to a chlorotoluene. Chlorobenzene has also been formylated under pressure.[6, 13] Dimethylaniline is probably formylated[14] to the expected *p*-dimethylaminobenzaldehyde, which, however, cannot be isolated since subsequent reactions occur with more dimethylaniline in the presence of the aluminum chloride to form the leuco base of crystal violet.

[8] Knorr and Weissenborn, U. S. pat. 1,776,154 [*C.A.*, **24**, 5307 (1930)].

[8a] Crounse, unpublished work.

[9] Crounse, *J. Am. Chem. Soc.*, **71**, 1263 (1949).

[10] Harding and Cohen, *J. Am. Chem. Soc.*, **23**, 594 (1901).

[11] Francesconi and Mundici, *Gazz. chim. ital.*, **32**, II, 467 (1902) [*J. Chem. Soc. Abs.*, **84** (I), 426 (1903)].

[12] Mundici, *Gazz. chim. ital.*, **34**, II, 114 (1904) [*J. Chem. Soc. Abs.*, **86** (I), 897 (1904)].

[13] Guthke, U. S. pat. 1,939,005 [*C.A.*, **28**, 1356 (1934)].

[14] Liston and Dehn, *Ind. Eng. Chem.*, **26**, 1073 (1934).

$$(CH_3)_2N\!\!-\!\!\langle\bigcirc\rangle + CO \xrightarrow[\text{HCl}]{\text{AlCl}_3} (CH_3)_2N\!\!-\!\!\langle\bigcirc\rangle\!\!-\!\!CHO$$

$$(CH_3)_2N\!\!-\!\!\langle\bigcirc\rangle\!\!-\!\!CHO + 2\langle\bigcirc\rangle\!\!-\!\!N(CH_3)_2 \xrightarrow{\text{AlCl}_3} \left[(CH_3)_2N\!\!-\!\!\langle\bigcirc\rangle\!\!-\right]_3\!\!CH$$

Phenol and phenol ethers could not be successfully formylated at atmospheric pressure in benzene as a solvent. This failure to react was attributed to the insolubility of the cuprous chloride in the reaction mixture.[15] It appears probable that formylation at high pressures where cuprous chloride is unnecessary might be successful.

Since nitrobenzene may be used as a solvent for formylation reactions,[4] it may be concluded that in general meta-directing groups in the benzene ring prevent substitution in the nucleus in which they are substituents.

Biphenyl is converted to p-phenylbenzaldehyde.[2,16] Hydrindene gives a 25% yield of the 5-aldehyde,[2] and a diisopropyl-ar-tetrahydronaphthalene furnishes a diisopropyl-ar-tetrahydronaphthaldehyde;[8] these are the only fused-ring compounds reported to undergo formylation. Naphthalene does not give naphthaldehyde.[17]

The synthesis of heterocyclic aldehydes by the Gattermann-Koch procedure has received almost no study. It has been reported that thiophene [18] decomposes during the course of the reaction and that only sufficient thiophene-2-aldehyde to be detected by odor is formed.

The reaction has been extended to the aliphatic and alicyclic series.[19] Cyclohexane yields 1-methyl-2-cyclohexanone under high-pressure formylation. The aliphatic hydrocarbons give ketones, and such reactions have proved to have practical application. Their discussion is beyond the scope of this chapter.

EXPERIMENTAL CONDITIONS

The most important variables in the Gattermann-Koch reaction are the condition and quantity of the catalyst, the carriers, the concentration of the hydrocarbons in the solvent, the pressure, and the temperature.

Catalysts. Anhydrous aluminum chloride has been the catalyst most commonly employed. Aluminum bromide,[20] however, was more success-

[15] Gattermann, Ber., 31, 1149 (1898).

[16] Hey, J. Chem. Soc., 1931, 2476.

[17] Dewar and Jones, J. Chem. Soc., 85, 212 (1904).

[18] Barger and Easson, J. Chem. Soc., 1938, 2100.

[19] Hopff, Ber., 64, 2739 (1931); Ber., 65, 482 (1932); Ger. pat. 512,718 [C.A., 25, 1258 (1931)]; Ger. pat. 520,154 [C.A., 25, 3664 (1931)].

[20] Reformatsky, J. Russ. Phys. Chem. Soc., 33, 154 (1901) [J. Chem. Soc. Abs., 80 (I), 327 (1901)].

294   ORGANIC REACTIONS

ful in the formylation of benzene at atmospheric pressure than aluminum chloride, although the latter is satisfactory at high pressures.[21] Some reports in the literature indicate that pretreatment of the aluminum chloride with moisture is advantageous when using high pressures. There is an optimum amount of water which must be added for satisfactory yields of benzaldehyde from benzene under specified conditions.[21,22] Exposure of aluminum chloride to moist air gives a very active catalyst.[9]

The amount of catalyst is an important factor. Usually a mole of aluminum chloride is used for each mole of hydrocarbon to be formylated. The ratio of aluminum chloride to benzene was studied carefully in the synthesis of benzaldehyde from benzene at different temperatures using a pressure of 1000 lb. per sq. in. and a reaction period of two hours.[21] In Table I are shown the results obtained at 25°, 35°, and 50° with changes in the molar ratio of aluminum chloride to benzene.

TABLE I

Effect of Quantity of Catalyst on Yield of Benzaldehyde

Molar Ratio $\frac{AlCl_3}{C_6H_6}$	Yield of Benzaldehyde %	
	Based on Benzene Converted	Based on Aluminum Chloride
At 25°		
0.3	20.6	68.7
0.5	31.5	63.0
0.75	48.6	64.8
1.0	65.4	65.4
At 35°		
0.3	20.5	68.3
0.5	33.8	67.6
0.75	39.9	53.2
At 50°		
0.3	18.6	61.9
0.5	33.0	66.0
0.75	39.4	52.5

[21] Holloway and Krase, *Ind. Eng. Chem.*, **25**, 497 (1933).
[22] Olson, U. S. pat. 1,935,914 [*C.A.*, **28**, 778 (1934)].

It was observed also that too much aluminum chloride in the reaction between isopropylbenzene and carbon monoxide gave decreased yields of p-isopropylbenzaldehyde though more hydrocarbon was consumed.[9] Excess aluminum chloride not only may convert aldehyde to the hydrocarbon and carbon monoxide but it also catalyzes the condensation of carbon monoxide and the hydrocarbon to anthracene and triphenylmethane derivatives.[23] It has been demonstrated by using tagged aldehydes that the aryl group holding the aldehyde does not become one of the aryl groups in the anthracene or triphenylmethane byproduct.

An industrial grade of aluminum chloride may be employed as catalyst. Its chief impurity is ferric chloride. Aluminum chloride containing titanium chloride as an impurity has been described as a valuable catalyst.[13] There are no statements in the literature which report any advantage in using highly purified aluminum chloride. A small amount of the preformed complex from aluminum chloride and the desired aldehyde is suggested as a promoter [24] and has proved successful in the synthesis of benzaldehyde.[21]

Carriers. When the Gattermann-Koch reaction is carried out at atmospheric pressure, a carrier is necessary.[1,2] The function is probably the acceleration of the reaction of carbon monoxide with hydrogen chloride. Cuprous chloride was the first such carrier discovered. Carbon monoxide is known to form a complex with cuprous chloride suitable for gas analysis in acid solution.[25] In anhydrous form this complex dissociates readily [26] but is more stable as the hydrate $CuCl \cdot CO \cdot 2H_2O$. The high rate of dissociation at atmospheric pressure may explain in part the slow rate of formylation as compared with that at high pressures.

Titanium tetrachloride [13] and nickelous chloride [2,27] have been reported to be almost as effective as cuprous chloride. Less efficient are cobaltous chloride, tungsten hexachloride, and ferric chloride.[27] Thus from 30 g. of toluene, 45 g. of aluminum chloride, and 2 g. of nickelous chloride a 54% yield of p-tolualdehyde resulted which is comparable to that obtained with cuprous chloride. 2,4,6-Trimethylbenzaldehyde was made from mesitylene in a similar manner. With ferric chloride as a carrier, only 14% yield of tolualdehyde was obtained from toluene; with tungsten hexachloride, the yield was only 5%, and with cobaltous chloride it was still lower.

[23] Hey, *J. Chem. Soc.*, **1935**, 72.
[24] Larson, U. S. pat. 1,989,700 [*C.A.*, **29**, 1834 (1935)].
[25] Snell and Biffen, *Commercial Methods of Analysis*, p. 609, McGraw-Hill, New York, 1944.
[26] Manchot and Friend, *Ann.*, **359**, 100 (1908).
[27] Korczynski and Mrozinski, *Bull. soc. chim. France*, [4] **29**, 459 (1921).

Concentration of the Hydrocarbon. Ordinarily the aromatic compound to be formylated is diluted with benzene, especially when the compound is an alkylbenzene with a labile alkyl group. Usually a ratio of benzene to aromatic compound of between 2 and 3 to 1 is satisfactory. The benzene inhibits the formation of dialkylbenzenes and thus lowers the amount of dialkylbenzaldehyde obtained as a by-product.

Pressure. Much of the work on the Gattermann-Koch reaction has been carried out at atmospheric pressure. Under these conditions the reaction mixture must be saturated with hydrogen chloride and kept so at all times by continual addition of the gas. At high pressures in an autoclave this is unnecessary. High pressures also increase the rate of absorption of carbon monoxide and increase the yield of product. The higher pressure apparently does not increase appreciably the rate of the transalkylation reaction but increases that of the formylation reaction. Carriers such as cuprous chloride are not necessary when working at high pressure,[9, 21] since benzene and isopropylbenzene have been successfully formylated without them. In the formylation of chlorobenzene and benzene,[13] it is claimed that the addition of titanium chloride is advantageous.

A pressure of 500 lb. per sq. in. has been suggested as satisfactory for formylation of isopropylbenzene.[9] In the formylation of benzene [21] a pressure of 1000 lb. per sq. in. was generally used although a pressure as low as 300 lb. was not appreciably less effective. As the pressure is increased from 700 lb. to 1000 lb., the yields gradually reach a constant value asymptotically.

Usually twice the length of time is required for completion of a formylation at atmospheric pressure as compared with high pressure (six or seven hours *versus* three or four).

Temperature. A temperature of 25–35° in formylations under pressure is often adequate,[9] although 50–60° has been found useful in certain reactions.[8, 13] Higher temperatures with a fixed ratio of aluminum chloride affected the yield of benzaldehyde from benzene unfavorably when the reactions were run beyond an optimum time; [21] tarry residues containing anthracene and triphenylmethane derivatives increased in quantity.[23] At atmospheric pressure a temperature range of 35–40° has been commonly employed.

Reagents and Apparatus. Since the Gattermann-Koch reaction involves two solids, two gases, and a liquid, good agitation is necessary whether operating at high or atmospheric pressure.

Carbon monoxide may be formed by the action of concentrated sulfuric acid upon formic acid. For high-pressure work it is convenient to use the gas obtained in cylinders under 800 lb. pressure.

In reactions at atmospheric pressure the hydrogen chloride, generated as used or from a cylinder, and the carbon monoxide may be combined and introduced into the reaction mixture through a common gas inlet. A convenient apparatus for this purpose has been described by Coleman and Craig.[28] More recently a procedure for simultaneous preparation of carbon monoxide and hydrogen chloride has been discovered.[29] This consists in the reaction of chlorosulfonic acid with formic acid. It was

$$HCOOH + ClSO_3H \rightarrow CO + HCl + H_2SO_4$$

found advantageous to add a volume of 100% sulfuric acid equal to that of the chlorosulfonic acid in order to reduce the vigor of the reaction. By employing an amount of chlorosulfonic acid adequate to neutralize 15% of water, commercial 85% formic acid may be substituted for anhydrous formic acid.

When working under high pressure, the reaction mixture is saturated with hydrogen chloride and placed in the autoclave before it is sealed. The carbon monoxide is then introduced.

The addition of nickel carbonyl to a mixture of the aromatic compound, aluminum chloride, and hydrogen chloride has served as a source of carbon monoxide in the formylation of benzene, toluene, xylene, and mesitylene.[17] The yields, however, are lower than in the usual method, and anthracene compounds appear to be formed in significant amounts.

If the reaction is carried out at atmospheric pressure, the reactor consists of a glass vessel fitted with an agitator, a gas inlet extending as near to the bottom of the flask or jar as possible, a thermometer, and an exit tube fitted as a bubble counter.[28]

For high-pressure work the catalytic hydrogenation rocking autoclave sold by the American Instrument Company has been satisfactory.[9] The autoclave should be lead lined to prevent corrosion.[9, 21] Copper has been reported to be satisfactory as a liner.[30] The use of an iron autoclave has been reported,[26] but the possibility of corrosion is a known risk. None of these metals has any known adverse effect on the reaction.

EXPERIMENTAL PROCEDURES

p-Tolualdehyde. (Atmospheric pressure, independent generation of carbon monoxide and hydrogen chloride, cuprous chloride carrier.) This preparation has been described in detail by Coleman and Craig in *Organic Syntheses*.[28]

[28] Coleman and Craig, *Org. Syntheses*, *Coll. Vol.* **2**, 583 (1943).
[29] Bert, *Compt. rend.*, **221**, 77 (1945).
[30] Hopff, U. S. pat. 1,976,682 [*C.A.*, **28**, 7263 (1934)].

p-Phenylbenzaldehyde.[16]   (Atmospheric pressure, cuprous chloride carrier.)   A stream of dry carbon monoxide and hydrogen chloride is passed for eight hours into a well-stirred solution of 60 g. of biphenyl in 240 ml. of dry benzene containing 90 g. of anhydrous aluminum chloride and 12 g. of cuprous chloride at 35–40°. After standing overnight the dark-colored semi-solid product is poured on ice. A yellow oil separates. The mixture is steam-distilled to remove benzene and unchanged biphenyl. The residue is extracted with ether, the extract is washed with dilute hydrochloric acid and with water, and the ether is evaporated. The semi-solid residue thus obtained is shaken with an excess of a saturated solution of sodium bisulfite, and after twelve hours the brown bisulfite compound is filtered, washed with ethanol and with ether, and warmed with aqueous sodium carbonate. The aldehyde is then collected, dried on a porous plate, and crystallized twice from petroleum ether (b.p. 80–100°). The yield of pale yellow plates, m.p. 60°, is 52 g. (73%).

p-Isopropylbenzaldehyde.[9],*   (High pressure, no carrier.)   A mixture of 210 g. (1.75 moles) of isopropylbenzene and 315 g. (4.05 moles) of benzene is saturated with hydrogen chloride and placed in a lead-lined rocking autoclave. Then 255 g. (1.92 moles) of aluminum chloride, which has been ground to 20 mesh, placed in a 1-in. layer in a shallow porcelain dish, and raked every fifteen minutes for two hours to induce hydration, is added. After the air in the autoclave is displaced with carbon monoxide, carbon monoxide is added until the pressure is 500 lb. per sq. in. The pressure is allowed to drop to 300 lb. per sq. in. The carbon monoxide pressure is returned to 500 lb. per sq. in., and the process is repeated until there is no pressure drop. The time of absorption is two and one-half hours, after which the reaction is allowed to proceed for another hour. The temperature of the reaction is 25–30°.

The reaction mixture is hydrolyzed by pouring it onto 2.5 kg. of ice acidified with 5 ml. of concentrated hydrochloric acid. The lower water layer is removed, and the oily layer is washed with 500 ml. of water and then with 500 ml. of 5% aqueous sodium carbonate solution. It is filtered to break the emulsion. After the lower alkaline layer has separated, the oily layer is washed twice with 500-ml. portions of water.

The oil is charged into a round-bottomed flask headed by a 36-in. fractionating column packed with glass helices. Most of the benzene is collected at atmospheric pressure. When the temperature of the liquid in the distilling flask reaches 131°, the flask is cooled to room temperature and the distillation is continued under a vacuum of 135 mm. This permits recovery of 40.5 g. of isopropylbenzene (b.p. 95°/135 mm.).

* The description of this procedure in ref. 9 is a condensed version.

THE GATTERMANN-KOCH REACTION

The system is cooled, and the vacuum is lowered to 35 mm. The next fraction consists of 11 g. of benzaldehyde (b.p. 83–88°/35 mm.) contaminated with a small amount of isopropylbenzene. On further distillation at this pressure, 126 g. of p-isopropylbenzaldehyde (b.p. 131–133°/35 mm.) is obtained, a yield of 60% based on the aluminum chloride and the unrecovered isopropylbenzene. The yield of 2,4-diisopropylbenzaldehyde (b.p. 151–152°/35 mm.) obtained on further distillation is 25 g. A residue of about 25 g. remains.

Generation of Carbon Monoxide and Hydrogen Chloride from Formic Acid and Chlorosulfonic Acid. An Erlenmeyer flask of suitable capacity is fitted with a two-holed rubber stopper. In one opening is placed a tube to lead off the generated gases; in the other is inserted a dropping funnel whose tip has been drawn to a capillary and whose over-all length permits the tip to be near the bottom of the flask. The dry generator is charged with the desired amount of technical 96–98% formic acid. Chlorosulfonic acid is placed in the dry dropping funnel and allowed to fill the capillary. The flow of chlorosulfonic acid into the formic acid is regulated by the rate of escape of the resulting gases. The rate of evolution of the gases can be increased or decreased by raising or lowering the temperature of the generating flask. The gases produced are anhydrous, and, therefore, no drying towers are needed.

When commercial 85% formic acid is used, the above apparatus is changed by the addition of a pressure equalizer between the top of the dropping funnel and the outlet tube, as shown for the hydrogen chloride generator of Fieser.[31] The 85% formic acid is placed in the dropping funnel and added through the capillary to a mixture of equal volumes of 100% sulfuric acid and chlorosulfonic acid. No drying towers are necessary.

In Table II are listed all the examples of the Gattermann-Koch reaction that have been found in the literature through 1946.

[31] Fieser, *Experiments in Organic Chemistry*, p. 394, D. C. Heath and Co., New York, 1941.

TABLE II

Compounds Prepared by the Gattermann-Koch Reaction

Starting Material	Product	Yield %	Pressure High	Pressure Atmospheric	Reference
Benzene	Benzaldehyde	65	+		21
	Benzaldehyde	85	+		6
	Benzaldehyde	90 *		+	4
	Benzaldehyde	—	+		22, 24, 35
	Benzaldehyde	—		+	20
	Benzaldehyde	25 †		+	17
Toluene	p-Tolualdehyde	85	+		6
	p-Tolualdehyde	85 *		+	4
	p-Tolualdehyde	—		+	1, 32
	p-Tolualdehyde	55		+	2
	p-Tolualdehyde	16 †		+	17
	p-Tolualdehyde	46		+	28
	p-Tolualdehyde	54 ‡		+	27
Ethylbenzene	p-Ethylbenzaldehyde	—		+	1
Chlorobenzene	p-Chlorobenzaldehyde	70 *		+	4
	p-Chlorobenzaldehyde	—	+		6, 13
tert-Butylbenzene	p-tert-Butylbenzaldehyde	—	+		5
Isopropylbenzene	p-Isopropylbenzaldehyde	60	+		9
	p-Isopropylbenzaldehyde	—		+	2
	p-Isopropylbenzaldehyde	—	+		33
	2,4-Diisopropylbenzaldehyde	—	+		9, 33
	2,4-Diisopropylbenzaldehyde	—		+	8
tert-Amylbenzene	p-tert-Amylbenzaldehyde	—	+		5
Cyclohexylbenzene	p-Cyclohexylbenzaldehyde	—	+		5
	p-Cyclohexylbenzaldehyde	14–16		+	7
(3-Methylcyclohexyl)-benzene	p-(3-Methylcyclohexyl)benzaldehyde	—	+		5
m-Xylene	2,4-Dimethylbenzaldehyde	46		+	2
	2,4-Dimethylbenzaldehyde	20 †		+	17
	2,4-Dimethylbenzaldehyde	—		+	1, 32
o-Xylene	3,4-Dimethylbenzaldehyde	—		+	1, 32
	3,4-Dimethylbenzaldehyde	58		+	2
p-Xylene	2,4-Dimethylbenzaldehyde	—		+	1
	2,4-Dimethylbenzaldehyde	45		+	2
Diisopropylbenzene	Diisopropylbenzaldehyde §	—		+	8
p-Cymene	Diisopropylmethylbenzaldehyde §	—	+		8
Diisopropyltoluene	Diisopropylmethylbenzaldehyde §	—	+		8
Diisopropyl-ar-tetrahydronaphthalene	Diisopropyl-ar-tetrahydronaphthaldehyde §	—	+		8
Diisopropylxylene	Diisopropyldimethylbenzaldehyde §	—	+		8
Pseudocumene	2,4,5-Trimethylbenzaldehyde	56		+	2
	2,4,5-Trimethylbenzaldehyde	—		+	34
Mesitylene	2,4,6-Trimethylbenzaldehyde	80		+	2
	2,4,6-Trimethylbenzaldehyde	—		+	1, 32
	2,4,6-Trimethylbenzaldehyde †	—		+	17
	2,4,6-Trimethylbenzaldehyde ‡	—		+	27
Biphenyl	p-Phenylbenzaldehyde	30		+	2
	p-Phenylbenzaldehyde	73		+	16
Hydrindene	5-Hydrindenaldehyde	25		+	2
Thiophene	2-Thiophenaldehyde	Negligible		+	18
Cyclohexane	1-Methyl-2-cyclohexanone	—	+		19
Dimethylaniline	Crystal violet leuco base	—	+		14
Triisopropylbenzene	Diisopropylbenzaldehyde §	—	+		8

* Nitrobenzene was used as solvent.
† Nickel carbonyl was used as the source of carbon monoxide.
‡ Nickelous chloride was used as catalyst.
§ Orientation unknown.

[32] Farbenfabriken vorm. Friedr. Bayer, Ger. pat. 98,706 [*Frdl.*, **5**, 97 (1897–1900)].

[33] Meuly, U. S. pats. 2,158,518–9 (*Chem. Zentr.*, **1938**, I, 3388).

[34] John, Gunther, and Rathmann, *Z. physiol. Chem.*, **268**, 104 (1941).

[35] Denman, Krebs, and Borchers, *Tech. Mitt. Krupp Tech.*, **6**, 59 (1938) [*C.A.*, **33**, 6257 (1939)].

CHAPTER 7

THE LEUCKART REACTION

MAURICE L. MOORE

Smith, Kline and French Laboratories

CONTENTS

INTRODUCTION

The Leuckart reaction is a process for the reductive alkylation of ammonia or primary or secondary amines by certain aldehydes and ketones. It is distinguished by the fact that the reduction is accomplished by formic acid or a derivative of formic acid and should be compared with the reductive alkylation using hydrogen discussed in Chapter 3 of Volume IV of *Organic Reactions*. The reaction is carried out by heating a mixture of the carbonyl compound and the formic acid salt or formyl derivative of ammonia or the amine. Primary and secondary amines produced in the reaction often are obtained as the formyl derivatives and must be recovered by hydrolysis; tertiary amines are obtained as the formates. The reaction may be illustrated by the following equations.

$$\begin{array}{c} R' \\ {\displaystyle >}CO + 2HCO_2NH_4 \\ R \end{array} \rightarrow \begin{array}{c} R' \\ {\displaystyle >}CHNHCHO + 2H_2O + NH_3 + CO_2 \\ R \end{array}$$

$$\begin{array}{c} R' \\ {\displaystyle >}CHNHCHO + H_2O \\ R \end{array} \rightarrow \begin{array}{c} R' \\ {\displaystyle >}CHNH_2 + HCO_2H \\ R \end{array}$$

Leuckart [1] discovered the reaction in an attempt to prepare benzylidenediformamide, $C_6H_5CH(NHCHO)_2$, by heating benzaldehyde with formamide in an experiment patterned after the preparation by Roth [2] of the corresponding acetamide derivative. The reaction with formamide was found to take a different course, leading to benzylamine and its formyl derivative, dibenzylamine and its formyl derivative, and tribenzylamine. Ammonium formate was found to react in the same

---

[1] Leuckart and co-workers, *Ber.*, **18**, 2341 (1885); **19**, 2128 (1886); **20**, 104 (1887); **22**, 1409, 1851 (1889).

[2] Roth, *Ann. Chem. Pharm.*, **154**, 72 (1870).

way as the amide, and benzophenone could be converted to benzohydrylamine by the use of conditions somewhat more drastic than those required with benzaldehyde. Leuckart's experiments with aliphatic aldehydes and ketones were not extensive,[3] but Wallach [4] and Kijner [5] applied the reaction to many such compounds. The method received little attention from other investigators until Ingersoll and his associates [6] reviewed the subject and applied the reaction to the synthesis of a series of substituted α-phenethylamines; since the appearance of this work the method has been employed extensively. Among the better-known modifications of the process are the preparation of trimethylamine [7] from ammonia, formaldehyde, and formic acid and the Eschweiler-Clarke [8,9] procedure for the methylation of primary and secondary amines by the aid of formaldehyde and formic acid.

MECHANISM OF THE REACTION

A single mechanism capable of accounting for all the variations of the Leuckart process can be postulated on the basis of the decomposition of the ammonium salt or of the amide, by thermal or hydrolytic means, respectively, to formic acid and ammonia or an amine. The base so formed may then react with the carbonyl compound to give an addition

product $\left(\begin{array}{c} \diagup \\ \diagup C \diagdown \end{array}\begin{array}{c} OH \\ N \diagdown \end{array}\right)$ which is reduced by formic acid to an amine

$\left(\diagup CH - N \diagdown\right)$; reaction of this amine with more formic acid leads to the salt or the amide. These transformations appear to be the only ones concerned in the formation of a tertiary amine from a carbonyl compound and the formate or formyl derivative of a secondary amine, but there are numerous other possible intermediates in the synthesis of primary and secondary amines. For example, the addition product from a carbonyl compound and ammonia or a primary amine may undergo

[3] Leuckart, J. prakt. Chem., [2] 41, 330 (1890).

[4] Wallach and co-workers, (a) Ber., 24, 3992 (1891); (b) Ann., 269, 347 (1892); (c) 272, 100 (1893); (d) 276, 296 (1893); (e) 289, 338 (1896); (f) 300, 283 (1898); (g) 343, 54 (1905).

[5] Kijner, J. Russ. Phys. Chem. Soc., 31, 877, 1033 (1899); 32, 381 (1900) [J. Chem. Soc. (Abs.), 78 (i), 277, 333, 629 (1900)].

[6] Ingersoll, Brown, Kim, Beauchamp, and Jennings, J. Am. Chem. Soc., 58, 1808 (1936).

[7] Sommelet and Ferrand, Bull. soc. chim. France, [4] 35, 446 (1924).

[8] Eschweiler, Ber., 38, 880 (1905).

[9] Clarke, Gillespie, and Weisshaus, J. Am. Chem. Soc., 55, 4571 (1933).

loss of water, and the imine so formed may be the intermediate which is
reduced to the amine (equation 1). Furthermore, when formamide is

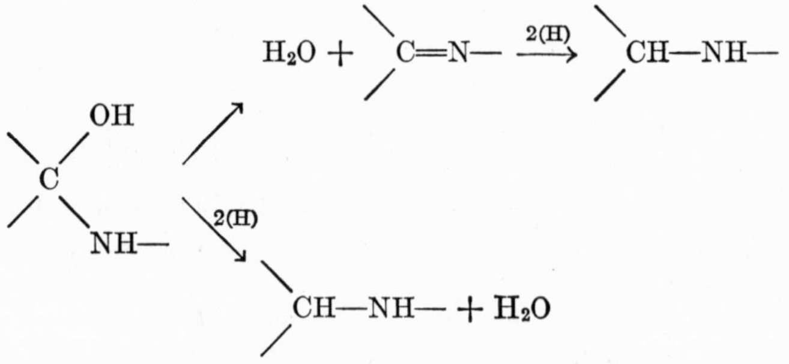

$$H_2O + \quad \overset{\diagdown}{\underset{\diagup}{C}}=N- \quad \overset{2(H)}{\longrightarrow} \quad \overset{\diagdown}{\underset{\diagup}{C}}H-NH-$$

$$\overset{\diagdown}{\underset{\diagup}{C}}\overset{OH}{\underset{NH-}{\diagup}} \qquad \overset{2(H)}{\searrow}$$

$$\overset{\diagdown}{\underset{\diagup}{C}}H-NH-\ +\ H_2O$$

(1)

present in the reaction mixture (either added as such or produced by
dehydration of ammonium formate) it may give rise to an addition
product capable of reduction directly to the formyl derivative of the
primary amine or of dehydration and reduction to the same substance.

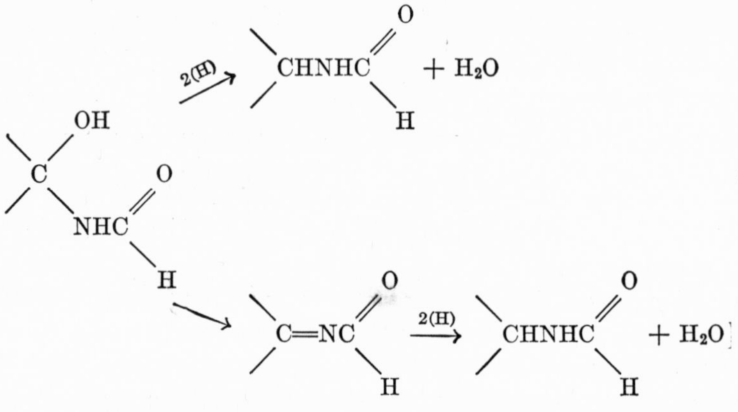

$$\overset{2(H)}{\longrightarrow} \quad \overset{\diagdown}{\underset{\diagup}{C}}HNHC\overset{O}{\underset{H}{\diagup\!\!/}} \ +\ H_2O$$

$$\overset{\diagdown}{\underset{\diagup}{C}}\overset{OH}{\underset{NHC}{\diagup}}\overset{O}{\underset{H}{\diagup\!\!/}}$$

(2)

$$\overset{\diagdown}{\underset{\diagup}{C}}=NC\overset{O}{\underset{H}{\diagup\!\!/}} \quad \overset{2(H)}{\longrightarrow} \quad \overset{\diagdown}{\underset{\diagup}{C}}HNHC\overset{O}{\underset{H}{\diagup\!\!/}}\ +\ H_2O$$

If the reacting amide is derived from a primary amine the addition
product cannot undergo dehydration but must be reduced directly if it
participates in the reaction. The formyl derivative of a secondary

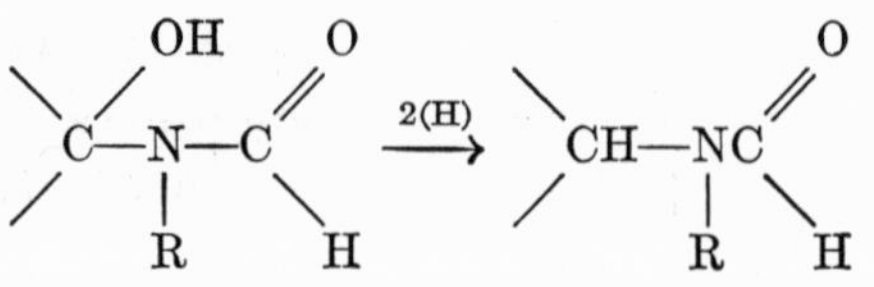

$$\overset{\diagdown}{\underset{\diagup}{C}}\overset{OH}{-}N\underset{R}{-}C\overset{O}{\underset{H}{\diagup\!\!/}} \quad \overset{2(H)}{\longrightarrow} \quad \overset{\diagdown}{\underset{\diagup}{C}}H\underset{R}{-}NC\overset{O}{\underset{H}{\diagup\!\!/}}$$

(3)

amine (HCONR$_2$) cannot give an addition product; evidently the first
step in its reaction must be hydrolysis.

Imines, $\diagup\!\!\mathrm{C}\!\!=\!\!\mathrm{N}\!\!-\!$, and addition products from carbonyl compounds

and ammonia or amines, $\diagup\!\!\mathrm{C}\!\!-\!\!\mathrm{N}\!\!\diagdown$ with OH group, were suggested in the preceding paragraphs as intermediates in the Leuckart reaction, intermediates which are reduced by formic acid. Benzalaniline, a representative imine, is reduced almost quantitatively to benzylaniline by heating at 140–160° with triethylammonium formate.[9a] No examples are available of the action of formic acid on the addition product of a carbonyl compound and ammonia or an amine; but p-dimethylaminophenylmethylcarbinol, a vinylog of the addition product from acetophenone and dimethylamine, is reduced to p-dimethylaminoethylbenzene in poor yield by heating at 130–135° with triethylammonium formate.[9a] Formic acid could not be used in these reductions since it led to the formation of resinous materials.

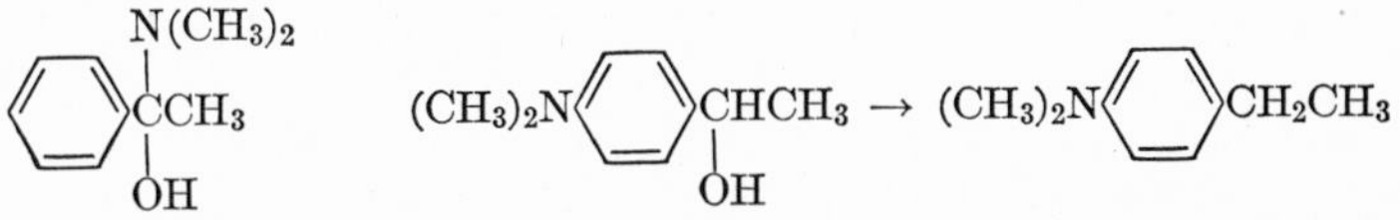

Much of the study [6,10,11,12] of the mechanism of the Leuckart process has been concerned with the reactions involved in the formation of primary amines. Inasmuch as the experimental temperature (150° or higher) usually employed is above that at which ammonium formate rapidly generates formamide and water it has been considered that formamide may be the true reagent even in preparations in which ammonium formate is employed. However, acetophenone in diethylene glycol at 120–130° does not react with formamide over a period of fifteen hours, whereas with ammonium formate under the same conditions a 10% yield of α-phenethylamine is obtained in four hours.[9a] At the higher temperatures ordinarily used, formamide could furnish ammonium formate in the following way.

$$\mathrm{\diagup\!\!C\!\!=\!\!O + HCONH_2 \rightleftarrows \diagup\!\!C\!\!=\!\!NCHO + H_2O}$$

$$\mathrm{HCONH_2 + H_2O \rightleftarrows HCO_2NH_4}$$

In experiments with acetophenone and formamide at 165–173°, the addition of anhydrous calcium sulfate brought down the yield of α-

[9a] Alexander and Wildman, *J. Am. Chem. Soc.*, **70**, 1187 (1948).
[10] Ingersoll, Brown, Levy, and Haynes, personal communication.
[11] Davies and Rogers, *J. Chem. Soc.*, **1944**, 126.
[12] Crossley and Moore, *J. Org. Chem.*, **9**, 529 (1944).

phenethylamine from 30% to 17%.[9a] The available evidence does not permit one to exclude either of the mechanisms shown in equations 1 and 2 on p. 304; both mechanisms may be operative under appropriate experimental conditions.

The reaction between benzophenone and formamide is catalyzed by ammonium formate, magnesium chloride, or ammonium sulfate, and it has been suggested that the catalyst polarizes the carbonyl group and thus facilitates the addition of formamide or ammonia.[12a]

Formyl derivatives of primary amines are stable substances, and many of them can be heated to 200° without undergoing any change. When they are heated to this temperature in the presence of Raney nickel, however, they furnish ketones.[12b] Formyl derivatives of second-

$$C_6H_5CHCH_3 \xrightarrow[200°]{\text{Raney nickel}} C_6H_5COCH_3$$
$$|$$
$$NHCHO$$

ary amines undergo the same reaction, but the yields of carbonyl compounds are poor.[12a]

$$C_6H_5CHCH_3 \xrightarrow[200°]{\text{Raney nickel}} C_6H_5COCH_3$$
$$|$$
$$CH_3NCHO$$

SCOPE OF THE REACTION

The method appears best adapted to aromatic aldehydes and water-insoluble ketones boiling at about 100° or higher. Higher aliphatic ketones, aromatic aldehydes and ketones, and certain terpenoid ketones have been used successfully, with yields of 40–90%. The application of the reaction to aliphatic aldehydes and ketones of lower molecular weight has been very limited. The method is definitely superior to that involving the formation and reduction of aldoximes and ketoximes and has succeeded where the reduction of oximes is unsatisfactory, particularly with compounds in which functional groups are present that are readily attacked by many reducing agents. Thus, the Leuckart method gives an 82% yield of pure α-p-chlorophenethylamine from p-chloroacetophenone, whereas the reduction of p-chloroacetophenone oxime with sodium and ethanol, sodium amalgam and acetic acid, or by catalytic means, proceeds in all instances with extensive removal of the nuclear halogen. p-Bromoacetophenone and m-nitroacetophenone are readily

[12a] Webers and Bruce, *J. Am. Chem. Soc.*, **70**, 1422 (1948).
[12b] Métayer and Mastagli, *Compt. rend.*, **225**, 457 (1947).

converted to the corresponding amines without disturbance of the halogen or nitro group.

The reaction is not limited to ammonium formate or formamide. Methyl formate has been used with a few primary amines. Substituted ammonium formates, such as monomethyl- or dimethyl-ammonium formate, react satisfactorily and lead to the formation of secondary and tertiary amines of mixed type that cannot be obtained easily by other methods. Thus, the N-methyl, N-ethyl, and N-butyl derivatives of α-phenethylamine are prepared in yields of 60–70% by the action of methyl-, ethyl-, and butyl-ammonium formates on acetophenone.[13, 14]

Methylation of Amines with Formaldehyde

The simplest aldehyde, formaldehyde, reacts very readily, and it is difficult to prevent the formation of tertiary amines. Formaldehyde reacts with ammonium formate and formic acid, but trimethylamine is the product isolated in highest yield.[7] Formaldehyde was first used alone [8] for the methylation reaction, but Clarke [9] obtained better yields (80%) by using an excess of formic acid with the formaldehyde. One molecular proportion (or a slight excess) of formaldehyde and two to four molecular proportions of formic acid are used for each methyl group introduced, indicating that it is mainly the formic acid that supplies the hydrogen involved in the reduction. The reaction is carried out on the steam bath. This variant of the Leuckart reaction, as mentioned earlier, is commonly known as the Eschweiler-Clarke procedure.

Ethylamine,[8] piperazine,[8] anabasine,[15] the benzylamines,[8,16,17] phenethylamines,[16] and methoxyphenethylamines [17] react to give almost theoretical yields of the corresponding tertiary amines. Secondary amines react as readily as primary amines to give the corresponding methyl derivatives although N-benzyl-3,4-dimethoxyphenethylamine [17] gives unsatisfactory results, probably owing to partial cyclization.[18] Dibenzylamine gives a 75% yield of the anticipated methyldibenzylamine, 6–12% of a more volatile base, probably dimethylbenzylamine, and a similar amount of benzaldehyde.[9] Further application of the process is illustrated by the complete methylation of ethylenediamine and tetramethylenediamine in yields of 92%.

[13] Novelli, *J. Am. Chem. Soc.*, **61**, 520 (1939).
[14] Busch and Lefhelm, *J. prakt. Chem.*, [2] **77**, 21, 23 (1908).
[15] Orechoff and Norkina, *Ber.*, **65**, 724 (1932).
[16] Decker and Becker, *Ber.*, **45**, 2404 (1912).
[17] Buck and Baltzly, *J. Am. Chem. Soc.*, **62**, 161 (1940); **63**, 1964 (1941); **64**, 2263 (1942).
[18] Buck, *J. Am. Chem. Soc.*, **56**, 1769 (1934).

The reaction fails with compounds in which strongly polar groups are attached to the nitrogen, such as amides, urea, guanidine, and hydroxylamine, as these appear to yield hydroxymethyl derivatives only. Moreover, the reaction cannot be applied successfully to the methylation of aniline, which on warming with formaldehyde and formic acid is converted into condensation products of high molecular weight.[19] On the other hand, it is reported that formaldehyde reacts with p-toluidine in an excess of 90% formic acid to give dimethyl-p-toluidine,[20] and with 2,4,6-tribromoaniline[9] and mesidine,[21] in which the active positions in the benzene nucleus are occupied, to form the dimethyl derivatives in 73–77% yields.

Some of the amino acids can be methylated by treatment with formaldehyde and formic acid.[9] For example, glycine yields 60–70% of dimethylglycine; complex, non-crystalline products as well as volatile bases, mainly trimethylamine, are formed also. α-Aminoisobutyric acid and α-phenyl-α-aminobutyric acid give 70–80% yields of the dimethyl derivatives, but the yield from β-aminopropionic acid is only 38%. However, with alanine none of the dimethyl derivative is isolated and 36% of the nitrogen is converted into methylamines. Similar results are obtained with leucine, glutamic acid, etc., in all of which an even greater proportion of the nitrogen is cleaved from the molecule.

Reactions of Higher Aliphatic Aldehydes

The Eschweiler-Clarke procedure is essentially specific for reactions with formaldehyde. Higher aldehydes usually fail to react or react in different ways at steam-bath temperatures. Thus, a mixture of acetaldehyde, ammonium formate, and formic acid yields no carbon dioxide on heating on the steam bath, and from the resulting bases only 2-methyl-5-ethylpyridine has been isolated.[9] Acetaldehyde and propionaldehyde give only tars when heated with mesidine or 2,4,6-tribromoaniline in formic acid.[21] However, a 63% yield of N,N'-dibutylpiperazine is obtained[22] upon refluxing butyraldehyde with piperazine in formic acid for three hours.

In the Leuckart method, valeraldehyde reacts with ammonium formate to give triamylamine,[4g] with aniline and formic acid to give diamylaniline, and with methylaniline and formic acid to give methyl-amylaniline.

[19] Wagner, J. Am. Chem. Soc., 55, 724 (1933).
[20] Eisner and Wagner, J. Am. Chem. Soc., 56, 1938 (1934).
[21] Emerson, Neumann, and Moundres, J. Am. Chem. Soc., 63, 972 (1941).
[22] Forsee and Pollard, J. Am. Chem. Soc., 57, 1788 (1935).

Reactions of Aromatic and Heterocyclic Aldehydes

When benzaldehyde is heated with an excess of ammonium formate to a temperature of 180° for several hours, 35–40% of pure tribenzylamine is isolated, along with varying quantities of N,N-dibenzylformamide, dibenzylamine, N-benzylformamide, and benzylamine.[1] Dibenzylamine and its formyl derivative are obtained in 10–15% yields; only small amounts of the monobenzylamine and its formyl derivative are isolated. Although a portion of the benzaldehyde remains unchanged, as much as 20% is converted into polymerized products. When refluxed for five days with piperazine in formic acid, benzaldehyde gives an 84% yield of N,N'-dibenzylpiperazine.[22]

Substitution in the ring of the aromatic aldehyde tends to reduce the reactivity toward the Leuckart reagents. Although the methoxybenzaldehydes give satisfactory yields of the formyl derivatives of the amines when treated with substituted ammonium formates,[23] it has been reported that some substituted benzaldehydes, such as piperonal, 6-nitropiperonal, and the hydroxy, nitro, and alkyl substituted benzaldehydes, are recovered unchanged from the reaction with formamide at 130–140°; in the presence of a trace of pyridine, the nitro and alkyl substituted benzaldehydes condense to give 40–60% of the bisamides, and the hydroxybenzaldehydes give about 65% of the benzalamides.[24]

$$O_2N\text{—}C_6H_4\text{—}CHO + 2HCONH_2 \xrightarrow[\text{5-8 hr.}]{140\text{–}180°} O_2N\text{—}C_6H_4\text{—}CH(NHCHO)_2 + H_2O$$

$$HO\text{—}C_6H_4\text{—}CHO + HCONH_2 \xrightarrow[\text{4 hr.}]{130\text{–}140°} HO\text{—}C_6H_4\text{—}CH\text{=}NCHO + H_2O$$

A 65% yield of the bisamide [25] is obtained by bubbling dry hydrogen chloride through a suspension of 6-nitroveratraldehyde in formamide for one hour at 45–50°.

Furfural is reported to be converted to furfurylamine by reaction with formamide,[26] although the yield is not indicated and no mention is

[23] Wojahn and Erdelmeier, *Arch. Pharm.*, **280**, 215 (1942).

[24] Pandya and coworkers, *Proc. Indian Acad. Sci.*, **15A**, 6 (1942) [*C.A.*, **36**, 6144 (1942)]; references to earlier papers on this work are given.

[25] Fetscher and Bogert, *J. Org. Chem.*, **4**, 71 (1939).

[26] Nabenhauer, Abstract of a paper presented at the 93rd meeting of the American Chemical Society, Chapel Hill, North Carolina, April, 1937.

made of the presence of any of the corresponding secondary or tertiary amines. N-Methylfurfurylamine,[26] N,N-dimethyl-, and N,N-diethylfurfurylamine [26,27] are prepared from N-methyl-, N,N-dimethyl-, and N,N-diethyl-formamide.

Reactions of Aliphatic Ketones

Acetone reacts with α-naphthylamine and methyl formate in an autoclave to produce isopropyl-α-naphthylamine.[28] Diethyl ketone [4g] is reported to yield 3-aminopentane acetate by reaction with ammonium formate in the presence of acetic acid, and pinacolone reacts with excess formamide to produce the formyl derivative of methyl-*tert*-butylcarbinamine in a yield of 52%.[6] The reaction has also been applied to a variety of methyl alkyl ketones (methyl propyl ketone,[10] methyl butyl ketone,[29] methyl amyl ketone,[10,29] methyl hexyl ketone,[5,10,29] and methyl cyclohexyl ketone [30]) to give the corresponding primary 2-aminoalkanes in yields of 30–60%. Dipropyl, dibutyl, and diheptyl ketones give yields of 40–80% of the primary amines.

Aliphatic ketones of certain types have been shown to be unsuitable for the reaction because of the formation of resinous by-products. Thus, minimum yields of primary amines are obtained from benzalacetone [6] or acetonylacetone.[10] It appears that the method is unsuitable for application to α,β-unsaturated ketones.

Phenylacetone, substituted phenylacetones,[31-38] and diphenylacetone [39] react to give primary amines in yields ranging from 20% to 70%. Secondary and tertiary amines are prepared in lower yields from these ketones in reactions with mono- or di-substituted amines and formic acid; the time necessary to complete such a reaction is longer.

[27] Weilmuenster and Jordon, *J. Am. Chem. Soc.*, **67**, 415 (1945).
[28] Speer, U. S. pat. 2,108,147 [*C.A.*, **32**, 2542 (1938)].
[29] Rohrmann and Shonle, *J. Am. Chem. Soc.*, **66**, 1516 (1944).
[30] Blicke and Zienty, *J. Am. Chem. Soc.*, **61**, 93 (1939).
[31] Johns and Burch, *J. Am. Chem. Soc.*, **60**, 919 (1938).
[32] Novelli, *Anales asoc. quím. argentina*, **27**, 169 (1939) [*C.A.*, **34**, 1627 (1940)].
[33] Bobranskii and Drabik, *J. Applied Chem. U.S.S.R.*, **14**, 410 (1941) [*C.A.*, **36**, 2531 (1942)].
[34] Elks and Hey, *J. Chem. Soc.*, **1943**, 15.
[35] Suter and Weston, *J. Am. Chem. Soc.*, **63**, 602 (1941); **64**, 533 (1942).
[36] Sugasawa, Kakemi, and Kazumi, *Ber.*, **73**, 782 (1940).
[37] Kakemi, *J. Pharm. Soc. Japan*, **60**, 11 (1940) [*C.A.*, **34**, 3748 (1940)].
[38] Nabenhauer, U. S. pat. 2,246,529 [*C.A.*, **35**, 6066 (1941)].
[39] Rajagopalan, *Proc. Indian Acad. Sci.*, **14A**, 126 (1941) [*C.A.*, **36**, 1603 (1942)].

Reactions of Aliphatic-Aromatic and Aliphatic-Heterocyclic Ketones

The Leuckart reaction has been applied successfully to many ali-phatic-aromatic ketones, such as acetophenone,[4g, 6, 10, 13, 31, 40, 41] propio-phenone,[10, 12] isobutyrophenone,[10] caprophenone,[12] and laurophenone,[12] with yields ranging from 50% to 85%. Acetophenones with a methyl group or halogen in the ring react as readily as the unsubstituted com-pound; the higher alkyl substituted and nitro derivatives appear to be less reactive, giving yields of 15–25% less even though the condensation time is longer.[6, 12, 13, 31, 42] Hydroxyl substituted aryl derivatives polymer-ize so readily in formic acid that the results are unsatisfactory.

α-Acetothienone,[43] α-propiothienone,[43] β-acetonaphthone,[6] p-phenyl-acetophenone,[6] and p-phenoxyacetophenone [6] readily undergo the reac-tion in 40–85% yields.

Secondary and tertiary amines can be readily prepared from the above aliphatic-aromatic ketones by the use of methyl-, ethyl-, butyl-, di-methyl-, or diethyl-amine, aniline, or naphthylamine in place of ammonia with the formic acid. Yields for the compounds of lower molecular weight are almost as good as with the primary amine, while compounds of higher molecular weight give slightly lower yields, and laurophenone gives no product when heated with dimethylamine and formic acid at 160–180° for twenty-eight hours.[12]

β-Benzoylpropionic acid is reported not to give the corresponding amine.[10]

γ-Nitro-β-phenylbutyrophenone is converted to 2,2′,4,4′-tetraphenyl-azadipyrromethine (I) in yields up to 33% by reaction with either ammonium formate or formamide.[11, 44] The corresponding substituted azamethines can be prepared in comparable yields from γ-nitro-β-(dimethylamino-, hydroxy-, methylenedioxy-, methoxy-, and nitro-phenyl)butyrophenones, γ-nitro-β-phenyl-p-methoxybutyrophenone, and γ-nitro-β-anisyl-p-methoxybutyrophenone. β-Benzoyl-α-phenyl-propionitrile also reacts with ammonium formate to give 2,2′,4,4′-tetra-phenylazadipyrromethine along with a small amount of the formyl derivative of 5-amino-2,4-diphenylpyrrole; if formamide is used instead of ammonium formate the substituted pyrrole becomes the major prod-uct (59%), unless the reaction is run for a very long time (seventeen hours), in which event the azamethine again predominates. As might

[40] Ingersoll, *Org. Syntheses, Coll. Vol.* **2**, 503 (1943).
[41] Ott, *Ann.*, **488**, 193 (1931).
[42] Geigy A.-G., Swiss pat. 211,783 [*C.A.*, **36**, 4634 (1942)].
[43] Blicke and Burckhalter, *J. Am. Chem. Soc.*, **64**, 477 (1942).
[44] Rogers, *J. Chem. Soc.*, **1943**, 590.

be expected from this observation, treatment of the isolated pyrrole with ammonium formate leads to the formation of the azamethine. A precursor of the pyrrole has been isolated, but, because of the ease with which it is converted into the pyrrole, it has not been identified with certainty. The mechanism of these remarkable reactions has not been elucidated, but the following equations have been suggested to account for the products obtained.

2,2',4,4'-Tetraphenylazadipyrromethine

Benzoins behave abnormally with the Leuckart reagent, giving chiefly glyoxalines along with lesser amounts of diazines. Benzoin reacts with ammonium formate [3] at 230° to give tetraphenylpyrazine (amarone) almost quantitatively along with a small amount of 2,4,5-triphenylglyoxaline (lophine). However, a 75% yield of 4,5-diphenylglyoxaline and a 10% yield of tetraphenylpyrazine result from heating the benzoin with formamide at 185–230°.[45] Similar products are obtained from anisoin, benzanisoin, and p-toluoin. The mechanism shown on p. 313 has been suggested to account for these products. The addition of acetic anhydride to a reaction mixture of benzoin and formamide leads to the formation of some N-desylformamide along with a 36% yield of 4,5-diphenylglyoxaline.[46] N-Desylaniline reacts with ammonium formate

[45] Novelli, *Anales asoc. quím. argentina*, **27**, 161 (1939) [*C.A.*, **34**, 1659 (1940)].
[46] Davidson, Weiss, and Jelling, *J. Org. Chem.*, **2**, 328 (1937).

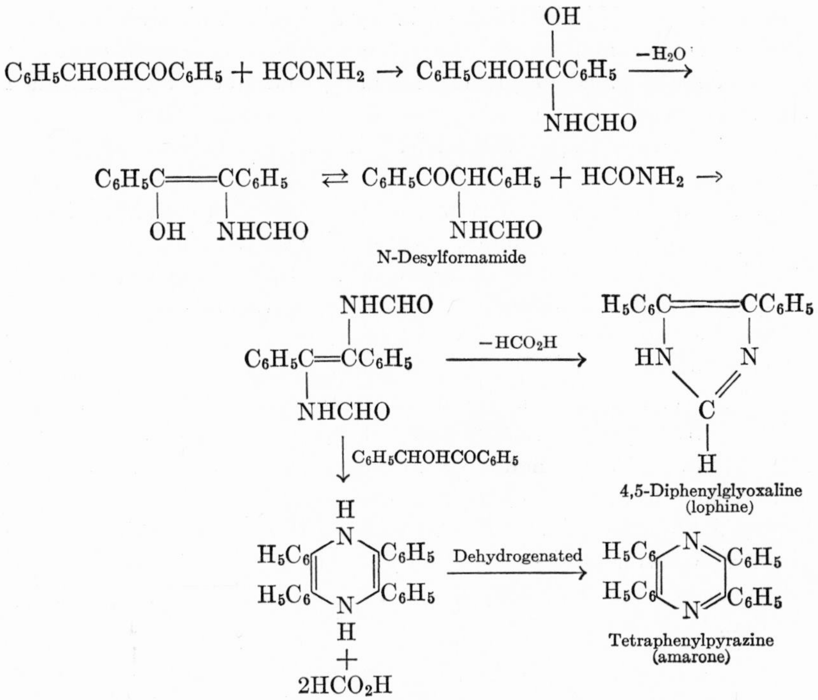

$$\text{C}_6\text{H}_5\text{CHOHCOC}_6\text{H}_5 + \text{HCONH}_2 \rightarrow \underset{\underset{\text{NHCHO}}{|}}{\overset{\overset{\text{OH}}{|}}{\text{C}_6\text{H}_5\text{CHOHCC}_6\text{H}_5}} \xrightarrow{-\text{H}_2\text{O}}$$

$$\underset{\underset{\text{OH}\quad\text{NHCHO}}{|\qquad|}}{\text{C}_6\text{H}_5\text{C}\!=\!\text{CC}_6\text{H}_5} \rightleftarrows \underset{\underset{\text{NHCHO}}{|}}{\text{C}_6\text{H}_5\text{COCHC}_6\text{H}_5} + \text{HCONH}_2 \rightarrow$$

N-Desylformamide

$$\underset{\underset{\text{NHCHO}}{|}}{\overset{\overset{\text{NHCHO}}{|}}{\text{C}_6\text{H}_5\text{C}\!=\!\text{CC}_6\text{H}_5}} \xrightarrow{-\text{HCO}_2\text{H}}$$

4,5-Diphenylglyoxaline
(lophine)

↓ C₆H₅CHOHCOC₆H₅

H
+
2HCO₂H

Dehydrogenated →

Tetraphenylpyrazine
(amarone)

to give a 40% yield of 4,5-diphenylglyoxaline instead of the expected 3,4,5-triphenylglyoxaline. N-Desyl-*p*-toluidine and N-(*p,p'*-dimethoxy-desyl)aniline undergo similar reactions with formamide.[47]

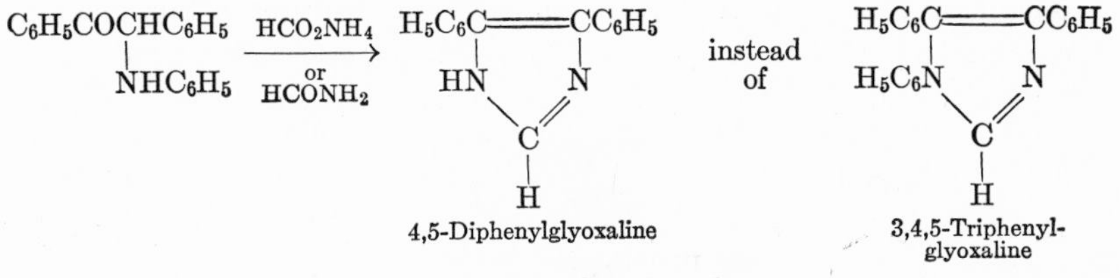

$$\underset{\underset{\text{NHC}_6\text{H}_5}{|}}{\text{C}_6\text{H}_5\text{COCHC}_6\text{H}_5}\ \overset{\text{HCO}_2\text{NH}_4}{\underset{\text{HCONH}_2}{\xrightarrow{\text{or}}}}$$

instead
of

4,5-Diphenylglyoxaline

3,4,5-Triphenyl-
glyoxaline

Reactions of Aromatic Ketones

Benzophenone reacts with 1.5 parts of solid ammonium formate, in a closed tube at 200–220° for four to five hours, to give an excellent yield of formylbenzohydrylamine, which may be hydrolyzed with ethanolic hydrochloric acid.[1] The reaction product is contaminated with some of the secondary amine, dibenzohydrylamine. With ammonia and

[47] Novelli and Somaglino, *Anales asoc. quím. argentina*, **31**, 147 (1943) [*C.A.*, **38**, 2957 (1944)].

formic acid, an 80% yield of the primary amine is obtained.[12, 48] Fluorenone and benzofluorenone [49] give the expected 9-aminofluorenes in yields of 65–75%. Benzoylbenzoic acid [10] yields chiefly an unidentified solid.

Reactions of Alicyclic Ketones

Cyclohexanone and its derivatives [4, 10, 50] have been converted to the corresponding primary amines, accompanied by varying quantities of the secondary amines. With more complicated cyclic ketones, such as camphor,[4, 6, 51, 52] fenchone,[4, 6] menthones,[4, 10, 53] carvomenthones,[53] and thujone,[54, 55] the reaction takes place less readily and requires a higher temperature or a longer time. No reaction occurs with menthone at 130° for three to four hours,[4] whereas an 80% yield of menthylamines is obtained from the reaction at 180–190° for twenty-five hours [10] or at 220–230° for five to six hours. A 20–35% conversion of carvomenthone to carvomenthylamines is obtained after forty-eight hours of refluxing at 130°.[53] Bornylamine is obtained in a yield of 55–65% from camphor.[4, 10] Carvone and α-bromocamphor are reported to be converted into neutral resins with only about 10% of the desired amines being isolated.[10]

Reactions of Quinones

p-Quinones also undergo the Leuckart reaction; [49] for example, the diformyl derivative of 9,10-diamino-9,10-dihydroanthracene is produced in the reaction of formamide with 9,10-anthraquinone. The free diamine can be obtained by hydrolysis with alcoholic potassium hydroxide.

o-Quinones, on the other hand, do not react normally but give the corresponding pyrazines. Thus, 1,2-anthraquinone is converted to bis-ang-dianthracenopyrazine (anthrazine). Acenaphthoquinone, substi-

$$\xrightarrow{\text{HCONH}_2}$$

[48] Mettler, Martin, Neracher, and Staub, U. S. pat. 2,276,587 [C.A., 36, 4633 (1942)].
[49] Schiedt, J. prakt. Chem., [2] 157, 203 (1941).
[50] Wegler and Frank, Ber., 70, 1279 (1937).
[51] Wegler and Ruber, Ber., 68, 1055 (1935).
[52] Tarbell and Paulson, J. Am. Chem. Soc., 64, 2842 (1942).
[53] Read et al., J. Chem. Soc., 1926, 2217; 1934, 231.
[54] Short and Read, J. Chem. Soc., 1938, 2016.
[55] Dickison and Ingersoll, J. Am. Chem. Soc., 61, 2477 (1939).

tuted acenaphthoquinones, phenanthraquinone, chrysenequinone, etc., undergo similar reactions with formamide. The addition of an aromatic aldehyde to a mixture of formamide with an *o*-quinone leads to the formation of an oxazole; for example, when chrysenequinone is treated with formamide in the presence of benzaldehyde, 2-phenylchryseneoxazole is isolated.

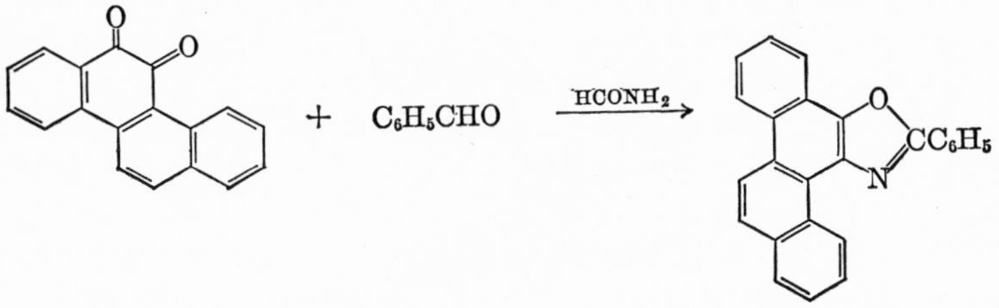

Reactions of a Pyrazolone and an Oxindole

4,4'-Methylidyne-*bis*(1-phenyl-3-methyl-5-pyrazolone) results from the reaction of formamide with 1-phenyl-3-methyl-5-pyrazolone, while methylidyne-*bis*(N-phenyloxindole) is the product from N-phenyloxindole.[49]

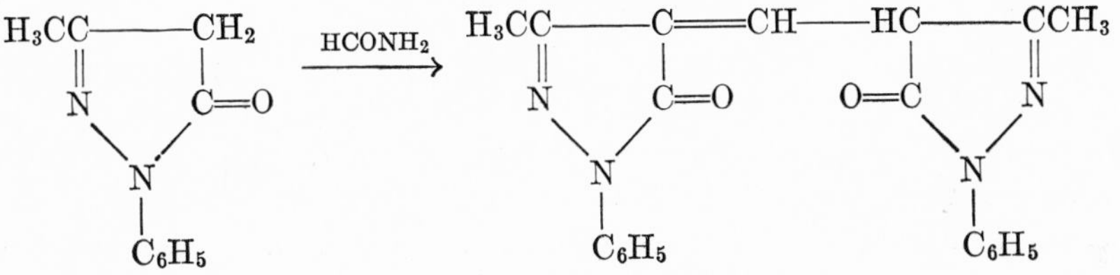

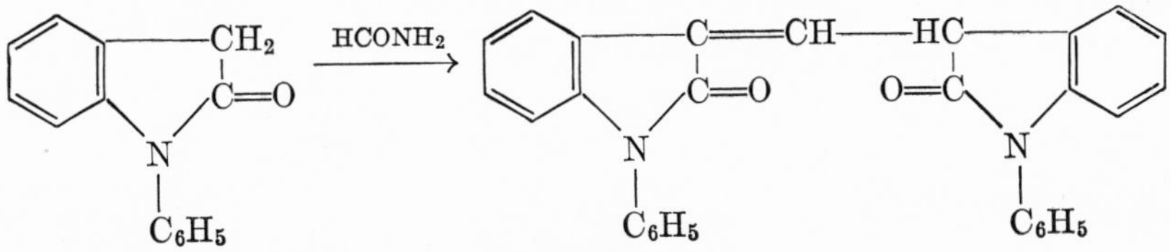

SIDE REACTIONS

The normal successive Leuckart reaction or reactions resulting in the formation of the secondary or the tertiary amine have been mentioned above as responsible for by-products in the preparation of primary and secondary amines. Under the influence of the bases present the carbonyl component of the reaction mixture may undergo condensations of the aldol type, some of the products of which may contain carbonyl groups capable of undergoing the Leuckart reaction. Although such side reactions have not been extensively investigated it is likely that they are concerned in the formation of the resinous by-products sometimes obtained.

EXPERIMENTAL CONDITIONS

The Ammonium Formate or Formamide

Much has been written about the effective reagent in the Leuckart reaction, but no very specific conclusions can be reached. Dry solid ammonium formate was used by Leuckart,[1] and by Wallach in his first experiments,[4] and the reaction mixture was heated at a temperature of 180–230° in a sealed tube. Later, Wallach obtained better yields by using a mixture of ammonia or substituted amine with formic acid. Formamide was used by Ott [41] and Ingersoll [10] in the preparation of α-phenethylamine from acetophenone. Anhydrous formamide alone is not a satisfactory reagent; the temperature required for the reaction is much higher, the yields are greatly decreased, and the sublimation of ammonium carbonate becomes troublesome. An ammonium formate-formamide reagent prepared by Ingersoll [6] from commercial ammonium carbonate-carbamate and formic acid gave excellent results in his experiments.

In many instances,[10, 12] the most satisfactory reagent appears to be formamide or ammonium formate supplemented by the addition of sufficient 90% formic acid to maintain a slightly acidic medium and to serve as an active reducing agent. One to three equivalents of formic acid is generally required, and occasional distillation of accumulated water may be necessary to maintain a suitably high reaction temperature. The presence of formic acid appears to diminish the aldol-type side reactions and traps ammonia that otherwise would appear as such or as the carbonate.

Wallach [4] used free formic or acetic acid with the intention of suppressing the formation of secondary and tertiary amines. The use of acetic acid with ammonium formate at 155° is reported to result in the formation of the acetate salt of the primary amine rather than the formyl derivative; acetophenone and ammonium formate give α-formylaminoethylbenzene, while the addition of acetic acid is stated to lead to the formation of α-aminoethylbenzene acetate.[4g]

The ketone and ammonium formate or formamide are usually employed in a molecular ratio of 1:4 or 1:5. The excess of ammonium formate tends to diminish the formation of secondary or tertiary amines, but ratios higher than 1:4 or 1:5 appear to be of little advantage. In a

series of experiments with acetophenone the percentage yields of amine
were 53, 62, 72, and 73, respectively, when the molar ratios of reagent to
ketone were 1:3, 1:3.5, 1:4, and 1:5.[6] Benzophenone and formamide
in the ratio of 1:6 give 43% yields of N-benzohydrylformamide. Under
the same conditions benzophenone and ammonium formate gave a 92%
yield. The addition of ammonium formate or magnesium chloride to the
benzophenone-formamide reaction mixture increased the yield of N-
benzohydryl formamide to 95%; the addition of ammonium sulfate
was not so effective. With benzophenone and formamide in the absence
of a catalyst the ratio of 1:18 was necessary in order to obtain a yield of
87%.[12a]

Temperature

The Leuckart reaction should be carried out at the lowest temperature
that will produce the desired product. With dry ammonium formate,
it has been necessary to heat the reagents in a sealed tube at 210–240°
for several hours. However, the use of an excess of formic acid or a
mixed ammonium formate-formamide reagent has made it possible to
carry out the reaction at a much lower temperature.[6] With such a
reagent, the reaction can be accomplished by refluxing at atmospheric
pressure, usually at temperatures in the range 150–180°; however,
temperatures of 175–190° for several hours are required for the conversion of hindered ketones of the terpenoid series. Most reaction
periods have been in the range of six to twenty-five hours at 160–185°,
but a few reactions with formamide have been carried out by refluxing
the reagents for as long as thirty hours.[31] The heating may be interrupted and resumed as desired.

In a comparative study of the condensation of α-methylphenylacetone
with the reagent from ammonia and formic acid, the percentage yields
of α,β-dimethyl-β-phenethylamine were 23, 47, and 50, respectively,
when the reactions were run for fifteen hours at 190–200°, 170–180°, and
160–170°. Experiments in which the reaction mixture was heated for
six hours at 190–200° and seven hours at 160–170° gave yields of 50%.
With hindered ketones, such as menthone, camphor, and fenchone, it is
advisable to heat at temperatures of 180–230°[4] or at 175–190°[6] for a
period of twelve to twenty hours in order to obtain maximum yields.

Solvent

Most of the Leuckart reactions are carried out in the absence of any
solvent other than the reagents themselves. Mixtures containing a
considerable proportion of formamide usually dissolve the ketone or

aldehyde upon heating. However, nitrobenzene has been used as a solvent with a few ketones that were insoluble in the hot reaction mixture, and it has been used to increase the reflux temperature of reaction mixtures containing low-boiling ketones.[6, 10]

Hydrolysis

The formyl derivatives obtained as intermediates in the reaction may be hydrolyzed to the amines by refluxing with acid or alkali. The use of 100–200 ml. of concentrated or 1:1 hydrochloric acid for each mole of ketone appears to be generally satisfactory, and the reaction is usually complete in from thirty minutes to one and one-half hours.[6, 13] When the entire reaction mixture is subjected to hydrolysis it may sometimes be desirable to employ concentrated hydrochloric acid, whereas if the formyl derivative is isolated and purified a 10% solution of hydrochloric acid may give better results.[12] Hydrolysis with 30% aqueous sodium hydroxide usually requires from twelve to twenty hours of refluxing, and the yield of amine is not as good.[41] In the alkaline hydrolysis of the material obtained by interaction of formamide and methyl α-phenyl-n-butyl ketone the yield of amine is only 5.3%, but when acid hydrolysis is employed the yield of amine is 86% based on the formyl derivative.[35] However, in the production of certain amines, such as thujylamine, it is desirable to hydrolyze the formyl derivative with alkali, inasmuch as acid solutions cause decomposition of the product.[55]

Isolation

The method of isolation of the free amine directly or following the hydrolysis of the formyl derivative varies with the properties of the product and the procedure used in hydrolysis. After an alkaline hydrolysis, the reaction mixture is extracted with an inert solvent, such as ether or benzene, and the amine is isolated by distillation or by conversion to the hydrochloride. Following an acid hydrolysis, the reaction mixture is cooled and neutralized with alkali before extraction with the inert solvent. Amines of higher molecular weight sometimes separate as crystalline salts directly from the cooled acid hydrolysis mixture. When a salt of the amine, rather than the formyl derivative, is present in the reaction mixture it is only necessary to neutralize the cooled mixture with alkali before extraction with the inert solvent.

EXPERIMENTAL PROCEDURES

Tri-*n*-amylamine [4g]

(Use of Ammonium Formate and Formic Acid)

A mixture of 20 g. of valeraldehyde, 30 g. of ammonium formate, and 10 ml. of formic acid is heated in a round-bottomed flask, equipped with a reflux condenser and suspended in a paraffin bath. The reaction begins at 90°, but the temperature is raised slowly to 130° and maintained there for three hours. The cooled residue is extracted with ether to remove the small quantity of non-basic material, and the base is liberated from the formate salt in the aqueous solution by neutralization with alkali. The base is separated, dried over solid potassium hydroxide, and distilled over sodium in a stream of hydrogen; it boils at 265–270°.

N,N-Dimethylfurfurylamine [27, 56]

(Use of Dimethylformamide and Formic Acid)

A mixture of 173 g. (2.5 moles) of dimethylformamide (b.p. 145–160°) and 54 g. (1 mole) of 85% formic acid is poured into a 1-l. distilling flask connected to a condenser. A dropping funnel is fitted into the neck of the flask so that its stem extends below the surface of the liquid. The flask is placed in an oil bath, the temperature of which is raised to 150–155°. Over a period of four to five hours, a mixture of 96 g. (1 mole) of redistilled furfural and 163 g. (3 moles) of 85% formic acid is added from the dropping funnel. The water and formic acid which distil are discarded. When all the furfural solution has been added, the receiver is changed and the temperature of the bath is gradually raised as long as distillation occurs. The distillate is made strongly acidic with dilute sulfuric acid, and the furfural and furfuryl alcohol are removed by steam distillation. The acid mixture is then made strongly alkaline by the cautious addition of sodium hydroxide solution; large amounts of dimethylamine are evolved. The alkaline mixture is steam-distilled to remove the tertiary amine. The N,N-dimethylfurfurylamine, which separates from the distillate upon the addition of 40% sodium hydroxide solution, is removed and the aqueous layer extracted twice with benzene. The base and benzene extracts are combined and dried over solid potassium hydroxide for twelve hours. The solvent is removed, and the residue is fractionated; the N,N-dimethylfurfuryl-

[56] Nabenhauer, private communication,

amine boils at 139–145°. Redistillation of the lower-boiling fractions yields more of the product. The pure base is obtained upon redistillation; b.p. 145–146°; yield 75 g. (60%).

α-(β-Naphthyl)ethylamine [6,40]

(Preparation and Use of Formamide-Formic Acid Reagent from Ammonium Carbonate-Carbamate and Formic Acid)

A 1-l. flask, containing 215 g. (4 mole equivalents of ammonia) of commercial ammonium carbonate-carbamate, is fitted with a cork bearing a thermometer that extends nearly to the bottom of the flask, a small separatory funnel, and a wide, bent tube attached to a short, wide condenser set for distillation. There is then added cautiously 215–230 g. (4.1 moles) of commercial 85–90% formic acid. When the reaction moderates, the mixture is heated cautiously and then slowly distilled until the temperature is about 165°. (The same amount of reagent can be prepared by distillation of 250 g. of commercial solid ammonium formate.) To the hot mixture 173 g. (1 mole) of β-acetonaphthone is added, the bent tube is replaced by a 20- to 30-cm. distilling column, and the heating is continued with a small flame. Water, ammonia, carbon dioxide, and a small amount of ketone distil. Some of the solid ketone and ammonium carbonate collect in the upper part of the column. This material may be removed with the aid of a little concentrated formic acid and returned to the reaction mixture. The mixture gradually becomes homogeneous as the reaction proceeds.

The distillation of water practically ceases when the temperature reaches 175–185°; the temperature of the mixture is then maintained at 175–185° for three to five hours. Termination of the reaction is indicated when the deposition of ammonium carbonate in the condenser no longer occurs. The mixture is cooled and stirred thoroughly with twice its volume of water. The aqueous layer is separated; formamide may be recovered from it. The crude, water-insoluble material is refluxed for forty to fifty minutes with 100 ml. of concentrated hydrochloric acid. The small amount of material that does not dissolve in the acid is extracted with small portions of warm benzene and discarded. The amine hydrochloride crystallizes from the cooled acid solution. It is collected and recrystallized from boiling water; the yield is 174 g. (84%), m.p. 198–199°.

Methyl-*tert*-butylcarbinamine [6,10]

(Use of a Solvent, Nitrobenzene)

To a flask containing the Leuckart reagent, prepared as described in the first paragraph of the preceding section, is added 100 g. (1 mole) of pinacolone dissolved in 100-150 g. of nitrobenzene. The reaction is carried out as described above, except that a heating period of about eight hours is required and it is difficult to maintain the temperature at a level higher than about 150-160°. The nitrobenzene and ketone which distil are returned to the reaction mixture from time to time. The nitrobenzene and unchanged pinacolone are removed by steam distillation following the hydrolysis of the formyl derivatives. The acid solution is then neutralized with sodium hydroxide, and the amine is distilled with steam into an excess of hydrochloric acid solution. The acidic solution is evaporated almost to dryness, treated cautiously with saturated potassium hydroxide solution, and extracted with ether. The ether solution of the amine is dried with sodium hydroxide flakes and distilled. The product boils at 102-103°; the yield is 52 g. (52%).

α-*p*-Chlorophenethylamine [10]

(Use of Formamide and Formic Acid)

A 1-l. round-bottomed flask, to which a narrow side tube has been attached for the insertion of a thermometer, is connected by a 19/38 or larger glass joint to an upright water-cooled condenser. The top of this condenser is joined by a wide, bent tube to a short condenser, arranged for downward distillation, and also is fitted with a small separatory funnel. The flask is charged with 310 g. (2 moles) of *p*-chloroacetophenone, 370 g. (about 8 moles) of 90-97% formamide, and 25 ml. of 90% formic acid. The flask is heated with a small flame; the mixture becomes homogeneous, and mild ebullition begins at about 160-165°. The temperature then rises somewhat, refluxing occurs, and a deposit of ammonium carbonate soon appears in the condenser. To prevent clogging and to maintain a slightly acidic reaction mixture, 20- to 25-ml. portions of 90% formic acid are added through the separatory funnel whenever ammonium carbonate is deposited or the odor of ammonia is detected.

The optimum reaction temperature is 175-180°; whenever it falls below about 165-170°, accumulated water is allowed to distil (by draining the reflux condenser) until the temperature rises again. Any ketone that distils with the water should be separated and returned. It is necessary to add a total of 200–250 ml. (4.5–5.0 moles) of formic acid, and the reaction requires ten to fourteen hours, depending upon the average temperature that has been maintained. The process may be interrupted and resumed at any time. The reaction is considered complete when ammonium carbonate is deposited only very slowly in the condenser.

When the reaction is complete the mixture is cooled and extracted with 250–300 ml. of benzene in several portions. The insoluble portion, chiefly formamide, is retained for recovery or may be used without purification for the next run. The benzene extract is distilled to remove the benzene, and the residue is refluxed for about an hour with 200 ml. of concentrated hydrochloric acid (sp. gr. 1.18). The cold mixture is extracted with benzene in order to remove a small amount (10–12 g.) of oily, acid-insoluble material; the benzene extract is discarded.

The aqueous portion is made strongly alkaline with 20–30% sodium hydroxide solution and distilled with steam until practically no more water-insoluble distillate is obtained; about 2.5–3 l. of distillate usually is sufficient. About 18–20 g. of nonvolatile, basic residue, presumably higher amines, remains in the distillation vessel. The distilled amine is extracted with 200–300 ml. of benzene and is dried by distillation of the benzene. The amine is best distilled under reduced pressure; b.p. 103–104°/11 mm.; yield 254–270 g. (82–87%). A small residue of less volatile material remains in the distilling flask.

α-Aminododecylbenzene [12]

(Use of Ammonia and Formic Acid)

One hundred and five grams (1.72 moles) of 28% aqueous ammonia and 88 g. (1.72 moles) of 90% formic acid are mixed carefully and poured into a 500-ml. three-necked flask, equipped with a dropping funnel, thermometer, and downward-directed condenser. The temperature is raised to 160° by distilling out water, and 89.5 g. (0.344 mole) of laurophenone is added in one portion. The temperature is maintained at 160-170° for twenty-two hours, and any ketone which distils is returned to the flask at intervals. The formyl derivative is hydrolyzed in the reaction mixture by refluxing for eight hours with 120 ml. of concentrated hydrochloric acid. After twelve hours at room temperature, 200 ml. of water is added and the compact crystalline mass of the hydrochloride is broken up with a glass rod and collected on a Büchner funnel. The α-aminododecylbenzene hydrochloride is washed three times with small portions of cold water and recrystallized from boiling water. The product weighs 76 g. (78%) and after recrystallization from boiling anhydrous ethanol melts at 115–116°.

α-(o-Chlorobenzyl)ethylamine [31]

(Use of Formamide)

A mixture of 24 g. of o-chlorobenzyl methyl ketone and 50 g. of form-amide in a 500-ml. flask is refluxed for thirty hours. The mixture is cooled, 100 ml. of 30% sodium hydroxide solution is added, and the alkaline mixture is refluxed for twelve hours to hydrolyze the formyl derivative of the amine. After cooling to room temperature, the reaction mixture is extracted with several portions of ether and the combined ether extract is shaken with 10% hydrochloric acid. Unchanged ketone may be recovered from the ether layer. The amine is recovered from the acid layer by the addition of sodium hydroxide and extraction with ether. The ether solution of the amine is dried over potassium hydroxide sticks and filtered. Dry hydrogen chloride gas is passed into the ether solution, and the precipitated hydrochloride of α-o-chlorobenzylethyl-amine is filtered and dried in a vacuum desiccator. The yield of amine hydrochloride is 15 g. (52%); m.p. 175–176°.

N,N-Dimethylbenzylamine [9]

(Eschweiler-Clarke Procedure)

One hundred and seven grams (1 mole) of benzylamine is added, with cooling, to 255 g. (5 moles) of 90% formic acid. Then 188 g. (2.2 moles) of 35% formaldehyde solution is added, and the mixture is heated on the steam bath under reflux for two to four hours after evolution of gas has ceased (eight to twelve hours in all). About 85 ml. (slightly more than one mole) of concentrated hydrochloric acid is then added, and the formic acid and any excess formaldehyde are evaporated on a steam bath. The colorless residue is dissolved in water and made alkaline by the addition of 25% aqueous sodium hydroxide, and the mixture is steam-distilled. The distillate is saturated with potassium hydroxide; the oil is separated, dried by heating with solid potassium hydroxide, and distilled over sodium. About 108 g. (80%) of N,N-dimethylbenzyl-amine, b.p. 176–180°, is obtained.

TABULAR SURVEY OF THE LEUCKART REACTION

In the tables which follow, examples of the Leuckart reaction described in the literature through 1945 have been tabulated. It is probable that the list is incomplete because the reaction frequently has been used as one step in a synthesis without being indexed or referred to as a Leuckart process. Since many of these reactions were carried out before the development of the modified procedures, it is likely that yields reported do not always represent the best that could be obtained. The arrangement of the carbonyl compounds in each table, or in groups of closely related compounds within a table, is alphabetical, and for each carbonyl compound the amines which react with it are also listed in alphabetical order.

TABLE I

LEUCKART REACTIONS WITH ALIPHATIC ALDEHYDES

Aldehyde	Reagent	Product	Yield %	Reference
Butyraldehyde	Piperazine + formic acid	N,N'-Dibutylpiperazine	63	22
Formaldehyde	Ammonia + formic acid	Trimethylamine	—	7
Formaldehyde	Benzylamine + formic acid	N,N-Dimethylbenzylamine	80	8, 9, 16
Formaldehyde	Butylamine + formic acid	N,N-Dimethylbutylamine	80	9
Formaldehyde	β-(2,5-Dimethoxyphenyl)ethylamine + formic acid	N,N-Dimethyl-β-(2,5-dimethoxyphenyl)ethylamine	Almost quantitative	17
Formaldehyde	β-(2,5-Dimethoxyphenyl)isopropylamine + formic acid	N,N-Dimethyl-β-(2,5-dimethoxyphenyl)isopropylamine	Almost quantitative	17
Formaldehyde	β-(2,5-Dimethoxyphenyl)propylamine + formic acid	N,N-Dimethyl-β-(2,5-dimethoxyphenyl)propylamine	Almost quantitative	17
Formaldehyde	Ethylamine + formic acid	N,N-Dimethylethylamine	—	8
Formaldehyde	Ethylenediamine + formic acid	Tetramethyl-1,2-diaminoethane	—	8
Formaldehyde	Tetramethylenediamine + formic acid	Tetramethyl-1,4-diaminobutane	92	9
Formaldehyde	Anabasine + formic acid	N-Methylanabasine	—	15
Formaldehyde	Benzylamylamine + formic acid	N-Methylbenzylamylamine	Almost quantitative	17
Formaldehyde	Benzylbutylamine + formic acid	Methylbenzylbutylamine	Almost quantitative	17
Formaldehyde	Benzyldodecylamine + formic acid	Methylbenzyldodecylamine	Almost quantitative	17
Formaldehyde	Benzylethylamine + formic acid	Methylbenzylethylamine	Almost quantitative	17
Formaldehyde	Benzylmethylamine + formic acid	Methylbenzylmethylamine	Almost quantitative	17
Formaldehyde	Benzylpropylamine + formic acid	Methylbenzylpropylamine	Almost quantitative	17
Formaldehyde	Dibenzylamine + formic acid	Methyldibenzylamine	75	9
Formaldehyde	β-(2,5-Dimethoxyphenyl)ethylmethylamine + formic acid	N,N-Dimethyl-β-(2,5-dimethoxyphenyl)ethylamine	Almost quantitative	17
Formaldehyde	β-(4-Methoxyphenyl)ethylbenzylamine + formic acid	N-Methyl-β-(4-methoxyphenyl)ethylbenzylamine	Almost quantitative	17
Formaldehyde	Piperazine + formic acid	N,N'-Dimethylpiperazine	—	8
Formaldehyde	Piperidine + formic acid	N-Methylpiperidine	80	9
Formaldehyde	Mesidine + formic acid	N,N-Dimethylmesidine	73	21
Formaldehyde	p-Toluidine + formic acid	N,N-Dimethyl-p-toluidine	—	20
Formaldehyde	2,4,6-Tribromoaniline + formic acid	N,N-Dimethyl-2,4,6-tribromoaniline	77	9
Formaldehyde	α-Aminoisobutyric acid + formic acid	α-Dimethylaminoisobutyric acid	80	9
Formaldehyde	β-Aminopropionic acid + formic acid	β-Dimethylaminopropionic acid	38	9
Formaldehyde	Glycine + formic acid	N,N-Dimethylglycine	60–70	9
Formaldehyde	α-Phenyl-α-aminobutyric acid + formic acid	α-Phenyl-α-dimethylaminobutyric acid	72	9
Valeraldehyde	Ammonium formate + formic acid	Triamylamine	—	4g
Valeraldehyde	Aniline + formic acid	N,N-Diamylaniline	—	4g
Valeraldehyde	Methylaniline + formic acid	N-Amyl-N-methylaniline	—	4g

TABLE II

LEUCKART REACTIONS WITH AROMATIC AND HETEROCYCLIC ALDEHYDES

Aldehyde	Reagent	Product	Yield %	Reference
o-Anisaldehyde	Ethylamine + formic acid	N-Ethyl-o-anisylamine	—	23
o-Anisaldehyde	Methylamine + formic acid	N-Methyl-o-anisylamine	—	23
m-Anisaldehyde	Ethylamine + formic acid	N-Ethyl-m-anisylamine	—	23
p-Anisaldehyde	Ethylamine + formic acid	N-Ethyl-p-anisylamine	—	23
p-Anisaldehyde	Methylamine + formic acid	N-Methyl-p-anisylamine	—	23
Benzaldehyde	Ammonium formate	Tribenzylamine, dibenzylamine, benzylamine	35–40 10–15 Trace	1
Benzaldehyde	Ammonium formate + formic acid	Tribenzylamine	—	4g
Benzaldehyde	Aniline + formic acid	N-Benzylaniline	—	4g
Benzaldehyde	Ethanolamine + formamide	N-Hydroxyethylbenzylamine	—	57
Benzaldehyde	Ethylamine + formic acid	N-Ethylbenzylamine	—	4g
Benzaldehyde	3-Methylcyclohexylamine + formic acid	N-Benzyl-3-methylcyclohexylamine	—	4g
Benzaldehyde	Piperazine + formic acid	N,N'-Dibenzylpiperazine	84	22
Benzaldehyde	Piperidine + formic acid	N-Benzylpiperidine	—	4g
Benzaldehyde	Piperidine + methyl formate	N-Benzylpiperidine	—	28
Furfural	Diethylamine + formic acid	N,N-Diethylfurfurylamine	—	27
Furfural	Dimethylamine + formic acid	N,N-Dimethylfurfurylamine	60	26, 27, 56
Furfural	Formamide	Furfurylamine	—	26
Furfural	Methylamine + formic acid	N-Methylfurfurylamine	—	26
Furfural	Methylformamide + formic acid	N-Methyldifurfurylamine	—	26
Furfural	Morpholine + formic acid	N-Furfurylmorpholine	—	26

[57] Wegler, U. S. pat. 2,251,245 [*C.A.*, **35**, 6975 (1941)].

TABLE III

LEUCKART REACTIONS WITH ALIPHATIC KETONES

Ketone	Reagent	Product	Yield %	Reference
Acetone	α-Naphthylamine + methyl formate	N-Isopropyl-α-naphthylamine	—	28
Diethyl ketone	Ammonium formate + acetic acid	3-Pentylamine	—	4g
Di-n-heptyl ketone	Ammonia + formic acid	8-Nonadecylamine	40	12
Diisobutyl ketone	Formamide + formic acid	2,6-Dimethyl-4-heptylamine	77	10
Diisopropyl ketone	Formamide + formic acid	2,4-Dimethyl-3-pentylamine	64	10
Di-n-propyl ketone	Formamide + formic acid	4-Heptylamine	25	10
Methyl amyl ketone	Ammonium carbonate-carbamate + formic acid	2-Heptylamine	28	10
Methyl amyl ketone	Ammonium formate	2-Heptylamine	55	29
Methyl butyl ketone	Ammonium formate	2-Hexylamine	—	29
Methyl cyclohexyl ketone	Ammonium formate	α-Cyclohexylethylamine	—	30
Methyl hexyl ketone	Ammonium formate	2-Octylamine	—	5, 29
Methyl hexyl ketone	Formamide + formic acid	2-Octylamine	60	10
Methyl propyl ketone	Ammonium carbonate-carbamate + formic acid	2-Pentylamine	10–37	10
Methyl octadecyl ketone	Ethanolamine + methyl formate	N-Hydroxyethyl-2-eicosylamine	85	57
Pinacolone	Ammonium carbonate-carbamate + formic acid	3,3-Dimethyl-2-butylamine	52	6
o-Chlorophenylacetone	Formamide	β-o-Chlorophenylisopropylamine	52	31
Di-(bromoveratryl) ketone	Ammonium carbonate + formic acid	Di-(bromoveratryl)carbinamine	—	37
α,α-Dimethylphenylacetone	Formamide	β,β-Dimethyl-β-phenylisopropylamine	76	35
Diphenylacetone	Ammonium formate	Dibenzylcarbinamine	—	39
Diveratryl ketone	Ammonium carbonate + formic acid	Diveratrylcarbinamine	—	36
α-Ethylphenylacetone	Formamide	β-Ethyl-β-phenylisopropylamine	63	35
p-Fluorophenylacetone	Formamide	β-p-Fluorophenylisopropylamine	—	35
3,4-Methylenedioxyphenylacetone	Ammonia + formic acid	β-3,4-Methylenedioxyphenylisopropylamine	20	34
α-Methylphenylacetone	Ammonia + formic acid	β-Methyl-β-phenylisopropylamine	58	12
α-Methylphenylacetone	Butylamine + formic acid	N-Butyl-β-methyl-β-phenylisopropylamine	16	12
α-Methylphenylacetone	Formamide	β-Methyl-β-phenylisopropylamine	60	35
α-Methylphenylacetone	Methylamine + formic acid	N,β-Dimethyl-β-phenylisopropylamine	16, 41	12, 35
Phenylacetone	Ammonia + formic acid	β-Phenylisopropylamine	27	12, 32
Phenylacetone	Ammonium formate	β-Phenylisopropylamine	—	33
Phenylacetone	Amylamine + formic acid	N-Amyl-β-phenylisopropylamine	50–70	32
Phenylacetone	Butylamine + formic acid	N-Butyl-β-phenylisopropylamine	50–70	12, 32
Phenylacetone	Diethylamine + formic acid	N,N-Diethyl-β-phenylisopropylamine	50–70	32
Phenylacetone	Dimethylamine + formic acid	N,N-Dimethyl-β-phenylisopropylamine	50–70	32
Phenylacetone	Ethylamine + formic acid	N-Ethyl-β-phenylisopropylamine	50–70	32
Phenylacetone	Formamide	β-Phenylisopropylamine	50–60	31
Phenylacetone	Methylamine + formic acid	N-Methyl-β-phenylisopropylamine	50–70 (22)	12, 32, 35
α-Propylphenylacetone	Formamide	β-Propyl-β-phenylisopropylamine	68	35
o-Tolylacetone	Formamide	β-o-Tolylisopropylamine	—	38
o-Tolylacetone	Methylamine + formic acid	N-Methyl-β-o-tolylisopropylamine	—	38
m-Tolylacetone	Formamide	β-m-Tolylisopropylamine	—	38
m-Tolylacetone	Methylamine + formic acid	N-Methyl-β-m-tolylisopropylamine	—	38
p-Tolylacetone	Formamide	β-p-Tolylisopropylamine	—	38
p-Tolylacetone	Methylamine + formic acid	N-Methyl-β-p-tolylisopropylamine	—	38

TABLE IV

LEUCKART REACTIONS WITH ALIPHATIC-AROMATIC AND ALIPHATIC-HETEROCYCLIC
KETONES

Ketone	Reagent	Product	Yield %	Reference
Acetophenone	Ammonium formate	α-Phenethylamine	—	4g, 40
Acetophenone	Ammonium formate + acetic acid	α-Phenethylamine	—	4g
Acetophenone	Ammonium carbonate-carbamate + formic acid	α-Phenethylamine	72–81	6, 10, 48
Acetophenone	Aniline + methyl formate	N-α-Phenethylaniline	—	28
Acetophenone	Butylamine + formic acid	N-Butyl-α-phenethylamine	78	13
Acetophenone	Ethylamine + formic acid	N-Ethyl-α-phenethylamine	70	13
Acetophenone	Formamide	α-Phenethylamine	50–60	31, 41
Acetophenone	Hydroxyethylformamide	N-Hydroxyethyl-α-phenethylamine	60	57
Acetophenone	Methylamine + formic acid	N-Methyl-α-phenethylamine	60	13
Acetophenone	α-Naphthylamine + methyl formate	N-α-Phenylethyl-α-naphthylamine	—	28
Acetophenone	1,3-Propanolamine + formamide	N-γ-Hydroxypropyl-α-phenethylamine	42	57
p-Bromoacetophenone	Ammonium carbonate-carbamate + formic acid	α-p-Bromophenethylamine	79	6
p-Bromoacetophenone	Ammonium formate	α-p-Bromophenethylamine	63	40
p-Bromoacetophenone	Butylamine + formic acid	N-Butyl-α-p-bromophenethylamine	70	13
p-Bromoacetophenone	Ethylamine + formic acid	N-Ethyl-α-p-bromophenethylamine	60	13
p-Bromoacetophenone	Methylamine + formic acid	N-Methyl-α-p-bromophenethylamine	70	13
p-Bromoheptanophenone	Ammonia + formic acid	α-p-Bromophenylheptylamine	—	28
p-Bromohexanophenone	Ammonia + formic acid	α-p-Bromophenylhexylamine	—	12
p-Chloroacetophenone	Ammonia + formic acid	α-p-Chlorophenethylamine	82	6
p-Chloroacetophenone	Ammonium formate	α-p-Chlorophenethylamine	65	40
p-Chloroacetophenone	Butylamine + formic acid	N-Butyl-α-p-chlorophenethylamine	80	13
p-Chloroacetophenone	Ethylamine + formic acid	N-Ethyl-α-p-chlorophenethylamine	80	13
p-Chloroacetophenone	Methylamine + formic acid	N-Methyl-α-p-chlorophenethylamine	70	13
p-Chloroheptanophenone	Ammonia + formic acid	α-p-Chlorophenylheptylamine	—	12
p-Chlorohexanophenone	Ammonia + formic acid	α-p-Chlorophenylhexylamine	—	12
p-Dimethylaminolaurophenone	Ammonia + formic acid	α-p-Dimethylaminophenyldodecylamine	—	7
p-Dodecylacetophenone	Ammonium formate	α-p-Dodecylphenethylamine	—	42, 48
Isobutyrophenone	Formamide + formic acid	α-Phenylisobutylamine	85	10
Laurophenone	Ammonia + formic acid	α-Phenyldodecylamine	78	12, 48
Laurophenone	Dimethylamine + formic acid	No product when heated at 160–170° for twenty-eight hours.	—	12
Laurophenone	Methylamine + formic acid	N-Methyl-α-phenyldodecylamine	53	12
p-Methoxyacetophenone	Ammonium carbonate-carbamate + formic acid	α-p-Methoxyphenethylamine	68	6
p-Methoxylaurophenone	Ammonia + formic acid	α-p-Methoxyphenyldodecylamine	—	7

TABLE IV—*Continued*

LEUCKART REACTIONS WITH ALIPHATIC-AROMATIC AND ALIPHATIC-HETEROCYCLIC
KETONES

Ketone	Reagent	Product	Yield %	Reference
o-Methylacetophenone	Ammonium carbonate-carbamate + formic acid	α-o-Tolylethylamine	70	6
p-Methylacetophenone	Ammonium carbonate-carbamate + formic acid	α-p-Tolylethylamine	72	6
p-Methylacetophenone	Ammonium formate	α-p-Tolylethylamine	72	40
p-Methylacetophenone	Butylamine + formic acid	N-Butyl-α-p-tolylethylamine	50	13
p-Methylacetophenone	Ethylamine + formic acid	N-Ethyl-α-p-tolylethylamine	60	13
p-Methylacetophenone	Formamide	α-p-Tolylethylamine	50–60	31
p-Methylacetophenone	Methylamine + formic acid	N-Methyl-α-p-tolylethylamine	50	13
p-Methylcaprophenone	Ammonia + formic acid	α-p-Tolylhexylamine	63	12
p-Methyllaurophenone	Ammonia + formic acid	α-p-Tolyldodecylamine	—	7
m-Nitroacetophenone	Ammonium carbonate-carbamate + formic acid	α-m-Nitrophenethylamine	56	6
p-Phenoxyacetophenone	Ammonium carbonate-carbamate + formic acid	α-p-Phenoxyphenethylamine	69	6, 48
p-Phenylacetophenone	Ammonium carbonate-carbamate + formic acid	α-p-Xenylethylamine	77	6
p-Phenylacetophenone	Ammonium formate	α-p-Xenylethylamine	66	40
Propiophenone	Ammonia + formic acid	α-Phenylpropylamine	65	10, 12
β-Acetonaphthone	Ammonium carbonate-carbamate + formic acid	α-(β'-Naphthyl)ethylamine	84	6
β-Acetonaphthone	Ammonium formate	α-(β'-Naphthyl)ethylamine	84	40
α-Acetothienone	Ammonium formate	α-(α'-Thienyl)ethylamine	51	43
α-Acetothienone	Methylamine + formic acid	N-Methyl-α-(α'-thienyl)ethylamine	45	43
α-Propiothienone	Formamide	α-(α'-Thienyl)propylamine	36	43
α-Propiothienone	Methylamine + formic acid	N-Methyl-α-(α'-thienyl)propylamine	27	43
Benzoin	Ammonium carbonate + formic and acetic acids	Desylamine	Small quantity	46

TABLE V

LEUCKART REACTIONS WITH AROMATIC KETONES

Ketone	Reagent	Product	Yield %	Reference
1,2-Benzofluorenone	Formamide	9-Amino-1,2-benzofluorene	—	49
2,3-Benzofluorenone	Formamide	9-Amino-2,3-benzofluorene	—	49
Benzophenone	Ammonia + formic acid	Benzohydrylamine	80	12, 48
Benzophenone	Ammonium formate	Benzohydrylamine	—	1
Fluorenone	Formamide	9-Aminofluorene	70–75	49

TABLE VI

LEUCKART REACTIONS WITH ALICYCLIC KETONES

Ketone	Reagent	Product	Yield %	Reference
Camphor	Ammonium carbonate-carbamate + formic acid	Bornylamines	62	6
Camphor	Ammonium carbonate + formic acid	Bornylamines	83	52
Camphor	Ammonium formate	Bornylamines	50–60	1, 4
Camphor	Methylformamide + formic acid	N-Methylbornylamines	60–75	51
Carvomenthone	Ammonium formate	Carvomenthylamine, dicarvomenthylamine	25	53
Cyclohexanone	Ammonium formate + acetic acid	Dicyclohexylamine	—	4g
Cyclohexanone	Benzylamine + formic acid	N-Cyclohexylbenzylamine	—	4g
Cyclohexanone	Cyclohexylamine + methyl formate	Dicyclohexylamine	—	28
Cyclohexanone	Ethanolamine + formamide	N-Hydroxyethylcyclohexyl-amine	65	57
Cyclohexanone	Formamide + formic acid	Cyclohexylamine, dicyclohexylamine	26 22	10, 50
Cyclohexanone	Laurylamine + methyl formate	N-Cyclohexyllaurylamine	—	28
Cyclohexanone	α-Naphthylamine + methyl formate	N-Cyclohexyl-α-naphthylamine	—	28
Cyclohexanone	Piperidine + methyl formate	N-Cyclohexylpiperidine	—	28
Fenchone	Ammonium carbonate-carbamate + formic acid	Fenchylamine	85	6
Fenchone	Ammonium formate	Fenchylamine	90	4
Menthone	Ammonium formate	Menthylamines	—	4, 53
1-Menthone	Ammonium formate + formamide + formic acid	Menthylamines	80	10
2-Methylcyclohexanone	Formamide + formic acid	2-Methylcyclohexylamine, di-2-methylcyclohexylamine	60 20	10
3-Methylcyclohexanone	Ammonium formate + formic acid	Di-3-methylcyclohexylamine	—	4g
3-Methylcyclohexanone	Amylamine + formic acid	N-Amyl-3-methylcyclohexyl-amine	—	4g
3-Methylcyclohexanone	Benzylamine + formic acid	N-Benzyl-3-methylcyclohexyl-amine	—	4g
3-Methylcyclohexanone	3-Methylcyclohexylamine + formic acid	Di-3-Methylcyclohexylamine	—	4g
Thujone	Ammonium carbonate-carbamate + formic acid	Thujylamine	55–77	10, 55

TABLE VII

LEUCKART REACTION WITH QUINONE

Quinone	Reagent	Product	Yield %	Reference
Anthraquinone	Formamide	9,10-Diamino-9,10-dihydroanthracene	90	49

CHAPTER 8

SELENIUM DIOXIDE OXIDATION

NORMAN RABJOHN

University of Missouri

CONTENTS

INTRODUCTION

Although it has been known [1] for a long time that organic compounds can be oxidized by selenium dioxide or selenious acid, only in recent years have these oxidizing agents found extensive application. It had been observed frequently that when commercial fuming sulfuric acid was used as an oxidizing agent (for example, in the introduction of hydroxyl groups into anthraquinone and its derivatives) the trace of selenium dioxide present in the acid was the active oxidizing agent.[2] The first practical use of selenium dioxide is recorded in a patent granted to the I.G. Farbenindustrie in 1930, which disclosed that 2-methylbenzanthrone could be oxidized to benzanthrone-2-carboxaldehyde.[3]

[1] Gmelin's *Handbuch der anorganischen Chemie*, Verlag Chemie, Berlin, 1907, pp. 756, 764.

[2] Brady, *Science Progress*, **28**, 100 (1933).

[3] I.G. Farbenind. A.-G., Ger. pat. 557,249 [*C.A.*, **27**, 304 (1933)].

Soon afterwards (1932), Riley, Morley, and Friend [4] undertook a systematic study of the oxidizing properties of selenium dioxide and showed that it oxidizes aldehydes and ketones of various types to 1,2-dialdehydes, aldoketones, and 1,2-diketones. This represented a marked advance in the method of preparation of many difficultly obtainable compounds and provided the impetus to many further studies of the oxidizing action of selenium dioxide. The results of these studies are the basis on which this chapter is written.

THE NATURE OF THE REACTION

Selenium dioxide oxidation is applicable to synthetic work, structural studies, analytical procedures, and a number of diverse reactions. It is associated generally with the conversion of active methyl or methylene groups to carbonyl groups as illustrated by the following equations.

$$RCOCH_3 + SeO_2 \rightarrow RCOCHO + Se + H_2O$$
$$RCOCH_2R' + SeO_2 \rightarrow RCOCOR' + Se + H_2O$$

The methyl or methylene groups can be activated by groups other than the carbonyl. Olefins and acetylenes are oxidized at the α-methylenic carbon atom to yield unsaturated alcohols. A methyl or methylene

$$2RCH_2CH{=}CHR' + SeO_2 \rightarrow 2RCHOHCH{=}CHR' + Se$$
$$2RCH_2C{\equiv}CR' + SeO_2 \rightarrow 2RCHOHC{\equiv}CR' + Se$$

group adjacent to one or more aromatic or heterocyclic rings is also converted to a carbonyl group. In a number of cases, the aldehyde is oxidized further to the corresponding carboxylic acid.

$$ArCH_3 + SeO_2 \rightarrow ArCHO + Se + H_2O$$
$$ArCH_2Ar' + SeO_2 \rightarrow ArCOAr' + Se + H_2O$$

Certain olefins undergo loss of hydrogen and addition of oxygen.

$$2RCH{=}CHR' + 3SeO_2 \rightarrow 2RCOCOR' + 3Se + 2H_2O$$

Acetylenic compounds which do not possess an active methylene group also undergo addition of oxygen.

$$RC{\equiv}CR' + SeO_2 \rightarrow RCOCOR' + Se$$

Selenium dioxide can bring about a still different type of reaction whereby oxygen does not enter the final product but the reacting molecule suffers dehydrogenation. Such reactions usually occur in systems where two carbon atoms carrying hydrogen atoms are situated between

[4] Riley, Morley, and Friend, *J. Chem. Soc.*, **1932**, 1875.

SELENIUM DIOXIDE OXIDATION 333

activating groups. A and A' may be doubly bonded carbon atoms,

$$2ACH_2CH_2A' + SeO_2 \rightarrow 2ACH{=}CHA' + Se + 2H_2O$$

carbonyl groups, ester groups, or aromatic nuclei.

In addition to these more general types of reactions, selenium dioxide will attack paraffin hydrocarbons, alcohols, phenols, mercaptans, sulfides, amines, hydrazines, amides, thioamides, acids, and a large number of other substances.

As yet, no completely satisfactory mechanism has been suggested to explain the varied behavior of selenium dioxide toward the countless organic compounds that it is capable of attacking. Mel'nikov and Rokitskaya [5-15] have published a series of papers on the mechanism of the selenium dioxide reaction. From a study of the rate constants of the reactions between selenium dioxide and a number of compounds in 75% acetic acid, they concluded that the oxidation takes place through the formation of an intermediate complex. From simple alcohols they were able to isolate dialkyl selenites which could be decomposed thermally to give the corresponding aldehydes, selenium, and water.

Guillemonat [16] has postulated the formation of selenium complexes from a study of the oxidation of 2-methyl-2-butene. He believes that the following series of reactions can occur with an olefin. (R is a radical containing an ethylenic bond.)

$$4RCH_2H + SeO_2 \rightarrow (RCH_2)_4Se + 2H_2O$$

$$(RCH_2)_4Se + H_2O \rightarrow (RCH_2)_2Se + RCH_3 + RCH_2OH$$

$$(RCH_2)_2Se + H_2O \rightarrow RCH_2OH + RCH_3 + Se$$

[5] Mel'nikov, Uspekhi Khim., 5, 443 (1936) [C.A., 30, 5180 (1936)].
[6] Mel'nikov, Fortschr. Chem. (Russ.), 5, 443 (1936) (Chem. Zentr., 1936, II, 2330).
[7] Mel'nikov and Rokitskaya, J. Gen. Chem. U.S.S.R., 7, 1532 (1937) [C.A., 31, 8502 (1937)].
[8] Mel'nikov and Rokitskaya, J. Gen. Chem. U.S.S.R., 7, 2738 (1937) [C.A., 32, 2903 (1938)].
[9] Mel'nikov and Rokitskaya, J. Gen. Chem. U.S.S.R., 8, 834 (1938) [C.A., 33, 1267 (1939)].
[10] Mel'nikov and Rokitskaya, J. Gen. Chem. U.S.S.R., 8, 1369 (1938) [C.A., 33, 4194 (1939)].
[11] Mel'nikov and Rokitskaya, J. Gen. Chem. U.S.S.R., 9, 1158 (1939) [C.A., 34, 1233 (1940)].
[12] Mel'nikov and Rokitskaya, J. Gen. Chem. U.S.S.R., 9, 1808 (1939) [C.A., 34, 3676 (1940)].
[13] Mel'nikov and Rokitskaya, J. Gen. Chem. U.S.S.R., 10, 1439 (1940) [C.A., 35, 2400 (1941)].
[14] Mel'nikov and Rokitskaya, J. Gen. Chem. U.S.S.R., 10, 1713 (1940) [C.A., 35, 3226 (1941)].
[15] Mel'nikov and Rokitskaya, J. Gen. Chem. U.S.S.R., 15, 657 (1945) [C.A., 40, 5702 (1946)].
[16] Guillemonat, Ann. chim., 11, 143 (1939).

Astin, Moulds, and Riley [17] agree that unstable organoselenium compounds are formed in many selenium dioxide oxidations. However, they maintain that the intermediate-complex theory would require the existence of a large number of different types of unstable compounds; a complicated addition of oxygen then would be necessary in the later stages of the reaction. An investigation [18] of the spectra of substances heated in selenium dioxide vapor suggests that the vapor is capable of providing oxygen atoms in a very low energy state. This may account for the formation of many unstable compounds. The dehydrogenating action of selenium dioxide indicates that the first process in many of the oxidations must be the removal of activated hydrogen atoms. This may or may not be followed by the addition of oxygen in a low energy state according to the nature of the dehydrogenated product.

THE SCOPE OF THE REACTION

The oxidation of compounds containing active methyl or methylene groups is perhaps the most valuable reaction of selenium dioxide. Desirable substances may be obtained from aldehydes and ketones. Even simple aliphatic aldehydes show the characteristic transformation of methylene or methyl groups to carbonyl groups. Acetaldehyde,[4,11,19] propionaldehyde,[4,11,19] and n-butyraldehyde,[4,11,19] for example, give yields of 90%, 30%, and 40%, respectively, of glyoxals. In a similar

$$CH_3CHO \xrightarrow{SeO_2} OHCCHO$$

$$CH_3CH_2CHO \xrightarrow{SeO_2} CH_3COCHO$$

$$CH_3CH_2CH_2CHO \xrightarrow{SeO_2} CH_3CH_2COCHO$$

manner, aliphatic ketones are converted to glyoxals or α-diketones. 2-Butanone [4,10,12,19] leads to a mixture of ethylglyoxal (17%) and biacetyl (1%), demonstrating the ability of selenium dioxide to attack both active methyl and methylene groups. Cyclic ketones [4,19] and mixed

$$CH_3COCH_2CH_3 \xrightarrow{SeO_2} CH_3CH_2COCHO + CH_3COCOCH_3$$

aliphatic-aromatic ketones [20] give satisfactory yields of diketones.

[17] Astin, Moulds, and Riley, *J. Chem. Soc.*, **1935**, 901.
[18] Emeléus and Riley, *Proc. Roy. Soc. London*, **140A**, 378 (1933).
[19] Imperial Chem. Ind., Brit. pat. 354,798 (*Chem. Zentr.*, **1932**, I, 288).
[20] Hatt, Pilgrim, and Hurran, *J. Chem. Soc.*, **1936**, 93.

CH₂   CH₂
/ \   / \
CH₂ CO   SeO₂   CH₂ CO
| | ──→ | | (35%)
CH₂ CH₂   CH₂ CO
\ /   \ /
CH₂   CH₂

$$C_6H_5CH_2COC_6H_5 \xrightarrow{SeO_2} C_6H_5COCOC_6H_5 \quad (88\%)$$

A large number of substituted benzyl ketones has been converted to diketones in very high yields. 2-Methylcyclohexanone [21] behaves anomalously when treated with selenium dioxide, dehydrogenation as

CH₃   CH₃
| |
CH   C
/ \   // \
CH₂ CO SeO₂   CH CO
| | ──→ | |
CH₂ CH₂   CH₂ CO
\ /   \ /
CH₂   CH₂

well as oxidation taking place.

Natural products, such as steroids and terpenes, which contain active methylene groups behave quite normally toward selenium dioxide.

Cholestanone [22,23] is converted to 2,3-cholestanedione (30%). Camphor [24-27] and isofenchone [28,29,30] give the corresponding 1,2-diketones.

[21] Godchot and Cauquil, *Compt. rend.*, **202**, 326 (1936).
[22] Stiller and Rosenheim, *J. Chem. Soc.*, **1938**, 353.
[23] Callow and Rosenheim, *J. Chem. Soc.*, **1933**, 387.
[24] Allard, *Bull. inst. pin*, **1934**, 127 [*C.A.*, **28**, 7255 (1934)].
[25] Evans, Ridgion, and Simonsen, *J. Chem. Soc.*, **1934**, 137.
[26] Vène, *Compt. rend.*, **216**, 772 (1943).
[27] Vène, *Bull. soc. sci. Bretagne*, **19**, 14 (1943–1944) (Pub. 1946) [*C.A.*, **41**, 739 (1947)].
[28] Alder, Stein, and Rickert, *Ann.*, **525**, 221 (1936).
[29] Ruzhentseva and Delektorskaya, *J. Gen. Chem. U.S.S.R.*, **10**, 1653 (1940) [*C.A.*, **35**, 3246 (1941)].
[30] Ruzhentseva and Delektorskaya, *Compt. rend. acad. sci. U.R.S.S.*, **29**, 41 (1940) [*C.A.*, **35**, 3622 (1941)].

(89%)

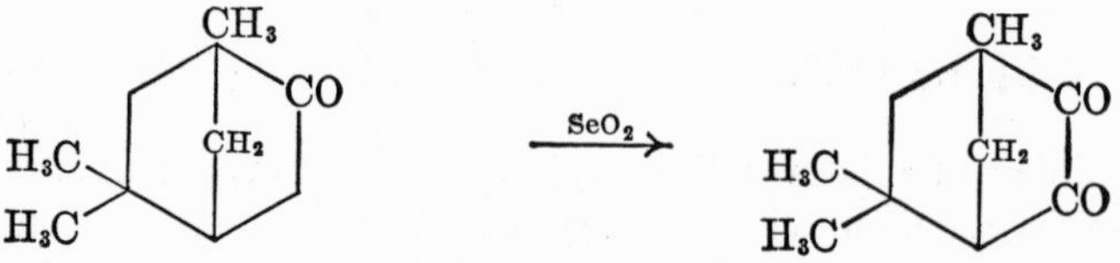

3-Benzylcamphor,[26, 27] on the other hand, suffers dehydrogenation to 3-benzylidenecamphor (95%).

A methylene group situated between two carbonyl groups, a carbonyl and an ester group, two ester groupings, two aromatic nuclei, or an aromatic group and a carboxyl group generally is changed to a carbonyl group. 2,4-Pentanedione [31] yields 2,3,4-pentanetrione. Ethyl aceto-

$$CH_3COCH_2COCH_3 \xrightarrow{SeO_2} CH_3COCOCOCH_3 \quad (29\%)$$

acetate [32] is transformed to ethyl α,β-diketobutyrate. Diethyl malo-

$$CH_3COCH_2CO_2C_2H_5 \xrightarrow{SeO_2} CH_3COCOCO_2C_2H_5 \quad (35\%)$$

nate [19, 32, 33] gives diethyl mesoxalate (32%), monoethyl mesoxalate, and diethyl oxalate. The last probably results from a disproportionation

$$CH_2(CO_2C_2H_5)_2 \xrightarrow{SeO_2} CO(CO_2C_2H_5)_2 + C_2H_5O_2CCOCO_2H + (CO_2C_2H_5)_2$$

of the diethyl mesoxalate.

Diphenylmethane [34, 35, 36] and fluorene [36, 37] are oxidized readily to ketones. Indene,[38] curiously, is reported to give hydrindene and a hydro-

$$C_6H_5CH_2C_6H_5 \xrightarrow{SeO_2} C_6H_5COC_6H_5 \quad (87\%)$$

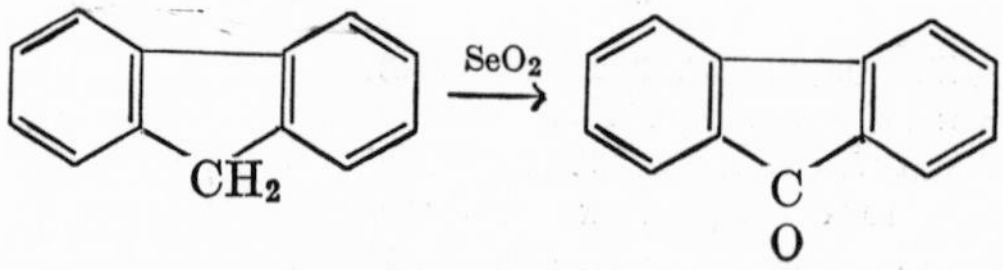

(65%)

[31] Piutti, *Gazz. chim. ital.*, **66**, 276 (1936).
[32] Müller, *Ber.*, **66**, 1668 (1933).
[33] Astin, Newman, and Riley, *J. Chem. Soc.*, **1933**, 391.
[34] DuPont, Allard, and Dulou, *Bull. soc. chim. France*, [4] **53**, 599 (1933).
[35] Fisher, *J. Am. Chem. Soc.*, **56**, 2056 (1934).
[36] Postowsky and Lugowkin, *Ber.*, **68**, 852 (1935).
[37] Badger, *J. Chem. Soc.*, **1941**, 535.
[38] Yokoyama, *J. Chem. Soc. Japan*, **59**, 262, 271 (1938) [*C.A.*, **32**, 9062 (1938)].

carbon C_9H_{10}.   Anthracene [17,36] and 7,16-dihydroheptacene [39] are converted to quinones, but phenanthrene [17,36] is scarcely attacked.   Benzyl

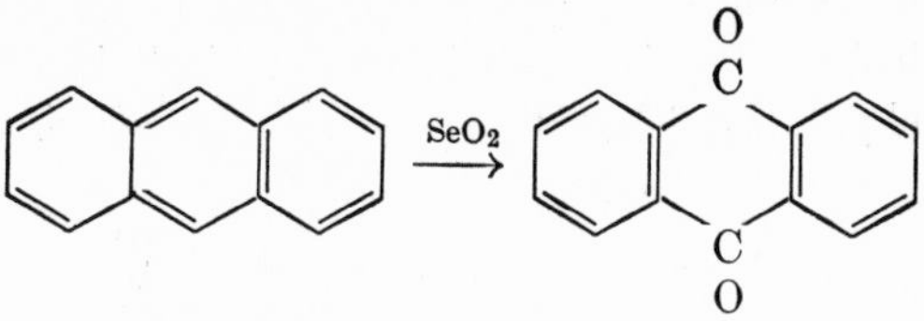

(76%)

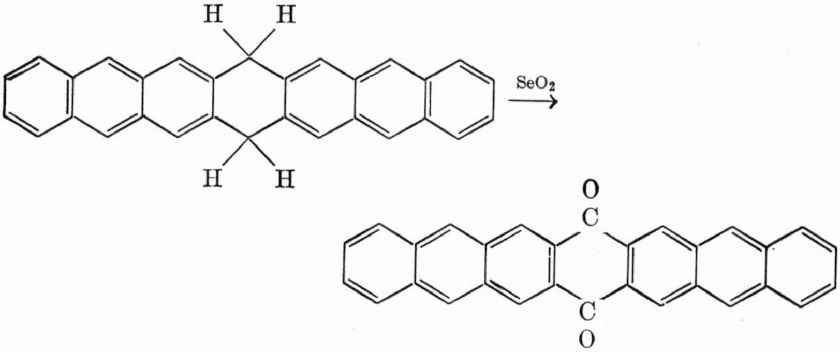

halides [35,40] yield benzaldehyde (49%), and toluene [41] gives benzoic acid.

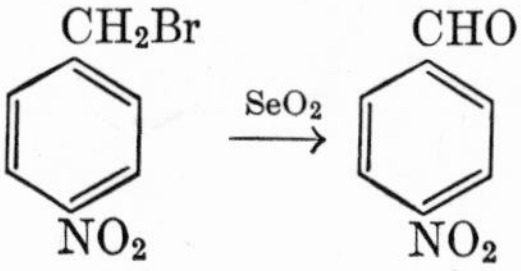

(56%)

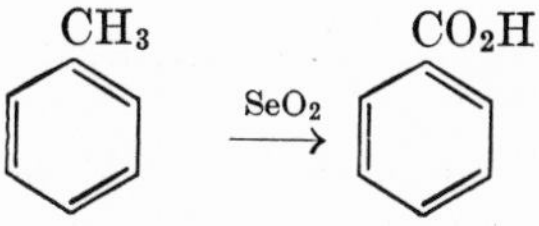

Triphenylmethane [35] is oxidized to triphenylcarbinol (15%).

Homophthalic acid [42] and its derivatives [43,44] demonstrate the activating effect of the benzene ring and the carboxyl group.

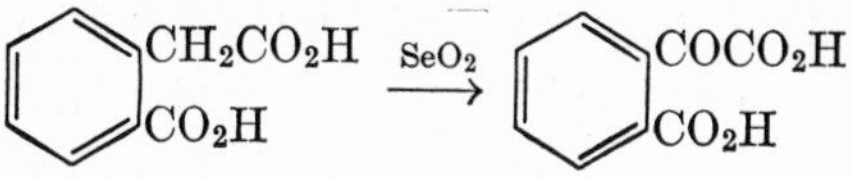

(80%)

[39] Clar, Ber., **75**, 1283, 1330 (1942).

[40] Michaelis and Landmann, Ber., **13**, 656 (1880).

[41] Deupree and Lyons, Proc. Indiana Acad. Sci., **46**, 101 (1937) [C.A., **32**, 498 (1938)].

[42] Chakravarti and Swaminathan, J. Indian Chem. Soc., **11**, 715 (1934) [C.A., **29**, 1080 (1935)].

[43] Chakravarti and Swaminathan, J. Indian Chem. Soc., **11**, 873 (1934) [C.A., **29**, 2942 (1935)].

[44] Chakravarti, Swaminathan, and Venkataraman, J. Indian Chem. Soc., **17**, 264 (1940) [C.A., **34**, 6254 (1940)].

Heterocyclic compounds are attacked also by selenium dioxide at an activated methyl or methylene group. Such groups in pyridine or quinoline derivatives are oxidized to either aldehyde or carboxyl groups. For example, 2-picoline [45,46] gives a mixture of picolinic acid and 2-pyridinecarboxaldehyde. 2,6-Lutidine [46] yields dipicolinic acid, and

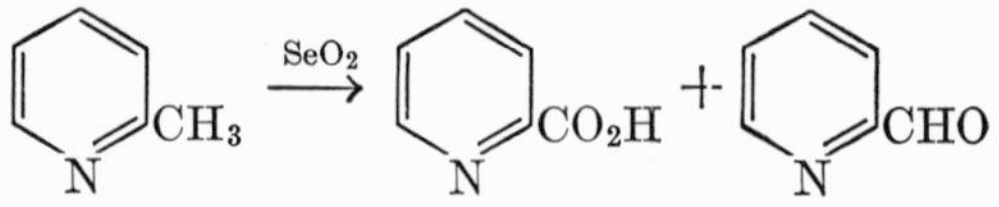

2,3,8-trimethylquinoline [47] is converted in 82% yield to 3,8-dimethylquinaldehyde. The conversion of 5,6-benzo-7-azahydrindene [45] to a keto

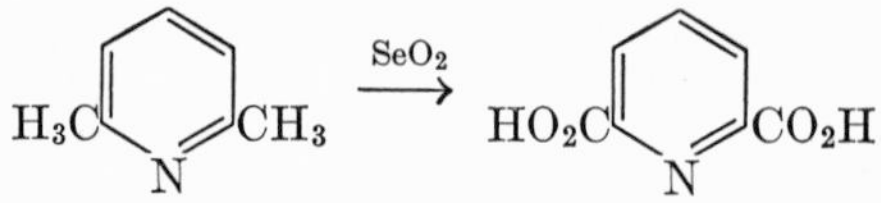

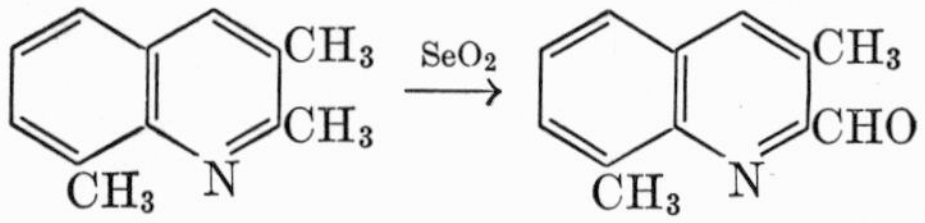

derivative illustrates the oxidation of an activated methylene group in a heterocyclic molecule. Selenium dioxide appears to show a greater

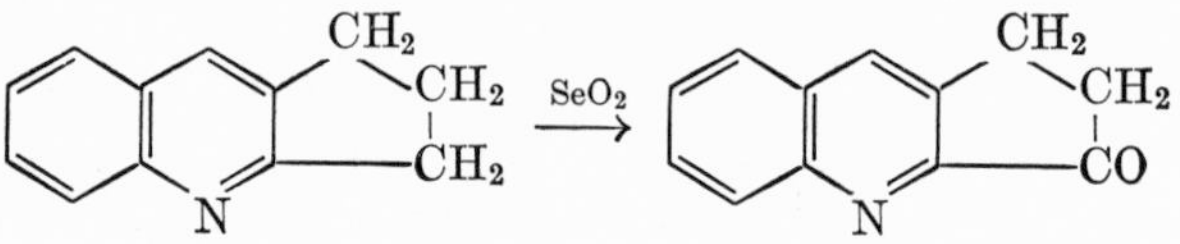

tendency to form acid derivatives with the nitrogen-containing heterocyclic compounds than with other substances.

The oxidation of olefinic compounds by selenium dioxide has led to a number of interesting and valuable results. Many of the materials available by this method are obtained only with considerable difficulty by other means. The simple olefins do not undergo oxidation at the α-methylenic carbon atom; however, olefins which contain at least five carbon atoms behave normally. 2-Pentene [16,48] is oxidized to 2-penten-4-ol, and 2-methyl-2-butene [16,48] yields 2-methyl-2-buten-1-ol. The be-

$$CH_3CH{=}CHCH_2CH_3 \xrightarrow{SeO_2} CH_3CH{=}CHCHOHCH_3$$

$$(CH_3)_2C{=}CHCH_3 \xrightarrow{SeO_2} HOCH_2C{=}CHCH_3$$
$$\qquad\qquad\qquad\qquad\qquad | \atop CH_3$$

[45] Borsche and Hartmann, Ber., 73, 839 (1940).
[46] Henze, Ber., 67, 750 (1934).
[47] Burger and Modlin, J. Am. Chem. Soc., 62, 1079 (1940).
[48] Riley and Friend, J. Chem. Soc., 1932, 2342.

havior of myrcene [49] shows that selenium dioxide is capable of taking an olefin beyond the alcohol stage.

$$
\begin{array}{l}
\underset{CH_3}{\overset{CH_3}{\diagdown}}\ \underset{CH_2=CH}{\overset{CH_2CH_2}{\diagup}}\ \overset{C=CH}{}\ \overset{C=CH_2}{}\ \xrightarrow{SeO_2}
\end{array}
$$

$$
\begin{bmatrix}
\underset{CH_3}{\overset{HOCH_2}{\diagdown}}\ \overset{C=CH}{}\ \underset{CH_2=CH}{\overset{CH_2CH_2}{\diagup}}\ \overset{C=CH_2}{} \\
\text{and} \\
\underset{CH_3}{\overset{HCO}{\diagdown}}\ \overset{C=CH}{}\ \underset{CH_2=CH}{\overset{CH_2CH_2}{\diagup}}\ \overset{C=CH_2}{}
\end{bmatrix}
$$

Mixture of myrcenones

Cyclic olefins behave like aliphatic olefins. Cyclohexene [16, 50, 51] can be oxidized to 1-cyclohexen-3-ol (50%) and cyclohexenone (6%).

$$
\text{cyclohexene} \xrightarrow{SeO_2} \text{1-cyclohexen-3-ol (CHOH)} + \text{cyclohexenone (CO)}
$$

3,5-Dimethyl-Δ^2-cyclohexenone [52] is converted to 3-hydroxy-2,6-dimethylquinone, which indicates that oxidation has occurred first at the

$$
\text{3,5-dimethyl-}\Delta^2\text{-cyclohexenone} \xrightarrow{SeO_2} \text{3-hydroxy-2,6-dimethylquinone}
$$

methylene group α to the double bond. This does not agree with the usual conception that the carbonyl group exerts the greater activating

[49] Delaby and Dupin, *Bull. soc. chim. France*, [5] **5**, 931 (1938); *Atti X° congr. intern. chim.*, **3**, 120 (1939) [*C.A.*, **33**, 8194 (1939)].

[50] Schwenk and Borgwardt, Ger. pat. 584,373 (*Chem. Zentr.*, **1933**, II, 3481).

[51] Arbuzov, Zelinskiĭ, and Shuĭkin, *Bull. acad. sci. U.R.S.S., Classe sci. chim.*, **1945**, 163 [*C.A.*, **40**, 3409 (1946)].

[52] Dane and Schmitt, *Ann.*, **536**, 196 (1938).

effect, as it does in 2-methyl-Δ^2-cyclopentenone.[53]   Cauquil[54] has re-

$$
\begin{array}{ccc}
\text{O} & & \text{O} \\
\big\| & & \big\| \\
\text{C} & & \text{C} \\
\diagup\diagdown & & \diagup\diagdown \\
\text{CH}_2 \quad \text{CCH}_3 & \xrightarrow{\;\text{SeO}_2\;} & \text{OC} \quad \text{CCH}_3 \\
\big| \quad\;\; \big\| & & \big| \quad\;\; \big\| \qquad (30\%) \\
\text{CH}_2\!-\!\!-\text{CH} & & \text{CH}_2\!-\!\!-\text{CH}
\end{array}
$$

ported that pulegone is oxidized by selenium dioxide in the presence of ethyl alcohol to a mixture of 1-methyl-4-isopropylidene-2,3-cyclohexane-dione, 1-methyl-4-isopropylidene-2,3,5-cyclohexanetrione, 1-methyl-2-ethoxy-4-isopropylidene-5-(or 6-)cyclohexen-3-one, and 1-methyl-4-iso-propylidene-6-ethoxy-5-(or 6-)cyclohexene-2,3-dione.   These results show the effect of activation of different methylene groups by a carbonyl group and an ethylenic linkage.

Simple acetylenic hydrocarbons behave similarly to olefins.   Both 1-heptyne[55] and ethylphenylacetylene[56] are oxidized at the α-methylenic carbon atom to give 3-hydroxy-1-heptyne (27%) and 1-phenyl-3-hydroxy-1-butyne (25%) respectively.   The ability of selenium dioxide

$$CH_3(CH_2)_3CH_2C\!\equiv\!CH \xrightarrow{\;SeO_2\;} CH_3(CH_2)_3CHOHC\!\equiv\!CH$$

$$CH_3CH_2C\!\equiv\!CC_6H_5 \xrightarrow{\;SeO_2\;} CH_3CHOHC\!\equiv\!CC_6H_5$$

to bring about direct oxidation at a double or triple bond is illustrated by acetylenes which possess no activated methylene groups.   Diphenyl-acetylene[36] is oxidized to benzil in 35% yield.   Stilbene[17, 36] and the

$$C_6H_5C\!\equiv\!CC_6H_5 \xrightarrow{\;SeO_2\;} C_6H_5COCOC_6H_5$$

lower olefins[48, 57] exhibit the same type of reaction.

$$C_6H_5CH\!=\!CHC_6H_5 \xrightarrow{\;SeO_2\;} C_6H_5COCOC_6H_5 \quad (86\%)$$

$$CH_3CH\!=\!CH_2 \xrightarrow{\;SeO_2\;} CH_3COCHO \quad (19\%)$$

Selenium dioxide is capable of producing a still different type of oxidation whereby oxygen does not enter the final product of the reaction.   The dehydrogenating action of selenium dioxide has been observed in systems where two carbon atoms possessing hydrogen atoms are

[53] Dane, Schmitt, and Rautenstrauch, *Ann.*, **532**, 29 (1937).
[54] Cauquil, *Compt. rend.*, **208**, 1156 (1939).
[55] Truchet, *Compt. rend.*, **196**, 706 (1933).
[56] Truchet, *Compt. rend.*, **196**, 1613 (1933).
[57] Imperial Chem. Ind., Fr. pat. 734,537 [*C.A.*, **27**, 999 (1933)]; Ger. pat. 574,162 [*C.A.*, **27**, 3486 (1933)].

between two activating groups. 1,4-Diketones, such as 2,5-hexane-dione [58,59] and 3-methyl-2,5-hexanedione,[59] are changed to olefins.

$$CH_3COCH_2CH_2COCH_3 \xrightarrow{SeO_2} CH_3COCH\!\!=\!\!CHCOCH_3 \quad (40\%)$$

$$CH_3COCH(CH_3)CH_2COCH_3 \xrightarrow{SeO_2} CH_3COC(CH_3)\!\!=\!\!CHCOCH_3 \,+$$
$$CH_3COC(CH_2OH)\!\!=\!\!CHCOCH_3$$

In the last reaction both dehydrogenation and oxidation have occurred. A similar dehydrogenation has been observed with certain terpenes. α-Phellandrene [60,61] is converted to a mixture of cymene and cumaldehyde.

Selenium dioxide also brings about a number of other reactions. For instance, substituted chalcones [62-65] are converted in good yields to flavones. Diphenylhydrazine [66] yields diphenylamine, and phenyl-

hydrazine derivatives [66] are dehydrogenated to diazonium salts. Numer-

$$(C_6H_5)_2NNH_2 \xrightarrow{SeO_2} (C_6H_5)_2NH \quad (94\%)$$

$$C_6H_5NHNH_2 \cdot HCl \xrightarrow{SeO_2} C_6H_5N_2{}^+Cl^-$$

[58] Armstrong and Robinson, *J. Chem. Soc.*, **1934**, 1650.
[59] Goldberg and Müller, *Helv. Chim. Acta*, **21**, 1699 (1938).
[60] Borgwardt and Schwenk, *J. Am. Chem. Soc.*, **56**, 1185 (1934).
[61] Hirayama, *J. Chem. Soc. Japan*, **59**, 67 (1938) [*C.A.*, **32**, 4969 (1938)].
[62] Bargellini, *Atti X° congr. intern. chim.*, **3**, 32 (1939) [*C.A.*, **34**, 1018 (1940)].
[63] Bargellini and Marini-Bettolo, *Gazz. chim. ital.*, **70**, 170 (1940).
[64] Chakravarti and Dutta, *J. Indian Chem. Soc.*, **16**, 639 (1939) [*C.A.*, **34**. 4735 (1940)].
[65] Mahal and Venkataraman, *J. Chem. Soc.*, **1936**, 569.
[66] Postowsky, Lugowkin, and Mandryk, *Ber.*, **69**, 1913 (1936).

ous sterol derivatives [23] are attacked by selenium dioxide; natural oils like cottonseed oil [67] are isomerized to give products with conjugated systems of double bonds. Skraup reactions [68] have been carried out using selenium dioxide, and even rubber [69] is transformed into a substance that appears to have been vulcanized.

An examination of the tables of selenium dioxide oxidations and reference to review articles [2, 5, 70-81] will show the amazing diversity of this interesting oxidizing agent.

EXPERIMENTAL CONDITIONS

Before attempting a selenium dioxide oxidation, it is advantageous to carry out a small-scale test and recover the precipitated selenium. If a reaction occurs and the calculated amount of selenium is not obtained, there is a good possibility that selenium-containing complexes have formed. Many such complexes are known [7, 75, 82-85] and often complicate the course of the reaction.

The important experimental variables in selenium dioxide oxidations appear to be few. Most important are the solvent and the reaction temperature. Sublimed selenium dioxide is employed most frequently, but occasionally an aqueous solution of selenious acid has been used.

A review of the literature shows that a great variety of solvents has been utilized. The list includes dioxane, acetic acid, acetic anhydride, ethanol, water, benzene, methanol, butyl alcohol, amyl alcohol, nitrobenzene, toluene, xylene, hexane, ether, carbon tetrachloride, anisole, pyridine, ethyl acetate, acetonitrile, and various combinations of these solvents. The first six have found much greater application than the others.

[67] Turk, Dawson, and Soloway, *Am. Paint J.*, **28**, 16, 18, 20 (1943) [*C.A.*, **38**, 547 (1944)].

[68] Kunz, Kochendoerfer, and Koeberle, U. S. pat. 2,001,201 [*C.A.*, **29**, 4377 (1935)].

[69] Fisher, *Ind. Eng. Chem.*, **31**, 1381 (1939).

[70] Hirayama, *Chem. Rev. (Japan)*, **5**, 134 (1939) [*C.A.*, **35**, 7935 (1941)].

[71] Kratzl, *Österr. Chem.-Ztg.*, **41**, 340 (1938) [*C.A.*, **32**, 9037 (1938)].

[72] Sa, *Rev. centro estud. farm. y bioquim.*, **27**, 19, 48 (1937) [*C.A.*, **31**, 5315 (1937)].

[73] Stein, *Angew. Chem.*, **54**, 146 (1941).

[74] Weygand, *Die Chemie*, **55**, 60 (1942).

[75] Waitkins and Clark, *Chem. Revs.*, **36**, 235 (1945).

[76] Vène, *Bull. soc. sci. Bretagne*, **18**, 87 (1942) [*C.A.*, **40**, 6047 (1946)].

[77] Vène, *Bull. soc. chim. France*, **12**, 506 (1945).

[78] Dupont, *Ind. chim. belge*, **10**, 307 (1939) [*C.A.*, **34**, 403 (1940)].

[79] Linstead, *Ann. Repts. on Progress Chem. (Chem. Soc. London)*, **34**, 238 (1937).

[80] Mayor, *Chimie & industrie*, **43**, 188 (1940).

[81] Naves and Igolen, *Bull. inst. pin*, **1935**, 234 [*C.A.*, **30**, 5487 (1936)].

[82] Backer and Strating, *Rec. trav. chim.*, **53**, 1113 (1934).

[83] Fuson, Weinstock, and Ullyot, *J. Am. Chem. Soc.*, **57**, 1803 (1935).

[84] Takamatsu, *J. Pharm. Soc. Japan*, **48**, 450 (1928) [*C.A.*, **22**, 3400 (1928)].

[85] Wierzchowski, *Roczniki Chem.*, **16**, 451 (1936) [*C.A.*, **31**, 1786 (1937)].

The solvent selected should not enter into the reaction either by undergoing oxidation itself or by combining with the desired product; both acetic acid and acetic anhydride show this latter property. They are useful when it is advantageous to isolate an acetate instead of a hydroxyl derivative. It is claimed [16] that acetic acid exerts a favorable effect during selenium dioxide oxidations. Acetic anhydride [36,86,87] can react with selenium dioxide to yield glyoxylic acid anhydride.

$$(CH_3CO)_2O \xrightarrow{SeO_2} (HCOCO)_2O$$

However, under normal experimental conditions the temperatures employed are not high enough to bring about this reaction. Acetic anhydride is often superior to acetic acid in that it does not lead to mixtures of hydroxyl compounds and acetates.

In several instances, alcohols are reported to form ethers as products of the oxidation reaction. Dihydro-α-dicyclopentadiene [88] yields the methyl, ethyl, and amyl ethers of dihydro-α-dicyclopentadien-3-ol when oxidized in the presence of methyl, ethyl, and amyl alcohol, respectively. Crotonaldehyde [87] gives β-methoxy-α-ketobutyraldehyde when methanol is used as the solvent. And, as previously stated, pulegone [54] in ethanol is oxidized to ethoxy derivatives.

The solvent may affect the nature of the end products of the reaction or influence the yield. For instance, 1-methylcyclohexene [89] in ethanol leads to a mixture of 1-methylcyclohexen-6-ol (35%) and 1-methylcyclohexen-6-one (27%). If, however, the reaction is carried out in water solution, a 90% yield of 1-methylcyclohexen-6-one results. Acetic acid, on the other hand, is reported [89] to give a 40% yield of 1-methylcyclohexen-6-ol acetate.

Studies of the oxidation of camphor in ethanol,[26] toluene,[26] xylene,[26] acetic anhydride,[24,25,26,27] and in the absence of a solvent [24] have produced yields of 27%, 89%, 89%, 95%, and 65%, respectively, of camphorquinone. Likewise, it has been found that 3-chlorocamphor [26,27] is not attacked by selenium dioxide in the presence of acetic acid but is transformed to camphorquinone when no solvent is used.

An examination [23] of the behavior of a series of sterols and bile acids toward selenium dioxide has shown that in aqueous-ethanolic solution marked differences in reactivity are observed. The separation of selenium takes place at room temperature with ergosterol, dihydroergosterol, lumisterol, calciferol, and apocholic acid. Many other sterols, mostly

[86] Hinsberg, *Ann.*, **260**, 40 (1890).
[87] Rappen, *J. prakt. Chem.*, **157**, 177 (1941).
[88] Alder and Stein, *Ann.*, **504**, 205 (1933).
[89] Urion, *Compt. rend.*, **199**, 363 (1934).

ergosterol derivatives, react readily at the temperature of the water bath. A third class, which includes nearly all the derivatives of cholesterol examined, does not react under these conditions, but reaction generally takes place at 100° in acetic acid or nitrobenzene. Most selenium dioxide oxidations can be carried out without the use of excessive temperatures. They are usually run at the boiling point of the solvent, and the commonly used solvents boil in the neighborhood of 100°. However, the oxidation of aromatic hydrocarbons, some dehydrogenation reactions, and the direct oxidation of double bonds appear to require higher temperatures. An interesting effect of temperature has been observed during the oxidation of $\Delta^{9,10}$-octahydronaphthalene [90] in acetic anhydride. At 0–5° the product of the reaction is $\Delta^{9,10}$-octahydro-1-naphthol acetate; at 25–30°, $\Delta^{9,10}$-octahydro-1-naphthol acetate and $\Delta^{9,10}$-octahydro-1,5-naphthalenediol diacetate; at 70°, $\Delta^{9,10}$-octahydro-1-naphthol acetate, $\Delta^{9,10}$-octahydro-1,5-naphthalenediol diacetate, and 1,2,3,5,6,7-hexahydro-1,5-naphthalenediol diacetate; and at 120–124°, only 1,2,3,5,6,7-hexahydro-1,5-naphthalenediol diacetate.

The isolation of the oxidation products usually involves merely the filtration of the reaction mixture to remove metallic selenium, distillation of the solvent, and then either crystallization or distillation of the residue. Only small amounts of selenium contaminate the residue if the usual procedure of employing the calculated amount of selenium dioxide is followed and the reaction is carried to completion. An excess of selenium dioxide can be removed by means of lead acetate, sulfur dioxide, or other reducing agents.

EXPERIMENTAL PROCEDURES

Preparation of Selenium Dioxide

A. By Combustion of Selenium in Oxygen and Nitrogen Dioxide.[91] The apparatus used is shown in the figure. One hundred grams of selenium is placed in the closed end of the tube, and nitrogen dioxide and

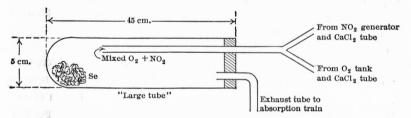

[90] Campbell and Harris, *J. Am. Chem. Soc.*, **63**, 2721 (1941).
[91] Naeser, *Inorganic Syntheses*, **1**, 117 (1939).

oxygen, dried over calcium chloride, are introduced through the Y tube. Some regulation of the gas flow is necessary to secure the best results. The gases must be mixed thoroughly before coming in contact with the selenium. It is desirable to use separate drying tubes for each gas, as the nitrogen dioxide contains a great deal of moisture. If a stopcock is placed between the nitrogen dioxide dryer and the Y tube, the calcium chloride may be changed without interrupting the flow of oxygen or the heating.

When all the air and moisture have been displaced from the tube, the selenium is heated strongly with a Bunsen flame. A white deposit of selenium dioxide forms on the surface of the selenium but sublimes as soon as the temperature becomes sufficiently high.

At the same time, the remaining selenium melts to a viscous mass and eventually burns with a pale blue flame. The sublimate collects on the gas-delivery tube and on the sides of the large tube. The exit gases are bubbled through water and then sodium hydroxide solution to remove the oxides of nitrogen. After all the selenium has reacted, the contents of the tube are allowed to cool while oxygen still is passing through the apparatus and the selenium dioxide is removed.

A yield of 114 g. (80%) is obtained readily by this method. There is always some loss of selenium due, perhaps, to the formation of the suboxide. The presence of tellurium as an impurity in the selenium also decreases the yield. Tellurium remains behind, presumably in the form of the oxide which is not volatilized readily.

The selenium dioxide is obtained in the form of a snow-white product which may be kept in a tightly stoppered bottle for an indefinite period of time. It may turn pink on exposure to air as the result of reduction by dust.

B. By Oxidation of Selenium with Nitric Acid.[92] One hundred milliliters of concentrated nitric acid is placed in a casserole or evaporating dish which is set on a sand bath. Heat is applied to the bath, and 60 g. of crude selenium is added cautiously in small portions to the nitric acid. The selenium should be scattered over the surface of the acid, and the frothing should be allowed to subside after each addition. By the time the reaction is completed, the sand bath should be at a temperature sufficient to start evaporation. Heating is continued until the residue appears dry. Care must be taken during the evaporation and subsequent cooling to keep the product broken up in order to avoid the formation of a hard, compact mass.

The residue is purified either by a wet treatment or by sublimation according to the procedure of Lenher.[93]

[92] Baker and Maxson, *Inorganic Syntheses*, **1**, 119 (1939).
[93] Lenher, *Am. Chem. J.*, **20**, 555 (1898).

ORGANIC REACTIONS

Wet Purification. The residue is treated with enough water to bring the selenium dioxide into solution, and, after filtration, 10 ml. of concentrated hydrochloric acid is added. A slow stream of sulfur dioxide is passed into the solution until heat is no longer evolved. This requires from two to five hours. Red selenium is deposited, but it changes to a pasty gray form which becomes brittle on standing for a few hours. This change is accelerated by boiling.

The selenium is removed by filtration, ground in a mortar, washed free of acid, dried, and finally heated over a Bunsen burner. After the mass has cooled, it is dissolved in concentrated nitric acid and evaporated as described previously. In order to ensure the complete removal of the nitric acid, the residue is dissolved in 75 ml. of water and evaporated again. The yield of white selenium dioxide is about 76 g. (90%).

Purification by Sublimation. The crude selenium dioxide, which may be contaminated with copper and other heavy metals present in the selenium, is pulverized and placed in an evaporating dish. The selenium dioxide is moistened with a small amount of nitric acid, and two nested funnels are inverted over the evaporating dish (a plug of glass wool is placed in the neck of the larger funnel). The dish is heated with an open flame, and the selenium dioxide condenses in long needle-like crystals on the walls of the funnels; m.p. 340°.

The results observed by Kaplan [94] during the oxidation of methylquinolines are of interest. He found that selenium dioxide, freshly prepared by the action of nitric acid on metallic selenium, whether used directly or purified by sublimation, gave good yields of quinolinealdehydes consistent with those reported originally by Kwartler and Lindwall.[95] However, selenium dioxide which was prepared in the same manner but allowed to stand for several months before use afforded poor yields of the aldehydes; these yields were not improved by sublimation of such aged selenium dioxide at the time of use. On the other hand, if the selenium dioxide was sublimed immediately after preparation and stored, the loss of effectiveness in a given length of time was less marked than with the unsublimed material. The change that occurred in the selenium dioxide was not determined.

Preparation of Phenylglyoxal [96]

In a 1-l. three-necked round-bottomed flask, fitted with a liquid-sealed stirrer and a reflux condenser, are placed 60 ml. of dioxane, 111 g. (1

[94] Kaplan, *J. Am. Chem. Soc.*, **63**, 2654 (1941).

[95] Kwartler and Lindwall, *J. Am. Chem. Soc.*, **59**, 524 (1937); Clemo and Hoggarth *J. Chem. Soc.*, **1939**, 1241.

[96] Riley and Gray, *Org. Syntheses*, **15**, 67 (1935).

mole) of selenium dioxide, and 20 ml. of water. The mixture is heated to 50–55° and stirred until the solid has gone into solution. Then 120 g. (1 mole) of acetophenone is added in one lot and the resulting mixture is refluxed with continued stirring for four hours. The hot solution is decanted from the precipitated selenium, and the dioxane and water are removed by distillation through a short column. The phenylglyoxal is distilled under diminished pressure from a 250-ml. Claisen flask, and the fraction boiling at 95–97°/25 mm. is collected. The yield is 93–96 g. (69–72%).

The aldehyde sets to a stiff gel on standing, probably as a result of polymerization. It may be recovered without appreciable loss by distillation. Phenylglyoxal may also be preserved in the form of the hydrate, which is prepared conveniently by dissolving the yellow liquid in 3.5–4 volumes of hot water and allowing crystallization to take place.

Preparation of 3,8-Dimethylquinoline-2-aldehyde [47]

A solution of 5 g. of 2,3,8-trimethylquinoline and 3.5 g. of selenium dioxide in 40 ml. of ethanol is boiled under reflux for six hours, and the precipitated selenium is filtered from the hot solution. The filtrate is concentrated, and 3.3 g. of the aldehyde is collected in the form of straw-colored needles. A reddish solid is precipitated by the addition of water to the mother liquor. It is removed by filtration and dissolved in 10 ml. of benzene, and the solution is shaken with 30 ml. of a saturated solution of sodium bisulfite for one hour. The crystalline addition product is filtered, washed with ether, and decomposed with dilute aqueous sodium carbonate. Another 1.2 g. of the aldehyde is obtained in this manner; the total yield is 82%. The aldehyde is purified by distillation under 1 mm. pressure followed by recrystallization from ethanol. It forms long colorless needles; m.p., 107–108°.

Preparation of cis-Δ^{5,6}-3,4-Cholestenediol [97]

A solution of 25 g. (0.22 mole) of selenium dioxide in 10 ml. of water and 500 ml. of acetic acid is warmed to 80° and mixed rapidly with a solution of 50 g. (0.13 mole) of cholesterol in 250 ml. of benzene which has been warmed also to 80°. The mixture immediately turns yellow and then red; it is refluxed on a steam bath for one hour. One hundred grams of sodium acetate is added, and, after heating for a few minutes, the black modification of selenium is deposited and removed by filtration. The filtrate is poured into 1 l. of half-saturated salt solution. The

[97] Rosenheim and Starling, *J. Chem. Soc.*, **1937**, 377.

---

benzene layer is separated, washed with water, dried over sodium sulfate, and concentrated under reduced pressure. The residue, which weighs 60 g., is suspended in 500 ml. of petroleum ether (b.p. 40–50°), allowed to settle in a tall cylinder, and washed twice by decantation with the same solvent. The crude, creamy-white product (26 g.), m.p., 174–175°, is crystallized once from acetone (Norit) and then from 85% ethanol. There is obtained 20 g. (39%) of the cis-diol in inch-long, monoclinic needles; m.p. 176–177°.

Preparation of Ninhydrin [98]

In a 2-l. three-necked flask fitted with a reflux condenser and a mechanical stirrer is placed 55 g. (0.5 mole) of sublimed selenium dioxide dissolved in 1.2 l. of dioxane and 25 ml. of water. The stirrer is started, and the solution is heated to approximately 60–70°. The flame is withdrawn, 73 g. (0.5 mole) of crude 1,3-diketohydrindene is added, and the resulting mixture is refluxed for six hours. A solid separates during this period and is filtered while the mixture is still hot. The filtrate is transferred to a distilling flask, and three-fourths of the dioxane is distilled. Between 400 and 500 ml. of water is added, and the solution is boiled to coagulate the tarry precipitate, which then is removed by filtration. The filtrate is concentrated by distillation to approximately 250 ml. and filtered. The filtrate is boiled with 1 g. of Norit, filtered again, concentrated to 125 ml., and allowed to stand at room temperature. The crude ninhydrin which crystallizes is filtered, the mother liquor concentrated, and a second crop of crystals obtained; the total yield of crude material is 36–38 g.

The impure ninhydrin is contaminated with a trace of selenious acid which acts as a bleaching agent and prevents the formation of the characteristic blue color reaction with α-amino acids. Crystallization from hot water with the aid of Norit furnishes 28–31 g. (31–35%) of long, colorless prisms of pure ninhydrin which gives none of the customary tests for selenium and produces the characteristic color reaction with α-amino acids. The purified product loses water of hydration and turns red between 125° and 130°, and finally it melts with decomposition at 241–243°.

SURVEY OF SELENIUM DIOXIDE OXIDATIONS

The following tables list the compounds which have been treated with selenium dioxide. The literature has been surveyed up to and including the August, 1947, Chemical Abstracts.

[98] Teeters and Shriner, J. Am. Chem. Soc., 55, 3026 (1933).

The compounds are divided into the following sections, which are arranged in alphabetical order: Acids and Acid Derivatives, Alcohols, Aldehydes, Hydrocarbons, Ketones, Nitrogen-Containing Compounds, Phenolic Compounds, Steroids, Sulfur-Containing Compounds, Terpenes, and Miscellaneous. These have been broken down further into a number of sub groups which are listed below. The attempt has been made to place compounds which contain more than one functional group according to the most dominant characteristic.

Since it has often been necessary to depend upon abstracts rather than the original articles, omissions of items such as the solvents used or the yields obtained do not always mean that the data have not been published.

INDEX TO TABLES

ACIDS AND ACID DERIVATIVES

Compound Treated	Solvent	Product	Yield %	Reference *
		ACIDS		
3,4-Dimethoxyhomo-phthalic acid	Xylene	2,3-Dimethoxy-phthalonic acid	—	43
4,6-Dimethoxyhomo-phthalic acid	Xylene	m-Opianic acid	—	42
5,6-Dimethoxyhomo-phthalic acid	Xylene	ψ-Opianic acid	—	42
Homophthalic acid	Xylene	Phthalonic acid	80	42
Hydrocyanic acid	$(CH_3CO)_2O$	Selenium + unidentified products	—	86
Lauric acid	None	Undecene	—	38
Leucine	None	$C_6H_{13}NO$	—	38
Levulinic acid	CH_3CO_2H	Not isolated	—	15
5-Methoxyhomophthalic acid	Xylene	4-Methoxyphthalonic acid	—	43
4,5-Methylenedioxy-homophthalic acid	Xylene	4,5-Methylenedioxy-phthalonic acid	—	44
Myristic acid	None	Tridecene	—	38
Palmitic acid	None	Pentadecene	—	38
Phenoxyacetic acid	H_2O	Diphenoxyacetic acid selenoxide	—	84
Propionic acid	—	Pyruvic acid	—	41
Pyruvic acid	CH_3CO_2H	Not isolated	—	15
Stearic acid	None	Heptadecene	—	38
Thiocyanic acid	H_2O	$Se + CO_2 + SO_4^= + H^+ + NH_4^+$	—	99
		ANHYDRIDES		
Acetic anhydride	None	Glyoxylic acid	17	36, 86, 87
1,2-Dimethyl-1,2,3,6-tetrahydrophthalic anhydride	$(CH_3CO)_2O$	1,2-Dimethyl-6-acetoxy-1,2,3,6-tetrahydrophthalic anhydride	—	100

* References 99–324 are on pp. 382–386.

ACIDS AND ACID DERIVATIVES—*Continued*

Compound Treated	Solvent	Product	Yield %	Reference *

ESTERS

Compound Treated	Solvent	Product	Yield %	Reference *
Diethyl cyclopentane-1,3-dione-2,5-dicarboxylate	Dioxane	Diethyl cyclopentane-1,3,4-trione-2,5-dicarboxylate	—	101
Diethyl glutaconate	CH_3CO_2H	Diethyl ketoglutaconate	—	102
Diethyl malate	None	Diethyl diketosuccinate + diethyl fumarate + ethyl hydrogen mesoxalate + oxalic acid + malic acid + ethyl hydrogen malate	—	17
Diethyl malonate	None	Diethyl mesoxalate + monoethyl ester of mesoxalic acid + diethyl oxalate	32	19, 32, 33
Diethyl β-ketoglutarate	None	Ethyl α,β-diketobutyrate	—	17
Diethyl succinate	None	Diethyl diketosuccinate + diethyl fumarate + ethyl hydrogen fumarate	— — 40	33
Diethyl tartrate	None	Diethyl ketohydroxysuccinate	11	103
Dimethyl tartrate	None	Dimethyl fumarate	—	103
Ethyl acetoacetate	Xylene	Ethyl α,β-diketobutyrate	35	32
Ethyl lactate	None	Ethyl pyruvate + $OHCCOCO_2C_2H_5$ or $OHCCHCO_2C_2H_5$ | OH	—	103
Ethyl β-methylcinnamate	Dioxane	β-Phenyl-$\Delta^{\alpha,\beta}$-butenolide	—	104
Ethyl β-phenylpropionate	None	Cinnamic acid	8	17
Tetrahydrofurfuryl acetate	CH_3CO_2H	No reaction	—	105

* References 99–324 are on pp. 382–386.

ALCOHOLS

Compound Treated	Solvent	Product	Yield %	Reference *
Benzyl alcohol	None	Benzaldehyde	100	33
n-Butyl alcohol	None	Ethylglyoxal	Trace	33
2,2-Dimesitylethanol	—	Mesitil	—	106
Ethyl alcohol	None	Glyoxal	41	7, 33
Isobutyl alcohol	—	Diisobutyl selenite	—	7
Methanol	—	Dimethyl selenite	—	7
α-Methylallyl alcohol	(C$_2$H$_5$)$_2$O, C$_2$H$_5$OH, or dioxane	α-Methylacrolein	62	107
β-Methylallyl alcohol	Hexyl alcohol or dioxane	β-Methylacrolein	50–60	108
n-Propyl alcohol	None	Methylglyoxal	Trace	7, 33
Tetrahydrofurfuryl alcohol	None	No reaction	—	109

ALDEHYDES

Acetaldehyde	None	Glyoxal	90	4, 11, 19
n-Butyraldehyde	None	Ethylglyoxal	45	4, 11, 19
Cinnamaldehyde	None	Hydrocinnamic acid	—	38
Crotonaldehyde	CH$_3$OH	β-Methoxy-α-keto-butyraldehyde	19	87
	(CH$_3$CO)$_2$O	β-Acetoxy-α-keto-butyraldehyde	—	87
	H$_2$O or CH$_3$CO$_2$H	Polymeric β-hydroxy-α-ketobutyralde-hyde	—	87
	(CH$_3$CO)$_2$O + CH$_3$CO$_2$H	Diacetate of croton-aldehyde	—	87
Heptaldehyde	CH$_3$CO$_2$H	Not isolated	—	11
Homopiperonal	—	3,4-Methylenedioxy-phenylglyoxal	—	110
Isobutyraldehyde	CH$_3$CO$_2$H	Not isolated	—	11
Isovaleraldehyde	CH$_3$CO$_2$H	Not isolated	—	11
Paraldehyde	Dioxane + CH$_3$CO$_2$H	Glyoxal†	74	111
Phenylacetaldehyde	None	Phenylglyoxal	35	4
Propionaldehyde	None	Methylglyoxal	30	4, 11, 19

* References 99–324 are on pp. 382–386.
† Isolated as the bisulfite addition product.

HYDROCARBONS

Compound Treated	Solvent	Product	Yield %	Reference *
		ALKANES		
Ethane	None	Glyoxal + acetic acid + carbon dioxide	—	48
		OLEFINS		
Ethylene	None	Glyoxal	82	48, 57, 112, 113
1-Hexene	CH_3CO_2H + $(CH_3CO)_2O$	2-Hexen-1-ol acetate + 1-hexen-3-ol acetate	—	16
2-Methyl-2-butene	CH_3CO_2H + $(CH_3CO)_2O$	2-Methyl-2-buten-1-ol acetate	—	16, 48
		Isoprene + tiglaldehyde + tiglic alcohol	—	
2-Methyl-2-pentene	CH_3CO_2H + $(CH_3CO)_2O$	2-Methyl-2-penten-1-ol acetate	—	16
3-Methyl-2-pentene	CH_3CO_2H + $(CH_3CO)_2O$	3-Methyl-3-penten-2-ol acetate + 2-ethyl-2-buten-1-ol acetate	—	16
3-Methyl-3-pentene	CH_3CO_2H + $(CH_3CO)_2O$	3-Methyl-3-penten-2-ol acetate	—	16
3-Nonene	CH_3CO_2H + $(CH_3CO)_2O$	Mixture of acetates of nonenols	—	16
4-Nonene	CH_3CO_2H + $(CH_3CO)_2O$	Mixture of acetates of nonenols	—	16
Olefins	—	Olefin oxides, glycols, etc.	—	114
2-Pentene	CH_3CO_2H + $(CH_3CO)_2O$	2-Penten-4-ol acetate	—	16, 48
2,3-Dimethyl-3-pentene	CH_3CO_2H + $(CH_3CO)_2O$	2-Isopropyl-2-buten-1-ol acetate	—	16
3-Phenyl-3-pentene	CH_3CO_2H + $(CH_3CO)_2O$	3-Phenyl-3-penten-2-ol acetate	—	16
Propylene	None	Methylglyoxal	19	48, 57
Stilbene	None	Benzil	86	17, 36
Styrene	—	No reaction	—	48
2,2,3-Trimethyl-3-pentene	CH_3CO_2H + $(CH_3CO)_2O$	2-tert-Butyl-2-buten-1-ol acetate	—	16

* References 99–324 are on pp. 382–386.

HYDROCARBONS—*Continued*

Compound Treated	Solvent	Product	Yield %	Reference *
		DIOLEFINS		
1,6-Dibiphenylene-1,5-hexadiene	$C_6H_5OCH_3$ + CH_3CO_2H	1,6-Dibiphenylene-hexatriene	—	115
1,3-Pentadiene	—	3-Pentene-1,2-diol	—	116
1,1,6,6-Tetraphenyl-1,5-hexadiene	CH_3CO_2H	1,1,6,6-Tetraphenyl-hexatriene	50	115
1,1,5,5-Tetraphenyl-1,4-pentadiene	—	1,1,2,2-Tetra-(β,β-diphenylvinyl) ethane	60	117
		CYCLOÖLEFINS		
Cyclohexene	CH_3CO_2H + $(CH_3CO)_2O$	1-Cyclohexen-3-ol acetate + cyclohexenone	50 6	16, 50, 51
	$(CH_3)_2CO$ + H_2O_2	*trans*-Cyclohexanediol	45	116
Cyclopentadiene	—	Cyclopentene-3,4-diol	—	116
Cyclopentene	$(CH_3CO)_2O$	Cyclopentenol acetate + cyclopentendiol diacetate	—	53
Dihydro-α-dicyclopentadiene	CH_3OH	Methyl ether of dihydro-α-dicyclopentadien-3-ol	—	88
	C_2H_5OH	Ethyl ether of dihydro-α-dicyclopentadien-3-ol	60	88
	$C_5H_{11}OH$	Amyl ether of dihydro-α-dicyclopentadien-3-ol	—	88
	$(CH_3CO)_2O$	Dihydro-α-dicyclopentadien-3-ol acetate	73	88
Dihydronordicyclopentadiene	CH_3CO_2H	Dihydro-exo-dicyclopentadien-3-ol acetate	38	118

* References 99–324 are on pp. 382–386.

HYDROCARBONS—*Continued*

Compound Treated	Solvent	Product	Yield %	Reference *
CYCLOÖLEFINS—*Continued*				
Dihydro-α-tricyclopentadiene	(CH₃CO)₂O	Dihydro-α-tricyclopentadien-3-ol acetate	80	88
Dihydro-β-tricyclopentadiene	(CH₃CO)₂O	Dihydro-β-tricyclopentadien-3-ol acetate	61	88
1,2-Dimethylcyclohexene	CH₃CO₂H + (CH₃CO)₂O	2,3-Dimethyl-1,3-cyclohexadiene + o-xylene	70	16, 119
1,6-Dimethylcyclohexene	CH₃CO₂H + (CH₃CO)₂O	2,3-Dimethyl-1,3-cyclohexadiene + o-xylene	—	16, 119
1-Ethylcyclohexene	CH₃CO₂H + (CH₃CO)₂O	1-Ethylcyclohexen-6-ol acetate	23	16
1-Ethylcyclopentene	CH₃CO₂H + (CH₃CO)₂O	1-Ethylcyclopenten-5-ol acetate	19	16
1-Methylcyclohexene	C₂H₅OH	1-Methylcyclohexen-6-ol + 1-methylcyclohexen-6-one	35, 27	89, 120
	H₂O	1-Methylcyclohexen-6-one	90	89
	CH₃CO₂H	1-Methylcyclohexen-6-ol acetate	40	89
3-Methylcyclohexene	CH₃CO₂H + (CH₃CO)₂O	6-Methylcyclohexen-3-ol acetate + 4-methylcyclohexen-3-ol + 1-methylcyclohexene + toluene	—	16
	CH₃CO₂H + (CH₃CO)₂O	6-Methylcyclohexen-3-ol acetate + 4-methylcyclohexen-3-ol acetate	—	119
4-Methylcyclohexene	CH₃CO₂H + (CH₃CO)₂O	4-,5-, and 6-Methylcyclohexen-3-ol acetates	—	16
	CH₃CO₂H + (CH₃CO)₂O	6-Methylcyclohexen-3-ol acetate + 4-methylcyclohexen-3-ol acetate + 4-methylcyclohexen-1-ol acetate	—	119

HYDROCARBONS—*Continued*

Compound Treated	Solvent	Product	Yield %	Reference *
		CYCLOÖLEFINS—*Continued*		
1-Methylcyclopentene	(CH₃CO)₂O	1-Methylcyclopenten-5-ol acetate	—	53
1-Methyl-2-*sec*-iso-octyl-1 (?)-cyclo-pentene	C₄H₉OH	Not isolated	—	121
9-Methyloctahydro-naphthalene	(CH₃CO)₂O	*cis*-9-Methyloctahy-dro-3-naphthol acetate	17	122
Δ⁹,¹⁰-Octahydronaph-thalene	(CH₃CO)₂O (0–5°)	Δ⁹,¹⁰-Octahydro-1-naphthol acetate	65	90
	(CH₃CO)₂O (25–30°)	Δ⁹,¹⁰-Octahydro-1-naphthol acetate + Δ⁹,¹⁰-octahydro-1,5-naphthalenediol diacetate	35 12.5	90
	(CH₃CO)₂O (70°)	Δ⁹ ¹⁰-Octahydro-1-naphthol acetate + Δ⁹,¹⁰-octahydro-1,5-naphthalenediol + 1,2,3,5,6,7-hexahy-dro-1,5-naphtha-lenediol diacetate	17	90
	(CH₃CO)₂O (120–124°)	1,2,3,5,6,7-Hexahy-dro-1,5-naphtha-lenediol diacetate	—	90
1,1,3,5-Tetramethyl-2 4-cyclohexadiene	CH₃CO₂H	2,2,4,4-Tetramethyl-3,5-cyclohexadien-one	—	123
1,1,4-Trimethyl-3-cyclo-heptene	C₂H₅OH	1,1,4-Trimethyl-3-cyclohepten-5-one + 1,1-dimethyl-3-cycloheptene-4-car-boxaldehyde	—	124
		ACETYLENES		
Acetylene	None	Glyoxal	6	48, 125
Phenylacetylene	None	Benzoic acid	—	36

* References 99–324 are on pp. 382–386.

HYDROCARBONS—*Continued*

Compound Treated	Solvent	Product	Yield %	Reference *
ACETYLENES—*Continued*				
Diphenylacetylene	None	Benzil	35	36
1-Phenyl-1-propyne	—	1-Phenyl-3-hydroxy-1-butyne	25	56
1-Heptyne	C_2H_5OH	3-Hydroxy-1-heptyne	27	55
1-Octyne	C_2H_5OH	3-Hydroxy-1-octyne	—	55
AROMATIC HYDROCARBONS				
Acenaphthene	None	Acenaphthylene + cis-acenaphthene glycol + trans-acenaphthene glycol	25 16	126
	CH_3CO_2H	Acenaphthylene + acenaphthylene glycol + polyacenaphthylene + dinaphthylenecyclobutane	—	127
Anthracene	None	Anthraquinone	76	36
	$C_6H_5NO_2$	Anthraquinone	73	17, 36
	H_2O	Anthraquinone	70	127a
Benzene	None	Not isolated	—	128
Bibenzyl	None	Benzil + stilbene	33 17.5	17
Chrysofluorene	H_2O	Chrysofluorenone	80	37
1,2,5,6-Dibenzofluorene	H_2O	1,2,5,6-Dibenzofluorenone	39	37
1,2,7,8-Dibenzofluorene	H_2O	1,2,7,8-Dibenzofluorenone	38	129
3,4,5,6-Dibenzofluorene	H_2O	3,4,5,6-Dibenzofluorenone	—	129
1,2,8,9-Dibenzopentacene	$C_6H_5NO_2$	1,2,8,9-Dibenzopentacene-6,13-quinone	—	130
9,10-Dihydroanthracene	CH_3CO_2H	Anthracene	60	127a

* References 99–324 are on pp. 382–386.

HYDROCARBONS—*Continued*

Compound Treated	Solvent	Product	Yield %	Reference *
AROMATIC HYDROCARBONS—*Continued*				
7,16-Dihydroheptacene	$C_6H_5NO_2$	7,16-Heptacene-quinone	—	39
6,15-Dihydrohexacene	$C_6H_5NO_2$	6,15-Hexacene-quinone	—	39
Diphenylmethane	None	Benzophenone	87	34, 35, 36
Fluorene	H_2O	Fluorenone	65	36, 37
Hexahydropyrene	CH_3CO_2H	Pyrene	60	127a
Indene	—	Hydrindene + C_9H_{10}	—	38
9-Methyldecalin	—	No reaction	—	131
as-Octahydroanthracene	H_2O	Anthraquinone	—	127a
s-Octahydroanthracene	H_2O	Anthraquinone	—	127a
Phenanthrene	None	Phenanthraquinone	3	17, 36
Polybenzyl	Dioxane	No reaction	—	132
Toluene	—	Benzoic acid	—	41
Triphenylmethane	None	Triphenylcarbinol	15	35
SUBSTITUTED AROMATIC HYDROCARBONS				
Benzyl chloride	None	Benzaldehyde	49	35, 40
2,4-Dinitrotoluene	C_2H_5OH or dioxane	No reaction	—	35
p-Nitrobenzal bromide	None	p-Nitrobenzoic acid	—	35
p-Nitrobenzyl bromide	None	p-Nitrobenzaldehyde	56	35
7(?)-Nitro-1,2,5,6-di-benzofluorene	H_2O	7(?)-Nitro-1,2,5,6-di-benzofluorenone	—	133
p-Nitrotoluene	None	p-Nitrobenzoic acid	—	35
2,4,6-Trinitrotoluene	C_2H_5OH or dioxane	No reaction	—	35
KETONES				
MONOKETONES				
Acetomesitylene	Dioxane	Mesitylglyoxal	82.5	134
Acetone	None	Methylglyoxal	60	4, 10, 12, 19, 135–138

* References 99–324 are on pp. 382–386.

KETONES—*Continued*

Compound Treated	Solvent	Product	Yield %	Reference *
MONOKETONES—*Continued*				
Acetophenone	Dioxane	Phenylglyoxal	70	4, 10, 13, 19, 96, 138, 139
9-Acetyloctahydro-anthracene	Dioxane	Octahydro-9-anthra-ceneglyoxal hydrate	83	140
2-Benzylbenzanthrone	None	2-Benzoylbenzan-throne	—	3
Benzyl 4-biphenylyl ketone	$(CH_3CO)_2O$	4-Phenylbenzil	95	20
Benzyl 4-bromophenyl ketone	$(CH_3CO)_2O$	4-Bromobenzil	97	20
Benzyl 4-chlorophenyl ketone	$(CH_3CO)_2O$	4-Chlorobenzil	98	20
Benzyl duryl ketone	Dioxane	Phenyl duryl dike-tone	—	141
Benzyl isoduryl ketone	Dioxane	Phenyl isoduryl dike-tone	81	142
Benzyl mesityl ketone	$(CH_3CO)_2O$	2,4,6-Trimethylbenzil	97	20
Benzyl methyl ketone	Dioxane	Phenyl methyl dike-tone	60	13, 143
Benzyl p-tolyl ketone	$(CH_3CO)_2O$	4-Methylbenzil	74	20
Benzyl 2,4,6-triiso-propylphenyl ketone	Dioxane	2,4,6-Triisopropyl-phenyl phenyl di-ketone	85	141, 144
Benzyl 4-(o-xylyl) ketone	$(CH_3CO)_2O$	3,4-Dimethylbenzil	98	20
Benzyl 4-(m-xylyl) ketone	$(CH_3CO)_2O$	2,4-Dimethylbenzil	—	20
Benzyl p-xylyl ketone	$(CH_3CO)_2O$	2,5-Dimethylbenzil	89	20
3-Bromoacetomesitylene	Dioxane	3-Bromomesityl-glyoxal	65	145
p-Bromoacetophenone	Xylene	p-Bromophenyl-glyoxal	55	13, 146
p-Bromobenzyl mesityl ketone	Dioxane	p-Bromophenyl mesi-tyl diketone	72	145
3-Bromo-5-nitroaceto-mesitylene	Dioxane	3-Bromo-5-nitromesi-tylglyoxal	90	145
2-Butanone	None	Ethylglyoxal + biacetyl	17 1	4, 10, 12, 19

* References 99–324 are on pp. 382–386.

KETONES—*Continued*

Compound Treated	Solvent	Product	Yield %	Reference *

MONOKETONES—*Continued*

Compound Treated	Solvent	Product	Yield %	Reference *
p-Chloroacetophenone	Xylene	p-Chlorophenyl-glyoxal	64	13, 146
Crotonophenone	Dioxane	No reaction	—	147
Cycloheptanone	C_2H_5OH	1,2-Cycloheptanedione	—	21
Cyclohexanone	C_2H_5OH	1,2-Cyclohexanedione	46	4, 19, 120 148
Cycloöctanone	C_2H_5OH	8-Ethoxy-1,2-cyclooctanedione	—	21
Cyclopentanone	C_2H_5OH	1,2-Cyclopentanedione	7	4
Desoxybenzoin	$(CH_3CO)_2O$	Benzil	88	20
3,5-Dibromoacetomesitylene	Dioxane	3,5-Dibromomesitylglyoxal	41.5	149
3,5-Dimethyl-Δ^2-cyclohexenone	CH_3CO_2H	3-Hydroxy-2,6-dimethylquinone	—	52
2,4-Dimethyl-6-methoxyacetophenone	Dioxane	2,4-Dimethyl-6-methoxyphenylglyoxal	—	150
2,4-Dimethyl-3-pentanone	CH_3CO_2H	Not isolated	—	10
Diphenylacetoin	—	1,4-Diphenyl-2,3-butanedione	—	151
3,4-Diphenylcyclopentanone	Dioxane	3,4-Diphenyl-3-cyclopentenone	—	152
2,3-Diphenylcyclopentenone	Dioxane	No reaction	—	153
Dypnone	Dioxane	2,4-Diphenylfuran	10	147
p-Ethoxyacetophenone	Dioxane	p-Ethoxyphenylglyoxal	40	154
3-Ethyl-5-hydroxy-6,7-dimethoxy-3,4-dihydro-1(2)-naphthalenone	CH_3CO_2H or C_2H_5OH	Red dye	—	155
2-Heptanone	CH_3CO_2H	Not isolated	—	14
4-Heptanone	CH_3CO_2H	Not isolated	—	10
2-Hydroxy-4'-benzyloxy-4,6-dimethoxychalcone	$C_5H_{11}OH$	4'-Benzyloxy-5,7-dimethoxyflavone	70	65

* References 99–324 are on pp. 382–386.

SELENIUM DIOXIDE OXIDATION361

KETONES—*Continued*

Compound Treated	Solvent	Product	Yield %	Reference *
MONOKETONES—*Continued*				
2-Hydroxy-4-benzyloxy-phenyl styryl ketone	$C_5H_{11}OH$	7-Benzyloxyflavone	34	156
2-Hydroxy-3-chloro-3',4'-dimethoxychalcone	$C_5H_{11}OH$	8-Chloro-3',4'-dimethoxyflavone	—	64
2-Hydroxy-5-chloro-3',4'-dimethoxychalcone	$C_5H_{11}OH$	6-Chloro-3',4'-dimethoxyflavone	—	64
2-Hydroxy-4-(β,γ-dihydroxypropoxy) phenyl styryl ketone	—	7-(β,γ-Dihydroxypropoxy)flavone	—	157
2-Hydroxy-4,5-dimethoxychalcone	$C_5H_{11}OH$	6,7-Dimethoxyflavone	—	63
2-Hydroxy-3,4-dimethoxycinnamylideneacetophenone	$C_5H_{11}OH$	7,8-Dimethoxy-2-styrylchromone	—	158
2-Hydroxy-3,4-dimethoxyfurfurylideneacetophenone	C_2H_5OH	7,8-Dimethoxy-2-(2-furyl)chromone	—	159
2-Hydroxy-4,5-dimethoxyfurfurylidenacetophenone	C_2H_5OH	6,7-Dimethoxy-2-(2-furyl)chromone	—	159
2-Hydroxy-4-methoxycinnamylideneacetophenone	$C_5H_{11}OH$	7-Methoxy-2-styrylchromone	—	158
2-Hydroxy-4-methoxyfurfurylideneacetophenone	$C_5H_{11}OH$	7-Methoxy-2-(2-furyl)chromone	—	159
2-Hydroxy-3-nitro-5-methyl-3',4'-dimethoxychalcone	$C_5H_{11}OH$	6-Methyl-8-nitro-3',4'-dimethoxyflavone	—	64
o-Hydroxyphenyl styryl ketone	$C_5H_{11}OH$	Flavone	42	156
2-Hydroxy-3,4,6,4'-tetramethoxychalcone	$C_5H_{11}OH$	5,7,8,4'-Tetramethoxyflavone	—	62
2-Hydroxy-4,5,4'-trimethoxychalcone	$C_5H_{11}OH$	6,7,4'-Trimethoxyflavone	—	63
p-Iodoacetophenone	CH_3CO_2H	Not isolated	—	13

* References 99–324 are on pp. 382–386.
* References 99–324 are on pp. 382–386.

KETONES—*Continued*

Compound Treated	Solvent	Product	Yield %	Reference *
		MONOKETONES—*Continued*		
3'-Keto-4,6-dimethoxy-1,2-cyclopentenonaphthalene	CH_3CO_2H	2',3'-Diketo-4,6-dimethoxy-1,2-cyclopentenonaphthalene	—	160
Ketotetrahydrobenzofluorene	Dioxane	No reaction	—	161
p-Methoxyacetophenone	CH_3CO_2H	Not isolated	—	13
p-Methylacetophenone	CH_3CO_2H	p-Methylphenylglyoxal	—	13, 146
2-Methylbenzanthrone	H_2O	Benzanthrone-2-carboxaldehyde	—	3
6-Methylbenzanthrone	H_2O	Benzanthrone-6-carboxaldehyde	—	3
9-Methyl-*meso*-benzanthrone	H_2O	*meso*-Benzanthrone-9-carboxaldehyde + *meso*-benzanthrone-9-carboxylic acid	24	162
10-Methyl-*meso*-benzanthrone	$C_6H_5NO_2$	*meso*-Benzanthrone-10-carboxaldehyde + *meso*-benzanthrone-10-carboxylic acid	32	162
3-Methyl-2-butanone	CH_3CO_2H	Not isolated	—	10
2-Methylcyclohexanone	C_2H_5OH	3-Methyl-Δ^3-1,2-cyclohexenedione	—	21
3-Methylcyclohexanone	C_2H_5OH	3-Methyl-Δ^3-1,2-cyclohexenedione	—	21
4-Methylcyclohexanone	C_2H_5OH	4-Methyl-1,2-cyclohexanedione + 4-methyl-6-ethoxy-Δ^2-cyclohexenone	—	21
Methyl cyclohexyl ketone	Dioxane	Cyclohexylglyoxal	59	163
2-Methyl-Δ^2-cyclopentenone	$(CH_3CO)_2O$	3-Methyl-Δ^3-1,2-cyclopentenedione	30	53
3-Methyl-1-tetralone	C_2H_5OH	2-Hydroxy-3-methyl-1,4-naphthoquinone + 3-methyl-1,2-naphthoquinone	45 —	164

* References 99–324 are on pp. 382–386.

KETONES—*Continued*

Compound Treated	Solvent	Product	Yield %	Reference *
		MONOKETONES—*Continued*		
2-Methyl-1,1'-di-naphthyl ketone	H_2O	2-Carboxy-1,1'-di-naphthyl ketone	56	165
2-Methyl-1,2'-dinaph-thyl ketone	H_2O	2-Carboxy-1,2'-di-naphthyl ketone	53	165
4-Methyl-1,2'-dinaph-thyl ketone	$C_6H_5NO_2$	4-Carboxy-1,2'-di-naphthyl ketone	—	166
Methyl α-naphthyl ketone	CH_3CO_2H	α-Naphthylglyoxal	44	167
Methyl β-naphthyl ketone	CH_3CO_2H	β-Naphthylglyoxal	72	167
1-(2-Methylnaphthyl) 3',4',5'-trimethyl-phenyl ketone	H_2O	1-(3',4',5'-Trimethyl-benzoyl)-2-naph-thoic acid acetoxy lactone	—	168
β-Naphthoflavanone	Xylene	β-Naphthoflavone	—	156
3-Nitroacetomesitylene	Dioxane	3-Nitromesitylglyoxal	72	145
m-Nitroacetophenone	CH_3CO_2H	Not isolated	—	13
m-Nitrobenzyl mesityl ketone	Dioxane	Mesityl *m*-nitro-phenyl diketone	81	145
p-Nitrobenzyl mesityl ketone	Dioxane	Mesityl *p*-nitrophenyl diketone	72	145
5-Nonanone	CH_3CO_2H	Not isolated	—	10
trans-Octahydro-2(1)-naphthalenone	C_2H_5OH	*trans*-Octahydro-2,3-naphthalenedione	50	169, 170
2-Octanone	CH_3CO_2H	Not isolated	—	10, 14
2-Pentanone	CH_3CO_2H	Not isolated	—	10, 12
3-Pentanone	—	Methyl ethyl diketone	—	10, 19
1-Phenylacetyl-3-nitro-4-methoxybenzene	$(CH_3CO)_2O$	3-Nitro-4-methoxy-benzil	66	171
Pinacolone	CH_3OH	*tert*-Butylglyoxal	52	10, 172, 173
Propiomesitylene	Dioxane	Methyl mesityl diketone	42	145
Propiophenone	C_2H_5OH	Methyl phenyl diketone	50	4, 19
Tetraphenylcyclo-pentadienone hydrate	CH_3CO_2H	2,3,4-Triphenyl-benzoylfuran	—	174

* References 99–324 are on pp. 382–386.

KETONES—*Continued*

Compound Treated	Solvent	Product	Yield %	Refer- ence *
	MONOKETONES—*Continued*			
3,3,5,6-Tetraphenyl-1-indanone	Dioxane	3,3,5,6-Tetraphenyl-1,2-indandione	—	152, 175
1-p-Toluoyl-2-methyl-naphthalene	H_2O	1-p-Toluoyl-2-naph-thoic acid	65	127a
2,4,6-Triethylaceto-phenone	Dioxane	2,4,6-Triethylphenyl-glyoxal	78.5	176
2,4,6-Triisopropyl-acetophenone	Dioxane	2,4,6-Triisopropyl-phenylglyoxal	82	145
	DIKETONES			
1,9-Anthindandione	$C_6H_5NO_2$	Aceanthrenequinone	—	177
Benzoyl-β-isoduryloyl-methane	Dioxane	Mesityl phenyl tri-ketone + $C_{36}H_{32}O_4Se$	—	83
1-Benzoyl-3,4,5,6-tetra-phenyl-7-keto-1,2,3,6-tetrahydro-3,6-meth-anobenzene	CH_3CO_2H	No reaction	—	178
2-Benzylanthraquinone	—	2-Benzoylbenzan-throne	—	3
Bicyclo-[3.3.0]-2,6-octanedione	C_2H_5OH	Unstable oil	—	179
1,3-Diacetylbenzene	Dioxane	m-Phenylenedi-glyoxal	—	180
1,4-Diacetylbenzene	$(CH_3CO)_2O$	p-Phenylenediglyoxal	—	181
1,5-Dibenzoyl-2,6-di-methylnaphthalene	$C_6H_5NO_2$	1,5-Dibenzoylnaph-thalene-2,6-dicar-boxylic acid	—	3
1,2-Dibenzoyl-1-propene	Dioxane	2-Phenyl-4-benzoyl-furan	63	147
Di-(β-isoduryloyl)-methane	Dioxane	Dimesityl triketone	—	182
1,3-Diketohydrindene	Dioxane	Ninhydrin	35	98
1,2-Dimesitoylethylene glycol	Dioxane	Dimesityl triketone	50	149

KETONES—*Continued*

Compound Treated	Solvent	Product	Yield %	Reference *
		DIKETONES—*Continued*		
Diphenylsuccindandione	CH_3CO_2H	$C_{31}H_{16}O_3$	90	183
2,5-Hexanedione	H_2O	Δ^3-2,5-Hexenedione	40	58, 59
3-Methyl-2,5-hexane-dione	H_2O	3-Methyl-Δ^3-2,5-hexenedione + 3-hydroxy-4-methyl-Δ^3-2,5-hexenedione	—	59
1-Methyl-4-isopropyl-idene-2,3-cyclohex-anedione	—	1-Methyl-4-isopropyl-idene-2,3,5-cyclo-hexanetrione	—	54
5-Methylnaphtho-anthraquinone	—	Naphthoanthraqui-none-5-carboxylic acid + naphtho-anthraquinone-5-carboxaldehyde	—	3
2-Methyl-1,4-naphtho-quinone	C_2H_5OH	No reaction	—	164
3-Methyl-1,2-naphtho-quinone	C_2H_5OH	2-Hydroxy-3-methyl-1,4-naphthoquinone	—	164
1,8-Naphthindandione	$C_6H_5NO_2$	Acenaphthenequi-none	—	177
2-Nitro-1,4-diacetyl-benzene	Dioxane	2-Nitrophenylene-1,4-diglyoxal	—	181
2,4-Pentanedione	C_2H_5OH	2,3,4-Pentanetrione	29	31
1-Phenyl-1,3-butane-dione	C_2H_5OH	Unidentified	—	31
Triphenylcyclopenta-dienedione	Dioxane	$C_{46}H_{30}O_4$	—	184
		TRIKETONES		
1,3,5-*tris*(Bromo-acetyl)benzene	Dioxane	1,3,5-Triglyoxalyl-benzene	—	181

* References 99–324 are on pp. 382–386.

NITROGEN-CONTAINING COMPOUNDS

Compound Treated	Solvent	Product	Yield %	Reference *
		AMINES		
Aniline	CH_3OH	$C_7H_{11}O_3NSe$	—	17
	None	Violet compound	—	128
	$C_2H_5OH +$ $(C_2H_5)_2O$	Blue-black solid	—	86
Ethoxyphenylenediamine	H_2O	Ethoxypiaselenol	—	185
Ethylamine	—	Solid, m.p. 150°	—	128
Methylaniline	CH_3OH	Not isolated	—	17
1,2-Naphthylenediamine	H_2O	Naphthopiaselenol	—	186
1,8-Naphthylenediamine	H_2O	$C_{20}H_{16}N_4Se$	—	187
o-Phenylenediamine	H_2O	Piaselenol	—	185
p-Toluidine	CH_3OH	Not isolated	—	17
o-Tolylenediamine	HCl	Methylchloropiaselenol	—	188
o-Tolylenediamine	H_2O	Methylpiaselenol	—	186
1,2,4-Triaminobenzene	H_2O	Aminopiaselenol	—	185
		HYDRAZINES		
p-Bromophenylhydrazine hydrochloride	H_2O	p-Bromobenzenediazonium chloride	—	66
Diphenylhydrazine	C_2H_5OH	Diphenylamine	94	66
1-Naphthylhydrazine hydrochloride	H_2O	1-Naphthalenediazonium chloride	—	66
2-Naphthylhydrazine hydrochloride	H_2O	2-Naphthalenediazonium chloride	—	66
m-Nitrophenylhydrazine hydrochloride	H_2O	m-Nitrobenzenediazonium chloride	—	66
p-Nitrophenylhydrazine hydrochloride	H_2O	p,p'-Dinitrodiazoaminobenzene + p-nitrodiazobenzeneimide	46 32	66
Phenylhydrazine	$C_2H_5OH +$ H_2O	Not isolated	—	86, 189
Phenylhydrazine hydrochloride	H_2O	Benzenediazonium chloride	—	66

* References 99–324 are on pp. 382–386.

NITROGEN-CONTAINING COMPOUNDS—*Continued*

Compound Treated	Solvent	Product	Yield %	Reference *
		HETEROCYCLIC COMPOUNDS		
Acridine	None	Dihydroacridine	—	38
5,6-Benzo-7-aza-hydrindene	—	1-Keto-5,6-benzo-7-azahydrindene	—	45
9-Benzylacridine	Xylene	9-Benzoylacridine	60	190
2-(o-Carboxyphenyl)-4-keto-1,2,3,4-tetrahydroquinoline lactam	C$_6$H$_6$	2-(o-Carboxyphenyl)-4-keto-1,4-dihydroquinoline lactam	—	191
6,7-Dimethoxylepidine	Dioxane	6,7-Dimethoxycinchoninaldehyde	71	192
2,3-Dimethylbenzo(h)-quinoline	C$_2$H$_5$OH	3-Methylbenzo(h)-quinoline-2-carboxylic acid	20	193
2,4-Dimethylbenzo(h)-quinoline	C$_2$H$_5$OH	Benzo(h)quinoline-2,4-dicarboxylic acid	—	193
1,3-Dimethyl-6,7-methylenedioxyisoquinoline	Dioxane	1,3-Dimethyl-6,7-methylenedioxoisoquinolinaldehyde	—	194
2-Ethyl-3-methyl-quinoline	Xylene	3-Methylquinaldic acid	—	46
Ethyl 1-phenyl-5-keto-2-pyrazoline-3-carboxylate	—	Diethyl 1,1'-diphenyl-5,5'-dihydroxy-4,4'-bipyrazole-3,3'-dicarboxylate	—	195
8-Ethylquinaldine	C$_2$H$_5$OH	8-Ethylquinaldaldehyde	90	196
Hydroquinine	Xylene	Hydroquininone	45	197
Lepidine	Dioxane	Cinchoninaldehyde + 1,2-bis(4-quinolyl)-ethene	58 100	94, 95, 198, 199, 200
2,6-Lutidine	Xylene	Dipicolinic acid	—	46
6-Methoxylepidine	Xylene	Quininaldehyde	56	95, 192
9-Methylacridine	Xylene	9-Acridinecarboxaldehyde	—	201
4-Methylbenzo(h)-quinoline	Xylene	Benzo(h)quinoline-4-carboxaldehyde	10	202

* References 99–324 are on pp. 382–386.

NITROGEN-CONTAINING COMPOUNDS—*Continued*

Compound Treated	Solvent	Product	Yield %	Reference *
		HETEROCYCLIC COMPOUNDS—*Continued*		
2-Methyl-4-hydroxy-quinazoline	—	4-Hydroxy-2-quinazolinecarboxaldehyde	—	203
1-Methylisoquinoline	Dioxane	Isoquinolinealdehyde	42	194
2-Methyl-4-ketoquinazoline	—	4-Ketodihydroquinazoline-2-carboxaldehyde	—	204
6-Methylphenanthridine	$CH_3CO_2C_2H_5$	6-Phenanthridinecarboxaldehyde	70	205
5-Methylquinoline	None	5-Quinolinecarboxaldehyde	—	206
6-Methylquinoline	None	6-Quinolinecarboxaldehyde	—	206
7-Methylquinoline	None	7-Quinolinecarboxaldehyde	91	206
8-Methylquinoline	None	8-Quinolinecarboxaldehyde	70	206
2-Methylquinoxaline	Xylene	2-Quinoxalinecarboxaldehyde	24	207
2-Methyl-1,2,3,4-tetrahydroacridine	—	2-Methyl-4-keto-1,2,3,4-tetrahydroacridine + 2-methylacridine	—	45
Nicotine	H_2SO_4	Nicotinic acid	75	208
8-Nitrolepidine	C_2H_5OH	8-Nitrocinchoninaldehyde	53	209, 210
Papaverine	CH_3CO_2H	Papaveraldine	—	211
1-Phenyl-3-methyl-4,5-diketo-2-pyrazoline	C_2H_5OH	1,1'-Diphenyl-3,3'-dimethyl-5,5'-dihydroxy-4,4'-bipyrazole	—	195
1-Phenyl-3-methylflavazole	—	No reaction	—	195
	CH_3CO_2H	Pyrazole blue	—	195
2-Picoline	$CH_3CO_2C_2H_5$	2-Pyridinecarboxaldehyde	—	45

* References 99–324 are on pp. 382–386.

NITROGEN-CONTAINING COMPOUNDS—*Continued*

Compound Treated	Solvent	Product	Yield %	Reference *
HETEROCYCLIC COMPOUNDS—*Continued*				
2-Picoline (*Continued*)	Xylene	Picolinic acid + 2-pyridinecarboxaldehyde	—	46
3-Picoline	H_2SO_4	Nicotinic acid	50	46, 208
Quinaldine	Dioxane	2-Quinolinecarboxaldehyde	50	46, 94
	Dioxane	Quinaldil	91	212
	Dioxane	2-Hydroxy-1,2-di-2-quinolylethanone (aged SeO_2)	84	94
	Xylene	2-Quinolinecarboxaldehyde	68	213
Quinoline	H_2SO_4	Nicotinic acid	75	208
1,2,3,4-Tetrahydroacridine	—	1,2,3,4-Tetrahydro-4-acridone + acridine	—	45
2,3,8-Trimethyl-5-nitroquinoline	C_2H_5OH	3,8-Dimethyl-5-nitroquinoline-2-carboxaldehyde	38	47
2,3,8-Trimethylquinoline	C_2H_5OH	3,8-Dimethylquinoline-2-carboxaldehyde	82	47
MISCELLANEOUS				
Ethyl diazoacetate	H_2O	Not isolated	—	214
Nitromethane	Dioxane	Formic acid	—	215

PHENOLIC COMPOUNDS

2-Acetoxy-1-naphthol	C_2H_5OH	No reaction	—	164
Anethole	—	p-Methoxycinnamaldehyde	—	216
4,4'''-Dihydroxyquaterphenyl	—	No reaction	—	217
Dimethyldihydroresorcinol	$CH_3CO_2C_2H_5$	Anhydrodimethone selenium oxide	—	45, 218

* References 99–324 are on pp. 382–386.

PHENOLIC COMPOUNDS—*Continued*

Compound Treated	Solvent	Product	Yield %	Reference *
Isoeugenol	—	No reaction	—	216
Isosafrole	—	Piperonylacrolein + dihydrosafrole + 3-ethoxysafrole + $C_{10}H_{10}O_3$ + $C_{10}H_8O_2Se$	—	85
3-Methyl-1-naphthol	C_2H_5OH	Not isolated	—	164
2-Naphthol	$CH_3CO_2C_2H_5$	*bis*(Hydroxynaphthyl) selenide	—	45
Phenol	—	$Se(C_6H_4OH)_2$	—	84
Safrole	—	α-Ketodihydrosafrole + β-ketodihydrosafrole + ethoxysafrole + piperonylacrolein	—	85

STEROIDS

$\Delta^{20,22}$-3α-Acetoxy-12-β-hydroxynorcholenic acid 23 → 12 lactone	$(CH_3CO)_2O$	$\Delta^{20,22}$-3α-Acetoxy-12β,21-dihydroxynorcholenic acid 23 → 12 lactone	—	219
Acetyldesacetylpseudobufotalin	—	Isolated as dioxime, $C_{19}H_{30}O_5N_2$	—	220
Allocholesterol	CH_3CO_2H	Not isolated	—	23
Δ^5-Androstene-3-*trans*-17-diol	CH_3CO_2H	Δ^5-3,4,7-Androstenetriol	—	221
Δ^5-3,17-Androstenediol diacetate	C_6H_6 + CH_3CO_2H	Δ^5-3,4,7-Androstenetriol	—	222
Apocholic acid	C_2H_5OH	β-Dihydroxycholadienic acid	60	23, 223 224
Bromodesoxysarsapogenin	C_6H_6 + CH_3CO_2H	No reaction	—	225
Bromodigitogenin triacetate	CH_3CO_2H	No reaction	—	226
23-Bromodiosgenin acetate	C_6H_6 + CH_3CO_2H	4-Hydroxybromodiosgenin acetate	—	227

* References 99–324 are on pp. 382–386,

STEROIDS—*Continued*

Compound Treated	Solvent	Product	Yield %	Reference *
Bromogitogenin diacetate	CH_3CO_2H	No reaction	—	226
Bromosarsapogenin	—	No reaction	—	105
Bromotigogenin acetate	CH_3CO_2H	No reaction	—	228
Calciferol (vitamin D_2)	C_2H_5OH	Not isolated	—	23
3-O-Carbethoxycholesterol	$(CH_3CO)_2O$	3-O-Carbethoxy-4-acetoxycholesterol + 3-O-carbethoxy-6-acetoxy-Δ^4-3-cholestenol	—	229
	CH_3CO_2H	3-O-Carbethoxy-4-acetoxycholesterol + 3-O-carbethoxy-6-acetoxy-Δ^4-3-cholestenol + cis-Δ^5-cholestene-3,4-diol carbonate	—	229
3-O-Carbomethoxycholesterol	$(CH_3CO)_2O$	3-O-Carbomethoxy-4-acetoxycholesterol + 3-O-carbomethoxy-6-acetoxy-Δ^4-3-cholestenol	—	229
	CH_3CO_2H	3-O-Carbomethoxy-4-acetoxycholesterol + 3-O-carbomethoxy-6-acetoxy-Δ^4-3-cholestenol + cis-Δ^5-cholestene-3,4-diol carbonate	—	229
Chlorogenin	CH_3CO_2H	Not isolated	—	230
Choladienic acid	C_2H_5OH	Not isolated	—	23
Cholatrienic acid	C_2H_5OH	Not isolated	—	23
3,6-Cholestanedione	C_2H_5OH or CH_3CO_2H	Not isolated	—	22, 23
α-Cholestanetriol	CH_3CO_2H	No reaction	—	23
Cholestanone	C_2H_5OH or CH_3CO_2H	2,3-Cholestanedione	30	22, 23
Cholestene	CH_3CO_2H	Not isolated	—	23
$\Delta^{8,14}$-Cholestene	C_2H_5OH	$\Delta^{8,14}$-Cholestadiene	—	231
Δ^4-3,6-Cholestenedione	CH_3CO_2H	Not isolated	—	22
Cholestenone	CH_3CO_2H	Not isolated	—	23
4-Cholesten-3-one	CH_3CO_2H	Not isolated	—	22

* References 99–324 are on pp. 382–386.

STEROIDS—*Continued*

Compound Treated	Solvent	Product	Yield %	Reference *
Cholesterilene	CH_3CO_2H	Not isolated	—	23
Cholesterol	$C_6H_6 +$	cis-$\Delta^{5,6}$-3,4-Choles-	38	97
	CH_3CO_2H	tenediol		
	$(CH_3CO)_2O$	cis-$\Delta^{5,6}$-3,4-Choles-	25	23, 232,
		tenediol diacetate +		324
		Δ^4-3,6-cholestene-	25	
		diol diacetate		
Cholesterol oxide	CH_3CO_2H	Not isolated	—	23
Cholesteryl acetate	CH_3CO_2H	cis-$\Delta^{5,6}$-3,4-Choles-	—	23, 97
		tenediol diacetate +		
		$trans$-$\Delta^{5,6}$-choles-		
		tenediol diacetate		
	CH_3CO_2H	4-Acetoxy-Δ^5-3-cho-	60	233
		lestenol + 3-acet-	5	
		oxy-Δ^5-4-choles-		
		tenol		
	$C_6H_6 +$	3-Acetyl-4-hydroxy-	—	234
	CH_3CO_2H	cholesterol		
	—	Δ^4-Cholesten-3β,6β-	—	235
		diol		
Cholesteryl benzoate	CH_3CO_2H	3-Benzoate of cis-Δ^5-	—	97
		3,4-cholestenediol		
		+ $trans$-3,4-choles-		
		tenediol-3,4-diben-		
		zoate		
	Dioxane	3-Benzoxyloxy-Δ^5-4-	70	233
		cholestenol		
	—	Δ^4-Cholesten-3β,6β-	—	235
		diol		
Cholesteryl bromide	CH_3CO_2H	Not isolated	—	23
Cholesteryl chloride	CH_3CO_2H	Not isolated	—	23
Cholesteryl ether	CH_3CO_2H	Not isolated	—	23
Cholesteryl propionate	$C_6H_6 +$	4-Propionyloxy-Δ^5-3-	—	233
	CH_3CO_2H	cholestenol		
Cholic acid	CH_3CO_2H	No reaction	—	23
Clionasterol	$(CH_3CO)_2O$	Δ^4-3,6-Cliostenediol	—	236, 237
		diacetate		
Coprostanone	C_2H_5OH or	Not isolated	—	22
	CH_3CO_2H			
Coprosterol	CH_3CO_2H	Not isolated	—	23

STEROIDS—*Continued*

Compound Treated	Solvent	Product	Yield %	Reference *
Dehydrodesoxycholic acid	CH_3CO_2H	No reaction	—	23
Dehydroergostenol	CH_3CO_2H	Not isolated	—	23
Dehydroergosterol	C_2H_5OH	Not isolated	—	23
Desoxycholic acid	CH_3CO_2H	No reaction	—	23
Desoxysarsasapogenin	$C_6H_6 + CH_3CO_2H$	Not isolated	—	225
α-3(β),7-Dibenzoyl-Δ⁵-cholestene	Dioxane + CH_3CO_2H	α-3(β),7-Dibenzoyl-oxy-Δ⁵-4(β)-choles-tenol	—	238
Digitaligenin	CH_3CO_2H	No reaction	—	23
Digitoxigenin	CH_3CO_2H	Not isolated	—	23
Dihydrochlorogenin	CH_3CO_2H	$C_{27}H_{40}O_5$	—	230
Dihydrodesoxysarsapo-genin	$C_6H_6 + CH_3CO_2H$	No reaction	—	225
Dihydroergosterol	$C_6H_6 + C_2H_5OH$	Dihydroergosterol oxide + ergosterol-D	—	23
Dihydroergosterol oxide	$(CH_3CO)_2O$	Ergosterol-B₃ acetate	—	23
	C_2H_5OH	Not isolated	—	23
Dihydrogitogenin	—	No reaction	—	226
α-Dihydrolanosteryl acetate	CH_3CO_2H	γ-Lanosteryl acetate	—	239
Dihydrosarsasapogenin	—	No reaction	—	105
Dihydrotigogenin	CH_3CO_2H	No reaction	—	228
Dihydroxycholadienic acid	CH_3CO_2H	Not isolated	—	23
3,12-Diketocholanic acid	CH_3CO_2H	Not isolated	—	22
α-Ergostene	C_2H_5OH	Not isolated	—	23
α-Ergostenol	C_2H_5OH	Dehydroergostenol	—	23, 223
β-Ergostenol	CH_3CO_2H	Not isolated	—	23
α-Ergostenone	C_2H_5OH	Not isolated	—	23
Ergosterol	$C_2H_5OH + C_6H_6$	Dehydroergosterol	—	23, 240
Ergosterol-B₃	C_2H_5OH	Not isolated	—	23
Ergosterol-D	C_2H_5OH	Not isolated	—	23
Ergosterol peroxide	C_2H_5OH	Not isolated	—	23
Ergosteryl benzoate	C_2H_5OH	Not isolated	—	23
Gitogenin	CH_3CO_2H	Not isolated	—	226
Gitoxigenin	CH_3CO_2H	Not isolated	—	23

* References 99–324 are on pp. 382–386.

STEROIDS—*Continued*

Compound Treated	Solvent	Product	Yield %	Reference *
5-Hydroxy-3,6-cholestanedione	CH_3CO_2H	Not isolated	—	23
3-Hydroxy-6-cholestanone	CH_3CO_2H	Not isolated	—	22
3-Hydroxy-6-cholestanone acetate	CH_3CO_2H	No reaction	—	23
12-Ketocholanic acid	CH_3CO_2H	No reaction	—	23
Ketohydroxyoestrin	CH_3CO_2H	Not isolated	—	23
Lanosteryl acetate	C_2H_5OH	Monoacetate of diol, $C_{30}H_{50}O_2$	—	239
Lumisterol	C_2H_5OH	Not isolated	—	23
Methyl β-3-acetoxy-$\Delta^{20,22}$-norallocholenate	$(CH_3CO)_2O$	β-3-Acetoxy-21-hydroxy-$\Delta^{20,22}$-norallocholenic acid lactone	—	241
Methyl apocholate	C_2H_5OH	β-Dihydroxycholadienic acid (after hydrolysis)	—	23, 223
Methyl dihydroxycholenate	C_2H_5OH	β-Dihydroxycholadienic acid (after hydrolysis)	—	23, 223
5-Methyl-Δ^8-3,6-norcholestenediol	C_2H_5OH	5-Methyl-Δ^8-3,6,11-norcholestenetriol	25	242
Oxycholestenone	CH_3CO_2H	Not isolated	—	23
Oxycholesterilene	CH_3CO_2H	No reaction	—	23
Pregnane carbonyl compounds	—	Pregnane polycarbonyl compounds	—	243
Δ^5-Pregnene-3(β),20(α)-diol diacetate	C_6H_6 + CH_3CO_2H	Δ^5-3,4,20-Pregnenetriol	—	222
Δ^5-Pregnene-3,17-diol-21-one	—	Δ^5-3,4,17,20,21-Pentahydroxypregnene + Δ^4-3,6,17,20,21-pentahydroxypregnane	—	244
Pseudocholestane	CH_3CO_2H	No reaction	—	23
Pseudocholestene	CH_3CO_2H	Not isolated	—	23
Pseudocholesterol	CH_3CO_2H	Not isolated	—	23
Pseudosarsasapogenin	—	Not isolated	—	245
Sarsasapogenin	—	Not isolated	—	105
Sitosterol	CH_3CO_2H	Not isolated	—	23

* References 99–324 are on pp. 382–386.

STEROIDS—*Continued*

Compound Treated	Solvent	Product	Yield %	Reference *
Sitosteryl acetate	C_6H_6 + CH_3CO_2H	4-Hydroxysitosterol diacetate + 6-hydroxysitosterol diacetate	—	246
	—	Δ^5-3,4-Stigmastenediol + Δ^5-3,4-sitostenediol + Δ^4-3,6-sitostenediol	—	247
Stigmasterol	CH_3CO_2H	Not isolated	—	23
1,9,10,11-Tetrahydro-1,2-cyclopentenophenanthrene	C_2H_5OH	9,10-Dihydro-1,2-cyclopentenophenanthrene	—	248
Tetrahydrodiosgenin triacetate	C_6H_6 + CH_3CO_2H	Δ^5-3,4-Dihydroxy cholestene (after hydrolysis)	—	249
Tetrahydrosarsasapogenin	—	No reaction	—	105
Tigogenin	CH_3CO_2H	Not isolated	—	228
Zymosterol	C_2H_5OH	Not isolated	—	23

SULFUR-CONTAINING COMPOUNDS

Compound Treated	Solvent	Product	Yield %	Reference *
3-Acetylthianaphthene	Dioxane	3-Thianaphtheneglyoxal	50	250
Acetylthiourea	H_2O	Not isolated	—	251
Allylthiourea	H_2O	Not isolated	—	251
Benzylthiourea	H_2O	Not isolated	—	251
Benzyl p-tolyl sulfone	—	No reaction	—	252
Diacetylthiourea	H_2O	Not isolated	—	251
Diethylbenzylthiourea	H_2O	Not isolated	—	251
Diethylthiourea	H_2O	Not isolated	—	251
Dimethylphenylthiourea	H_2O	Not isolated	—	251
Disulfides	—	Sulfoxides + sulfones	—	5
Dithiocarbamates	ROH	Selenium dithiocarbamates	—	253
Ethyl ethanesulfenate	—	No reaction	—	254
2-Hydroxythianaphthene	C_2H_5OH	Isothioindigo	—	255, 256

* References 99–324 are on pp. 382–386.

SULFUR-CONTAINING COMPOUNDS—*Continued*

Compound Treated	Solvent	Product	Yield %	Reference *
3-Hydroxythianaphthene	C_2H_5OH	Thioindigo	—	255
2-Methylbenzothiazole	Xylene	2-Benzothiazolecarboxaldehyde	20	207
Methylthiourea	H_2O	Not isolated	—	251
Phenylthiourea	H_2O	Not isolated	—	251
Thioacetamide	H_2O	Not isolated	—	251
Thiobenzamide	H_2O	Not isolated	—	251
Thiophenol	—	Diphenyl disulfide + $(C_6H_5S)_2Se$	—	86
Thiourea	H_2O	Not isolated	—	251
Trimethylthiourea	H_2O	Not isolated	—	251

TERPENES

Abietic acid	C_2H_5OH	6-Hydroxyabietic acid	26	23, 257
	—	Dehydroabietic acid	—	258
6-Acetoxyepicamphor	$(CH_3CO)_2O$	6-Acetoxycamphorquinone	57	259
$\Delta^{12,13,18,19}$-2-Acetoxy-11-ketoöleadiene	Dioxane	$C_{32}H_{46}O_5$	—	260
$\Delta^{10,11,12,13,18,19}$-2-Acetoxy-11-ketoöleatriene	CH_3CO_2H	$C_{32}H_{46}O_5$	—	260
2-Acetoxy-5-oxocamphane	$(CH_3CO)_2O$	2-Acetoxy-5,6-camphanedione	—	259
β-Amyradienol acetate	Dioxane	β-Amyradienedionol acetate	—	261
β-Amyradienonyl acetate	CH_3CO_2H	O_5-Acetate	65	262
β-Amyradienonyl benzoate	CH_3CO_2H	O_5-Benzoate	—	262
β-Amyradienyl acetate	CH_3CO_2H	β-Amyrenonyl acetate	—	263
β-Amyranonyl acetate enol acetate	—	No reaction	—	264
β-Amyratrienol acetate	CH_3CO_2H	β-Amyradiendionyl acetate	—	265
β-Amyrene	CH_3CO_2H	Dehydro-β-amyrene	—	266
β-Amyrenonyl acetate	CH_3CO_2H	O_5-Acetate	68	262

TERPENES—*Continued*

Compound Treated	Solvent	Product	Yield %	Reference *
β-Amyrenonyl benzoate	CH_3CO_2H	O_5-Benzoate	60	262
β-Amyrin acetate	CH_3CO_2H	Dehydro-β-amyrin acetate	—	266, 267
	Dioxane	β-Amyradienediol acetate	44	261
δ-Amyrin acetate	Dioxane	β-Amyradienediol acetate	—	261
β-Amyrin benzoate	CH_3CO_2H	Dehydro-β-amyrene benzoate	—	23, 266
β-Amyranonol acetate	Dioxane	Enol-β-amyrandionol acetate	—	268
Arnidenediol diacetate	—	Diacetylarnidenaldiol	—	269
3-Benzylcamphor	None	3-Benzylidenecamphor	95	26, 27
Betulinol diacetate	CH_3CO_2H, $(CH_3CO)_2O$, or C_6H_6	Diacetoxylupenal	—	270
Borneol	None	Camphorquinone	60	24, 271
3-Bromocamphor	CH_3CO_2H	No reaction	—	26
	None	Camphorquinone	55	26
Camphene	—	Camphene selenide	—	272
Camphor	C_2H_5OH	Camphorquinone	73	26, 27
	Toluene	Camphorquinone	89	26, 27
	Xylene	Camphorquinone	89	26, 27
	$(CH_3CO)_2O$	Camphorquinone	95	24, 25, 26, 27
	None	Camphorquinone	65	24
Camphoric mononitrile	Toluene	Camphoric anhydride	11	27
Carvomenthene	CH_3CO_2H	Cymene + carvotanacetone + carvotanacetol acetate	24 28	273
	C_2H_5OH	Carvotanacetone	26	50, 60
Caryophyllene	C_4H_9OH	Resin	—	274
	$(CH_3CO)_2O$	Caryophyllenol acetate	—	275
Cedrene	$(CH_3CO)_2O$	Cedrenol acetate	80	276, 277
	C_4H_9OH	Cedrenal	—	276
3-Chlorocamphor	CH_3CO_2H	No reaction	—	26
	None	Camphorquinone	32	26, 27
l-α-Curcumene	C_2H_5OH	No reaction	—	278
l-β-Curcumene	C_2H_5OH	l-β-Curcumenal	—	278

* References 99–324 are on pp. 382–386.

TERPENES—*Continued*

Compound Treated	Solvent	Product	Yield %	Reference *
Cyclocitral	C_2H_5OH	Safranal	—	279
Cymene	—	Cumaldehyde	—	280
Dihydrocaryophyllene	C_4H_9OH	Dihydrocaryophyl-lenealdehyde	36	274
Dihydrolycorinone	CH_3CO_2H	No reaction	—	281
Dipentene	—	Ketone group at 8-position + cymene + cumaldehyde	—	50, 280
d-Epicamphor	$(CH_3CO)_2O$	5,6-Diketocamphane	—	282
l-Epicamphor	$(CH_3CO)_2O$	Camphorquinone	74	282
3-Ethylcamphor	—	Camphorquinone + 3-ethylidenecamphor	12	26, 27
R-Homocamphenilone	—	Carbocamphenilo-none	—	283
3-Hydroxycamphor	C_2H_5OH	Camphorquinone	40	26, 27
	None	Camphorquinone	85	26, 27
Iso-α-amyrenonol acetate	CH_3CO_2H	Iso-α-amyradienonol acetate	50	284
Iso-α-amyrenonol benzoate	CH_3CO_2H	Iso-α-amyradienonol benzoate	—	284
Iso-β-amyrenonyl acetate	CH_3CO_2H	Acetate; m.p. 208°	—	285
Isoborneol	—	Camphorquinone	—	271
α-Isocamphenilone	$(CH_3CO)_2O$	α-Isocamphenilqui-none	66	286
Isofenchone	$(CH_3CO)_2O$	Isofenchoquinone	—	28, 29
l-Isofenchone	$(CH_3CO)_2O$	Isofenchoquinone	—	30
Isonitrosocamphor	C_2H_5OH	α-Camphoric mononi-trile + camphoric anhydride	20 12	26
	Toluene	α-Camphoric mononi-trile + camphoric anhydride	36 36	26
	None	α-Camphoric mononi-trile + camphoric anhydride	23 27	26, 27
Isonoragathenol acetate	C_6H_6	α,β-Ketone, $C_{11}H_{32}O_3$ (after dehydrogena-tion)	—	287

* References 99–324 are on pp. 382–386.

TERPENES—*Continued*

Compound Treated	Solvent	Product	Yield %	Reference *
2-Keto-1,7-dimethyl-7-norcamphanecarboxylic acid	CH_3CO_2H	o-Oxoisoketopinic acid	—	288
Leucodrin	—	No reaction	—	289
d-Limonene	—	Cymene + mixture of terpene alcohols and aldehydes or ketones	—	290
α-Lupene	CH_3CO_2H or C_6H_6	Lupenal	45	291, 292
Lupeol	$(CH_3CO)_2O$	Lupenalol acetate	—	269
Lupeol acetate	$(CH_3CO)_2O$	Lupenediol diacetate + ketolupeol acetate	50	293, 294
	C_6H_6	Ketolupeol acetate	60	293
	CH_3CO_2H	Lupenalol acetate	58	292
Lupeol benzoate	C_6H_6	A ketolupeol benzoate	53	293
	$(CH_3CO)_2O$	Ketolupeol benzoate	42	294
Menthene	C_2H_5OH	Δ^3-Menthen-5-one	12	50, 60
Menthol	C_2H_5OH	Hydroxythymoquinone + thymol + menthone	—	271
Menthone	C_2H_5OH	Hydroxythymoquinone	8	295
	C_2H_5OH	Diosphenol	15	4
Methyl $\Delta^{12,13,18,19}$-2-acetoxy-11-keto-30-oleadienate	Dioxane	$C_{33}H_{46}O_7$	—	260
Methyl acetyldehydrooleanolate	CH_3CO_2H	Diketodehydro ester, $C_{33}H_{46}O_6$, + methyl oleanolate	—	296
Methyl acetyldesoxyglycyrrhetate	CH_3CO_2H	Methyl acetyldehydrodesoxyglycyrrhetate	—	297
Methyl acetyloleanolate	CH_3CO_2H	Methyl acetyldehydroöleanolate	—	298
Methyl acetylsumaresinoate	CH_3CO_2H	Methyl acetyldehydrosumaresinoate	—	298
Methyl ketoacetyloleanolate	CH_3CO_2H	Acetate, $C_{33}H_{46}O_7$	—	262

* References 99–324 are on pp. 382–386.

TERPENES—Continued

Compound Treated	Solvent	Product	Yield %	Reference [*]
Myrcene	C_2H_5OH	Myrcenol + myrcenal + myrcenone	—	49
4-p-Nitrophenylcamphor	$(CH_3CO)_2O$	4-p-Nitrophenylcamphorquinone	—	299
Nopinene	H_2O	Pinocarvone + pinocarveol	35 —	34, 300
	C_2H_5OH	Pinocarveol + carvopinone	42	301
	$(CH_3CO)_2O$ or CH_3CO_2H	Pinocarveol + pinocarvyl acetate + carvopinone + pinocarvone	—	302
	C_2H_5OH, $(CH_3)_2CO$, C_6H_6, C_6H_{14}, $(C_2H_5)_2O$, CCl_4, C_5H_5N, H_2O, or none	Mixture of carvopinone and pinocarvone	—	303
A-Nordihydrobetulonic acid	Dioxane	Tricarboxylic acid anhydride, $C_{29}H_{44}O_5$	—	304
A-Nordihydrobetulonic acid methyl ester	Dioxane	Methyl tricarboxylic acid anhydride ester, $C_{30}H_{46}O_5$	70	304
Norfriedalone	CH_3CO_2H	Norfriedelenone	—	305
Norfriedelenone	Dioxane	Norfriedelenedione	—	305
α-Phellandrene	C_2H_5OH	Cumaldehyde + cymene	—	60, 61
Pinene	—	Myrtenol + myrtanol + nopinene + pinadiene	—	306, 307
	C_2H_5OH	Myrtenal + myrtenol	11 35	272, 308, 309
	C_2H_5OH	Verbenone	35	34, 310
	None	$C_{10}H_{14}O$	—	50, 311
Pinocarveol	C_2H_5OH	Carvopinone	25	302
Piperitone	C_2H_5OH	Thymol + hydroxythymoquinone	78	60, 61

[*] References 99–324 are on pp. 382–386.

TERPENES—*Continued*

Compound Treated	Solvent	Product	Yield %	Reference *
Pulegone	C_2H_5OH	1-Methyl-4-isopropyl-idene-2,3-cyclo-hexanedione + 1-methyl-4-isopropyl-idene-2,3,5-cyclo-hexanetrione + 1-methyl-4-isopropyl-idene-2-ethoxy-5-(or -6)-cyclohexen-3-one + 1-methyl-4-isopropylidene-6-ethoxy-5-(or 6-) cyclohexene-2,3-dione	—	54
Santenone	CH_3CO_2H	Santenonequinone	100	312, 313
α-Terpineol	—	Hydroxycarvone	—	314
Tetrahydroyobyrine-carboxylic acid	C_5H_5N	Tetrahydroyobyrone-carboxylic acid	—	315
Verbanone	C_2H_5OH	Verbenone	—	316
Yobyrine	Xylene or $(CH_3CO)_2O$	Yobyrone	—	315

MISCELLANEOUS

Compound Treated	Solvent	Product	Yield %	Reference *
Acetylegonol	CH_3CO_2H	*bis*-2-(Acetyl-Δ³-egonolyl)selenide + *bis*-2-(acetyle-gonolyl) selenide	—	317
	$(CH_3CO)_2O$	Noregonolonidin ace-tate + α-*bis*(ace-tylegonolyl) selen-ide + β-*bis*(acetyl-egonolyl) selenide	—	318
3,4-Benzoxanthene	—	3,4-Benzoxanthone	—	319
Castor oil	H_2O	Rubberlike substance	—	320
Cottonseed oil	—	Conjugated unsatu-rated oils	—	67
Crotonaldehyde di-methyl acetal	CH_3OH	β-Methoxy-α-keto-butyraldehyde	—	87

* References 99–324 are on pp. 382–386.

382 ORGANIC REACTIONS

MISCELLANEOUS—*Continued*

Compound Treated	Solvent	Product	Yield %	Reference *
Dibutylmercury	None	$(C_4H_9Hg)_2SeO_3$	—	9
Diethylmercury	None	$(C_2H_5)_2Se +$ $(C_2H_5Hg)_2SeO_3$	—	9
Diisoamylmercury	None	$(iso\text{-}C_5H_{11}Hg)_2SeO_3$	—	9
Dipropylmercury	None	$(C_3H_7Hg)_2SeO_3$	—	9
Glucose	H_2O	Not isolated	—	321
Linseed oil	—	Conjugated unsaturated oils	—	67
Lorchel	H_2SO_4	Not isolated	—	322
Rubber	—	Product resembling vulcanized rubber	—	69
Sucrose	H_2O	Not isolated	—	214
Tetrahydroösajetin trimethyl ether	CH_3CO_2H	Tetrahydroösajetinone trimethyl ether	25	323
Tetrahydropomiferitin tetramethyl ether	CH_3CO_2H	Tetrahydropomiferitinone tetramethyl ether	20	323
Triphenylarsine	C_6H_6	Triphenylarsine oxide + triphenylarsine selenide	—	9
Triphenylphosphine	C_6H_6	Triphenylphosphine oxide + triphenylphosphine selenide	—	9
Triphenylstibine	C_6H_6	Triphenylstibine oxide + triphenylstibine selenide	—	9

* References 99–324 are on pp. 382–386.

REFERENCES TO TABLES

99 Hall, *Ind. Eng. Chem., Anal. Ed.*, **10**, 395 (1938).
100 Ziegler, Schenck, Krockow, Siebert, Wenz, and Weber, *Ann.*, **551**, 1 (1942).
101 Ruggli and Doebel, *Helv. Chim. Acta*, **29**, 600 (1946).
102 Cornforth and Cornforth, *J. Chem. Soc.*, **1946**, 755.
103 Astin and Riley, *J. Chem. Soc.*, **1934**, 844.
104 Torrey, Kuck, and Elderfield, *J. Org. Chem.*, **6**, 289 (1941).
105 Marker and Rohrmann, *J. Am. Chem. Soc.*, **61**, 846 (1939).
106 Fuson, Southwick, and Rowland, *J. Am. Chem. Soc.*, **66**, 1109 (1944).
107 Röhm and Haas, Ger. pat. 634,501 [*C.A.*, **31**, 420 (1937)].
108 Kautter, U. S. pat. 2,171,727 [*C.A.*, **34**, 115 (1940)].
109 Paillard and Szasz, *Helv. Chim. Acta*, **26**, 1856 (1943).

[110] Kawai and Ashino, *Bull. Chem. Soc. Japan*, **13**, 480 (1938) [*C.A.*, **32**, 8389 (1938)].

[111] Ronzio and Waugh, *Org. Syntheses*, **24**, 61 (1944).

[112] Blacet and Moulton, *J. Am. Chem. Soc.*, **63**, 868 (1941).

[113] Gardner, U. S. pat. 2,366,724 [*C.A.*, **39**, 2767 (1945)].

[114] Dreyfus, Fr. pat. 770,420 [*C.A.*, **29**, 474 (1935)].

[115] Schmitt, *Ann.*, **547**, 103 (1941).

[116] Seguin, *Compt. rend.*, **216**, 667 (1943).

[117] Wittig and Obermann, *Ber.*, **68**, 2214 (1935).

[118] Bartlett and Schneider, *J. Am. Chem. Soc.*, **68**, 6 (1946).

[119] Guillemonat, *Compt. rend.*, **206**, 1126 (1938).

[120] Butz, Davis, and Gaddis, *J. Org. Chem.*, **12**, 122 (1947).

[121] Rydon, *J. Chem. Soc.*, **1939**, 1544.

[122] Burnop and Linstead, *J. Chem. Soc.*, **1940**, 720.

[123] Schmitt, *Ann.*, **547**, 256 (1941).

[124] Barbier, *Helv. Chim. Acta*, **23**, 524, 1477 (1940).

[125] Jouve, *Bull. soc. chim. France*, [3] **25**, 489 (1901).

[126] Monti, *Gazz. chim. ital.*, **68**, 608 (1938).

[127] Monti, *Atti X° congr. intern. chim.*, **3**, 256 (1939) [*C.A.*, **33**, 9316 (1939)].

[127a] Badger, *J. Chem. Soc.*, **1947**, 764.

[128] Chabrié, *Bull. soc. chim. France*, [3] **2**, 788 (1889).

[129] Martin, *J. Chem. Soc.*, **1941**, 679.

[130] Clar, *Ber.*, **76**, 257 (1943).

[131] Clemo and Dickenson, *J. Chem. Soc.*, **1935**, 735.

[132] Shriner and Berger, *J. Org. Chem.*, **6**, 305 (1941).

[133] Cook and Preston, *J. Chem. Soc.*, **1944**, 553.

[134] Gray and Fuson, *J. Am. Chem. Soc.*, **56**, 739 (1934).

[135] Bersin and Nafziger, *Ber.*, **69**, 560 (1936).

[136] Hahn and Schales, *Ber.*, **67**, 1816 (1934).

[137] Henze and Müller, *Z. physiol. Chem.*, **214**, 281 (1933).

[138] Riley, U. S. pat. 1,955,890 [*C.A.*, **28**, 4067 (1934)].

[139] Bousset, *Bull. soc. chim. France*, [5] **6**, 986 (1939).

[140] Arnold and Rondestvedt, *J. Am. Chem. Soc.*, **67**, 1265 (1945).

[141] Fuson, Byers, Sperati, Foster, and Warfield, *J. Org. Chem.*, **10**, 69 (1945).

[142] Fuson, Armstrong, Wallace, and Kneisley, *J. Am. Chem. Soc.*, **66**, 1274 (1944).

[143] Wegmann and Dahn, *Helv. Chim. Acta*, **29**, 1247 (1946).

[144] Fuson and Soper, *J. Am. Chem. Soc.*, **65**, 915 (1943).

[145] Fuson and Soper, *J. Org. Chem.*, **9**, 193 (1944).

[146] Arnold and Fuson, *J. Am. Chem. Soc.*, **58**, 1295 (1936).

[147] Fuson, Fleming, and Johnson, *J. Am. Chem. Soc.*, **60**, 1994 (1938).

[148] Rauh, Smith, Banks, and Diehl, *J. Org. Chem.*, **10**, 199 (1945).

[149] Fuson, McBurney, and Holland, *J. Am. Chem. Soc.*, **61**, 3246 (1939).

[150] Fuson, McKeever, Rabjohn, and Gray, *J. Am. Chem. Soc.*, **65**, 1028 (1943).

[151] Ruggli and Zeller, *Helv. Chim. Acta*, **28**, 741 (1945).

[152] Allen and Rudoff, *Can. J. Research*, **15B**, 321 (1937).

[153] Burton and Shoppee, *J. Chem. Soc.*, **1939**, 567.

[154] Kipnis, Soloway, and Ornfelt, *J. Am. Chem. Soc.*, **69**, 1231 (1947).

[155] Wallenfels, *Ber.*, **74**, 1428 (1941).

[156] Mahal, Rai, and Venkataraman, *J. Chem. Soc.*, **1935**, 866.

[157] Nadkarni and Wheeler, *J. Univ. Bombay*, **6**, Pt. II, 107 (1937) [*C.A.*, **32**, 3765 (1938)].

[158] Marini-Bettolo, *Gazz. chim. ital.*, **72**, 201 (1942).

[159] Marini-Bettolo, *Gazz. chim. ital.*, **71**, 635 (1941).

[160] Martin and Robinson, *J. Chem. Soc.*, **1943**, 491.

[161] Lothrop and Coffman, *J. Am. Chem. Soc.*, **63**, 2564 (1941).

[162] Copp and Simonsen, *J. Chem. Soc.*, **1942**, 209.

[163] Rubin, Paist, and Elderfield, *J. Org. Chem.*, **6**, 260 (1941).

[164] Weygand and Schröder, *Ber.*, **74**, 1844 (1941).

384   ORGANIC REACTIONS

[165] Cook, J. Chem. Soc., **1932**, 1472.
[166] Buckley, J. Chem. Soc., **1945**, 561.
[167] Goldyrev and Postovskiĭ, J. Gen. Chem. U.S.S.R., **10**, 39 (1940) [C.A., **34**, 4732 (1940)].
[168] Martin, J. Chem. Soc., **1943**, 239.
[169] Ganapati, J. Indian Chem. Soc., **15**, 407 (1938) [C.A., **33**, 565 (1939)].
[170] Ganapati, Current Sci., **6**, 448 (1938) [C.A., **32**, 4973 (1938)].
[171] Borsche and Barthenheier, Ann., **553**, 250 (1942).
[172] Fuson, Gray, and Gouza, J. Am. Chem. Soc., **61**, 1937 (1939).
[173] Fuson and Robertson, J. Org. Chem., **7**, 466 (1942).
[174] Putter and Dilthey, J. prakt. Chem., **149**, 183 (1937).
[175] Allen and Gates, J. Am. Chem. Soc., **64**, 2439 (1942).
[176] Fuson, Emerson, and Gray, J. Am. Chem. Soc., **61**, 480 (1939).
[177] I.G. Farbenind. A.-G., Fr. pat. 729,191 (Chem. Zentr., **1933**, II, 783).
[178] Allen, Bell, Bell, and Van Allan, J. Am. Chem. Soc., **62**, 656 (1940).
[179] Wawzonek, J. Am. Chem. Soc., **65**, 839 (1943).
[180] Ruggli and Theilheimer, Helv. Chim. Acta, **24**, 899 (1941).
[181] Ruggli and Gassenmeier, Helv. Chim. Acta, **22**, 496 (1939).
[182] Fuson, Matuszeski, and Gray, J. Am. Chem. Soc., **56**, 2099 (1934).
[183] Brand, Gabel, Ott, Müller, and Fleischhauer, Ber., **69**, 2504 (1936).
[184] Allen, Massey, and Nicholls, J. Am. Chem. Soc., **59**, 679 (1937).
[185] Hinsberg, Ber., **22**, 2895 (1889).
[186] Hinsberg, Ber., **22**, 862 (1889).
[187] Hinsberg, Ber., **52**, 21 (1919).
[188] Hinsberg, Ber., **23**, 1393 (1890).
[189] Gutbier, Z. anorg. Chem., **32**, 257 (1902).
[190] Buu-Hoi and Lecocq, Rec. trav. chim., **64**, 250 (1945).
[191] Diesbach, Rey-Bellet, and Kiang, Helv. Chim. Acta, **26**, 1869 (1943).
[192] Levitz and Bogert, J. Org. Chem., **10**, 341 (1945).
[193] Schenck and Bailey, J. Am. Chem. Soc., **63**, 2331 (1941).
[194] Barrows and Lindwall, J. Am. Chem. Soc., **64**, 2430 (1942).
[195] Ohle and Melkonian, Ber., **74**, 398 (1941).
[196] Glenn and Bailey, J. Am. Chem. Soc., **63**, 639 (1941).
[197] McKee and Henze, J. Am. Chem. Soc., **66**, 2020 (1944).
[198] Kaplan and Lindwall, J. Am. Chem. Soc., **65**, 927 (1943).
[199] Clemo and Hoggarth, J. Chem. Soc., **1939**, 1241.
[200] MacDonald, J. Am. Chem. Soc., **69**, 1219 (1947).
[201] Monti, Atti accad. nazl. Lincei, Classe sci. fis. mat. e nat., **24**, 145 (1936) [C.A., **31**, 4321 (1937)].
[202] Gobeil and Hamilton, J. Am. Chem. Soc., **67**, 511 (1945).
[203] Monti, Atti X° congr. intern. chim., **3**, 255 (1939) [C.A., **33**, 9305 (1939)].
[204] Monti, Atti accad. nazl. Lincei, Classe sci. fis. mat. e nat., **28**, 96 (1938) [C.A., **33**, 2897 (1939)].
[205] Ritchie, J. Proc. Roy. Soc. N. S. Wales, **78**, 164 (1945) [C.A., **40**, 879 (1946)].
[206] Rodionov and Berkengeĭm, J. Gen. Chem. U.S.S.R., **14**, 330 (1944) [C.A., **39**, 4076 (1945)].
[207] Borsche and Doeller, Ann., **537**, 39, 53 (1938).
[208] Woodward, Badgett, and Kaufman, Ind. Eng. Chem., **36**, 544 (1944).
[209] Johnson and Hamilton, J. Am. Chem. Soc., **63**, 2864 (1941).
[210] Krahler and Burger, J. Am. Chem. Soc., **64**, 2417 (1942).
[211] Menon, Proc. Indian Acad. Sci., **19A**, 21 (1944) [C.A., **39**, 390 (1945)].
[212] Linsker and Evans, J. Am. Chem. Soc., **68**, 947 (1946).
[213] Monti, Atti accad. nazl. Lincei, **18**, 505 (1933) [C.A., **28**, 4733 (1934)].
[214] Karve, J. Indian Chem. Soc., **2**, 128 (1925) [C.A., **20**, 694 (1926)].
[215] Rabjohn and Harjes, unpublished work.
[216] Monti, Gazz. chim. ital., **74**, 23 (1944).

217 Harley-Mason and Mann, *J. Chem. Soc.*, **1940**, 1379.
218 Stamm and Gossrau, *Ber.*, **66**, 1558 (1933).
219 Plattner and Pataki, *Helv. Chim. Acta*, **27**, 1544 (1944).
220 Ōno, *J. Pharm. Soc. Japan*, **60**, 559 (1940) [*C.A.*, **35**, 2902 (1941)].
221 Ruzicka and Plattner, *Helv. Chim. Acta*, **20**, 809 (1937).
222 Marker, Crooks, and Wittbecker, *J. Am. Chem. Soc.*, **63**, 777 (1941).
223 Callow, *J. Chem. Soc.*, **1936**, 462.
224 Plattner, Ruzicka, and Holtermann, *Helv. Chim. Acta*, **28**, 1660 (1945).
225 Marker and Rohrmann, *J. Am. Chem. Soc.*, **61**, 1284 (1939).
226 Marker and Rohrmann, *J. Am. Chem. Soc.*, **61**, 2724 (1939).
227 Marker, Turner, Shabica, and Ulshafer, *J. Am. Chem. Soc.*, **63**, 1032 (1941).
228 Marker and Rohrmann, *J. Am. Chem. Soc.*, **61**, 1516 (1939).
229 Paige, *J. Chem. Soc.*, **1943**, 437.
230 Marker and Rohrmann, *J. Am. Chem. Soc.*, **61**, 3479 (1939).
231 Eck and Hollingsworth, *J. Am. Chem. Soc.*, **64**, 140 (1942).
232 Butenandt and Hausmann, *Ber.*, **70**, 1154 (1937).
233 Petrow, Rosenheim, and Starling, *J. Chem. Soc.*, **1943**, 135.
234 Marker and Rohrmann, *J. Am. Chem. Soc.*, **61**, 3022 (1939).
235 Urusibara, *Bull. Chem. Soc. Japan*, **16**, 182 (1941) [*C.A.*, **36**, 486 (1942)].
236 Bergmann and Kind, *J. Am. Chem. Soc.*, **64**, 473 (1942).
237 Kind and Bergmann, *J. Org. Chem.*, **7**, 341 (1942).
238 Petrow and Starling, *J. Chem. Soc.*, **1946**, 749.
239 Bellamy and Dorée, *J. Chem. Soc.*, **1941**, 176.
240 Montignie, *Bull. soc. chim. France*, [4] **51**, 144 (1932).
241 Ruzicka, Plattner, and Pataki, *Helv. Chim. Acta*, **25**, 425 (1942).
242 Petrow, *J. Chem. Soc.*, **1939**, 998.
243 Miescher and Wettstein, U. S. pats. 2,323,276 and 2,323,277 [*C.A.*, **38**, 222 (1944)].
244 Soc. pour l'ind. chim. à Bâle, Brit. pat. 497,394 [*C.A.*, **33**, 3812 (1939)].
245 Marker and Rohrmann, *J. Am. Chem. Soc.*, **62**, 521 (1940).
246 Marker, Kamm, and Wittle, *J. Am. Chem. Soc.*, **60**, 1071 (1938).
247 Mitui, *J. Agr. Chem. Soc. Japan*, **15**, 795 (1939) [*C.A.*, **34**, 383 (1940)].
248 Robinson and Slater, *J. Chem. Soc.*, **1941**, 376.
249 Marker and Turner, *J. Am. Chem. Soc.*, **63**, 767 (1941).
250 Hansch and Lindwall, *J. Org. Chem.*, **10**, 381 (1945).
251 Werner, *Sci. Proc. Roy. Dublin Soc.*, **22**, 387 (1941) [*C.A.*, **35**, 5415 (1941)].
252 Connor, Fleming, and Clayton, *J. Am. Chem. Soc.*, **58**, 1386 (1936).
253 Russell, U. S. pat. 2,347,128 [*C.A.*, **38**, 6301 (1944)].
254 Meuwsen and Gebhardt, *Ber.*, **70**, 792 (1937).
255 Chovin, *Compt. rend.*, **215**, 419 (1942).
256 Chovin, *Bull. soc. chim. France*, [5] **11**, 91 (1944).
257 Fieser and Campbell, *J. Am. Chem. Soc.*, **60**, 159 (1938).
258 Lombard, *Compt. rend.*, **213**, 793 (1941).
259 Asahina, Ishidate, and Tukamoto, *Ber.*, **69**, 349 (1936).
260 Jeger, Norymberski, and Ruzicka, *Helv. Chim. Acta*, **27**, 1532 (1944).
261 Ruzicka, Jeger, and Norymberski, *Helv. Chim. Acta*, **25**, 457 (1942).
262 Mower, Green, and Spring, *J. Chem. Soc.*, **1944**, 256.
263 Picard and Spring, *J. Chem. Soc.*, **1941**, 35.
264 Jones and Verrill, *J. Chem. Soc.*, **1940**, 1512.
265 Newbold and Spring, *J. Chem. Soc.*, **1944**, 532.
266 Ruzicka, Müller, and Schellenberg, *Helv. Chim. Acta*, **22**, 767 (1939).
267 Ruzicka and Jeger, *Helv. Chim. Acta*, **24**, 1236 (1941).
268 Ruzicka and Jeger, *Helv. Chim. Acta*, **24**, 1178 (1941).
269 Dieterle and Schreiber, *Arch. Pharm.*, **279**, 312 (1941).
270 Ruzicka, Brenner, and Rey, *Helv. Chim. Acta*, **25**, 161 (1942).
271 Hirayama, *J. Chem. Soc. Japan*, **59**, 683 (1938) [*C.A.*, **32**, 9072 (1938)].
272 Zacharewicz, *Roczniki Chem.*, **16**, 290 (1936) [*C.A.*, **30**, 8191 (1936)].

[273] Tabuteau, *Compt. rend.*, **200**, 244 (1935).
[274] Rydon, *J. Chem. Soc.*, **1939**, 537.
[275] Treibs, *Ber.*, **71**, 1794 (1938).
[276] Treibs, *Ber.*, **70**, 2060 (1937).
[277] Treibs, *Ber.*, **76**, 160 (1943).
[278] Carter, Copp, Rao, Simmonsen, and Subramaniam, *J. Chem. Soc.*, **1939**, 1504.
[279] I.G. Farbenind. A.-G., Ger. pat. 638,940 [*C.A.*, **31**, 3070 (1937)].
[280] Hirayama, *J. Chem. Soc. Japan*, **59**, 229 (1938) [*C.A.*, **32**, 9072 (1938)].
[281] Kondo and Katura, *Ber.*, **73**, 112 (1940); *J. Pharm. Soc. Japan*, **60**, 101 (1940) [*C.A.*, **34**, 3751 (1940)].
[282] Asahina, Ishidate, and Momose, *Ber.*, **67**, 1432 (1934).
[283] Hückel and Kirschner, *Chem. Ber.*, **80**, 41 (1947).
[284] Ruzicka, Rüegg, Volli, and Jeger, *Helv. Chim. Acta*, **30**, 140 (1947).
[285] Green, Mower, Picard, and Spring, *J. Chem. Soc.*, **1944**, 527.
[286] Nametkin and Kagan, *J. Gen. Chem. U.S.S.R.*, **16**, 885 (1946) [*C.A.*, **41**, 2019 (1947)].
[287] Ruzicka and Bernold, *Helv. Chim. Acta*, **24**, 1167 (1941).
[288] Ishidate, Kawahata, and Nakazawa, *Ber.*, **74**, 1707 (1941).
[289] Rapson, *J. Chem. Soc.*, **1939**, 1085.
[290] Sebe, *J. Chem. Soc. Japan*, **62**, 16 (1941) [*C.A.*, **37**, 4063 (1943)].
[291] Jones and Meakins, *J. Chem. Soc.*, **1941**, 757.
[292] Ruzicka and Rosenkranz, *Helv. Chim. Acta*, **23**, 1311 (1940).
[293] Ruzicka and Rosenkranz, *Helv. Chim. Acta*, **22**, 778 (1939).
[294] Jones and Meakins, *J. Chem. Soc.*, **1940**, 1335.
[295] Hirayama, *J. Chem. Soc. Japan*, **58**, 1383 (1937) [*C.A.*, **32**, 4157 (1938)].
[296] Kon and Ross, *J. Chem. Soc.*, **1942**, 741.
[297] Bilham, Kon, and Ross, *J. Chem. Soc.*, **1942**, 535.
[298] Ruzicka, Grob, and F. Ch. van der Sluys-Veer, *Helv. Chim. Acta*, **22**, 788 (1939).
[299] Nametkin and Sheremet'eva, *Compt. rend. acad. sci. U.R.S.S.*, **38**, 131 (1943) [*C.A.*, **37**, 6657 (1943)].
[300] Zacharewicz, *Roczniki Chem.*, **17**, 630 (1937) [*C.A.*, **32**, 4157 (1938)].
[301] Joshel and Palkin, *J. Am. Chem. Soc.*, **64**, 1008 (1942).
[302] Stallcup and Hawkins, *J. Am. Chem. Soc.*, **64**, 1807 (1942).
[303] Stallcup and Hawkins, *J. Am. Chem. Soc.*, **63**, 3339 (1941).
[304] Ruzicka, Brenner, and Rey, *Helv. Chim. Acta*, **24**, 515 (1941).
[305] Ruzicka, Jeger, and Ringnes, *Helv. Chim. Acta*, **27**, 972 (1944).
[306] Dupont, Slawinski, and Zacharewicz, *Roczniki Chem.*, **17**, 154 (1937) [*C.A.*, **31**, 6220 (1937)].
[307] Dupont and Zacharewicz, *Compt. rend.*, **200**, 759 (1935).
[308] Dupont and Zacharewicz, *Bull. soc. chim. France*, [5] **2**, 533 (1935).
[309] Dupont, Zacharewicz, and Dulou, *Compt. rend.*, **198**, 1699 (1934).
[310] Schwenk and Borgwardt, *Ber.*, **65**, 1601 (1932).
[311] Schwenk and Borgwardt, U. S. pat. 1,974,727 [*C.A.*, **28**, 7262 (1934)].
[312] Ishidate and Sano, *Ber.*, **74**, 1189 (1941).
[313] Chakravarti, *J. Indian Chem. Soc.*, **12**, 319 (1944) [*C.A.*, **39**, 2499 (1945)].
[314] Dupont, *Ind. chim. belge*, **11**, 3 (1940) [*C.A.*, **34**, 2353 (1940)].
[315] Witkop, *Ann.*, **554**, 83 (1943).
[316] Guha and Rao, *J. Indian Inst. Sci.*, **22A**, 326 (1939) [*C.A.*, **34**, 3255 (1940)].
[317] Kawai and Yamagami, *J. Chem. Soc. Japan*, **59**, 876 (1938) [*C.A.*, **32**, 9085 (1938)].
[318] Kawai and Yamagami, *Ber.*, **71**, 2438 (1938).
[319] Baddar and Gindy, *Nature*, **157**, 409 (1946).
[320] Fokin, *J. Russ. Phys. Chem. Soc.*, **45**, 285 (1913) [*C.A.*, **7**, 2316 (1913)].
[321] de Coninck and Chauvenet, *Compt. rend.*, **141**, 1234 (1905).
[322] Reif, *Z. Untersuch. Lebensm.*, **71**, 435 (1936) (*Chem. Zentr.*, **1936**, II, 2044).
[323] Wolfrom and Moffett, *J. Am. Chem. Soc.*, **64**, 311 (1942).
[324] Montignie, *Bull. soc. chim. France*, [5] **1**, 290 (1934).

CHAPTER 9

THE HOESCH SYNTHESIS

Paul E. Spoerri and Adrien S. DuBois *

Polytechnic Institute of Brooklyn

CONTENTS

* Present address, Fuld Bros , Inc.

INTRODUCTION

The Hoesch synthesis * consists in the condensation of a nitrile with a phenol, a polyhydric phenol, or a phenolic ether to form a hydroxyaryl or alkoxyaryl ketone.[3] Usually, equimolar quantities of the reactants are dissolved in dry ether, preferably in the presence of a catalyst such as zinc chloride (or ferric chloride), and dry hydrogen chloride is introduced. When phenols are used, imino ether hydrochlorides are sometimes formed as by-products and occasionally represent the only product of the reaction.

$$RCN + C_6H_4(OH)_2 \rightarrow RCOC_6H_3(OH)_2$$

$$RCN + C_6H_5OH \rightarrow \underset{\underset{NH \cdot HCl}{\|}}{RCOC_6H_5}$$

This synthesis, which is an extension of the Gattermann aldehyde reaction,[5, 6] is closely related to several well-known procedures leading to ketones, such as the Fries [7] and the Nencki [8] reactions.

The Hoesch synthesis has proved to be the most convenient synthetic method for certain polyhydroxyacylophenones and polyhydroxybenzophenones. In these classes, there are twenty-five natural products which have been prepared by this procedure. Among these hydroxy ketones are anthelmintics, antidiarrhetics, and antiseptics. The Hoesch reaction with phloroglucinol has been proposed as a method of converting nitriles to solid derivatives.[9]

Certain substituted nitriles do not undergo the Hoesch reaction because of the influence of one or more additional functional groups.

---

* A polemical discussion has appeared between Hoesch [1] and Houben [2] concerning the priority of the discovery of the reaction between alkyl or aryl nitriles and phenols. Since Hoesch was the first to publish a description of this condensation [3] and since, in articles by Houben [4] prior to the appearance of the paper by Hoesch, no mention is made that this type of reaction was either carried out or contemplated, the name "Hoesch reaction" is accepted in this chapter. Houben's claim to priority rests on the basis [2a] that he had suggested privately the possibility of this reaction before the appearance of the early work of Hoesch.

[1] Hoesch, *Ber.*, **60**, 389, 2537 (1927).

[2] Houben, (a) *Ber.*, **59**, 2880 (1926); (b) *Ber.*, **60**, 1554 (1927); (c) *Ber.*, **61**, 1597 (1928).

[3] Hoesch, (a) *Ber.*, **48**, 1122 (1915); (b) Hoesch and von Zarzecki, *Ber.*, **50**, 462 (1917).

[4] Houben and Schmidt, *Ber.*, **46**, 2447, 3616 (1913).

[5] Gattermann, *Ber.*, **31**, 1149, 1765 (1898).

[6] Calloway, *Chem. Revs.*, **17**, 327 (1935).

[7] Blatt, *Organic Reactions*, I, 342, John Wiley & Sons, 1942.

[8] Nencki and Sieber, *J. prakt. Chem.*, **23**, 147 (1881).

[9] Howells and Little, *J. Am. Chem. Soc.*, **54**, 2451 (1932); Shriner and Fuson, *The Systematic Identification of Organic Compounds*, 3rd ed., John Wiley & Sons, p. 204, 1948,

When an α,β-unsaturated nitrile and a phenol react under the conditions used for the Hoesch synthesis, the phenol adds to the olefinic double bond with formation of a saturated nitrile which hydrolyzes and cyclizes to a dihydrocoumarin.[10] Such reactions have been referred to as "abnormal" Hoesch reactions, although the nitrile group is not involved

$$C_6H_5CH{=}CHCN + HO\!\!\overbrace{}\!\!OH \xrightarrow{HCl} \underset{\underset{C_6H_5}{\overset{|}{}}}{HO\!\!\overbrace{}\!\!\overset{OH}{\underset{CHCH_2CN}{}}} \rightarrow$$

$$HO\!\!\overbrace{}\!\!\overset{\displaystyle O}{\underset{\underset{\underset{C_6H_5}{|}}{CH}}{\overset{\diagdown}{\underset{CH_2}{CO}}}}$$

in the initial condensation. Nitriles, other than the α,β-unsaturated nitriles, which yield "abnormal" products appear to be limited almost exclusively to those with a reactive functional group beta to the nitrile group, such as β-halo, β-hydroxy, β-carbethoxy, β-benzoyloxy, β-aldehydo, β-keto, and β-ketimino nitriles. γ-Chlorobutyronitrile also gives an "abnormal" product. The products obtained in the "abnormal" reactions are usually β-arylpropionic acids or β-arylpropionitriles, coumarins, or dihydrocoumarins.

The normal Hoesch synthesis is also applicable to the formation of pyrryl ketones from nitriles and certain pyrroles.

$$RCN + \overbrace{\underset{\underset{H}{N}}{}} \rightarrow \underset{\underset{H}{\underset{\overset{\|}{NH\cdot HCl}}{N}}}{\overbrace{}}CR \rightarrow \underset{\underset{H}{N}}{\overbrace{}}COR$$

A further extension of the Hoesch synthesis is found in the condensation of thiocyanates with phenols or polyhydric phenols to yield thio esters.

$$RSCN + HO\!\!\overbrace{}\!\!OH \rightarrow \underset{\underset{NH\cdot HCl}{\overset{\|}{}}}{HO\!\!\overbrace{}\!\!\overset{OH}{\underset{CSR}{}}} \rightarrow HO\!\!\overbrace{}\!\!\overset{OH}{\underset{COSR}{}}$$

[10] Fischer and Nouri, *Ber.*, **50**, 693 (1917).

MECHANISM

Hoesch assumed that the reaction involved three separate steps:
(a) Formation of imino chlorides;

$$RCN + HCl \rightarrow RCCl$$
$$\parallel$$
$$NH$$

(b) Interaction of imino chlorides with phenol to give ketimine hydrochlorides;

$$\begin{array}{ccc} RCCl + C_6H_4(OH)_2 & \rightarrow & RCC_6H_3(OH)_2 \\ \parallel & & \parallel \\ NH & & NH \cdot HCl \end{array}$$

(c) Hydrolysis of the ketimine hydrochlorides to ketones.

$$RCC_6H_3(OH)_2 \rightarrow RCOC_6H_3(OH)_2$$
$$\parallel$$
$$NH \cdot HCl$$

In substantiation of this view, Tröger and Luning [11] isolated the imino chloride from chloroacetonitrile and hydrogen chloride, and Stephen [12] condensed this addition product with resorcinol to form chlororesaceto-phenone. Several investigators have isolated and identified the intermediate ketimine hydrochlorides from a variety of Hoesch reactions.[2a, 13, 14, 15]

Stephen suggested a different mechanism.[12] He postulated that the imino chloride reacted initially with a phenolic hydrogen rather than with a nuclear hydrogen, thus forming an imino ether which might then (1) rearrange to a ketimine hydrochloride ("normal" Hoesch reaction), or (2) if properly constituted condense internally to a coumarin or dihydrocoumarin ("abnormal" Hoesch reaction). This mechanism is untenable,[2a, 16] since imino ether hydrochlorides cannot be rearranged

[11] Tröger and Luning, J. prakt. Chem., [2] **69**, 347 (1904).
[12] Stephen, J. Chem. Soc., **117**, 1529 (1920).
[13] Houben and Fischer, J. prakt. Chem., [2] **123**, 89 (1929).
[14] Korczynski and Nowakowsky, Bull. soc. chim. France, [4] **43**, 329 (1928).
[15] Sonn, (a) Ber., **50**, 1292 (1917); (b) Ber., **51**, 821 (1918).
[16] Chapman, J. Chem. Soc., **121**, 1676 (1922).

to ketimine hydrochlorides under the influence of heat with or without a catalyst. Moreover, the fact that phenol ethers undergo the Hoesch reaction with the same ease as phenols [3, 17-20] offers additional evidence against an intermediate imino ether.

The "abnormal" Hoesch reaction appears to be merely addition of the phenol to the olefinic double bond of the α,β-unsaturated nitrile.[10, 21, 22] The extraordinary susceptibility to addition of the olefin linkage in such nitriles makes this seem likely. The other nitriles which have been reported as undergoing "abnormal" reactions may be divided into three groups: (1) β-hydroxy, β-carbethoxy, β-benzoyloxy, and β-halo; (2) β-aldehydo, β-keto, β-ketimino; (3) γ-halo nitriles.

The mechanism of the initial reaction involved in the first group may be the direct elimination of water, ethanol, hydrogen chloride, etc., between the functional group in the nitrile and a nuclear hydrogen of the phenol, or the substituted nitrile may be converted *in situ* to an α,β-unsaturated nitrile to which the phenol then adds. In the second group, enolization will result in the formation of an α,β-unsaturated

nitrile to which the phenol may add or which may lose water or ammonia by direct reaction with a nuclear hydrogen of the phenol. The members of the third group, the γ-halo nitriles, appear to condense directly with the phenol rather than through an unsaturated intermediate.

[17] Houben and Fischer, *Ber.*, **60**, 1759 (1927).
[18] Shinoda, *J. Pharm. Soc. Japan*, No. **548**, 834 (1927) [*C.A.*, **22**, 768 (1928)].
[19] Slater and Stephen, *J. Chem. Soc.*, **117**, 309 (1920).
[20] Sonn, (a) *Ber.*, **51**, 1829 (1918); (b) *Ber.*, **52**, 923 (1919).
[21] Langley and Adams, *J. Am. Chem. Soc.*, **44**, 2320 (1922).
[22] Marsh and Stephen, *J. Chem. Soc.*, **127**, 1633 (1925).

SCOPE AND LIMITATIONS

Variations in the Phenols, Phenolic Ethers, and Nitriles

A wide variety of nitriles has been condensed with a relatively restricted number of phenols.[22a] Phenol and substituted monohydric phenols sometimes react with nitriles to give as products imino ether hydrochlorides, many times to the exclusion of any ketone. Phenol and β-naphthol with acetonitrile, chloroacetonitrile, dichloroacetonitrile, phenylacetonitrile, and benzonitrile give 42 to 74% yields of imino ethers.[2a] Phenetole with chloro- or bromo-acetonitrile gives very low yields (8%) of ketones.[17] On the other hand, trichloroacetonitrile reacts smoothly with anisole, phenetole, o-cresyl ethyl ether, m-cresyl ethyl ether, phenyl ether, and veratrole to give ketones, usually in yields varying from 50 to 100%. α-Naphthol reacts with acetonitrile to yield both imino ether and ketone (38%); the yields of ketones from α-naphthol and chloroacetonitrile (55–83%), trichloroacetonitrile (50%), phenylacetonitrile (40%), and benzonitrile (18%) indicate the wide variation that may be expected in this reaction, dependent upon the structure of the nitrile. Similarly, α-naphthyl ethyl ether reacts to give ketones with acetonitrile (2–5%), chloroacetonitrile (86%), and trichloroacetonitrile (95%); anthranyl methyl ether with acetonitrile and benzonitrile also results in formation of ketones. An excess of nitrile with mono- and poly-hydric phenols and their ethers tends to increase the yield of ketones.[17]

Extensive investigations on the condensation of nitriles with resorcinol, phloroglucinol, and their ethers indicate that this reaction is very satisfactory for forming polyhydroxy ketones. The yields of ketones from phloroglucinol or its ethers with aliphatic nitriles except those of very complex character are over 70%; resorcinol or its ethers usually give lower yields. Aromatic nitriles do not react so readily as aliphatic nitriles. In only one instance has the introduction of two ketone groups been noted: acetonitrile and phloroglucinol dimethyl ether yield a mix-

---

[22a] Reactions have been described in which an aromatic hydrocarbon or a heterocyclic compound replaces the phenol or phenolic ether. Although these reactions are, strictly speaking, beyond the scope of this chapter, the synthesis of pyrryl ketones is described on p. 397; and the reader's attention is called to the fact that trichloroacetonitrile in the presence of aluminum chloride and hydrogen chloride reacts with benzene, toluene, o-, m-, and p-xylene, mesitylene, naphthalene, and thiophene to yield ω-trichloroacetophenone (70%), ω-trichloro-p-methylacetophenone (93%), ω-trichloro-3,4-dimethylacetophenone (60%), ω-trichloro-2,4-dimethylacetophenone (94%), ω-trichloro-2,5-dimethylacetophenone (83%), trichloroacetimidomesitylene (73%), a mixture of ω-trichloroacetonaphthones (29%), and α-trichloroacetylthiophene (35%). See Houben and Fischer, *J. prakt. Chem.,* [2] **123**, 313 (1929).

ture of 1-hydroxy-3,5-dimethoxy-2,6-diacetobenzene and 2-hydroxy-4,6-dimethoxyacetophenone or, possibly, 4-hydroxy-2,6-dimethoxyacetophenone.[18]

Of the other polyhydric phenols that have been investigated, orcinol reacts readily to give the corresponding ketones with acetonitrile (63%), benzonitrile (66%), and β-phenylpropionitrile, but not with succinonitrile. 1,2,4-Trihydroxybenzene condenses with p-chlorobenzonitrile to give a 55% yield of ketone; pyrogallol, with the same nitrile, gives a 25% yield of ketone, but with benzonitrile or succinonitrile it does not react. The Hoesch reaction is reported not to take place with catechol or hydroquinone.[14, 23, 24, 25]

Aliphatic dinitriles react with resorcinol and phloroglucinol less readily than mononitriles and usually give mono ketonic acids by the condensation of one nitrile group and hydrolysis of the other. From phloroglucinol and malononitrile or glutaronitrile, a small yield of diketone is reported.[15a, 26] Apparently dinitriles have not been successfully condensed with any phenols other than those mentioned. In dinitriles

with one aromatic nitrile group and one aliphatic, only the aliphatic group appears to react.[27]

Cyanogen, which may be considered a dinitrile, reacts with resorcinol to give a mixture of the tetrahydroxybenzil and the dihydroxyphenyl-

[23] Dalal and Nargund, J. Univ. Bombay, 7, Pt. 3, 189 (1938) [C.A., 33, 3778 (1939)].

[24] Badhwar, Baker, Menon, and Venkataraman, J. Chem. Soc., 1931, 1541.

[25] Bresson and Culbertson, Proc. Iowa Acad. Sci., 36, 266 (1929) [C.A., 25, 1230 (1931)].

[26] Yamashita, Sci. Repts. Tohoku Imp. Univ., 1st series, 24, 192 (1935) [C.A., 29, 7316 (1935)].

[27] Yamashita, Sci. Repts. Tohoku Imp. Univ., 1st series, 22, 167 (1933) [C.A., 27, 3927 (1933)].

glyoxylic acid; with orcinol and 2,4-dimethyl-3-carbethoxypyrrole only the glyoxylic acids or derivatives are reported.

By reaction with ethyl cyanocarbonate instead of cyanogen, 2,5-dimethyl-3-carbethoxypyrrole is converted to the ester of the same glyoxylic acid. From 2,4-dimethyl-3-acetylpyrrole, the 5-glyoxylic ester is formed. The yields are excellent (75–97%).

The reactivity of aromatic nitriles is affected adversely by certain *ortho* substituents; *o*-cyano-,[27, 28] *o*-nitro-,[29, 30] *o*-chloro-,[31] and *o*-methylbenzonitrile[31] do not react either with resorcinol or phloroglucinol. Even in benzyl cyanide, which contains an aliphatic nitrile group, certain *ortho* substituents cause a reduction in the yield of ketone and sometimes prevent the reaction.[28] *o*-Cyano-[27, 28] and *o*-chloro-benzyl cyanide[31] react with phloroglucinol, but the *o*-nitro derivative does not. However, halogen, alkyl, hydroxyl, alkoxyl, and nitro substituents in the *meta* and *para* positions of benzonitrile or benzyl cyanide do not interfere with the reaction.

[28] Yamashita, *Sci. Repts. Tohoku Imp. Univ.*, 1st series, **18**, 615 (1929) [*C.A.*, **24**, 2443 (1930)].

[29] Yamashita, *Sci. Repts. Tohoku Imp. Univ.*, 1st series, **18**, 129 (1929) [*C.A.*, **24**, 98 (1930)].

[30] Yamashita, *Sci. Repts. Tohoku Imp. Univ.*, 1st series, **24**, 205 (1935) [*C.A.*, **29**, 7316 (1935)].

[31] Orito, *Sci. Repts. Tohoku Imp. Univ.*, 1st series, **18**, 121 (1929) [*C.A.*, **24**, 98 (1930)].

If a nitrile contains an α-halogen or α-hydroxy substituent, the initial condensation is often followed by ring closure to a coumarone.[19,30,32,33,34]

The nitriles of α-keto acids, RCOCN, react (a) with one molecule of a phenol to form the normal condensation product, a 1,2-diketone,[22] or (b) with two molecules of a phenol to give more complex substances. Thus, acetyl cyanide and propionyl cyanide condense with resorcinol or phloroglucinol to give the expected diketones.[35] Aroyl cyanides, on the other hand, were first reported to undergo a similar reaction,[22] but further investigation indicated that the condensation takes place between one mole of the benzoyl cyanide and two of the phenol to give imino lactones.[36] The keto group of the aroyl cyanide condenses with two molecules of the phenol followed subsequently by cyclization. Upon hydrolysis, the imino lactone is converted to the lactone.

A few attempts to carry out intramolecular Hoesch reactions have met with very limited success; [37] α-2-naphthoxymethylmandelonitrile was converted to 2-hydroxy-2-phenyl-1,4-α-naphthopyranone.[38]

[32] Karrer and Ferla, *Helv. Chim. Acta*, **4**, 203 (1921).
[33] Klarmann, *J. Am. Chem. Soc.*, **48**, 2358 (1926).
[34] Sonn, *Ber.*, **50**, 1262 (1917).
[35] Borsche and Diacont, *Ber.*, **63**, 2740 (1930).
[36] (a) Borsche and Walter, *Ber.*, **59**, 461 (1926); (b) Borsche, Walter, and Niemann, *Ber.*, **62**, 1360 (1929).
[37] Stevens, *J. Chem. Soc.*, **1927**, 178.
[38] Badhwar and Venkataraman, *J. Chem. Soc.*, **1932**, 2420.

In the Hoesch synthesis involving phenol ethers a single isomer is usually obtained. With certain ethers, however, two isomers have been isolated; thus iretol (4-methoxyphloroglucinol) and chloroacetonitrile give 4,6-dihydroxy-5-methoxycoumaran-3-one and 4,6-dihydroxy-7-methoxycoumaran-3-one;[39] orcinol monomethyl ether and acetonitrile give 2-hydroxy-6-methoxy-4-methyl- and 2-hydroxy-4-methoxy-6-methyl-acetophenone.[3a] Phloroglucinol dimethyl ether and piperonylonitrile give 2-hydroxy-4,6-dimethoxy-3',4'-methylenedioxybenzophenone and 4-hydroxy-2,6-dimethoxy-3',4'-methylenedioxybenzophenone.[13] If zinc chloride is used as a catalyst only the latter compound is obtained; if ferric chloride is employed both result.[13]

The condensation of aniline and acetonitrile to give p-aminoaceto-phenone is the only reaction reported between an aromatic amine and a nitrile.[40]

Since imino chlorides are intermediates in the initial step of the Hoesch reaction, various imino chlorides may be substituted for the nitriles. Thus benzanilide imino chlorides react with resorcinol to give the Schiff's bases of the ketones which are then hydrolyzed to the corresponding ketones.[12, 16]

"Abnormal" Hoesch Reactions

The "abnormal" Hoesch reactions run smoothly, but only a few yields have been reported. The reactions of β-aldehydo, β-ketimino, or β-keto nitriles, with resorcinol or phloroglucinol or their alkylated derivatives, fall within the scope of the von Pechmann reaction.[15b, 41-44] All the com-

[39] Shriner, Matson, and Damschroder, J. Am. Chem. Soc., 61, 2322 (1939).
[40] Hao-Tsing, J. Am. Chem. Soc., 66, 1421 (1944).
[41] Baker and Robinson, J. Chem. Soc., 127, 1981 (1925).
[42] Ghosh, J. Chem. Soc., 109, 105 (1916).
[43] von Meyer, J. prakt. Chem., [2] 67, 342 (1903).
[44] von Pechmann and Duisberg, Ber., 16, 2119 (1883).

pounds represented by the general formulas RCOCH(Ar)CN, ArCOCH$_2$-CN, ArC(=NH)CH$_2$CN, ArCOOCH=C(Ar)CN, and HCOCH(Ar)CN give coumarins. An oxocoumarin is obtained from resorcinol and malonitrile or ethyl cyanoacetate in 80% yield. β-Hydroxy-, β-chloro-, and β-carbethoxy-propionitrile react with resorcinol, its monomethyl ether,

orcinol, and phloroglucinol to give in good yields β-arylpropionic acids or the corresponding dihydrocoumarins.[21, 45]

By the use of excess phenol in the absence of a catalyst, ketones sometimes can be isolated in low yields.[45] Acrylonitrile and certain cinnamonitriles are converted smoothly to dihydrocoumarins.[10, 22] γ-Chlorobutyronitrile and resorcinol form γ-(2,4-dihydroxyphenyl)butyric acid in 21% yield.

Reactions with Pyrroles

In a limited number of reactions pyrroles have been used in the Hoesch synthesis and pyrryl ketones have been formed. Both aliphatic nitriles [46-50] and aromatic nitriles [49] have been employed. Acetonitrile has

[45] Chapman and Stephen, *J. Chem. Soc.*, **127**, 885 (1925).
[46] Blicke, Faust, Gearien, and Warzynski, *J. Am. Chem. Soc.*, **65**, 2465 (1943).
[47] Fischer, Schneller, and Zerweck, *Ber.*, **55**, 2390 (1922).
[48] Fischer, Weiss, and Schubert, *Ber.*, **56**, 1194 (1923).
[49] Seka, *Ber.*, **56**, 2058 (1923).
[50] Kalle and Co., Ger. pat. 365,092 [*Frdl.*, **14**, 518 (1926)].

been condensed with 2,4-dimethylpyrrole (54%) and with 2,4-dimethyl-3-carbethoxypyrrole; chloroacetonitrile, with pyrrole (20%), 2,4-dimethylpyrrole, 2,4,5-trimethylpyrrole (57%), 2,5-dimethyl-3-carbethoxypyrrole (75%), and 2-methylindole (20%). 2-Methylindole gives excellent yields with benzyl cyanide, ethyl cyanoacetate, and benzoyl cyanide (70%).[49] Cyanogen and ethyl cyanocarbonate [47] have been

condensed in good yields with 2,4-dimethyl-3-carbethoxypyrrole, 2,4-dimethyl-3-acetylpyrrole, and 2,5-dimethyl-3-carbethoxypyrrole.

Reactions with Thiocyanates

Early in the study of the Friedel and Crafts reaction [52] it was demonstrated that phenyl thiocyanate and anisole or related phenol ethers react in the presence of aluminum chloride to give thio esters. It was established much later that this reaction takes place with certain phenols under the experimental conditions of the Hoesch synthesis. Thus, resorcinol or phloroglucinol or orcinol and methyl, ethyl, and n-butyl thiocyanates yield the corresponding imino thio ester hydrochlorides which can be hydrolyzed to thio esters.[53] Phenyl thiocyanate is reported to react with resorcinol, orcinol, and phloroglucinol to give quite stable

imino thio esters which, unlike the corresponding alkyl derivatives, yield acid amides on hydrolysis with hydrochloric acid.[53,54]

A reaction between phenols and isothiocyanates can occur under the conditions of the Hoesch synthesis. Although this condensation involves neither a nitrile group nor an imino chloride, nevertheless, it is of interest in connection with the condensation of phenols and thiocyanates. Ethyl,

[51] Spath and Fuchs, Monatsh., 42, 267 (1921).
[52] Tust and Gattermann, Ber., 25, 3528 (1892).
[53] Kaufmann and Adams, J. Am. Chem. Soc., 45, 1745 (1923).
[54] Borsche and Niemann, Ber., 62, 1743 (1929).

allyl, α-naphthyl, and phenyl isothiocyanates react with α-naphthol, pyrogallol, resorcinol, or phloroglucinol to give amides of thio acids.[55, 56]

SELECTION OF EXPERIMENTAL CONDITIONS

The usual procedure for the Hoesch synthesis is to dissolve equimolar quantities of nitrile and phenol in dry ether and to pass in dry hydrogen chloride to saturation while the reaction mixture is carefully protected from moisture by means of a calcium chloride tube. The temperature has usually been maintained at about 0°. Various procedures are described involving different time factors for completion of the reaction. Sometimes the reaction mixture has been worked up almost immediately after saturation with the hydrogen chloride; sometimes the reaction mixture has been held at 0° from a few hours to a few days.[57] No recommendation with respect to the time necessary is possible though it appears advisable to allow the reaction mixture to stand at least several hours with those nitriles which react slowly with the hydrogen chloride. Hydrogen bromide has been employed in place of hydrogen chloride only in rare instances [58] and probably should be considered only when hydrogen chloride may cause some undesirable side reaction such as the replacement of an active bromine in the nitrile by chlorine.

Dry ether is the solvent that leads to the best yields of product. Glacial acetic acid is a possible substitute for ether and is a better solvent for the imino chlorides; [15b, 59] the yields of ketones, however, are usually lower. Other solvents that have been used successfully are chloroform-ether,[14] methyl acetate,[17] and ethyl bromide; [17] those reported as unsuitable are acetic anhydride,[17] dioxane,[17] amyl ether,[14] and benzene.[14]

Anhydrous zinc chloride is a desirable though not indispensable catalyst.[17, 19] In general the yields are better if a catalyst is used.[17] Ferric chloride sometimes has advantages over zinc chloride,[17] but comparative experiments have not been sufficiently numerous to make it possible to predict which is to be preferred. Aluminum chloride, a more powerful catalyst, is sometimes necessary.[60]

[55] Karrer and Weiss, *Helv. Chim. Acta*, **12**, 554 (1929).
[56] Mayer and Mombour, *Ber.*, **62**, 1921 (1929).
[57] Robinson and Venkataraman, (*a*) *J. Chem. Soc.*, **1926**, 2344; (*b*) **1929**, 61.
[58] Freudenberg, Fikentscher, and Harder, *Ann.*, **441**, 157 (1925).
[59] Borsche and Niemann, *Ber.*, **62**, 2043 (1929).
[60] Krollpfeiffer, *Ber.*, **56**, 2360 (1923).

When the reaction with hydrogen chloride is complete the hydrolysis and isolation of the ketone may be accomplished in a number of ways. If the ketimine hydrochloride is very insoluble, it may be filtered from the ether and hydrolyzed. Isolation of the ketimine is attended with greater success if a catalyst has not been employed in the reaction. It is reported that the ketimine hydrochlorides may be converted into the less-soluble sulfates by dissolving the hydrochlorides in water and adding dilute sulfuric acid or aqueous ammonium sulfate.[2a,3a]

The reaction mixture containing the ketimine hydrochloride may be treated with water and the ether layer removed. The aqueous solution is then heated, and the ketone which separates is filtered or extracted with a solvent. Sometimes ethanol or aqueous ethanol increases the rate of hydrolysis, but the isolation of pure ketone is often more difficult under these conditions.[12] The hydrolysis may be facilitated by the addition of dilute aqueous ammonia,[3a,58] sodium hydroxide,[61] calcium carbonate,[34] dilute hydrochloric acid,[12] or dilute sulfuric acid.[62]

EXPERIMENTAL PROCEDURES

Phloroacetophenone. Detailed directions for the preparation of this ketone from phloroglucinol and acetonitrile in 74–87% yield are given in *Organic Syntheses*.[63]

4-Hydroxy-1-acetonaphthone and Acetimino-α-naphthyl Ether Hydrochloride.[2a] Dry hydrogen chloride is bubbled through a solution of 14.4 g. of α-naphthol and 4.1 g. of acetonitrile in absolute ether while the mixture is cooled in an ice bath. After twelve hours the solution takes on a dark-green color and small, green needles of 4-hydroxy-1-acetonaphthone ketimine hydrochloride are deposited in the bottom of the flask. The separation of crystals is complete in three to four days. The supernatant liquid is then decanted from the product, which is crystallized from glacial acetic acid, filtered, washed with ether, and dried. The needles decompose slowly above 200° and finally melt with blackening at 251°. The hydrochloride is stable in the air and is not hygroscopic. The free 4-hydroxy-1-acetonaphthone ketimine, which is insoluble in water, ethanol, and ether, is obtained by treatment with aqueous sodium carbonate.

The ketimine hydrochloride is boiled with water until the white 4-hydroxy-1-acetonaphthone separates from the solution. The crystals

[61] Bauer and Schoder, *Arch. Pharm.*, **259**, 53 (1921).
[62] Shoesmith and Haldane, *J. Chem. Soc.*, **125**, 113 (1924).
[63] Gulati, Seth, and Venkataraman, *Org. Syntheses, Coll. Vol.* **2**, 522 (1943).

are filtered, dried, crystallized from benzene, and washed with petroleum ether; m.p. 198°.

On standing for six to eight weeks, the mother liquors from the crystallization of the ketimine hydrochloride deposit large, pale-green crystals of acetimino-α-naphthyl ether hydrochloride. These are pulverized, dissolved in hot glacial acetic acid, and filtered, and the solution is cooled. The imino ether hydrochloride is precipitated with absolute ether, filtered, washed with ether, and dried; white, very hygroscopic crystals are obtained which decompose above 200°.

β-(2,4-Dihydroxyphenyl)propionic Acid.[21] In a 2-l. round-bottomed flask protected with a calcium chloride tube are placed 130 g. of c.p. resorcinol, 90 g. of pure β-chloropropionitrile, and 700 ml. of dry ether. To this solution is added 40 g. of zinc chloride which has been freshly fused and then powdered, dry hydrogen chloride is passed in for five hours, and the flask is allowed to stand for thirty-six hours longer. The mass of crystals that separates is sticky and hard to handle because of the presence of zinc chloride; it is filtered from the red solution and washed with dry ether. The original filtrate is again stoppered and allowed to stand for forty-eight hours, during which time an additional 39 g. of solid separates. After filtering and allowing the filtrate to stand for a week longer, 25 g. more of crystals is obtained.

The total quantity of crystals is dissolved in 450 ml. of water and heated on a steam bath for four hours. An oily layer of β-(2,4-dihydroxyphenyl)propionic acid lactone first separates and solidifies if the heating is interrupted. The layer, however, is not removed, but the reaction mixture is heated further, causing the lactone to go gradually into solution. This solution is cooled and allowed to stand for some hours after which 86.5 g. of β-(2,4-dihydroxyphenyl)propionic acid crystallizes and is filtered. The aqueous filtrate, upon evaporation in vacuum to 175 ml. and cooling, yields a second crop of crystals which weighs 22.5 g. Further concentration and cooling of the filtrate yield only inorganic salts. The total yield of product is thus 109 g. (56%). The substance is almost always light brown, and this color is difficult to remove even after several crystallizations from water with decolorizing carbon. The substance always separates from the aqueous solution very slowly. In spite of the color, the product melts sharply at 165° with decomposition, the same temperature as that of the white material obtained by hydrolysis of the pure lactone.

2-Chloroacetylpyrrole.[46] A mixture of 13.6 g. of pyrrole, 20.8 g. of chloroacetonitrile, and 100 ml. of ether is cooled with ice and saturated with hydrogen chloride in such a manner that moisture is excluded.

The precipitated imine hydrochloride is filtered, dissolved in 100 ml. of water, and heated for two hours on a steam bath. The black, solid product is powdered and extracted with carbon tetrachloride in a Soxhlet apparatus; yield 5.7 g. (20%), m.p. 117–119°.

Methyl Thio-β-resorcylate Monohydrate.[53] A 1.5-l. wide-mouthed bottle is equipped with a three-holed rubber stopper through which are passed a mechanical stirrer with a mercury seal, an inlet tube with a wide mouth reaching to the bottom of the bottle, and an outlet tube which extends through the stopper and to which is attached a small upright water condenser, the upper end of which is closed with a tube leading through a sulfuric acid wash bottle. In the bottle are placed 110 g. of resorcinol, 73 g. of methyl thiocyanate, 136 g. of anhydrous zinc chloride, and 275 ml. of anhydrous ether. The stirrer is started, and the mixture is agitated for about an hour, until solution is complete. Dry hydrogen chloride is then bubbled into the solution for thirty to forty hours while rapid agitation is maintained constantly. Noticeable warming takes place at the beginning and continues for two to three hours.

After fifteen to twenty-five hours the separation of crystals begins and continues for some time until complete. The mixture is allowed to settle, and the clear mother liquors are decanted. The methyl thio-β-resorcylate imide hydrochloride thus obtained is crystallized twice from hot 15% hydrochloric acid, washed with cold acetone, and then dried at 100–110°. The product is practically pure white and melts at 244–245° (cor.) with decomposition.

The pure imido thio ester hydrochloride is dissolved in three to five times its weight of water, the solution is cooled, and sufficient saturated sodium bicarbonate solution is added to make the mixture alkaline. The methyl thio-β-resorcylate imide which precipitates is filtered and washed with water and then crystallized from methanol; small yellow needles, m.p. 197–199° (cor.) with decomposition.

A solution of 35 g. of once-recrystallized methyl thio-β-resorcylate imide hydrochloride in 1.5 l. of water and 5 ml. of concentrated hydrochloric acid is refluxed for five hours. Upon cooling 25 g. of methyl thio-β-resorcylate monohydrate separates. This is purified by dissolving in a little boiling ethanol to which bone charcoal is added, filtering and reprecipitating with water, and finally recrystallizing from 50% ethanol; colorless needles, m.p. 70–71° (cor.).

TABULAR SURVEY OF THE HOESCH REACTION

In the five tables that follow are listed the imino ethers, ketones, and other products reported in the literature covered by *Chemical Abstracts* through 1947 as having been prepared by the Hoesch and "abnormal" Hoesch reactions.

TABLE I

IMINO ETHER HYDROCHLORIDES *

Reactants	Products	Yield %	Reference
Phenol			
CH_3CN	Acetiminophenyl ether hydrochloride	55	2a
$ClCH_2CN$	Chloroacetiminophenyl ether hydrochloride	73	2a
Cl_2CHCN	Dichloroacetiminophenyl ether hydrochloride	70	2a
Cl_3CCN	Trichloroacetiminophenyl ether hydrochloride	74	2a
$C_6H_5CH_2CN$	Phenylacetiminophenyl ether hydrochloride	42	2a
C_6H_5CN	Benziminophenyl ether hydrochloride	60	2a
α-Naphthol			
CH_3CN	Acetimino-α-naphthyl ether hydrochloride	—	2a
β-Naphthol			
CH_3CN	Acetimino-β-naphthyl ether hydrochloride	45	2a
$ClCH_2CN$	Chloroacetimino-β-naphthyl ether hydrochloride	52	2a

* No catalyst was used in the preparation of these imino ether hydrochlorides.

TABLE II

KETONES AND COUMARANONES

Reactants	Products	Yield %	References *
Anisole			
Cl₃CCN	4-Methoxy-ω-trichloroacetophenone	70	17
o-Bromoanisole			
Cl₃CCN	4-Methoxy-3-bromo-ω-trichloroacetophenone	5	17
Phenetole			
ClCH₂CN	4-Ethoxy-ω-chloroacetophenone	8	17
BrCH₂CN	4-Ethoxy-ω-bromoacetophenone	8	17
Cl₃CCN	4-Ethoxy-ω-trichloroacetophenone	73–100	17
1-Ethoxy-2-methylbenzene			
Cl₃CCN	4-Ethoxy-3-methyl-ω-trichloroacetophenone	79	17
1-Ethoxy-3-methylbenzene			
Cl₃CCN	4-Ethoxy-2-methyl-ω-trichloroacetophenone	50–70	17
Phenyl ether			
Cl₃CCN	4-Phenoxy-ω-trichloroacetophenone	—	17
1-Naphthol			
CH₃CN	4-Hydroxy-1-acetonaphthone	38	2a, 17
ClCH₂CN	4-Hydroxy-1-chloroacetonaphthone	55–83	2a, 17
Cl₃CCN	4-Hydroxy-1-trichloroacetonaphthone	50	17
C₆H₅CH₂CN	4-Hydroxy-1-phenylacetonaphthone	40	17
C₆H₅CN	4-Hydroxy-1-benzonaphthone	18	17
1-Ethoxynaphthalene			
CH₃CN	4-Ethoxy-1-acetonaphthone	2–5	17
ClCH₂CN	4-Ethoxy-1-chloroacetonaphthone	86	17
Cl₃CCN	4-Ethoxy-1-trichloroacetonaphthone	95	17
9-Methoxyanthracene			
CH₃CN	9-Methoxy-10-anthryl methyl ketone	— †	60
C₆H₅CN	9-Methoxy-10-anthryl phenyl ketimine hydrochloride	—	60
Veratrole			
Cl₃CCN	3,4-Dimethoxy-ω-trichloroacetophenone	55	17
Resorcinol			
CH₃CN	2,4-Dihydroxyacetophenone	70–94	2a, 3a, 19
n-C₅H₁₁CN	n-Amyl 2,4-dihydroxyphenyl ketone	27	64
CH₂(CN)₂	ω-Cyano-2,4-dihydroxyacetophenone	—	15a
CN(CH₂)₂CN	β-2,4-Dihydroxybenzoylpropionic acid	21	23, 65
CN(CH₂)₃CN	γ-2,4-Dihydroxybenzoylbutyric acid	—	26
CN(CH₂)₄CN	δ-2,4-Dihydroxybenzoylvaleric acid	—	26
ClCH₂CN	2,4-Dihydroxy-ω-chloroacetophenone	90 ‡	12, 20a
	6-Hydroxy-2,3-dihydro-2(1)-benzofuranone	—	34
BrCH₂CN	2,4-Dihydroxy-ω-bromoacetophenone	60–100	17, 20b, 66
HOCH₂CN	2,4-Dihydroxy-ω-hydroxyacetophenone	38	67
	6-Hydroxy-2(1)-benzofuranone	—	19
CH₃OCH₂CN	2,4-Dihydroxy-ω-methoxyacetophenone	70	19
C₂H₅OCH₂CN	2,4-Dihydroxy-ω-ethoxyacetophenone	—	20b
C₆H₅OCH₂CN	2,4-Dihydroxy-ω-phenoxyacetophenone	—	20b
C₆H₅COOCH₂CN	2,4-Dihydroxy-ω-benzoyloxyacetophenone	80	68
C₆H₅CH₂CN	2,4-Dihydroxy-ω-phenylacetophenone	50–75	69
p-ClC₆H₄CH₂CN	2,4-Dihydroxy-ω-p-chlorophenylacetophenone	—	69a
m-NO₂C₆H₄CH₂CN	2,4-Dihydroxy-ω-m-nitrophenylacetophenone	47	28
p-CH₃C₆H₄CH₂CN	2,4-Dihydroxy-ω-p-methylphenylacetophenone	—	69a

* References 64–110 are on p. 412.
† Aluminum chloride as catalyst in benzene as solvent.
‡ No catalyst employed.

TABLE II—*Continued*

KETONES AND COUMARANONES

Reactants	Products	Yield %	References *
Resorcinol—Continued			
C$_6$H$_5$CONHCH$_2$CN	2,4-Dihydroxy-ω-benzoylaminoacetophenone	40	66
C$_2$H$_5$OCONHCH$_2$CN	2,4-Dihydroxy-ω-carbethoxyaminoacetophenone	51	66
C$_2$H$_5$O$_2$COCH$_2$CN	2,4-Dihydroxy-ω-carbethoxyoxyacetophenone	—	66
C$_2$H$_5$CN	2,4-Dihydroxypropiophenone	31	70
CH$_3$CHOHCN	6-Hydroxy-3-methyl-2(1)-benzofuranone	— ‡	19
C$_6$H$_5$CH$_2$CH$_2$CN	2,4-Dihydroxy-β-phenylpropiophenone	50 ‡	33, 71
3,4-(CH$_3$O)$_2$C$_6$H$_3$CH$_2$CH$_2$CN	2,4-Dihydroxy-β-(3,4-dimethoxyphenyl)propiophenone	22 ‡	72
3,4-(CH$_2$O$_2$)C$_6$H$_3$CH$_2$CH$_2$CN	2,4-Dihydroxy-β-piperonylpropiophenone	48 ‡	72
6-Br-3,4-(CH$_2$O$_2$)C$_6$H$_3$CH$_2$CH$_2$CN	2,4-Dihydroxy-β-6-bromopiperonylpropiophenone	47	73
n-C$_3$H$_7$CN	2,4-Dihydroxybutyrophenone	25	70
(CH$_3$)$_2$CHCHOHCN	2,4-Dihydroxy-α-hydroxycaprophenone	15	30
(CH$_3$)$_2$CHCHClCN	3-Isopropyl-6-hydroxy-2,3-dihydro-2(1)-benzofuranone	20	30
C$_{11}$H$_{23}$CN	2,4-Dihydroxylaurophenone	20	70
C$_6$H$_5$CN	2,4-Dihydroxybenzophenone	30–40	3a, 74
o-CH$_3$COOC$_6$H$_4$CN	3-Hydroxyxanthone	18	75
m-ClC$_6$H$_4$CN	2,4-Dihydroxy-3'-chlorobenzophenone	52	31
p-ClC$_6$H$_4$CN	2,4-Dihydroxy-4'-chlorobenzophenone	39	31
2,4-(CH$_3$COO)$_2$C$_6$H$_3$CN	2,4,2',4'-Tetrahydroxybenzophenone	—	75
4-HO-3-CH$_3$OC$_6$H$_3$CN	2,4,4'-Trihydroxy-3'-methoxybenzophenone	20	3b
3,4-(CH$_2$O$_2$)C$_6$H$_3$CN	2,4-Dihydroxy-3',4'-methylenedioxybenzophenone	37 §	13
2-CH$_3$OC$_6$H$_4$CHOHCN	2,4-Dihydroxy-2'-methoxybenzoin	—	76
C$_6$H$_5$CCl=NC$_6$H$_5$	2,4-Dihydroxybenzophenone	20 ‡	12, 16
4-C$_2$H$_5$O$_2$COC$_6$H$_4$CCl=NC$_6$H$_5$	2,4,4'-Trihydroxybenzophenone	— ‡	12
CNCN	2,4,2',4'-Tetrahydroxybenzil and 2,4-dihydroxyphenylglyoxylic acid	— ‡	32
CH$_3$COCN	1-(2,4-Dihydroxyphenyl)propane-1,2-dione	—	35
C$_2$H$_5$COCN	1-(2,4-Dihydroxyphenyl)butane-1,2-dione	70	35
C$_6$H$_5$COCN	2,4-Dihydroxybenzil	— ‡ǁ	22
	2,4,2',4'-Tetrahydroxytriphenylacetic acid lactone	65	36a
o-CH$_3$OC$_6$H$_4$COCN	2,4-Dihydroxy-2'-methoxybenzil	— ‡	22
p-CH$_3$OC$_6$H$_4$COCN	2,4,2',4'-Tetrahydroxy-4''-methoxytriphenylacetic acid lactone	50 ‡¶ǁ	36a
	2,4-Dihydroxy-4'-methoxybenzil	—	22
3,4,5-(CH$_3$O)$_3$C$_6$H$_2$COCN	2,4-Dihydroxy-3',4',5'-trimethoxybenzil	— ‡¶	22
p-ClC$_6$H$_4$COCN	2,4,2',4'-Tetrahydroxy-4''-chlorotriphenylacetic acid imino lactone	— ǁ	36b
Resorcinol monomethyl ether			
CH$_3$CN	4-Hydroxy-2-methoxy- and 2-hydroxy-4-methoxy-acetophenone	27 each	3a
CN(CH$_2$)$_2$CN	β-2-Hydroxy-4-methoxybenzoylpropionic acid	—	23
ClCH$_2$CN	4-Hydroxy-2-methoxy- and 2-hydroxy-4-methoxy-ω-chloroacetophenone	—	20b
HOCH$_2$CN	6-Methoxy-2(1)-benzofuranone	—	19
CH$_3$OCH$_2$CN	2-Hydroxy-4-methoxy-ω-methoxyacetophenone	— ‡	19

* References 64–110 are on p. 412.
‡ No catalyst employed.
§ Ferric chloride as catalyst.
ǁ Aluminum chloride as catalyst in the absence of a solvent.
¶ Chloroform-ether as solvent.

TABLE II—*Continued*

KETONES AND COUMARANONES

Reactants	Products	Yield %	References *
Resorcinol monomethyl ether—Continued			
CH₃CHOHCN	6-Methoxy-3-methyl-2(1)-benzofuranone	—	19
p-CH₃OC₆H₄CH₂CN	2-Methoxy-4-hydroxy-ω-p-methoxyphenylacetophenone	—	77
	and as a by-product 2-hydroxy-4-methoxy-ω-p-methoxy-phenylacetophenone		
	2-Hydroxy-4-methoxy-ω-p-methoxyphenylacetophenone	—	78
Resorcinol dimethyl ether			
CH₃CN	2,4-Dimethoxyacetophenone	—	18
ClCH₂CN	2,4-Dimethoxy-ω-chloroacetophenone	60	20a
BrCH₂CN	2,4-Dimethoxy-ω-bromoacetophenone	—	66
HOCH₂CN	2,4-Dimethoxy-ω-hydroxyacetophenone	— ‡	19
C₂H₅O₂COCH₂CN	2,4-Dimethoxy-ω-carbethoxyoxyacetophenone	—	66
Cl₃CCN	2,4-Dimethoxy-ω-trichloroacetophenone	100	17
6-Hydroxy-3-methylbenzofuran			
ClCH₂CN	5-Chloroaceto-3-methyl-6-hydroxybenzofuran	—	79
C₆H₅CN	5-Benzoyl-3-methyl-6-hydroxybenzofuran	—	80
p-HOC₆H₄CN	5-(4'-Hydroxybenzoyl)-3-methyl-6-hydroxybenzofuran	—	81
p-CH₃OC₆H₄CN	5-(4'-Methoxybenzoyl)-3-methyl-6-hydroxybenzofuran	—	81
3,4-(HO)₂C₆H₃CN	5-(3',4'-Dihydroxy)-3-methyl-6-hydroxybenzofuran	—	79
6-Hydroxy-3-methyl-2,3-dihydro-benzofuran			
C₆H₅CN	3-Methyl-5-benzoyl-6-hydroxy-2,3-dihydrobenzofuran	—	80
2-Methylresorcinol (2,6-Dihydroxy-1-methylbenzene)			
CH₃CN	2,4-Dihydroxy-3-methylacetophenone	—	82
CH₃OCH₂CN	2,4-Dihydroxy-3-methyl-ω-methyoxyacetophenone	—	82
Orcinol			
CH₃CN	2,4-Dihydroxy-6-methylacetophenone	63	3a
C₆H₅CH₂CH₂CN	2,4-Dihydroxy-6-methyl-β-phenylpropiophenone	— ‡	71
C₆H₅CN	4,6-Dihydroxy-2-methylbenzophenone	66	3a
CNCN	6-Hydroxy-4-methyl-3-keto-2,3-dihydro-2(1)-benzofuranone	— ‡	32
Orcinol monomethyl ether			
CH₃CN	2-Hydroxy-4-methoxy-6-methyl- and 4-hydroxy-2-methoxy-6-methyl-acetophenone	27, 32	3a
Pyrogallol			
o-CH₃COOC₆H₄CN	2,3,4,2'-Tetrahydroxybenzophenone	18	75
p-ClC₆H₄CN	2,3,4-Trihydroxy-4'-chlorobenzophenone	25	14
2,4-(CH₃COO)₂C₆H₃CN	2,3,4,2',4'-Pentahydroxybenzophenone	18	75
1,2,4-Trihydroxybenzene			
CH₃CN	2,4,5-Trihydroxyacetophenone	Poor	83
CH₃OCH₂CN	2,4,5-Trihydroxy-ω-methoxyacetophenone	50	83
p-ClC₆H₄CN	2,4,5-Trihydroxy-4'-chlorobenzophenone	55	14
3,4-(CH₃COO)₂C₆H₃CN	2,4,5,3',4'-Pentahydroxybenzophenone	24 ¶	14
Phloroglucinol			
CH₃CN	2,4,6-Trihydroxyacetophenone	74–93	3a, 57, 63
C₂H₅CN	2,4,6-Trihydroxypropiophenone	73	84
n-C₃H₇CN	2,4,6-Trihydroxybutyrophenone	72	84, 85
iso-C₃H₇CN	2,4,6-Trihydroxyisobutyrophenone	—	85
n-C₄H₉CN	2,4,6-Trihydroxyvalerophenone	85	84

* References 64–110 are on p. 412.
‡ No catalyst employed.
¶ Chloroform-ether as solvent.

TABLE II—*Continued*

KETONES AND COUMARANONES

Reactants	Products	Yield %	References *
Phloroglucinol—Continued			
iso-C$_4$H$_9$CN	2,4,6-Trihydroxyisovalerophenone	—	86
n-C$_5$H$_{11}$CN	2,4,6-Trihydroxycaprophenone	27–69	69b, 84, 87
iso-C$_5$H$_{11}$CN	2,4,6-Trihydroxyisocaprophenone	37	84
CNCH$_2$CN	bis(2,4,6-Trihydroxyphenyl)methane and ω-cyano-2,4,6-trihydroxyacetophenone	— ‡	15a
CN(CH$_2$)$_3$CN	γ-2,4,6-Trihydroxybenzoylbutyric acid and α,γ-bis(2,4,6-trihydroxybenzoyl)propane	15	26
CN(CH$_2$)$_4$CN	δ-2,4,6-Trihydroxybenzoylvaleric acid	—	26
ClCH$_2$CN	2,4,6-Trihydroxy-ω-chloroacetophenone and 4,5-dihydroxy-2,3-dihydro-2(1)-benzofuranone	— ‡	34
HOCH$_2$CN	4,6-Dihydroxy-2(1)-benzofuranone	—	19
CH$_3$OCH$_2$CN	2,4,6-Trihydroxy-ω-methoxyacetophenone	75	19, 57b
CH$_3$CH$_2$CHClCN	4,6-Dihydroxy-3-ethyl-2,3-dihydro-2(1)-benzofuranone	—	33
C$_6$H$_5$COOCH$_2$CN	2,4,6-Trihydroxy-ω-benzoyloxyacetophenone	74 ‡	68
C$_6$H$_5$CH$_2$CN	2,4,6-Trihydroxy-ω-phenylacetophenone	—	69a, 87
o-ClC$_6$H$_4$CH$_2$CN	2,4,6-Trihydroxy-ω-(2'-chlorophenyl)acetophenone	20	31
p-ClC$_6$H$_4$CH$_2$CN	2,4,6-Trihydroxy-ω-(4'-chlorophenyl)acetophenone	—	69a
p-HOC$_6$H$_4$CH$_2$CN	2,4,6-Trihydroxy-ω-(4'-hydroxyphenyl)acetophenone	16–20 ‡	88, 89
p-CH$_3$OC$_6$H$_4$CH$_2$CN	2,4,6-Trihydroxy-ω-(4'-methoxyphenyl)acetophenone	71,‡ 92	89, 90
o-CNC$_6$H$_4$CH$_2$CN	2,4,6-Trihydroxy-ω-(2'-cyanophenyl)acetophenone	—	27
m-CNC$_6$H$_4$CH$_2$CN	2,4,6-Trihydroxy-ω-(3'-cyanophenyl)acetophenone	—	27
p-CNC$_6$H$_4$CH$_2$CN	2,4,6-Trihydroxy-ω-(4'-cyanophenyl)acetophenone	—	27
o-O$_2$NC$_6$H$_4$CH$_2$CN	2,4,6-Trihydroxy-ω-(2'-nitrophenyl)acetophenone	25	28
m-O$_2$NC$_6$H$_4$CH$_2$CN	2,4,6-Trihydroxy-ω-(3'-nitrophenyl)acetophenone	60	28
p-O$_2$NC$_6$H$_4$CH$_2$CN	2,4,6-Trihydroxy-ω-(4'-nitrophenyl)acetophenone	54	28
C$_6$H$_5$CH$_2$CH$_2$CN	2,4,6-Trihydroxy-ω-phenylpropiophenone	— ‡	33, 71
p-HOC$_6$H$_4$CH$_2$CH$_2$CN	2,4,6-Trihydroxy-ω-(4'-hydroxyphenyl)propiophenone	16 ‡	88
p-CH$_3$COOC$_6$H$_4$CH$_2$CH$_2$CN	2,4,6-Trihydroxy-ω-(4'-hydroxyphenyl)propiophenone	60	91
p-CH$_3$C$_6$H$_4$CH$_2$CH$_2$CN	2,4,6-Trihydroxy-ω-(4'-methylphenyl)propiophenone	—	69a
CH$_3$CH$_2$CHBrCN	4,6-Dihydroxy-3-ethyl-2,3-dihydro-2(1)-benzofuranone	—	33
C$_6$H$_5$CN	2,4,6-Trihydroxybenzophenone	63	3a, 51, 87
m-ClC$_6$H$_4$CN	2,4,6-Trihydroxy-3'-chlorobenzophenone	67	31
p-ClC$_6$H$_4$CN	2,4,6-Trihydroxy-4'-chlorobenzophenone	43	31
o-HOC$_6$H$_4$CN	1,3-Dihydroxyanthrone	—	92
	2,4,6,2'-Tetrahydroxybenzophenone	—	74
m-HOC$_6$H$_4$CN	2,4,6,3'-Tetrahydroxybenzophenone	37	92
p-HOC$_6$H$_4$CN	2,4,6,4'-Tetrahydroxybenzophenone	15	92
3,4-(HO)$_2$C$_6$H$_3$CN	2,4,6,3',4'-Pentahydroxybenzophenone	37	3b
4-HO-3-CH$_3$OC$_6$H$_3$CN	2,4,6,4'-Tetrahydroxy-3'-methoxybenzophenone	33	3b
5-NO$_2$-2-HOC$_6$H$_3$CN	1,3-Dihydroxy-7-nitroxanthone	—	93
3,4-(CH$_2$O$_2$)C$_6$H$_3$CN	2,4,6-Trihydroxy-3',4'-methylenedioxybenzophenone	36	94
CH$_3$COCN	1-(2,4,6-Trihydroxyphenyl)propane-1,2-dione	70	35
C$_6$H$_5$COCN	2,4,6-Trihydroxybenzil	— ‡‖	22
	2,4,6,2',4',6'-Hexahydroxytriphenylacetic acid imino lactone	90	36b
o-CH$_3$OC$_6$H$_4$COCN	2,4,6-Trihydroxy-2'-methoxybenzil	— ‡	22

* References 64–110 are on p. 412.

‡ No catalyst employed.

‖ Aluminum chloride as catalyst in the absence of a solvent.

TABLE II—Continued

KETONES AND COUMARANONES

Reactants	Products	Yield %	References *
Phloroglucinol—Continued			
p-CH₃OC₆H₄COCN	2,4,6-Trihydroxy-4'-methoxybenzil	— ‡¶‖	22
	2,4,6,2',4',6'-Hexahydroxy-4''-methoxytriphenylacetic acid imino lactone	—	36b
3,4,5-(CH₃O)₃C₆H₂COCN	2,4,6-Trihydroxy-3',4',5'-trimethoxybenzil	— ‡¶	22
p-ClC₆H₄COCN	2,4,6,2',4',6'-Hexahydroxy-4''-chlorotriphenylacetic acid imino lactone	— ‖	36b
Phloroglucinol monomethyl ether			
n-C₃H₇CN	4,6-Dihydroxy-2-methoxybutyrophenone	—	85a
C₆H₅CN	2,6-Dihydroxy-4-methoxybenzophenone	—	95
CH₃OCH₂CN	2,4-Dihydroxy-ω,6-dimethoxyacetophenone	60	96
C₆H₅COOCH₂CN	2,4-Dihydroxy-6-methoxy-ω-benzoyloxyacetophenone	7	96
Phloroglucinol dimethyl ether			
CH₃CN	2-Hydroxy-4,6-dimethoxyacetophenone and 1-hydroxy-3,5-dimethoxy-2,6-diacetylbenzene	—	18
CH₃OCH₂CN	ω,2,4-Trimethoxy-6-hydroxyacetophenone and a small amount of ω,2,6-trimethoxy-4-hydroxyacetophenone	24	97
C₆H₅COOCH₂CN	2,4-Dimethoxy-6-hydroxy-ω-benzoyloxyacetophenone	56	96
C₆H₅CN	2- and 4-Hydroxy-2,6-dimethoxybenzophenone	—	98
p-HOC₆H₄CH₂CN	2,4-Dimethoxy-6-hydroxy-ω-(p-hydroxyphenyl)-acetophenone and a small amount of 2,6-dimethoxy-4-hydroxy-ω-(p-hydroxyphenyl)acetophenone	19	99
3,4-(CH₂O₂)C₆H₃CN	2-Hydroxy-4,6-dimethoxy- and 4-hydroxy-2,6-dimethoxy-3',4'-methylenedioxybenzophenone	11 §	13
3,4-(CH₂O₂)C₆H₃CN	4-Hydroxy-2,6-dimethoxy-3',4'-methylenedioxybenzophenone	33	13
Phloroglucinol trimethyl ether			
CH₃CN	2,4,6-Trimethoxyacetophenone	85	13, 18
ClCH₂CN	2,4,6-Trimethoxy-ω-chloroacetophenone	— ‡	58
BrCH₂CN	2,4,6-Trimethoxy-ω-bromoacetophenone	— ‡	58
p-HOC₆H₄CH₂CN	2,4,6-Trimethoxy-ω-(p-hydroxyphenyl)acetophenone	10	99
3,4-(CH₃O)₂C₆H₃CH₂CN	2,4,6-Trimethoxy-ω-(3',4'-dimethoxyphenyl)acetophenone	32	100, 101
C₆H₅CHBrCN	2,4,6-Trihydroxy-α-bromo-α-phenylacetophenone	45	58
3,4-(CH₃COO)₂C₆H₃CN	2,4,6-Trimethoxy-3',4'-dihydroxybenzophenone	16 **	13
4-HO-3-CH₃OC₆H₃CN	2,4,6,3'-Tetramethoxy-4'-hydroxybenzophenone	12	14
3,4-(CH₂O₂)C₆H₃CN	2,4,6-Trimethoxy-3',4'-methylenedioxybenzophenone	65 §	13
	2,4,6-Trimethoxy-3',4'-methylenedioxybenzophenone	46	13
1,3,5-Trihydroxy-2-methylbenzene			
n-C₃H₇CN	2,4,6-Trihydroxy-3-methylbutyrophenone	—	85b
1,3,5-Trihydroxy-2-isoamylbenzene			

(structural formulas at bottom)

CH₃O—C₆H₂(—OCH₂CO₂CH₃)—CH₃O, —CH₂CN	CH₃O—C₆H₂(—OCH₂CO₂CH₃)—CH₃O, with HO— ring bearing CH₂CH₂CH(CH₃)₂, —OH, —COCH₂—, ÖH	—	86

* References 64–110 are on p. 412.
‡ No catalyst employed.
§ Ferric chloride as catalyst.
‖ Aluminum chloride as catalyst in the absence of a solvent.
¶ Chloroform-ether as solvent.
** Acetic acid as solvent.

TABLE II—*Continued*

KETONES AND COUMARANONES

Reactants	Products	Yield %	References *
1,3-Dihydroxy-5-methoxy-2-methyl-benzene			
p-CH₃OC₆H₄CH₂CN	2,4-Dihydroxy-6-methoxy-3-methyl-ω-(p-hydroxyphenyl)-acetophenone	44	102
1,3-Dihydroxy-5-methoxy-4-methyl-benzene			
n-C₃H₇CN	2,6-Dihydroxy-4-methoxy-3-methylbutyrophenone	—	103
1,3-Dimethyl-2,4,6-trihydroxy-benzene			
n-C₃H₇CN	2,4,6-Trihydroxy-3,5-dimethylbutyrophenone	—	85
1,3,5-Trihydroxy-2-methoxybenzene			
ClCH₂CN	4,6-Dihydroxy-5-methoxycoumaran-3-one and 4,6-dihydroxy-7-methoxycoumaran-3-one	31, 50	39
1-Hydroxy-3,4,5-trimethoxybenzene			
ClCH₂CN	2-Hydroxy-4,5,6-trimethoxy-ω-chloroacetophenone	42	39
p-CH₃OC₆H₄CH₂CN	2-Hydroxy-4,5,6-trimethoxy-ω-(p-methoxyphenyl)aceto-phenone	—	104
1,3-Dihydroxy-2,5-dimethoxy-benzene			
CH₃CN	2,4-Dihydroxy-3,6-dimethoxyacetophenone	—	105
ClCH₂CN	2,4-Dihydroxy-3,6-dimethoxy-ω-chloroacetophenone	25	39
CH₃OCH₂CN	2,4-Dihydroxy-ω,3,6-trimethoxyacetophenone	72 ‡	106
1,3-Dihydroxy-4,5-dimethoxy-benzene			
CH₃OCH₂CN	2,6-Dihydroxy-ω,3,4-trimethoxyacetophenone	— ‡	106
p-CH₃OC₆H₄CH₂CN	2,6-Dihydroxy-3,4-dimethoxy-ω-(p-methoxyphenyl)-acetophenone	29	107
1,4-Dimethoxy-3,5-dibenzyloxy-benzene			
CH₃CN	2,4-Dihydroxy-3,6-dimethoxyacetophenone	75	108
CH₃OCH₂CN	2,4-Dihydroxy-ω,3,6-trihydroxyacetophenone	62	109
	2-Hydroxy-4-benzyloxy-ω,3,6-trimethoxyacetophenone	31	110

* References 64–110 are on p. 412.
‡ No catalyst employed.

TABLE III

PRODUCTS FROM "ABNORMAL" HOESCH REACTION PRODUCTS

Reactants	Products	Yield %	Reference
2-Naphthol			
$C_6H_5COOCH=C(C_6H_5)CN$	2-Phenyl-3,4-β-naphthopyrone	—	38
Resorcinol			
$CH_3COCH(C_6H_5)CN$	7-Hydroxy-3-phenyl-4-methylcoumarin	—	41
$HCOCH(C_6H_5)CN$	7-Hydroxy-3-phenylcoumarin	—	24
$C_6H_5COOCH=C(C_6H_5)CN$	7-Hydroxy-3-phenylcoumarin	—	24
$C_6H_5C(=NH)CH_2CN$	7-Hydroxy-4-phenylcoumarin	— †	15b
$C_6H_5CH(CN)COCO_2C_2H_5$	3-Phenyl-4-carbethoxy-7-hydroxycoumarin	— ‡	59
$CNCH_2CO_2C_2H_5$	7-Hydroxy-4-oxocoumarin	—	15a, 61
$HOCH_2CH_2CN$	β-(2,4-Dihydroxyphenyl)propionic acid	—	21
$ClCH_2CH_2CN$	β-(2,4-Dihydroxyphenyl)propionic acid	56 §	21
	β-(2,4- and 2,6-Dihydroxyphenyl)propionic acid	71	45
	β-(2,4- and 2,6-Dihydroxyphenyl)propionic acid; 2,4- and 2,6-dihydroxyphenyl β-2,4-dihydroxyphenethyl ketone	—	45
$C_2H_5O_2COCH_2CH_2CN$	Same four products as above	—	45
$ClCH_2CH_2CH_2CN$	γ-(2,4-Dihydroxyphenyl)butyric acid	21	21
$C_6H_5CH=CHC(Cl)=NH$	7-Hydroxy-4-phenylhydrocoumarin	— †	12
Resorcinol monomethyl ether			
$HCOCH(C_6H_5)CN$	7-Methoxy-3-phenylcoumarin	—	24
$ClCH_2CH_2CN$	β-(2-Hydroxy-4-methoxyphenyl)propionic acid	—	45
	β-(2-Hydroxy-4-methoxyphenyl)propionic acid and β-(2-hydroxy-4-methoxyphenyl)propionitrile	—	21
Acetyl resorcinol monomethyl ether			
$C_6H_5COOCH=C(C_6H_5)CN$	7-Methoxy-3-phenylcoumarin	—	24
Orcinol			
$C_6H_5COOCH=C(C_6H_5)CN$	7-Hydroxy-5-methyl-3-phenylcoumarin	—	24
$C_6H_5CH(CN)COCO_2C_2H_5$	3-Phenyl-4-carbethoxy-7-hydroxycoumarin	— ‡	59
$ClCH_2CH_2CN$	5-Methyl-7-hydroxyhydrocoumarin	40	21
$CH_2=CHCN$	5-Methyl-7-hydroxyhydrocoumarin	—	21
Pyrogallol			
$C_6H_5COOCH=C(C_6H_5)CN$	7,8-Dihydroxy-3-phenylcoumarin	—	24
Phloroglucinol			
$HCOCH(C_6H_5)CN$	5,7-Dihydroxy-3-phenylcoumarin	—	24
$C_6H_5C(=NH)CH_2CN$	5,7-Dihydroxy-4-phenylcoumarin	— ‡	15b
p-$CH_3OC_6H_4C(=NH)$-CH_2CN	5,7-Dihydroxy-4-(4'-methoxyphenyl)coumarin	— ‡	15b
p-$CH_3OC_6H_4COCH_2CN$	5,7-Dihydroxy-4-(4'-methoxyphenyl)coumarin	— ‡	20a
$2,4$-$(CH_3O)_2C_6H_3COCH_2CN$	5,7-Dihydroxy-4-(2',4'-dimethoxyphenyl)coumarin	— ‡	20a
$3,4$-$(HO)_2C_6H_3COCH_2CN$	5,7-Dihydroxy-4-(3',4'-dihydroxyphenyl)coumarin	— ‡	20a
$C_6H_5CH(CN)COCO_2C_2H_5$	3-Phenyl-4-carbethoxy-5,7-dihydroxycoumarin	— ‡	59
$CH_2(CN)_2$	5,7-Dihydroxy-4-oxocoumarin	—	15a, 18
$CNCH_2CO_2C_2H_5$	5,7-Dihydroxy-4-oxocoumarin ketimine	— †	15a
$ClCH_2CH_2CN$	5,7-Dihydroxyhydrocoumarin	50	21
$C_6H_5CH=CHCN$	5,7-Dihydroxy-4-phenylhydrocoumarin	90	10
p-$HOC_6H_4CH=CHCN$	5,7-Dihydroxy-4-(4'-hydroxyphenyl)hydrocoumarin	30	10
1,2,4-Triacetoxybenzene			
$HCOCH(C_6H_5)CN$	6,7-Dihydroxy-3-phenylcoumarin	—	38
Phloroglucinol dimethyl ether			
$HCOCH(4$-$CH_3OC_6H_4)CN$	5,7-Dimethoxy-3-(4'-methoxyphenyl)coumarin	—	24
3,4,5-Trimethoxyphenol			
$HCOCH[3,4,5$-$(CH_3O)_3C_6H_2]CN$	5,6,7-Trimethoxy-3-(3',4',5'-trimethoxyphenyl)coumarin	—	24
α-2-Naphthoxymethyl-mandelonitrile (self-condensation)	2-Hydroxy-2-phenyl-1,4-β-naphthopyranone	—	38

† No catalyst employed.
‡ Acetic acid as solvent.
§ Excess phenol and no catalyst used.

TABLE IV

Pyrryl Ketones *

Reactants	Products	Yield %	Reference
Pyrrole			
$ClCH_2CN$	2-Chloroacetylpyrrole	20	46
2,4-Dimethylpyrrole			
CH_3CN	2,4-Dimethyl-5-acetylpyrrole	54	48
$ClCH_2CN$	2,4-Dimethyl-5-chloroacetylpyrrole	96	48
2,4,5-Trimethylpyrrole			
$ClCH_2CN$	2,4,5-Trimethyl-3-chloroacetylpyrrole	57	47
2,4-Dimethyl-3-carbethoxypyrrole			
CH_3CN	2,4-Dimethyl-3-carbethoxy-5-acetylpyrrole	—	47, 50
C_6H_5CN	2,4-Dimethyl-3-carbethoxy-5-benzoylpyrrole	92	50
$CNCO_2C_2H_5$	Ethyl 2,4-dimethyl-3-carbethoxypyrryl-5-glyoxylate	75	47
$CNCN$	2,4-Dimethyl-3-carbethoxypyrryl-5-glyoxylic acid nitrile	—	47
$CNCH_2CN$	2,4-Dimethyl-3-carbethoxy-5-cyanoacetylpyrrole	70	47
2,4-Dimethyl-3-acetylpyrrole			
$CNCO_2C_2H_5$	Ethyl 2,4-dimethyl-3-acetylpyrrole-5-glyoxylate	84	47
2,5-Dimethyl-3-carbethoxypyrrole			
$ClCH_2CN$	2,5-Dimethyl-3-carbethoxy-4-chloroacetylpyrrole	75	47
$CNCO_2C_2H_5$	Ethyl 2,5-dimethyl-3-carbethoxypyrryl-4-glyoxylate	97	47
2-Methylindole			
$ClCH_2CN$	2-Methyl-3-chloroacetylindole	—	50
$CNCH_2CO_2C_2H_5$	Ethyl 2-methylindole-3-β-aminoacrylate	70	49
$C_6H_5CH_2CN$	2-Methyl-3-phenylacetylindole	70	49
C_6H_5CN	2-Methyl-3-benzoylindole	70	15a

* All the pyrryl ketones were prepared without using a catalyst.

TABLE V

Imino Thio Esters

Reactants	Products	Reference
Resorcinol		
CH_3SCN	Methyl thio-β-resorcylate imide hydrochloride	53
C_2H_5SCN	Ethyl thio-β-resorcylate imide hydrochloride	53
$n\text{-}C_4H_9SCN$	Butyl thio-β-resorcylate imide hydrochloride	53
C_6H_5SCN	Phenyl thio-β-resorcylate imide hydrochloride	53, 54
Orcinol		
C_6H_5SCN	Methyl 2,4-dihydroxy-6-methylthiobenzoate imide hydrochloride	54
Phloroglucinol		
CH_3SCN	Methyl 2,4,6-trihydroxythiobenzoate imide hydrochloride	53
C_6H_5SCN	Phenyl 2,4,6-trihydroxythiobenzoate imide hydrochloride	54

REFERENCES TO TABLES

[64] A. S. DuBois, M.S. Thesis, Brooklyn Polytechnic Institute, 1944.

[65] Murai, *Bull. Chem. Soc. Japan*, **1**, 129 (1926) [*C.A.*, **20**, 2995 (1926)]; *Sci. Repts. Tohoku Imp. Univ.*, **15**, 675 (1926) (*Chem. Zentr.*, **1927**, I, 1156).

[66] Sonn and Falkenheim, *Ber.*, **55**, 2975 (1922).

[67] Karrer and Biedermann, *Helv. Chim. Acta*, **10**, 441 (1927).

[68] Heap and Robinson, *J. Chem. Soc.*, **1926**, 2336.

[69] (a) Chapman and Stephen, *J. Chem. Soc.*, **123**, 404 (1923); (b) Houben and Wollenweber, *Biochem. Z.*, **204**, 448 (1929); (c) Klarmann, *J. Am. Chem. Soc.*, **48**, 791 (1926); (d) Klarmann, U. S. pat. 1,596,613 [*C.A.*, **20**, 3332 (1926)]; (e) Farbwerke vorm. Meister Lucius and Bruning, Brit. pat. 157,854 [*Frdl.*, **14**, 518 (1926)].

[70] DuBois, unpublished data.

[71] Baker, *J. Chem. Soc.*, **127**, 2349 (1925).

[72] Baker and Robinson, *J. Chem. Soc.*, **127**, 1424 (1925).

[73] Baker, *J. Chem. Soc.*, **1926**, 1074.

[74] Karrer, *Helv. Chim. Acta*, **4**, 992 (1921).

[75] Atkinson and Heilbron, *J. Chem. Soc.*, **1926**, 2688.

[76] Ishidate, *J. Pharm. Soc. Japan*, **1927**, No. 542, 47 (*Chem. Zentr.*, **1927**, II, 251).

[77] Wessely, Lechner, and Dinjaški, *Monatsh.*, **63**, 201 (1933).

[78] Anderson and Marrian, *J. Biol. Chem.*, **127**, 649 (1939).

[79] Karrer, Glattfelder, and Widmer, *Helv. Chim. Acta*, **3**, 541 (1920).

[80] Karrer and Widmer, *Helv. Chim. Acta*, **2**, 454 (1919).

[81] Karrer, Rudlinger, Glattfelder, and Waitz, *Helv. Chim. Acta*, **4**, 718 (1921).

[82] Rangaswami and Seshadri, *Proc. Indian Acad. Sci.*, **8A**, 214 (1938) [*C.A.*, **33**, 2122 (1939)].

[83] Healy and Robinson, *J. Chem. Soc.*, **1934**, 1625.

[84] Howells and Little, *J. Am. Chem. Soc.*, **54**, 2451 (1932).

[85] (a) Karrer, *Helv. Chim. Acta*, **2**, 466 (1919); (b) Farbwerke vorm. Meister Lucius and Bruning, Brit. pat. 157,854 [*Frdl.*, **14**, 518 (1926)]; (c) Farbwerke vorm. Meister Lucius and Bruning, Brit. pat. 364,883 [*Frdl.*, **14**, 1423 (1926)].

[86] Kenny, Robertson, and George, *J. Chem. Soc.*, **1939**, 1601.

[87] Klarmann and Figdor, *J. Am. Chem. Soc.*, **48**, 803 (1926).

[88] Zemplen, Csuros, Gerecs, and Aczel, *Ber.*, **61**, 2486 (1928).

[89] Baker and Robinson, *J. Chem. Soc.*, **1926**, 2713.

[90] Shriner and Hull, *J. Org. Chem.*, **10**, 288 (1945).

[91] Fischer and Nouri, *Ber.*, **50**, 611 (1917).

[92] Nishikawa and Robinson, *J. Chem. Soc.*, **121**, 839 (1922).

[93] Yumoto, *J. Pharm. Soc. Japan*, **48**, 49 (1928) (*Chem. Zentr.*, **1928**, II, 50).

[94] Späth and Bretschneider, *Monatsh.*, **49**, 429 (1928).

[95] Karrer, *Helv. Chim. Acta*, **2**, 486 (1919).

[96] Kuhn, Löw, and Trischmann, *Ber.*, **77**, 202 (1944).

[97] Row and Seshadri, *Proc. Indian Acad. Sci.*, **23A**, 23 (1946) [*C.A.*, **40**, 5050 (1946)].

[98] Karrer and Lichtenstein, *Helv. Chim. Acta*, **11**, 789 (1928).

[99] Zemplen, Bognar, and Farkas, *Ber.*, **76**, 267 (1943).

[100] Carrara and Cohn, *Gazz. chim. ital.*, **56**, 134 (1926).

[101] Freudenberg, *Ann.*, **446**, 87 (1926).

[102] Shriner and Hull, *J. Org. Chem.*, **10**, 228 (1945).

[103] Karrer and Widmer, *Helv. Chim. Acta*, **3**, 392 (1920).

[104] E. J. Matson, Ph.D. Thesis, University of Illinois, 1939.

[105] Wessely and Moser, *Monatsh.*, **56**, 100 (1930).

[106] Baker, Nodzu, and Robinson, *J. Chem. Soc.*, **1929**, 74.

[107] Shriner and Stephenson, *J. Am. Chem. Soc.*, **64**, 2737 (1942).

[108] Sastri and Seshadri, *Proc. Indian Acad. Sci.*, **24A**, 243 (1946) [*C.A.*, **41**, 2417 (1947)].

[109] Rao, Rao, and Seshadri, *Proc. Indian Acad. Sci.*, **19A**, 88 (1944) [*C.A.*, **39**, 301 (1945)].

[110] Sastri and Seshadri, *Proc. Indian Acad. Sci.*, **24A**, 238 (1946) [*C.A.*, **41**, 2417 (1947)].

CHAPTER 10

THE DARZENS GLYCIDIC ESTER CONDENSATION

Melvin S. Newman

The Ohio State University

and

Barney J. Magerlein

The Upjohn Company

CONTENTS

INTRODUCTION

The Darzens glycidic ester condensation involves the condensation of an aldehyde or ketone with an α-halo ester to produce an α,β-epoxy ester (glycidic ester). The most frequently used condensing agents are sodium ethoxide and sodium amide.

$$R'COR'' + R'''CHXCO_2C_2H_5 \xrightarrow[\text{(NaNH}_2)]{\text{C}_2\text{H}_5\text{ONa}}$$

$$\underset{R''}{\overset{R'}{\diagdown}}\underset{O}{\diagup}C\text{———}\underset{}{\overset{R'''}{\mid}}CCO_2C_2H_5 + NaX + C_2H_5OH$$
(NH₃)

The glycidic esters are of interest primarily because they can be converted into aldehydes and ketones having a higher carbon content than the original aldehydes or ketones. This transformation occurs after hydrolysis to and decarboxylation of the epoxy acids and is accompanied by rearrangement when an aldehyde is formed.

$$\underset{R''}{\overset{R'}{\diagdown}}\underset{O}{\diagup}C\text{———}\underset{}{\overset{R'''}{\mid}}C\text{—}CO_2H \xrightarrow[(-CO_2)]{\Delta} \underset{R''}{\overset{R'}{\diagdown}}CHCOR''' \quad \text{or} \quad R''\text{—}\underset{R'''}{\overset{R'}{\diagup}}CCHO$$

The first synthesis of a glycidic ester was performed by Erlenmeyer,[1] who obtained ethyl β-phenyl-α,β-epoxypropionate by condensing benzaldehyde with ethyl chloroacetate by means of sodium. It remained for Darzens, however, to develop and generalize this reaction.[2-13] He

[1] Erlenmeyer, Jr., Ann., **271**, 161 (1892).
[2] Darzens, Compt. rend., **139**, 1214 (1904).
[3] Darzens, Compt. rend., **141**, 766 (1905).
[4] Darzens, Compt. rend., **142**, 214 (1906).
[5] Darzens and Lefebure, Compt. rend., **142**, 714 (1906).
[6] Darzens, Compt. rend., **144**, 1123 (1907).
[7] Darzens, Compt. rend., **145**, 1342 (1907).
[8] Darzens, Compt. rend., **150**, 1243 (1910).
[9] Darzens and Rost, Compt. rend., **151**, 758 (1910).
[10] Darzens, Compt. rend., **152**, 443 (1911).
[11] Darzens and Sejourné, Compt. rend., **152**, 1105 (1911).
[12] Darzens and Leroux, Compt. rend., **154**, 1812 (1912).
[13] Darzens, Compt. rend., **195**, 884 (1932).

preferred sodium ethoxide as the condensing agent. Shortly after the appearance of Darzens' first paper, Claisen [14] reported that sodium amide could be used as the condensing agent. The glycidic ester condensation has not been applied as widely as one would expect in view of the number and variety of compounds that can be prepared by its use.

Darzens [15, 16, 17] has described another procedure which involves the reaction of aldehydes and ketones with ethyl dichloroacetate and dilute magnesium amalgam. The first product of this reaction is a β-hydroxy α-chloro ester which is quantitatively converted to a glycidic ester by treatment with sodium ethoxide. Alternatively, the hydroxy chloro esters may be dehydrated to yield α-chloro unsaturated esters.

$$R'COR'' + CHCl_2CO_2C_2H_5 \xrightarrow{Mg \cdot Hg} \begin{matrix} R' \\ \diagdown \\ CCHClCO_2C_2H_5 \\ \diagup \quad | \\ R'' \quad OMgCl \end{matrix}$$

$$\downarrow H_2O$$

$$\begin{matrix} R' \\ \diagdown \\ CCHClCO_2C_2H_5 \\ \diagup \quad | \\ R'' \quad OH \end{matrix}$$

$$\xleftarrow{P_2O_5}$$

$$\downarrow C_2H_5ONa$$

$$\begin{matrix} R' \\ \diagdown \\ C=C-CO_2C_2H_5 \\ \diagup \quad | \\ R'' \quad Cl \end{matrix} \qquad \begin{matrix} R' \\ \diagdown \\ C \quad\quad CHCO_2C_2H_5 \\ \diagup \diagdown \quad \diagup \\ R'' \quad\quad O \end{matrix}$$

The mechanism of glycidic ester formation probably involves the addition of the enolate of the halo ester to the carbonyl group of the aldehyde or ketone,* followed by an intramolecular nucleophilic dis-

---

* Early ideas involving addition of the condensing agent to the carbonyl group of the aldehyde or ketone, Fourneau and Billeter, *Bull. soc. chim. France*, [5] **6**, 1616 (1939), or the conversion of the aldehyde or ketone to its enolate by the base, Rutowski and Dajew, *Ber.*, **64**, 693 (1931), appear inadequate. Scheibler and Tutundzitsch, *Ber.*, **64**, 2916 (1931), first suggested the formation of the enolate of the halo ester, but their detailed mechanism appears unnecessarily complicated.

[14] Claisen, *Ber.*, **38**, 693 (1905).
[15] Darzens, *Compt. rend.*, **151**, 883 (1910).
[16] Darzens, *Compt. rend.*, **203**, 1374 (1936).
[17] Darzens and Lévy, *Compt. rend.*, **204**, 272 (1937).

placement on carbon. The function of the basic condensing agent is to convert the halo ester to its enolate.

$$ClCH_2CO_2C_2H_5 + C_2H_5ONa \rightarrow [ClCHCO_2C_2H_5]^-Na^+ + C_2H_5OH$$
$$\text{(NaNH}_2) \qquad\qquad\qquad\qquad\qquad\qquad \text{(NH}_3)$$

$$R'COR'' + [ClCHCO_2C_2H_5]^-Na^+ \rightarrow \left[\begin{array}{c} R' \quad O \\ \diagdown C CHCO_2C_2H_5 \\ R'' \quad Cl \end{array} \right]^- Na^+$$

$$\searrow$$

$$\begin{array}{c} R' \qquad O \\ C\text{————}CHCO_2C_2H_5 + NaCl \\ R'' \end{array}$$

Evidence supporting the formation of the enolate of the chloro ester is the fact that about 79% of the theoretical amount of ammonia is evolved on treating a suspension of sodium amide in ether with ethyl chloroacetate.[18, *] It has been shown that the sodium enolates of ketones react with chloro esters to give glycidic esters.[18, 19] This result is consistent with the above mechanism if it is postulated that the enolate of the ketone reacts with the chloro ester to convert it to its enolate.

$$\begin{array}{c} ONa \\ | \\ CH_3C\text{==}CH_2 + ClCH_2CO_2C_2H_5 \rightarrow CH_3COCH_3 + [ClCHCO_2C_2H_5]^-Na^+ \end{array}$$

SCOPE AND LIMITATIONS

Carbonyl Components

Of the many types of aldehydes and ketones from which the desired condensation products have been isolated, only formaldehyde,[4] monosubstituted acetaldehydes,[4] and a few terpene ketones, such as carvone and pulegone,[4] give generally poor yields. Aromatic aldehydes containing alkyl, alkoxy, methylenedioxy, and chloro groups give fair to good yields. Although no study of the effect of steric hindrance has been made, 2,4,6-trimethylbenzaldehyde is reported to give the expected product,[20] but in unstated yield. Aliphatic ketones, including methyl ketones, α,β-unsaturated ketones, and cyclic ketones, react smoothly.

---

* The hypothesis that a halo ester may form an enolate is supported by the observation that chloromalonic ester may be alkylated to form benzylchloromalonic ester by treatment with sodium ethoxide followed by benzyl chloride, Conrad, *Ann.*, **209**, 241 (1881).

[18] Unpublished experiments by Newman and Magerlein at the Ohio State University.
[19] Rutowski and Dajew, *Ber.*, **64**, 693 (1931).
[20] Chuit and Bolle, *Bull. soc. chim. France*, [4] **35**, 200 (1924).

The successful use of a Mannich base, 2-dimethylaminocyclohexanone, has been reported,[21] but the analogous 4-dimethylamino-2-butanone failed to give the expected ester.[21] Aromatic and aromatic-aliphatic ketones give very satisfactory yields. The presence of a nuclear chlorine atom appears to improve the yield somewhat.[18] Although a fairly representative group of aldehydes and ketones has been investigated, no systematic study of the effect of the structure of the carbonyl component on the yield of glycidic ester has been reported.

Halogenated Esters

As a rule, chloro esters are preferable to bromo or iodo esters although bromo esters have been used successfully. With cyclohexanone, it has been shown that the p-toluenesulfonate of ethyl glycolate may be substituted for the chloro ester.[22] With ethyl chloroacetate, isobutyro phenone yields the glycidic ester, whereas with ethyl iodoacetate it yields an alkylation product, ethyl β,β-dimethyl-β-benzoylpropionate, with ethyl bromoacetate a mixture of the two products results.[23]

$$C_6H_5COCH(CH_3)_2 \begin{cases} \xrightarrow{ClCH_2CO_2C_2H_5} \quad \begin{array}{c} (CH_3)_2CH \quad O \\ \diagdown \diagup \diagdown \\ C\!-\!\!-\!\!-CHCO_2C_2H_5 \\ \diagup \\ C_6H_5 \end{array} \quad (A) \\ \\ \xrightarrow{BrCH_2CO_2C_2H_5} \text{Mixture of A and B} \\ \\ \xrightarrow{ICH_2CO_2C_2H_5} C_6H_5COC(CH_3)_2CH_2CO_2C_2H_5 \quad (B) \end{cases}$$

Very little is known of the condensation of halo esters other than halo acetates, halo propionates, and halo butyrates, ethyl α-chlorolaurate being the only example of a higher ester described.[13]

The effect of the alkyl group of the halo ester on reactivity or yield has not been investigated to any extent. If sodium amide is the condensing agent, the ethyl ester is preferable to the methyl ester because of increased formation of chloroacetamide with the methyl ester.[14] In experiments involving acetone, benzaldehyde, acetophenone, and cyclohexanone the following alkyl chloroacetates and chloropropionates gave yields comparable to those obtained with methyl and ethyl esters:[18]

[21] Howton, J. Org. Chem., **12**, 379 (1947).

[22] Newman and Magerlein, J. Am. Chem. Soc., **69**, 469 (1947).

[23] Haller and Ramart-Lucas, Compt. rend., **159**, 143 (1914); Ger. pat. 586,645 [Frdl. **20**, 781 (1935)].

propyl and isopropyl, allyl, cyclohexyl, n-amyl, benzyl, and 2-ethylhexyl; with β-methallyl and tetrahydrofurfuryl esters the yields were lower. There is some evidence that better yields of condensation products may be obtained with halo amides. An 80% yield of glycide amide is obtained from acetone and the diethylamide of chloroacetic acid [24] whereas with ethyl chloroacetate [2, 14, 19] much lower yields result. However, it has not been shown that the glycidic amides can be hydrolyzed and decarboxylated to give aldehydes or ketones in improved yields.

More complex halo esters, such as ethyl β-hydroxy-α-chloropropionate,[25] ethyl α,β-dichloropropionate,[25] and ethyl α-bromo-β,β-diethoxypropionate,[26] have failed to undergo the glycidic ester condensation.

Other Halogenated Compounds

Certain other halogenated compounds have been used in place of halo esters. α-Halo ketones have been condensed with a variety of aldehydes to yield α,β-epoxyketones.[27-31]

$$RCHO + ClCH_2COR' \xrightarrow{C_2H_5ONa} RCH{-}CHCOR'$$

These epoxyketones may condense with a second molecule of halo ketone to yield $\alpha,\beta,\gamma,\delta$-diepoxyketones.[28a]

$$RCH{-}CHCOR' + ClCH_2COR' \xrightarrow{C_2H_5ONa}$$

$$RCH{-}CHC{-}CHCOR'$$
$$R'$$

When 1,4-dibromo-1,4-dibenzoylbutane is treated with sodium cyanide,[32] diethylamine,[32] sodium acetate,[32] or the sodium derivative

[24] von Schickh, *Ber.*, **69**, 971 (1936).
[25] Yarnall and Wallis, *J. Org. Chem.*, **4**, 284 (1939).
[26] Oroshnik and Spoerri, *J. Am. Chem. Soc.*, **67**, 721 (1945).
[27] Widman, (a) *Ann.*, **400**, 86 (1913); (b) *Ber.*, **49**, 477 (1916).
[28] Bodforss, (a) *Ber.*, **49**, 2795 (1916); (b) *Ber.*, **51**, 192 (1918); (c) *Ber.*, **52**, 142 (1919).
[29] Jörlander, (a) *Ber.*, **49**, 2782 (1916); (b) *Ber.*, **50**, 406, 1457 (1917).
[30] Freudenberg and Stoll, *Ann.*, **440**, 41 (1924).
[31] Murakami and Irie, *Proc. Imp. Acad. (Tokyo)*, **10**, 568 (1934) [*C.A.*, **29**, 1818 (1935)].
[32] Kao and Fuson, *J. Am. Chem. Soc.*, **54**, 313 (1932).

of malonic ester [33] a cyclic epoxyketone is produced; with molecular silver the debrominated analog is obtained.[33]

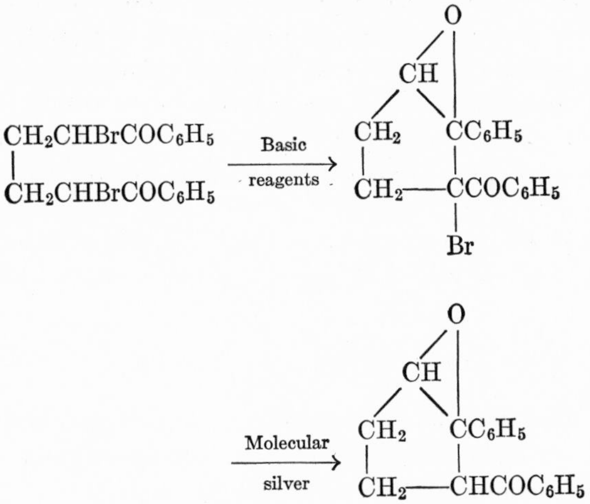

$$CH_2CHBrCOC_6H_5 \atop CH_2CHBrCOC_6H_5 \quad \xrightarrow[\text{reagents}]{\text{Basic}}$$

O
╱＼
CH
╱ ＼
CH_2 CC_6H_5
CH_2——$CCOC_6H_5$
                Br

$$\xrightarrow[\text{silver}]{\text{Molecular}}$$

O
╱＼
CH
╱ ＼
CH_2 CC_6H_5
CH_2——$CHCOC_6H_5$

A number of substituted halides of the benzyl [34,35,36] and benzal [34b] types has been condensed with aldehydes and ketones to give epoxy and α-haloepoxy compounds in yields which, although usually not stated, were often good. Stereoisomeric forms of the epoxy compounds were occasionally separated.

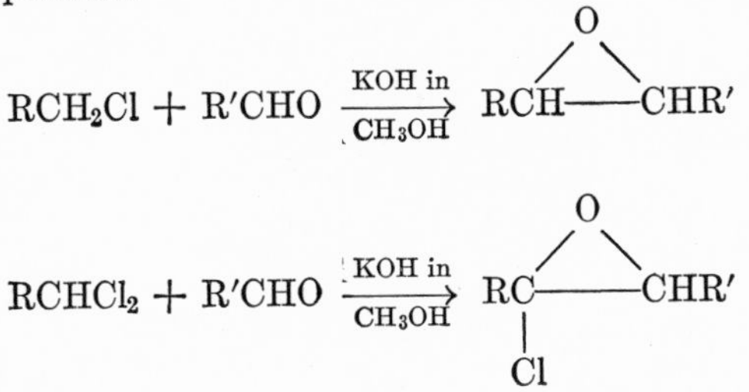

$$RCH_2Cl + R'CHO \xrightarrow[\text{CH}_3\text{OH}]{\text{KOH in}} \overset{\displaystyle O}{\overset{\diagup\diagdown}{RCH\!-\!\!-\!\!-CHR'}}$$

$$RCHCl_2 + R'CHO \xrightarrow[\text{CH}_3\text{OH}]{\text{KOH in}} \overset{\displaystyle O}{\overset{\diagup\diagdown}{RC\!-\!\!-\!\!-CHR'}} \atop Cl$$

The aldehydes used include benzaldehyde, o-, m-, and p-nitrobenzaldehyde, p-methoxybenzaldehyde, diphenylacetaldehyde, cinnamaldehyde, and furfural; the ketones were fluorenone and 2,7-dibromofluorenone. As halides, o- and p-nitrobenzyl chloride, 9-chlorofluorene, and 9-bromo-10-anthrone were used.

[33] Kao, *J. Am. Chem. Soc.*, **62**, 356 (1940).

[34] (a) Hatzig, Inaugural dissertation, Strasbourg, 1909; (b) Barrow, Inaugural dissertation, Strasbourg, 1909; (c) Chrzescinski, Inaugural dissertation, Strasbourg, 1911.

[35] Kleucker, *Ber.*, **55**, 1634 (1922).

[36] Bergmann and Hervey, *Ber.*, **62**, 902 (1929).

Side Reactions

Few investigators have studied the non-glycidic-ester portion of the reaction products. Some unchanged ketone may usually be recovered. Possible contaminants of the glycidic esters are the isomeric oxygen or carbon alkylation products formed by alkylation of the enolate of the ketone by the halo ester. The boiling ranges reported for the glycidic esters usually cover 5–10°, so that such contamination is entirely possible. The condensation product from β-ionone and ethyl chloroacetate is considered to be a mixture of three isomeric products: glycidic ester; α-keto ester; and the enolic form of the latter.[37] Halogen in the condensation products indicates the presence of an α-halogen α,β-unsaturated ester.[14] High-boiling products, including resinous material, are frequently noted. These may result from self-condensation of the aldehyde or ketone [38] or of the halo ester; ethyl chloroacetate in ether reacts with sodium to yield an ethoxy chloro acetoacetate of undetermined structure.[39] Vacuum distillation of high-boiling glycidic esters should be done at as low a temperature as possible in order to guard against rearrangement to an α-keto ester.[40, 41, 42]

SELECTION OF EXPERIMENTAL CONDITIONS

The reactions are carried out under strictly anhydrous conditions preferably in an inert atmosphere. Often no solvent is used, care being taken to prevent undue temperature rise when the condensing agent is added. It seems best to add the condensing agent to a mixture of the reaction components, of which the halo ester is preferably in some excess.[37] It has been found [18] advantageous to use 1.6 moles of chloro ester and 1.6 moles of alkoxide to 1 mole of ketone. During the first stage of the reaction it is well to keep the mixture cold, temperatures as low as −80° being recommended.[43] However, in a few cases no reaction occurs at −80°, and a temperature of 0° appears to be preferable.[18] After reaction periods ranging from a few hours to a few days, the mixture is usually heated for an hour on a steam bath. The reaction mixture is then treated with dilute acid and the organic products are generally

[37] Milas, Lee, Sakal, Wohlens, MacDonald, Grossi, and Wright, *J. Am. Chem. Soc.*, **70**, 1584 (1948).

[38] Weidlich and Daniels, *Ber.*, **72**, 1596 (1939).

[39] Fittig and Erlenbach, *Ann.*, **269**, 15 (1892).

[40] Troell, *Ber.*, **61**, 2498 (1928).

[41] Kohler, Richtmyer, and Hester, *J. Am. Chem. Soc.*, **53**, 211 (1931).

[42] Pointet, *Compt. rend.*, **148**, 417 (1909).

[43] Yarnall and Wallis, *J. Org. Chem.*, **4**, 270 (1939).

separated by vacuum distillation. At least one glycidic ester rearranged into an α-keto ester at the high temperature needed for vacuum
distillation,[40, 41, 42] but this rearrangement seems not to be general.

The most frequently used condensing agents are sodium ethoxide and
sodium amide. Of these, sodium ethoxide is the reagent of choice in
the few reactions where both have been employed.[18, 37, 40, 44, 45] The use
of powdered sodium in various solvents seems to be promising.[46] The
sodium ketyl prepared from benzophenone has been used with fair
success in one reaction.[19]

The effect of solvent on the yields of glycidic esters has not been
extensively investigated. Better yields were obtained in the condensation of cyclohexanone with ethyl α-chloropropionate without solvent
than with ether, benzene, or benzene-petroleum ether.[25] A variety of
inert solvents has been used, but the experiments do not permit a conclusion concerning the importance of the solvent. Aromatic hydrocarbons have been recommended as solvents in preparations carried out
with the aid of metallic sodium; in the presence of such solvents the
sodium chloride formed in the reaction separates in a colloidal suspension
and does not coat the sodium.[46]

CONVERSION OF GLYCIDIC ESTERS INTO ALDEHYDES AND KETONES

Hydrolysis of glycidic esters to and decarboxylation of the resulting
glycidic acids usually yield ketones or aldehydes. R' and R'' may

represent hydrogen or alkyl or aryl groups, or may be joined in a ring.
If R''' is hydrogen an aldehyde always results; if a methyl group, methyl
ketones are formed. The effect of other groups in the R''' position has

[44] Linstead and Mann, *J. Chem. Soc.*, **1930**, 2070.

[45] Kayser, *Ann. chim.*, [11] **6**, 170 (1936).

[46] Knorr, Laage, and Weissenborn, Ger. pat. 591,452 [*C.A.*, **28**, 2367 (1934)], U. S. pat.
1,899,340 [*C.A.*, **27**, 2962 (1933)].

received little attention: when R''' is ethyl, an ethyl ketone is obtained; [47] when R''' is n-decyl, an aldehyde results.[13]

The conversion of glycidic esters to acids may be effected by the usual alkaline hydrolysis. A special hydrolysis [14] involves treatment of the ester with one equivalent of sodium ethoxide in absolute ethanol followed by addition of exactly one equivalent of water; addition of dry ether then causes the precipitation of the sodium salt of the glycidic acid.

For the most part, the glycidic acids are converted into the aldehydes or ketones by heating to the decomposition point. Better yields of methyl cyclohexyl ketone may be obtained from α-methyl-α,β-epoxy-cyclohexylideneacetic acid by two modifications of the above treatment (which gives a 41% yield).[43] In one, the sodium salt of the glycidic acid is heated with sodium hydroxide at 300° (yield 45–56%); in the other, the glycidic acid is treated with dry hydrogen chloride, and the crude chloro hydroxy acid thus obtained is then heated with semicarbazide hydrochloride in pyridine (yield 75%).

The optimum conditions for pyrolysis of the glycidic acid derived from the condensation of β-ionone and ethyl chloroacetate involve heating in pyridine at 130–135° for one to two hours.[37] When this same glycidic acid is decarboxylated by heating in the presence or absence of powdered glass or by passage in the vapor phase under reduced pressure over freshly reduced copper on pumice at 140–160°, products having slightly different properties from those of the product obtained by the pyridine method are obtained.[37] Another group of workers recommends heating in the presence of a small amount of copper powder as the best method for decarboxylating and rearranging this same glycidic acid and the isomeric acid obtained from α-ionone and ethyl chloroacetate,[47a] while a third group of workers reports that no special decarboxylation procedure is necessary for the glycidic ester from β-ionone and ethyl chloroacetate: the glycidic ester is hydrolyzed with cold methanolic sodium hydroxide, the product is extracted in the usual way with ether, and the aldehyde is obtained by vacuum distillation.[47b]

A systematic study of the best conditions for the conversion of glycidic esters to aldehydes or ketones is obviously to be desired, and such a study would contribute much to the wider synthetic use of glycidic esters.

[47] Mousseron and Granger, Compt. rend., 218, 358 (1944); Mousseron, Winternitz, Granger, Claret, Trinquier, and Combes, Bull. soc. chim. France, 1947, 598.

[47a] Heilbron, Johnson, Jones, and Spinks, J. Chem. Soc., 1942, 727.

[47b] Isler, Huber, Ronco, and Kofler, Helv. Chim. Acta, 30, 1911 (1947).

REACTIONS OF GLYCIDIC ESTERS

In addition to their conversion to aldehydes and ketones, discussed in the preceding section, the glycidic esters undergo a number of other reactions which should prove to be valuable in synthetic work. In the paragraphs which follow, examples of these reactions are given. No attempt has been made to list all the examples of any one reaction, but it is believed that all the types of reactions are included.

Rearrangement to α- or β-Keto Esters. It has already been pointed out (pp. 420 and 421) that a glycidic ester on heating to a high temperature may undergo rearrangement to a keto ester. Ethyl β,β-diphenylglycidate is isomerized to ethyl β,β-diphenyl-α-ketopropionate on distillation.[40, 41, 42]

$$(C_6H_5)_2C \overset{\displaystyle O}{\overset{\diagup \diagdown}{\rule{1.5em}{0pt}}} CHCO_2C_2H_5 \rightarrow (C_6H_5)_2CHCOCO_2C_2H_5$$

Ethyl β-phenylglycidate, on passage in the vapor state over infusorial earth at 310°, yields the ester of phenylmalonaldehydic acid.[48]

$$C_6H_5CH \overset{\displaystyle O}{\overset{\diagup \diagdown}{\rule{1.5em}{0pt}}} CHCO_2C_2H_5 \rightarrow C_6H_5CH \overset{\diagup CHO}{\underset{\diagdown CO_2C_2H_5}{}}$$

Reactions with Hydrogen Halides. The addition of hydrogen chloride in dry ether in the cold to ethyl β,β-dimethylglycidate and to ethyl α,β,β-trimethylglycidate results in the formation of α-hydroxy β-chloro esters.[8] This reaction complements the addition of hypochlorous acid to the corresponding substituted acrylates which yields the isomeric α-chloro β-hydroxy esters.

$$CH_3C \overset{\displaystyle O}{\overset{\diagup \diagdown}{\rule{1.5em}{0pt}}} \underset{\displaystyle CH_3 \quad R}{\overset{\displaystyle}{CCO_2C_2H_5}} \xrightarrow{HCl} \underset{\displaystyle CH_3 \quad R}{\overset{\displaystyle Cl \quad OH}{CH_3C \rule{1.5em}{0pt} CCO_2C_2H_5}} \quad R = H, CH_3$$

Hydrogen bromide reacts similarly,[8] but hydrogen iodide yields the acrylate.[8] This latter reaction constitutes another * method for pre-

---

* A summary of the methods of preparing α,β-unsaturated acids by condensation methods is given in the chapter on the Perkin reaction by J. R. Johnson in *Organic Reactions*, Vol. I, p. 233, John Wiley & Sons, New York, 1942.

[48] Tiffeneau and Levy, *Anales soc. quím. argentina*, **16**, 144 (1928) [*C.A.*, **24**, 2450 (1930)].

paring α,β-unsaturated esters and might be developed into a procedure

$$CH_3\overset{O}{\overset{\diagup\diagdown}{C}}\underset{CH_3}{|}CHCO_2C_2H_5 + 2HI \rightarrow CH_3C{=}\underset{CH_3}{\underset{|}{C}}HCO_2C_2H_5 + H_2O + I_2$$

for the quantitative determination of glycidic esters.

Reactions with Ammonia and Amines. Depending upon the reaction conditions, glycidic esters may yield either glycidic amides, hydroxy amino esters, or hydroxy amino amides on treatment with ammonia or amines. The orientation of the hydroxy amino amides appears in doubt. If ammonia or an aliphatic amine is used it is claimed that α-hydroxy β-amino amides are obtained, whereas with an aromatic amine the reverse orientation results.[49]

$$C_6H_5CHOHCHCONHAr \underset{Aromatic}{\overset{ArNH_2}{\longleftarrow}} C_6H_5\overset{O}{\overset{\diagup\diagdown}{C}}H{-}CHCO_2C_2H_5 \underset{Aliphatic}{\overset{RNH_2}{\longrightarrow}}$$
$$\underset{NHAr}{|} \qquad\qquad\qquad\qquad\qquad\qquad C_6H_5CHCHOHCONHR$$
$$\qquad\qquad\qquad\qquad\qquad\qquad\qquad\qquad\qquad\qquad \underset{NHR}{|}$$

It is stated that with ethyl β,β-dimethylglycidate and aniline or methylaniline an α-anilino-β-hydroxy ester is produced,[24] whereas in a patent the reverse orientation is claimed.[50]

$$CH_3\overset{O}{\overset{\diagup\diagdown}{C}}\underset{CH_3}{|}CHCO_2C_2H_5 + C_6H_5NHR \rightarrow CH_3\overset{CH_3}{\overset{|}{C}}\underset{RNC_6H_5}{|}{-}CHOHCO_2C_2H_5 \quad R = H, CH_3$$

It appears that more work is required before assignment of structure of such amino hydroxy compounds can safely be made by analogy.

With phenylhydrazine, the amide[24] or ethyl ester[51] of β,β-dimethyl-glycidic acid yields 1-phenyl-3,3-dimethyl-4-hydroxy-5-pyrazolidone.

$$CH_3\overset{O}{\overset{\diagup\diagdown}{C}}\underset{CH_3 \quad (OC_2H_5)}{|}CHCONH_2 + C_6H_5NHNH_2 \xrightarrow[10\ hours]{150-180°} \underset{(CH_3)_2C{-}{-}NH}{\overset{HOCH{-}CO}{|\qquad\qquad}}\diagdown NC_6H_5$$

[49] (a) Fourneau and Billeter, *Bull. soc. chim. France.* [5] **6**, 1616 (1939); (b) [5] **7**, 593 (1940); (c) Fourneau and Maréchal, *ibid.*, [5] **12**, 990 (1945).
[50] Schickh, Ger. pat. 583,243 [*C.A.*, **28**, 260 (1934)].
[51] Schickh, Ger. pat. 588,045 [*C.A.*, **28**, 1360 (1934)].

Reduction. The reduction of glycidic esters by heating in alcohols with sodium is said to yield mixtures of the saturated acid and of the corresponding primary alcohol. No details of the experimental procedure or yields are reported.[52] By a similar reduction, β,β-diphenyl-

$$\underset{}{RCH}\overset{\displaystyle O}{\overbrace{}}CHCO_2C_2H_5 \rightarrow RCH_2CH_2COOH + RCH_2CH_2CH_2OH$$
$$R = n\text{-}C_3H_7\text{—} \quad \text{and} \quad C_6H_5\text{—}$$

$$CH_3CH_2\underset{\displaystyle |}{\overset{\displaystyle O}{C}}\overbrace{}CHCO_2C_2H_5 \rightarrow CH_3CH_2\underset{\displaystyle |}{C}HCH_2CH_2OH$$
$$CH_3 CH_3$$

glycidic ester is reported to yield β,β-diphenyl-α-hydroxypropionic acid.[53] However, in view of the previously mentioned rearrangement of this glycidic ester to form a keto ester on vacuum distillation,[40, 41, 42] it is possible that the reduction was carried out on the rearranged product.

Grignard Reaction. The product resulting from the action of methylmagnesium iodide on ethyl β,β-diphenylglycidate[54] followed by hydrolysis is claimed to be β,β-diphenyl-α-hydroxybutyric acid. However, the proof of structure consisted in establishing the non-identity of the reaction product (m.p. 167°) with β,β-diphenyl-β-hydroxy-α-methylpropionic acid (m.p. 101°). The alternative possibility, β,β-diphenyl-α-hydroxy-α-methylpropionic acid, was not ruled out. This latter product would be formed if the glycidic ester rearranged to the α-keto ester.

$$(C_6H_5)_2C\overset{\displaystyle O}{\overbrace{}}CHCO_2C_2H_5 + CH_3MgI \xrightarrow{\text{Hydrolysis}}$$

$$(C_6H_5)_2\underset{\displaystyle |}{C}CHOHCO_2H \text{ (m.p. 167°)}$$
$$CH_3$$

$$(C_6H_5)_2\underset{\displaystyle |}{C}OHCHCO_2H \text{ (m.p. 101°)}$$
$$CH_3$$

Hydration. Hydration of the *cis* form of ethylene oxide dicarboxylic acid yields *dl*-tartaric acid, whereas the *trans* form yields a mixture of about 40% *dl*-tartaric and 60% *meso*-tartaric acid.[55]

[52] Verley, *Bull. soc. chim. France*, [4] **35**, 487 (1924).
[53] Billon-Bardon, *Compt. rend.*, **188**, 1412 (1929).
[54] Bardon and Ramart, *Compt. rend.*, **183**, 214 (1926).
[55] Kuhn and Ebel, *Ber.*, **58**, 919 (1925).

$$\underset{cis}{O{\Large\triangleleft}\begin{matrix}CHCO_2H\\[4pt]CHCO_2H\end{matrix}} \xrightarrow{\;H_2O\;} dl\text{-Tartaric acid} \overset{40\%}{\longleftarrow} \underset{trans}{O{\Large\triangleleft}\begin{matrix}CHCO_2H\\[4pt]CHCO_2H\end{matrix}}$$

$$\underset{60\%}{\swarrow}$$ meso-Tartaric acid

Reaction with Active Methylene Groups. Although details and proof of structure are not given, it is stated that β,β-dimethylglycidic ester and β-phenylglycidic ester react with sodioacetoacetic ester and sodiomalonic ester, respectively, to yield substituted γ-butyrolactones.[56]

$$(CH_3)_2C\overset{O}{\overbrace{}}CHCO_2C_2H_5 + CH_3COCHNaCO_2C_2H_5 \rightarrow (CH_3)C\underset{O\underline{}CO}{\overset{CO_2C_2H_5}{-CHCHCOCH_3}}$$

$$C_6H_5CH\overset{O}{\overbrace{}}CHCO_2C_2H_5 + CHNa(CO_2C_2H_5)_2 \rightarrow C_6H_5CH\underset{O\underline{}CO}{\overset{CO_2C_2H_5}{CHCHCO_2C_2H_5}}$$

THE DICHLOROACETATE SYNTHESIS

Darzens has discovered a series of reactions starting with ethyl dichloroacetate which promises to be of wide applicability. The dichloro ester condenses with aldehydes and ketones in the presence of dilute magnesium amalgam to give excellent yields of α-chloro β-hydroxy esters which can be converted to glycidic esters or to α-chloroacrylic esters.[15, 16, 17]

$$RCOR + CHCl_2CO_2C_2H_5 \xrightarrow[\text{Ether}]{Mg\cdot Hg} \underset{OH}{\overset{R}{RCCHClCO_2C_2H_5}}$$

$$\swarrow{P_2O_5} \qquad\qquad \downarrow{NaOC_2H_5}$$

$$\underset{R}{RC}\overset{R}{\underset{O}{\diagdown\diagup}}CHCO_2C_2H_5$$

$$\overset{R}{RC}{=}CClCO_2C_2H_5 \qquad\qquad \downarrow\begin{matrix}1.\ \text{Hydrolysis}\\2.\ \text{Decarboxylation}\end{matrix}$$

$$\downarrow\begin{matrix}NaOH\\H_2O\end{matrix}$$

$$\overset{R}{\underset{R}{\diagdown}}CHCOCO_2H \xrightarrow{\text{Heat}} \overset{R}{\underset{R}{\diagdown}}CHCHO + CO_2$$

[56] Chelintsey and Osetrova, *J. Gen. Chem. U.S.S.R.*, **7**, 2373 (1937) [*C.A.*, **32**, 2099 (1938)].

The α-chloro β-hydroxy esters are formed in almost theoretical yields from ketones. Aliphatic aldehydes, which with α-chloro esters give poor yields of glycidic esters, give yields of 40% to 68% of α-chloro β-hydroxy esters. Ethyl dibromoacetate may replace the dichloro ester, calcium and zinc amalgams the magnesium amalgam, and benzene may replace ether as solvent.[16]

The halohydrin esters are quantitatively converted into glycidic esters by treatment with one equivalent of sodium ethoxide. Alternatively, they may be dehydrated to α-chloroacrylates in high yield by phosphorus pentoxide.

The overall conversion of the halohydrin esters to disubstituted acetaldehydes may be effected by two paths as indicated by the above chart. The path involving hydrolysis of the chloroacrylate and decarboxylation of the resulting α-keto acid is recommended by Darzens.[17] The dichloro ester synthesis merits more study and wider use.

EXPERIMENTAL PROCEDURES

Methyl α-Methyl-α,β-epoxycyclohexylideneacetate. (Use of sodium methoxide.) [18] A solution of 49 g. (0.5 mole) of cyclohexanone and 98 g. (0.5 mole) of methyl α-chloropropionate in 200 ml. of anhydrous ether is placed in a flask which has been previously dried by heating with a flame while being swept out with dry nitrogen. The entire reaction is carried out in an atmosphere of dry nitrogen. The reactants are cooled to 5°, and 45.5 g. (0.8 mole) of commercial sodium methoxide (95% pure, The Matheson Company) is added over a period of one hour during which time the reaction mixture is cooled in an ice-water bath and vigorously stirred. The reaction mixture is permitted to warm slowly to room temperature and is stirred for twenty hours, after which the mixture is hydrolyzed by the addition of a cold solution of 30 ml. of concentrated hydrochloric acid in 200 ml. of water. The ether solution is separated and washed successively with two 100-ml. portions of water, 100 ml. of saturated sodium bicarbonate solution, 50 ml. of water, and 100 ml. of saturated sodium chloride solution. After filtration through anhydrous sodium sulfate and distillation of the ether, 78 g. (85%) of methyl α-methyl-α,β-epoxycyclohexylideneacetate is obtained by vacuum distillation, b.p. 116–118°/8.5 mm.

Ethyl α-Methyl-β-p-tolylglycidate. (Use of sodium ethoxide, bromo ester, and an aromatic aldehyde.) [57] To a solution of 90 g. (0.5 mole) of ethyl α-bromopropionate and 60 g. (0.5 mole) of p-tolualdehyde, cooled in an ice-salt bath, 34 g. (0.5 mole) of freshly prepared sodium ethoxide

[57] Ruzicka and Ehmann, *Helv. Chim. Acta,* **15,** 160 (1932).

is added over a period of three to four hours. The mixture is stirred overnight with cooling, two hours at room temperature, and finally warmed six hours in a water bath. Ice water is then added, the mixture is acidified with acetic acid, and the product is extracted with ether. After drying and removing the solvent 62.5 g. (56%) of the glycidic ester is obtained, b.p. 148–152°/12 mm.

Ethyl β-Methyl-β-phenylglycidate. (Use of sodium amide.) Detailed directions for the preparation of this ester in 62–64% yield from ethyl chloroacetate and acetophenone with sodium amide as the condensing agent are given in *Organic Syntheses*.[58]

Hydratropaldehyde. (Conversion of a glycidic ester to an aldehyde.) [58, 59] To a stirred solution of 274 g. (6.85 moles) of sodium hydroxide in 770 ml. of water is added 708 g. (3.44 moles) of ethyl β-methyl-β-phenylglycidate. After being stirred for nine hours at 45–50°, the solution is acidified to Congo red with 6 N hydrochloric acid. The glycidic acid is extracted with benzene and distilled with superheated steam [59] at 180°. This treatment decarboxylates the glycidic acid over a period of four to five hours, the aldehyde being removed continuously as formed. The aldehyde is extracted from the distillate with benzene and is vacuum-distilled to yield 268 g. (58%) of product, b.p. 101–102°/ 21–22 mm. Alternatively [58] the original hydrolysate, acidified to Congo red, is steam-distilled at atmospheric pressure for about eighty hours, approximately 125 l. of distillate being collected. After extraction with benzene and distillation, the yield is 310 g. (67%).

Ethyl β-p-Chlorophenylglycidate. (Use of powdered sodium.) [46] Over a period of two hours a solution of 49 g. (0.45 mole) of ethyl chloroacetate and 60 g. (0.43 mole) of p-chlorobenzaldehyde is added to 10 g. (0.48 mole) of powdered sodium suspended in 150 ml. of xylene. Water is then added, and the xylene fraction containing the product is worked up as previously described. The pure product boils at 155–160°/4 mm.; yield 75 g. (66%).

Ethyl α-Chloro-β-hydroxy-β-phenylbutyrate. (Use of magnesium amalgam and ethyl dichloroacetate.) [16] A magnesium amalgam is prepared by warming a mixture of 7.5 g. of magnesium with 375 g. of mercury under a stream of hydrogen. The amalgam is cooled under hydrogen, and a solution of 36 g. (0.3 mole) of acetophenone and 48 g. (0.3 mole) of ethyl dichloroacetate in 300 ml. of anhydrous ether is added with stirring and cooling. After being stirred for six to ten hours the mixture is poured on ice containing acetic acid and the organic portion is worked

[58] Allen and Van Allen, *Org. Syntheses*, **24**, 82 (1944).
[59] Newman and Closson, *J. Am. Chem. Soc.*, **66**, 1553 (1944).

up in the usual fashion.   Vacuum distillation gives 68 g. (92%) of product, b.p. 166–167°/5 mm.

EXAMPLES OF THE DARZENS GLYCIDIC ESTER CONDENSATION

The literature has been covered through 1947.   The compounds are listed according to the increasing carbon content of the empirical formula of the glycidic ester as in the *Chemical Abstracts Formula Index*.

The typical procedure involves slow addition of the condensing agent to a cooled mixture of the carbonyl compound and halo ester with or without a solvent.   The condensing agents are:

A. The sodium alkoxide corresponding to the alkyl group of the halo ester.

B. Sodium amide.

C. Sodium, usually powdered.

TABLE I

GLYCIDIC ESTERS

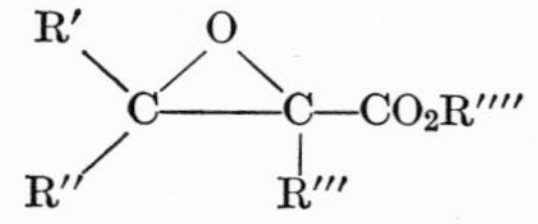

$$R'{-}\underset{R''}{C}\diagup\!\!\!\!\overset{O}{}\!\!\!\!\diagdown\underset{R'''}{C}{-}CO_2R''''$$

Carbonyl Component	Glycidic Ester Formula				Condensing Agent	Yield %	References *
	R'	R''	R'''	R''''			
Formaldehyde	H	H	CH₃—	C₂H₅—	A	20–30	4
Acetaldehyde	CH₃—	H	H	C₂H₅—	C	—	19
Acetone	CH₃—	CH₃—	H	C₂H₅—	†	47 ‡	19
Acetone	CH₃—	CH₃—	H	C₂H₅—	C	53	19
					A	60	2
Acetaldehyde	CH₃—	H	CH₃—	C₂H₅—	B	59 §	14
Propionaldehyde	C₂H₅—	H	H	C₂H₅—	A	20–30	4
Acetone	CH₃—	CH₃—	CH₃—	C₂H₅—	A	20–30	4
Butanone	C₂H₅—	CH₃—	H	C₂H₅—	A	—	3
					A	56	44
					B	34	14, 60
Furfural	C₄H₃O—	H	H	C₂H₅—	C	—	61
					A	96(?)	20
Furfural	C₄H₃O—	H	CH₃—	CH₃—	A ‖	73	62
Mesityl oxide	C₄H₇—	CH₃—	H	C₂H₅—	A	58 ¶	63

Carbonyl compound	R	R'	R''	Ester	Method	Yield (%)	Reference
Cyclopentanone	—(CH₂)₄—		H	C₂H₅—	A	41	64
Butanone	C₂H₅—	CH₃—	CH₃	C₂H₅—	A	—	3
3-Methyl-2-butanone	iso-C₃H₇—	CH₃—	H	C₂H₅—	C	—	65
2-Pentanone	C₃H₇—	CH₃—	H	C₂H₅—	B	50	14
3-Pentanone	C₂H₅—	C₂H₅—	H	C₂H₅—	B	50	14
Benzaldehyde	C₆H₅—	H	CH₃	CH₃—	A	54	18
Furfural	C₄H₃O—	H	H	C₂H₅—	A **	50	4
Cyclohexanone	—(CH₂)₅—		H	C₂H₅—	A	68	43
Cyclohexanone	—(CH₂)₅—		CH₃	CH₃—	A	65	4
Cyclopentanone	—(CH₂)₄—		CH₃	C₂H₅—	A	85	18
3-Methylbutanal	iso-C₄H₉—	H	CH₃	C₂H₅—	A	35	43
2-Pentanone	C₃H₇—	CH₃—	CH₃	C₂H₅—	A	20–30	4
o-Chlorobenzaldehyde	o-C₆H₄Cl—	H	CH₃	CH₃—	C	—	3
p-Chlorobenzaldehyde	p-C₆H₄Cl—	H	H	C₂H₅—	A	70	62
Benzaldehyde	C₆H₅—	H	H	C₂H₅—	B	66	46
Acetophenone	C₆H₅—	CH₃—	H	CH₃—	A	50	4
2-Methylcyclohexanone	—CHCH₃(CH₂)₄—		H	C₂H₅—	B	25	14
3-Methylcyclohexanone ††	—CH₂CHCH₃(CH₂)₃—		H	C₂H₅—	A	70	21
3-Methylcyclohexanone	—CH₂CHCH₃(CH₂)₃—		H	C₂H₅—	B ‡‡	—	66
4-Methylcyclohexanone	—(CH₂)₂CHCH₃(CH₂)₂—		H	C₂H₅—	A	—	5
4-Methylcyclohexanone	—(CH₂)₂CHCH₃(CH₂)₂—		CH₃	CH₃—	A	60	67

* References 60–87 are on pp. 439–440.

† Ethyl chloroacetate was added to the sodium enolate of the ketone prepared from sodium amide in ether.

‡ The yield was based on the chloro ester.

§ An impure product containing chloro ester and chloro amide.

‖ The α-bromo ester was used.

¶ A mixture of methyl and ethyl esters was employed.

** This experiment was run at −80° with no solvent.

†† An optically active ketone was used, and an optically active aldehyde was obtained.

‡‡ The α-bromo ester was used.

TABLE I—*Continued*

GLYCIDIC ESTERS

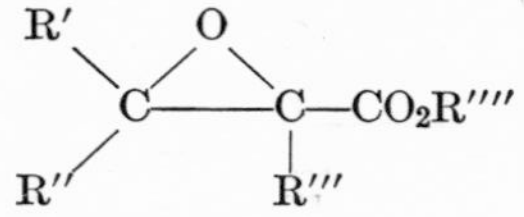

$$\underset{R''}{\overset{R'}{\diagdown}}C\overset{O}{\diagup\diagdown}C\underset{CO_2R''''}{\overset{R'''}{\diagup}}$$

Carbonyl Component	Glycidic Ester Formula				Condensing Agent	Yield %	References*
	R'	R''	R'''	R''''			
Cyclohexanone	—(CH$_2$)$_5$—		CH$_3$—	C$_2$H$_5$—	A	—	6
3,4-Methylenedioxybenzaldehyde (piperonal)	C$_7$H$_5$O$_2$—	H	H	C$_2$H$_5$—	C	—	68
Benzaldehyde	C$_6$H$_5$—	H	CH$_3$—	C$_2$H$_5$—	A	50, 71	4, 18
p-Tolualdehyde	C$_7$H$_7$—	H	H	C$_2$H$_5$—	C	—	46
Acetophenone	C$_6$H$_5$—	CH$_3$—	H	C$_2$H$_5$—	A	60–64	2, 58
					B	—, 64	14, 69
o-Methoxybenzaldehyde	o-C$_7$H$_7$O—	H	CH$_3$—	CH$_3$—	A	75	62
m-Methoxybenzaldehyde	m-C$_7$H$_7$O—	H	CH$_3$—	CH$_3$—	A	82	62
p-Methoxybenzaldehyde	p-C$_7$H$_7$O—	H	H	C$_2$H$_5$—	C	—	46, 68
1-Cyclohexenyl methyl ketone	C$_6$H$_5$—	CH$_3$—	H	C$_2$H$_5$—	A	—	9
6-Methyl-5-hepten-2-one	C$_6$H$_{11}$—	CH$_3$—	H	C$_2$H$_5$—	A §§	45	70, 71
					A ‖	30	70
6-Methyl-6-hepten-2-one	**C$_6$H$_{11}$—**	CH$_3$—	H	C$_2$H$_5$—	A	—	72
2-Methylcyclohexanone	—CHCH$_3$(CH$_2$)$_4$—		CH$_3$—	C$_2$H$_5$—	A	—	6

Carbonyl Compound	R	R′	Ester	Method	Yield (%)	Reference
3-Methylcyclohexanone	$-CH_2CHCH_3(CH_2)_3-$		C_2H_5-	A	—	6
3-Methylcyclohexanone (active)	$-CH_2CHCH_3(CH_2)_3-$		C_2H_5-	B	—	47
4-Methylcyclohexanone	$-(CH_2)_2CHCH_3(CH_2)_2-$		C_2H_5-	A	—	6
2-Octanone	$C_6H_{13}-$	CH_3-	C_2H_5-	C	41	49a
6-Methyl-2-heptanone	$C_6H_{13}-$	CH_3-	C_2H_5-	A	—	2
3,4-Methylenedioxybenzaldehyde (piperonal)	$C_7H_5O_2-$	H	C_2H_5-	A ¶¶	48	73
Acetophenone	C_6H_5-	CH_3-	C_2H_5-	A	—, 35	4; 3, 18
Phenylacetone	C_7H_7-	CH_3-	C_2H_5-	B	60–63	14
p-Tolualdehyde	C_7H_7-	H	C_2H_5-	A	56	2
p-Ethylbenzaldehyde	C_8H_9-	H	C_2H_5-	A	—	74
2,4-Dimethylbenzaldehyde	C_8H_9-	H	C_2H_5-	C	42	57
Propiophenone	C_6H_5-	C_2H_5-	C_2H_5-	C	—	46
p-Tolyl methyl ketone	C_7H_7-	CH_3-	C_2H_5-	A	—	46
p-Methoxybenzaldehyde	$CH_3OC_6H_4-$	H	C_2H_5-	B	66	45
p-Methoxybenzaldehyde	$CH_3OC_6H_4-$	H	CH_3-	A	—	14
p-Methoxyacetophenone	$CH_3OC_6H_4-$	CH_3-	C_2H_5-	A	72	75, 76; 4
2,3-Dimethoxybenzaldehyde	$(CH_3O)_2C_6H_3-$	H	C_2H_5-	C	—	62; 69; 77
"1-Ketoöctahydropyridocoline"	(ring structure)	H	C_2H_5-	B	40***	78

* References 60–87 are on pp. 439–440.
§§ Petroleum ether, b.p. 100–120°, was used as solvent.
‖‖ No solvent was employed.
¶¶ The α-bromo ester was used.
*** Neither the glycidic acid nor the aldehyde could be prepared from this ester.

TABLE I—*Continued*

GLYCIDIC ESTERS

$$R' \quad O \quad R''''$$
$$\diagdown \quad \diagup \quad $$
$$C \underset{|}{\overset{|}{-}} C - CO_2R''''$$
$$R'' \qquad R'''$$

Carbonyl Component	R'	R''	R'''	R''''	Condensing Agent	Yield %	References*
				Glycidic Ester Formula			
3-Methylcyclohexanone	—CH$_2$CHCH$_3$(CH$_2$)$_3$—		C$_2$H$_5$—	C$_2$H$_5$—	B	—	47
2-Dimethylaminomethyl cyclo-hexanone	—CHCH$_2$N(CH$_3$)$_2$(CH$_2$)$_4$—		H	C$_2$H$_5$—	A	43–58	21
Acetone	CH$_3$—	CH$_3$—	H	CH$_3$(CH$_2$)$_3$- CH(C$_2$H$_5$)CH$_2$—	A	46	67
2-Nonanone	C$_7$H$_{15}$—	CH$_3$—	H	C$_2$H$_5$—	A	60–63	2
2-Octanone	C$_6$H$_{13}$—	CH$_3$—	CH$_3$—	C$_2$H$_5$—	A	—	3
3,4-Dimethoxybenzaldehyde	(CH$_3$)$_2$C$_6$H$_3$—	H	CH$_3$—	CH$_3$—	A	70	62
Benzaldehyde	C$_6$H$_5$—	H	C$_2$H$_5$—	C$_3$H$_7$—	A	67	67
p-Isopropylbenzaldehyde	C$_9$H$_{11}$—	H	H	C$_2$H$_5$—	C, A	—	20, 46
2,4,6-Trimethylbenzaldehyde	C$_9$H$_{11}$—	H	H	C$_2$H$_5$—	A	—	20
2,4,5-Trimethylbenzaldehyde	C$_9$H$_{11}$—	H	H	C$_2$H$_5$—	A	—	20
p-Methylacetophenone	C$_7$H$_7$—	CH$_3$—	CH$_3$—	C$_2$H$_5$—	A	58	3
Propiophenone	C$_6$H$_5$—	C$_2$H$_5$—	H	iso-C$_3$H$_7$	A	—	67
Isobutyrophenone	C$_6$H$_5$—	iso-C$_3$H$_7$—	H	C$_2$H$_5$—	B	—	23

Compound					Method	Yield	Reference
p-Methylacetophenone	C7H7—	CH3—	H	iso-C3H7—	A	47	67
Butyrophenone	C6H5—	C3H7—	H	C2H5—	A	60-63	2
p-Ethylacetophenone	C8H9—	CH3—	H	C2H5—	A	60-63	2
4-Phenyl-2-butanone	C8H9—	CH3—	iso-C3H7—	C2H5—	C	—	69
p-Methoxybenzaldehyde	CH3OC6H4—	H	H	CH3—	A†††	70	62
β-Decalone	β-C10H16<		H	C2H5—	A	90, 71	12, 49a
					C	80	69
2-Nonanone	C7H15—	CH3—	CH3—	C2H5—	A	—	3
2-Decanone	C8H17—	CH3—	H	C2H5—	C	—	69
5,6,7,8-Tetrahydro-1-naphthaldehyde	C10H11—	H	H	C2H5—	C	—	46
p-sec-Butylbenzaldehyde	C10H13—	H	H	C2H5—	C	—	46
2-Methyl-5-isopropylbenzaldehyde	C10H13—	H	CH3—	C2H5—	A	—	20
p-Isopropylbenzaldehyde	C9H11—	H	H	C2H5—	A	40	79
p-Isopropylacetophenone	C9H11—	CH3—	CH3—	C2H5—	C	—	69
β-Decalone	β-C10H16<		CH3—	C2H5—	A	—	12
2-Undecanone	C9H19	CH3—	H	C2H5—	A	60-63	2, 75
					C	—	69
Benzophenone	C6H5—	C6H5—	H	CH3—	A	—	41
Methyl 1-naphthyl ketone	1-C10H7—	CH3—	H	C2H5—	A	45	7
Methyl 2-naphthyl ketone	2-C10H7—	CH3—	H	C2H5—	A	—	7
Isobutylacetophenone ‡‡‡	C10H13—	CH3—	H	C2H5—	A	60-63	2
2,2-Dimethyl-3-(carbethoxymethyl)-cyclobutyl methyl ketone	C10H17O2—	CH3—	H	C2H5—	A	50 §§§	80
2-Isopropyl-2-(carbethoxymethyl)-cyclopropyl methyl ketone	C10H17O2—	CH3—	H	C2H5—	A	32 ‖‖‖	81

* References 60-87 are on pp. 439-440.
†† The bromo ester was used.
††† The position of the isobutyl group was not stated.
‡‡‡ Forty-six per cent of the keto ester was recovered.
§§§ Forty-five per cent of the keto ester was recovered.
‖‖‖ Twenty-five per cent of the keto ester was recovered.

TABLE I—*Continued*

Glycidic Esters

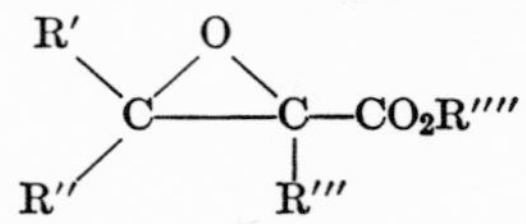

Glycidic Ester Formula

$$\text{R}' \,\text{C} \overset{\text{O}}{\diagup\diagdown} \text{C} \begin{smallmatrix} \text{CO}_2\text{R}''''\\ \text{R}'''\end{smallmatrix}$$

Carbonyl Component	R'	R''	R'''	R''''	Condensing Agent	Yield %	References *
2-Undecanone	C9H19—	CH3—	CH3—	C2H5—	A	—	3
Benzophenone	C6H5—	C6H5—	H	C2H5—	A	75 ¶¶¶	19, 40, 41, 42
2,4-Diisopropylbenzaldehyde	C12H17—	H	H	C2H5—	C	—	46
4-(p-Isopropylphenyl)-2-butanone	C11H15—	CH3—	H	C2H5—	C	—	69
α-Ionone	C11H17—	CH3—	H	C2H5—	A	34	47a, 63a
β-Ionone	C11H17—	CH3—	H	C2H5—	A	55, 80	47a,b, 63b, 82
Tetrahydroionone	C11H21—	CH3—	H	C2H5—	C	73	69
Acetone	CH3—	CH3—	n-C10H21—	C2H5—	A	70	13
6,10-Dimethyl-2-undecanone	C11H23—	CH3—	H	C2H5—	C	69	69
p-Methylbenzophenone	C7H7—	C6H5—	H	C2H5—	B	—	42
p-Methoxybenzophenone	C7H7O—	C6H5—	H	C2H5—	B	—	42
5-(2,2,6-Trimethylcyclohexenyl)-3-pentanone	C11H21—	C2H5—	H	C2H5—	C	—	69

Reactant							Ref.
Dibenzyl ketone	C_7H_7—	C_7H_7—	H	C_2H_5—	A	—	83
3-Methoxy-4-benzyloxybenzaldehyde	$C_{14}H_{13}O_2$	H	CH_3—	C_2H_5—	****	—	84
Cyclohexanone	—$(CH_2)_5$—		n-$C_{10}H_{21}$—	C_2H_5—	A	—	13
Acetophenone	C_6H_5—	CH_3—	n-$C_{10}H_{21}$—	C_2H_5—	A	—	13
Dehydroandrosterone	(steroid structure: H_3C, H_3C, HO)	CH_3—	CH_3—	C_2H_5—	A	—	25, 85

* References 60–87 are on pp. 439–440.
¶¶ The product is an α-keto ester, not a glycidic ester.
**** The condensing agent was not mentioned. A bromo ester was used.

TABLE II

Glycidic Amides

The procedures are similar to those used in the glycidic ester reactions. The condensing agents used are the following: A. Sodium ethoxide.   B. Sodium amide.   C. Sodium.

Carbonyl Compound	Glycidic Amide Formula $$\underset{R''}{\overset{R'}{\diagdown}}\mathrm{C}\!\!\diagup\!\!\overset{\mathrm{O}}{\underset{R'''}{\mathrm{C}}}\!\!-\!\!\overset{\mathrm{O}}{\mathrm{C}}\!\!-\!\!R'''' $				Con-densing Agent	Yield %	References *
	R'	R''	R'''	R''''			
Acetone	CH₃—	CH₃—	H	NH₂—	C	80	24
					A	55	86
3-Pentanone	C₂H₅—	C₂H₅—	H	NH₂—	A †	—	86
					B †	—	86
Cyclohexanone	—(CH₂)₅—		H	NH₂—	—	—	86
Benzaldehyde	C₆H₅—	H	H	NH₂—	—	—	86
Acetone	CH₃—	CH₃—	H	N(C₂H₅)₂—	B	80	24
Benzaldehyde	C₆H₅—	H	CH₃—	NHCH₃—	A ‡	75–80	24
Propiophenone	C₆H₅—	C₂H₅—	H	NH₂—	A	80	24
1-Phenyl-2-propanone	C₇H₇—	CH₃—	H	NH₂—	—	—	86
1-Phenoxy-2-propanone	C₇H₇O—	CH₃—	H	NH₂—	—	—	86
Acetophenone	C₆H₅—	CH₃—	H	N(CH₃)₂—	—	—	86
Citral	C₉H₁₅—	H	H	NH₂—	A	70	24
Benzaldehyde	C₆H₅—	H	H	NHC₆H₅—	A	—	28c

* References 60–87 are on pp. 439–440.

† Procedure A gave an amide m.p. 104°; procedure B, an amide m.p. 148°.

‡ The α-bromoamide was used.

TABLE III

α-CHLORO β-HYDROXY ESTERS

The procedure involves the addition of a mixture of ketone and α,α-dichloro ester in ether to dilute (1 to 50) magnesium amalgam. All the α-chloro β-hydroxy esters were converted in high yield to epoxy esters by treatment with alkaline reagents.

Carbonyl Component	Product	Yield %	References *
Acetaldehyde	$CH_3CHOHCHClCO_2C_2H_5$	40	17
Acetone	$(CH_3)_2COHCHClCO_2C_2H_5$	—	15, 16
Isobutyraldehyde	$(CH_3)_2CHCHOHCHClCO_2C_2H_5$	68	17
Cyclopentanone	$(CH_2)_4=COHCHClCO_2C_2H_5$	—	17
Cyclohexanone	$(CH_2)_5=COHCHClCO_2C_2H_5$	97	17
Benzaldehyde	$C_6H_5CHOHCHClCO_2C_2H_5$	—	17
Heptaldehyde	$CH_3(CH_2)_5CHOHCHClCO_2C_2H_5$	57	17
Acetophenone	$C_6H_5COHCHClCO_2C_2H_5$	95	16
Dehydroandrosterone acetate †		—	87

* References 60–87 are on pp. 439–440.

† This reaction failed when dehydroandrosterone was used, Ercoli and Mamoli, *Chimica e Industria*, **1937**, 435.

REFERENCES TO TABLES

[60] Neustadter, *Monatsh.*, **27**, 889 (1906).

[61] Asahina and Fujita, *J. Pharm. Soc. Japan*, No. 490, 1084 (1922) [*C.A.*, **17**, 2578 (1923)].

[62] Wolf, Ger. pat. 702,007 [*C.A.*, **36**, 95 (1942)].

[63] (a) Ishikawa and Matsuura, *Sci. Repts. Tokyo Bunrika Daigaku*, **3A**, 173 (1937) [*C.A.*, **31**, 7851 (1937)]; (b) Cymerman, Heilbron, Jones, and Lacey, *J. Chem. Soc.*, **1946**, 500.

[64] Newman, *J. Am. Chem. Soc.*, **57**, 732 (1935).

[65] Brunner and Farmer, *J. Chem. Soc.*, **1937**, 1039.

[66] von Auwers, *Ann.*, **415**, 147 (1918).

[67] Newman, Magerlein, and Wheatley, *J. Am. Chem. Soc.*, **68**, 2112 (1946).

[68] Rosenmund and Dornsaft, *Ber.*, **52**, 1740 (1919).

[69] Knorr and Weissenborn, Ger. pat. 602,816 [*C.A.*, **29**, 1438 (1935)].

[70] Doeuvre, *Bull. soc. chim. France*, [4] **45**, 710 (1929).

[71] Fester and Pucci, *Ber.*, **69**, 2017 (1936).

[72] Verley, *Bull. soc. chim. France*, [4] **35**, 608 (1924).

[73] Elks and Hey, *J. Chem. Soc.*, **1943**, 15.

[74] Darzens, U. S. pat. 830,213 [C.A., 1, 251 (1907)].

[75] Darzens, Ger. pat. 174,279 [C.A., 1, 950 (1907)].

[76] Dutta, J. Indian Chem. Soc., 18, 233 (1941).

[77] Mauthner, J. prakt. Chem., [2] 148, 95 (1937).

[78] Clemo, Romage, and Raper, J. Chem. Soc., 1931, 3190.

[79] Bradfield, Pritchard, and Simonsen, J. Chem. Soc., 1937, 760.

[80] Ruzicka and Trebler, Helv. Chim. Acta, 4, 666 (1921).

[81] Ruzicka and Koolhaas, Helv. Chim. Acta, 15, 944 (1932).

[82] Milas, U. S. pat. 2,369,156 [C.A., 39, 5043 (1945)]; U. S. pats. 2,369,160–2,369,167 incl. [C.A., 39, 5046 (1945)]; U. S. pat. 2,415,834 [C.A., 41, 3483 (1937)].

[83] Scheibler and Tutundzitsch, Ber., 64, 2916 (1931).

[84] Robinson and Lowe, Eng. pat. 519,894 [C.A., 36, 875 (1942)].

[85] Yarnall and Wallis, J. Am. Chem. Soc., 59, 951 (1937); Yarnall and Wallis, J. Org. Chem., 4, 270 (1939).

[86] Fourneau, Billeter, and Bovet, J. pharm. chim., 19 (1934) [C.A., 28, 5179 (1934)].

[87] Miescher and Kagi, Helv. Chim. Acta, 22, 184 (1939); Chemistry & Industry, 57, 276 (1938).

INDEX

Numbers in **bold-face** type refer to experimental procedures.